SHOULD WE FALL BEHIND

SHOULD WE FALL BEHIND

by Sharon Duggal

Bluemoose

First published in 2020 by
Bluemoose Books Ltd
25 Sackville Street
Hebden Bridge
West Yorkshire
HX7 7DJ

www.bluemoosebooks.com

British Library Cataloguing-in-Publication data
A catalogue record for this book is available from the British Library

Paperback 978-1-910422-61-8

Hardback 978-1-910422-60-1

Printed and bound in the UK by Short Run Press

For my family and friends

1. JIMMY

Jimmy Noone drifted, alone in a cold subway, falling away with the day as it faded to shadow. He dreamt of balloons: sky-blue, bought by his father to mark his third birthday. The balloons were set free one by one from the bedroom window as Jimmy, holding onto his brother's hand, urged them to float higher and higher over brick terraces into a sea of platinum cloud. Their mother smiled weakly, propped up in bed drinking tea, rubbing heavy eyelids between gulps, mug balanced on her swollen belly. His earliest memories always came unexpectedly. Somewhere above the ground there was a clatter and it echoed loudly, jolting dreams away. He was no longer alone. A woman was slumped opposite, head cocked against an image of a sapphire-blue kingfisher. She was young, even younger than him; just a girl really.

The subway was hidden beneath dull office blocks and a sprawling budget hotel. Its walls were painted with fresh murals, bright enough to shock: rainbow lorikeets perched on branches surrounded by hummingbirds dancing across a swimming-pool sky; shades of cyan, turquoise and teal – colours at once both green and blue, and not of the drab English city above. The subway led to a municipal car park on the other side of the road. Each morning at seven, Vivaldi's *Four Seasons* played into it from the hotel through a concealed speaker; music arrived on a tang of fried bacon, wafting over the linger of stale piss. The same music played at six in the evening, drowning out the rumble of rush hour as darkness slipped in and everything needed gee-ing up.

When Jimmy told the girl his name, she flinched and pushed her back against the wall.

'Jimmy Noone,' he repeated softly. 'Like midday. Noon with an E. 'N.O.O.N.E.'

She closed her eyes and turned her face away as the music soared. Jimmy reached into his rucksack, pulled out a tattered paperback and pretended to focus on words obscured in murky twilight.

When she spoke it was barely above a whisper. Her voice trembled.

'Did I imagine it?' she said.

'The music?' he shook his head. 'It's real but only plays out a couple of times a day.'

'I don't know if I'm dreaming or not anymore.'

'Me neither,' he replied.

Grimy fluorescent tubes flickered and a smoky light appeared, throwing muted shapes across surfaces. The girl wore a frayed denim jacket, hugged tight around her small frame. Her face was oval: unblemished, wheatish skin not yet the pallid slate-grey of time-served street dwellers.

'I'm Betwa,' she said eventually.

'It's a nice name.' He hadn't heard of it before. He asked about it.

'It's a river in India, near where my mother was born, but I've never been there. It confuses people; the name, I mean. They want to call me something else, something they understand.'

He liked listening to her. Beneath her reticence he sensed a tiny glint of light: no slurring of words, no bitterness, not yet. She was different from others he'd met on the streets. Something about her made him want to hold his palms up to the world and halt the pull of it before it was too late.

When she spoke again, Betwa said, 'I don't suppose anyone ever asks what Jimmy means?'

September flipped into October that night; the change in the air was palpable. Jimmy wondered how the year could almost be gone already, how time could slip away without consequence. He didn't like that it moved on so swiftly while his life was mired, stuck in a kind of sinkhole, dragging only downwards. The rain didn't touch them that night but the cold did. It was hard for anyone to get warm with concrete next to bone; even in a sleeping bag, bones are cold. He knew it was the same for the girl: she was slight, like a teenager, snappable. He wanted to tell her he wasn't much different: layers of clothing made him seem bulky and he was tall, but he was just as fragile.

She fell asleep quickly and he watched, trying hard to keep his own eyes open. Her hair was shoulder-length, the same charred-wood colour as his own. It fell gently across her cheek. When he slept, dreams were sporadic, like Nan's old cine film. Soft fingers stroked his pitted skin, brushing away tobacco strands from the beard which obscured his face and made him into someone else, someone older. The dream fingers belonged to his mother. He tried to grasp them but the moment flitted away, onto the next frame. He woke, bereft, longing to feel heat from another body, warm breath on his skin. Across the subway, the girl slept leaning into her rucksack, arms clasped around her knees. Jimmy touched his hair, spat on his fingers and tried to tame the wildness of it.

In the morning, Betwa agreed to walk with him up to the brown river which divided the city.

'Don't be on your own, not if you can help it,' he said, and she followed him out into the day.

At first she was quiet so he rambled on about finding the subway a few weeks earlier.

'I wanted it for myself but I knew that couldn't happen; there were already empty bottles and bits of cardboard when I arrived.'

A stream of drifters passed through. Most disappeared as suddenly as they appeared; he was always glad when they'd gone. He told her about the man called Alan who spoke with slobber trickling from his scaly lips. He mimicked the man's broad accent.

Fuck you, Jimmy. You think others haven't been here before? You're not the first bugger to think he's found a special place just for him but out here we're all family, right? This is no place for a selfish cunt. You don't wanna be here alone, lad.

He recognised the traces of fear in the girl's eyes when he talked about Alan so he changed the subject to things he'd learnt about the music in the subway: how it was sometimes like thunder, sometimes like sleet. It was, he said, written almost four hundred years ago by a sickly composer for the poverty-stricken orphans he worked with.

Betwa said 'I've never heard of music in an underpass,' and Jimmy thought she sounded even younger than she was.

He told her about a bloke called Ringo who went into a frenzy when the music began. *It's the fucking DWP theme tune. They're playing it to torture us,* Ringo said. Jimmy knew he'd heard it before, in shopping centre lifts and clinical waiting rooms but somewhere else too and it was only when Ringo kicked off he remembered holding the phone while his nan strutted off to make a cup of tea. *You hang on there for me Jimmy lad,* she'd said. *They keep you waiting for hours with that awful music screeching at you. I can't stand it. It breaks your spirit, so it does. They'd do anything to stop you from claiming what's yours. Poor man that Vivaldi fella, us all hating him because of them using his music like that.*

Some time later, in the warmth of the local library, Jimmy learnt the irony of it: Vivaldi died a pauper, more in common with the benefit claimants than the over-paid PR consultants and civil servants in wood-panelled offices selecting music for the hold.

'But what about the underpass?' Betwa said, so he described the hotel guests in shiny shoes who shuffled through with trolley suitcases, pretending not to see the people at their feet. Some of those guests complained about the stench and the Swamp

Thing look of them and one morning the police arrived earlier than the music.

'I woke up with a boot in my face,' Jimmy said.

He'd returned to the subway soon after the police left and stood at the entrance while a man in an orange boiler suit jet-sprayed the stink away, drowning out the sound of Vivaldi's *Spring* with the whoosh of water.

'Something keeps drawing me back,' he said.

He knew he shouldn't get too attached to a place but the subway with its birds and its music was the closest he'd been to comfort since his brother Ant left him alone with their father.

The more Jimmy spoke, the more Betwa relaxed and after an hour of walking, the conversation flowed more freely.

'I never knew my dad,' she said. 'Mama never mentioned him. She was just seventeen. Younger than me now. She'd only been in England a short while. We could've been sisters.'

There were grandparents, aunties and uncles she'd never met; shielded by her mother from the shame her people wore as a response to her existence.

Jimmy listened intently but walked with a small gap between them so his bad odours didn't overpower her. She somehow managed to retain a faint aroma of fresh mint, orange blossom, washing powder; smells of a clean life. He tried to absorb them, breathing her in deeply.

They stopped for a rest by a gated square surrounded by grand buttermilk buildings: floor to ceiling windows, curtains flung open flaunting lofty rooms, picture rails, gilt-edged paintings.

'I'm hungry,' Betwa said.

'It'll pass,' he told her.

'I hope so, I can't get used to it. I keep thinking I'm going to collapse and there'll be nobody to pick me up.'

He felt for her. It had taken him weeks to learn to ride waves of hunger, to predict the high tides, and when they might recede.

5

He didn't tell her how those waves sometimes swelled until they became unfathomable. Instead, he opened a wheelie bin, peered inside. Nothing. He opened another and another until finally he pulled out a length of stale baguette and held it up like a trophy.

'Picnic, madam?' he said with a bow before jumping the iron gate.

Betwa laughed and when he stretched out his hand to help her over the railings the touch of her made him shiver. They sat slouched on a bench beneath an old laburnum tree, scraping out bits of dry bread from a rock-hard crust, kicking their legs to shoo away greedy pigeons burbling around their ankles.

Betwa pointed to a large Regency house opposite. 'I'd like to live there,' she said.

Jimmy tossed the stony end of the baguette to the ground and watched as the birds scavenged. Soon drops of rain began to splutter down.

'Come on,' he said. 'We definitely don't want wet clothes.'

On the way back, they slipped past office workers and shoppers in good coats hurrying home for the weekend through the chill of dusk. They reached the subway just as the sky turned violent and buildings became silhouettes. Later, swaddled in darkness, leaning on hummingbirds, Betwa talked about her mother again.

'The river of my name flowed through her village. She always wanted to return there but she never managed it, She died before she got to go home. Nothing can be as cruel as that.'

Jimmy thought for a while. 'I dunno,' he said.

'She was still everywhere in the house,' Betwa said. 'The smell of her face cream on cushions; a strand of her hair wrapped around the top of a shampoo bottle. I couldn't bear it; I had to sit on the edge of the bath, holding on while all the shower water wasted away.' She paused. 'I miss the sound of her voice.'

She was quiet for a long time and he held her silence until she broke it. 'What about you, Jimmy? How come you're living it up down here?'

He smiled. 'I'll tell you another time.' Her story was enough for one night.

She laid her head on his shoulder and closed her eyes. Her hair smelled of rain and wet leaves now and the sound of her steady breathing made tears swell and spill over.

Days passed more quickly than hours did before Betwa, and Jimmy knew he'd already talked more to her than anyone else in months. One morning, just before rain seeped into the subway and threatened to soak their things, he told her about the Seroxat and other drugs.

'When I didn't have a doctor to give it me any more I had to find alternatives. I thought it was the only way to be, out here.'

He felt as if he was relating someone else's miserable life.

'But I stopped.' he said, 'because this way there might be some kind of hope.' He knew it didn't make sense. It was a stubborn thing, hope.

She said she understood but how could she? It was too early for her.

In their third week together, she said, 'I've seen a poster, Jimmy. There's a festival on the Common. Come with me. It's free and there might be music.'

The Common was up towards the river, more than a couple of miles away. They walked briskly and after a while Betwa removed her jacket and he offered to hold it.

'You're quite the gentleman, Mr Noone,' she teased.

He was pleased to be able to offer her anything.

The festival appeared in the distance as a low murmur buzzing with possibility. They headed towards it and as they neared they saw the Common: a throbbing green lung amidst an ailing greyscape of tower-blocks stacked up against the muddy river. The festival rose through the middle in a bellow of noise and smoke and a patchwork of colour. Horns beeped as traffic clogged up on the road alongside it. Smells of candy floss and cooking oil bloated the air, causing a sharp twist inside Jimmy's gut. People jostled around them, weaving between cars and buses in the direction of whirring Twister-rides and the thuddy reverb of bass guitar. In the distance, a tiny boy, four maybe five years old, stood on the edge of the grass sobbing as distracted revellers wandered by. Betwa ran to him without hesitation. Jimmy tried to catch up but a pram blocked his way so he watched as she knelt on one knee and put her face near to the child's. She whispered something in his ear and gently wiped his tears with the tips of her fingers then pointed him towards a thin woman in a smart lemon-yellow jacket frantically pushing through the crowd. Jimmy smiled. Above the roar, the woman screeched the boy's name.

'Oscar, Oscarrr!'

The noise she made was alarming. A sudden hush cloaked the crowd and the moment was suspended, gripping the air until the woman's gaze fell on Betwa and then the tone of her voice shifted.

'Don't touch him! Get your filthy hands off him,' she shouted.

The moment unpaused. People stared. Some gathered around Betwa and the boy, kettling them. A man in a Vampire Weekend tee-shirt grabbed the child's trembling shoulder, yanked him in close and raised the flat of his hand right up to Betwa's nose. The woman in the yellow jacket was a few feet from her child now. She continued to shout, her flushed cheeks streaked with make-up. Her voice rose over the grumble of traffic and the clangour of pop music. 'Get away from him!' she said firmly.

Betwa's face crumpled. 'He was... I was just...'

The boy wriggled free and ran to his mother. She dropped to her knees and they embraced. The child sobbed into her breast as she squeezed him tightly. Onlookers dispersed and the festival atmosphere returned swiftly.

'What, no thank you?' Jimmy said to the woman as he reached the spot where she knelt. She ignored him and nestled into her child, covering the top of his head in kisses.

'For fuck's sake,' Jimmy muttered under his breath. 'You lost him; my friend here was just trying to help.'

He turned to look for Betwa. Only seconds had passed but she was gone. He scanned the crowd: a multi-coloured sea of people, young and old, a mess of shape and noise. He couldn't see her. He moved through the throng, shouting, yelling her name over and over. No hush fell over the revellers and no moment was suspended; there was no pause, no alarm, no echoes of his desperation, no empathetic looks in the faces of strangers. He pushed his hair away from his face and climbed on to a bench to get a better view. A few people looked up, rolling their eyes at his raggedy-ness; they turned away quickly like people do from the news when the dead in the bomb-blasts and earthquakes don't look like them.

Jimmy still couldn't see Betwa even from the raised position. He clambered down and walked around the dodgems and the Waltzer ride, amongst dancers and sugared-up children, through discarded plastic bottles and half-eaten hot-dogs looking for her, clinging on to her jacket. He walked and called her name until daylight slipped away behind the high-rise buildings and only embers of the festival remained.

Later, by the bins at the back of Tesco's, where the street sleepers waited like Dickensian poor-boys for *past the sell-by date* sandwiches, he asked the others about her.

'The lass has probably gone home, back to her family. Someone would have come for her. Even a charming fuckhead like you, Jimmy-boy, is no substitute for a good ruby murray and a clean bed,' Alan said.

'No. That's not it.' Jimmy shook his head.

He trudged back to the subway and waited, until the gaudy dazzlement of the murals made his eyes ache and Vivaldi's *Four Seasons* drilled in his ears long after the music ended. He waited and waited, missing her quiet company. Three, four days passed, he couldn't recall. Then he rolled up his sleeping bag, shoved Betwa's jacket and his book into his rucksack and began walking, retracing steps they'd made together. First he went to the gated square where they'd jumped the railings. He sat on the bench under the laburnum tree, drifting in and out of an anxious sleep until an old man in tweeds and moccasins poked him with a walking stick and told him to *bugger off*. He looked behind bins, in half-loaded skips and empty doorways, amongst the ramshackle shelters and burnt-out vehicles under the graffiti-covered flyover which cut through the centre of the city. He walked, from south of the river over an old iron footbridge, and carried on walking, away from the only streets he knew in that cacophonous place.

2. RAYYA

The sound of shattering glass broke Rayya's sleep. She'd been dreaming of running across a plain with arms outstretched and her face towards the sun. Once awake it was difficult to get back off, so she lay in bed listening to the rustle of leaves, waiting for dawn to slip in through a gap in the drapes. It soon came, as a shimmer of maroon light and she rose to open the curtains, scanning the morning for the source of the earlier disturbance. Somehow, she noticed, the world had changed colour without ceremony and where only yesterday it seemed everything was cloaked in velvet green, now leaves were amber and brittle, swirling in the autumn breeze. Clouds hung low above rooftops opposite. It was hard to judge the temperature outside from the bedroom: even in the mildest days the central heating was on all the time; Satish had to be kept warm now his body had stopped functioning. She pushed open the sash window and breathed in the crisp air. The day was already a soft soup of noise: a low hum of traffic and the distant babble of sleepless babies being pushed around the park by somnambulant parents. Shifnal Road, with its brick-built properties, seemed solid enough but sound travelled easily between the houses. As Rayya stood near to the window, close to the wall of the adjoining house, she heard the murmur of the child next door singing to her toys. She smiled, pulled her dressing gown tight around her body and wondered if the child too had been woken in the night by the sound of breaking glass.

When Rayya first moved to Shifnal Road with Satish nearly fifty years earlier, no-one had wanted to live in the shabby little houses which lined those streets. The properties were cheap but many lay empty until people like them, those invited to take up new lives in this old country, started to make homes in the area. At first, an English family lived in the house next door. Their four young sons often scrambled over the fence separating the gardens in search of footballs gone astray. Rayya welcomed them with sweet sticky jalebi, bought especially, which they devoured before rubbing the syrup off their chins with their wrists and clambering back over the wall. The parents of the boys were Janet and John, names like the people in books at the school where Rayya worked. They never spoke to her or to Satish and at the side of their front bay window they displayed a newspaper cutting of a suited man raising his fist, fully visible to the Jamaican milkman and the Bangladeshi postman; the headline declared *England for the English.*

'They hate us,' Satish said in their mother tongue when he first saw the poster. 'Just because our skin is darker than theirs. Imagine the stupidity of it.'

'Satish, this also happens in India as you well know,' Rayya replied.

'Yes my darling, of course I know. It's why we came here for this supposedly better life.'

'Dreams are never the reality we imagine,' she said.

Satish continued. 'So much for the freethinking, liberated Europeans I used to read about. Sometimes I don't know what's worse, the *pindus* and the priests back home clinging on to their ridiculous divisions or the rulers of this country, peddling their racism to distract the poor from the true engineers of poverty; both are the same at the end of the day. Don't you agree, darling?'

She nodded. There was little they didn't agree on, including the causes of inequality in the world which kept Satish endlessly occupied.

Rayya often watched the next-door boys as they played in the scraggy park across the road, too. She would wave to them if they caught her eye. Sometimes one would smile, scan for onlookers and then, very occasionally give a little wave back. When she saw them, she imagined her own future offspring, perhaps one of each sex, running around the park with other British children, kicking balls or flying paper aeroplanes which she and Satish had folded. Then, as time passed, the next-door boys grew up and moved on and the daydreams of her own children became a deep and distant hollow within her.

'What will be will be,' Satish said when they came back from medical appointments or received test results.

'But I don't want to accept it, Satish. I want to have a baby. Our child – me and you combined in one being. I want to give you this gift.' Tears streamed as she spoke.

'Rayya,' Satish said as he kissed her wet face, 'when you used to run past me in Tilak Nagar, all I ever wanted was you. You agreeing to marry me was the greatest gift I could have wished for. Children come and then they go again, off to make their own lives, just as we did. But you and me, we'll be together forever.'

Rayya understood the truth in his consolations but she also knew there was a huge hole inside her which was irreparable. The void existed in a different way for Satish: in unplayed cricket games and unexplained theorems, in the joy of the *Apu Trilogy* and the stories of Tagore or Narayan which he would never get to hand on like a gleaming baton or precious heirloom; but these were things which, nevertheless, could one day be gently put aside. Then, when Janet and John's oldest boy came to visit with his own newborn baby swaddled in a sling at his chest, Rayya wept for two days without abate. She wept for the years slipped away, and for Satish who she knew longed to be a father despite his conciliatory words; she wept at the fact she would never be able to give him such joy, and for the dreams they once concocted together of a life which had never worked out quite as they'd hoped. But most of all she wept for herself in grief, knowing she would never be a mother. The longing for a child remained as a tight knot in her heart, but any talk of it was quietly put away into a place only she could reach.

When Janet and John moved away, it was without so much as a nod to the neighbours they'd lived beside for well over a decade. The house stood empty for many months before a jovial young Cypriot man moved in and invited Rayya and Satish into an abode they'd never before entered. The man was called Kostas; he chatted to them as if he were their long lost friend, asking questions about the neighbourhood and how it was for them to have come from elsewhere and live in such a place. That evening, they ate *avgolemono* soup together and, beneath postcards of Kostas' island home, still squinting from the tart lemony broth, they raised a large glass of ouzo to mark the anniversary of the death of the fascist Franco and Rayya saw something of Satish's boyhood revitalised in him.

The evening with their new neighbour was the first of many, always with music and food, Greek or Indian, beer or ouzo, and always with impassioned conversation which reminded all three of them they were part of a much bigger world. But, less than seven years later, Kostas died in a circumstance which was never fully explained and suddenly their good friend, one of the few people to ever treat them as equals, was no more. Instead Kostas' impetuous young nephew was their neighbour. A few years after the passing of his uncle, Nikos Makrides divided the house into two flats: the ground floor he kept for his own young family and the top floor was rented out to a succession of tenants who came and went, often before Rayya had got used to their faces. Eventually, Nikos moved to a more salubrious neighbourhood and later the ground floor was sold off, to two women (friends unable to buy their own places, Rayya guessed) while upstairs was rented more permanently to a beautiful little girl and her impenetrable young mother. Rayya had lived in the area far longer than most but she remained a stranger, and now, with Satish the way he was, she wondered sometimes if there was anyone around she could actually call a friend anymore.

Next door, the child's singing appeared to come to an abrupt halt; Rayya wondered why. She returned to the window to survey the day now it had properly settled in, but it took a moment for her to see the person by the car at the back of the gardens. She stared and when the young man caught her eye she stepped backwards into the bedroom. In the shadows, she suddenly remembered an incident from the day before, of a similar young man being kicked in a doorway by Nikos; it was the wild black hair which seemed familiar but whether it was the same person or not she couldn't tell, not with her eyesight weakening as it was. The previous incident had disturbed her enough to describe it to Satish on her return from her hurried shopping trip that morning.

'Honestly, Satish you would be appalled at how someone, someone we know and have spent time with, can kick a poor unfortunate boy lying on the ground defenceless. Kostas was such a sweet and gentle man, how this nephew of his could behave in such a heartless way is incredible to me, don't you agree? I can hardly think they are of the same blood anymore.'

Now she rushed down the landing to tell Satish about the man behind the gardens, to ask if they could possibly be one and the same? Her husband's room was dark on entry and stifling as it always was in the mornings. She opened the curtains, watching his face closely for the minutest glimmer of movement as a new light washed over him. She wanted a sign to show he was awake; there was none. His eyes remained closed, just as she had positioned them the night before. She lifted his eyelids gently with her fingertips and kissed his brow.

'Good morning, darling,' she said with a cheerfulness which became more strained each day.

When Satish first started to become ill their conversations were unmarked by the deterioration in his physical health. He was weak but the chatter flowed, just as it always had after daytimes spent apart. But, as time moved forward, he spoke less and less and as his body became progressively devoid of animation so too did his voice become devoid of words. Rayya couldn't remember the exact moment their conversations became her monologues but over time she came to accept nods and smiles as prompts and responses. It wasn't long before the nods were reduced to blinks and the smiles became glares. But she knew Satish could hear her so she still shared everything with him; whilst his body may have closed down his brain still processed thoughts and memories, she was certain of it.

'Satish,' Rayya said, 'there is a man outside. He is just a boy really. He looks so skinny. He is sleeping in the bashed up car. Remember I told you about the car?' She gently stroked Satish's cheek as she spoke. His eyes displayed no discernible emotion; they didn't need to, she knew what lay behind: it terrified her to think of his devastating sadness and, worse, his desperate and dreadful fear.

She put drops into his eyes and reached for a tissue from the nearby table to wipe the corners of his mouth where a tiny stream of peach-coloured liquid dribbled out, then she sat on her chair beside him, as she did every morning, slipped on her glasses and began to read. Yesterday they'd finished *A Fine Balance* after many weeks. Today she was starting *A House For Mr Biswas*. They were among his favourites. He'd read each one many times over, including out loud to Rayya, and the characters were as familiar as relatives to them both. She recited the first few lines and then stopped suddenly, laid the book on her lap and said, 'Can you believe it, Satish? I think this boy in the car is the same one silly dumbo Nikos Makrides was kicking yesterday. Remember I told you about this? I think he needs our help, the boy not Nikos I mean.' She picked up the book and thumbed the pages. 'I know you would reprimand me for uttering such a superstitious thing, but I think he's here because he needs us. I'm meant to help him. What do you think, Satish?'

She was surprised by the bounce in her own voice. She got up and straightened Satish's covers and opened the window for just a few seconds to let some air into the fuggy room.

'Well,' she continued. 'I know you'd agree it's our duty at least to help this boy. It's what we've always believed isn't it? To stretch out our hands to those in trouble.'

She stood up and placed the book on the vacated chair.

'Today reading will have to wait,' she said. 'I've decided. I'm going to make him *roti*, Satish. It is the only thing I can think of to help him. The poor thing looks like he may not have eaten properly for weeks, and well, I may as well take my chance to be the *dadi-ma* I should have been by now. Is this not what everyone thinks of us old Indian ladies, that we are only useful to cook and to feed? Apparently it is all we are good for, so, yes, why not? I will feed him, this is what I should do, *hai na*?'

In the kitchen, Rayya grabbed the only onion from the wire basket next to the hob and held on to it while she looked in the fridge. The shelves were empty besides a small carton of milk, a slab of butter and some garlic and ginger paste. The cupboard next to the cooker was equally scant but behind cans of minestrone soup and plum tomatoes she found a couple of tins of boiled chickpeas. It was enough.

As spicy aromas permeated the oblong room, Rayya wondered when she'd last cooked a proper meal. Now, with Satish's only sustenance administered through a tube there was no pleasure in cooking, not just for herself. Eating was a function, carried out at set hours without joy. These days she ate mostly from tins and packets: supermarket brand soups, dehydrated noodle pots, Batchelor's Savoury Rice, and cheap microwave meals which only ever tasted of plastic and salt. At a push, she sometimes made herself an omelette, adding a little garlic and garam masala for flavour. Once a week she'd boil a simple dhal and eat it with pitta from the Turkish bakery along the high street for as many meals as it would last. She bolted food down, often standing in the kitchen as she ate. There was no point sitting alone in the dim dining room with no-one to talk to. And to eat by Satish, as he lay inanimate upstairs, would be both cruel and vulgar.

The smell of sizzling onion reminded Rayya of the first meal she'd cooked after their wedding: a concoction of lamb and tomatoes with far too much green chilli in the sauce. Satish, eager to try his new wife's culinary skills, tasted a large spoonful straight from the pan. His face turned an immediate shade of scarlet, glistening as he spluttered and coughed, fanning his mouth with his hands. Two glasses of water and a bowl of plain yoghurt later, he gently suggested they visit the Delhi street market nearby to eat *bhel poori* as an appetiser. There they sat on wooden benches outside Gobi's Dhaba on the edge of the bustling square in the centre of Tilak Nagar. Gobi was familiar to them both from the local streets and, when he saw the henna on Rayya's hands, he insisted the bhel poori was on the house, followed by complementary pakora and freshly cooked keema kebabs. The food was delivered with a hearty slap on the back for Satish and a polite bow for Rayya. The following day, Satish brought more yogurt and stirred it into the cold lamb dish. He added extra tomatoes, a little sugar and a squeeze of lemon and that evening they ate the reheated meal with piles of rice as beads of sweat dripped down their noses and onto their plates. From then on, they cooked together in the evenings, feeding one another little tastes of sauce, adding extra salt or chilli as needed. And so they learnt to perfect the *saag* Rayya loved so much and the *bhindi* and *baingan bhata* which were Satish's favourites. Over time, the art of cooking improved for both husband and wife and became a beloved shared pleasure. Sometimes, if either was inadvertently heavy-handed with the spice, they recalled their first meal as a married couple and laughed at how they had tried so hard to play at being grown-ups in those first few weeks of setting up home. Later, in their little English terraced house, they made simpler versions of their favourite dishes after busy days at work, sitting in their cosy dining room, taking hours over the meal, each with a tall glass of icy beer at hand and the music of Jagjit Singh or Pandit Ravi Shankar in the background. Their conversations ranged from the local news stories from the streets of the city they now lived in to developments back home in India. Often they just chatted about people they'd encountered, those who had been interesting or kind to them. Rayya missed the sound of Satish's voice. She stirred the onions, lowered the gas and returned to the bedroom where he lay.

'I am making him *chole*, Satish. Do you think he'll like Punjabi food?' She leaned over him as she spoke, swabbing his mouth with a dampened cotton wool bud. 'I'll be careful with the *mirch*', she said cheerfully, searching his face for a tiny hint of a smile but it was rigid. He had now been without any movement for over six months but she still worried she might miss a tic in his cheek or a flicker in his eye. 'Who wouldn't like Punjabi food, eh?' she said.

While the chickpea curry was thickening on the stove, Rayya put enough flour and water into a bowl to make a fist-sized ball of dough. She dusted off the *tava*, floured the wooden chopping board and rolled out four perfectly round chapatis and proceeded to cook them, shifting the flatbread from *tava* to open flame and wincing when the fire caught the tips of her fingers. When all four chapatis were cooked, she set one aside and wrapped the remaining three in tin foil, placed them on top of a plastic container filled with the curry, wrapped a tea towel around the bundle to keep in the heat and made herself a cup of tea which she carried up to the bedroom. She sat next to Satish, reading from *A House For Mr Biswas* between sips. When the chapter was complete, she said,

'I can still make chapatis, Satish. I haven't made them for many months now, not just for myself. But each one blew up like a little balloon first time. I've made them for the boy in the car. I know you'll probably think I should just leave him to find his own way but it's breaking my heart to think of him sleeping outside in the cold. We didn't have much when were young but somehow this is different. This boy, well he must have had a very bad time to be in this position. And he is an Englishman. Can you believe it?'

On the last gulp of tea, Rayya heard the front gate creak. She stood and looked out of the window. 'Carers are here, Satish. Time for you to be fed too, my darling,' she said.

3. TULI

Tuli climbed onto the edge of the bed and lifted the curtain. Her room overlooked the gardens at the back of the house and immediately below her window she could see raised flower beds and a vegetable patch which belonged to the flat downstairs. Next door there was just a yard: grass paved over with brown stone, a washing line and one sad-looking apple tree which stretched over the fence, partially shading the lawn beneath. Beyond the gardens was a space where Grace once told her Mr Makrides was going to build a pottery shed. At the time, Tuli asked her mother what a pottery shed was. Mummy said,

'It's a place to make nice things out of clay, like you do with play dough.'

She showed Tuli what clay looked like on her phone and they both watched, transfixed, as large wrinkled hands worked with a slop of grey mud, transforming it into a bowl like the ones they ate breakfast cereal from. Tuli was astounded.

'It's like magic. I didn't know magic could happen in a scruffy place at the back of gardens,' she said.

A noise in the quietest part of the night disturbed her but she didn't look out into the dark then because it was when ghosts and other bad things came alive. She waited, and suddenly it was morning so she peered from the edge of the curtain towards the pottery-shed space, all the while singing to Freddy Teddy and her dolly with the stuck hair, unaware that in the room next door the old woman who smiled but never spoke was looking towards the same spot for the same reason. She dropped the curtain when she heard noises down the landing, cupping her hands over her ears to block out the sound of Mummy's loud in-a-rush voice but it still poured into her head.

'Tuli, are you up? You'll have to go downstairs again. I'll be back soon. Tuli. Can you hear me?'

'Yes, Mummy,' she said flopping onto the floor but her own voice was a tiny whisper and even she could barely hear it.

Downstairs was where Grace and Mandy lived. Sometimes they looked after her when school was closed and Mummy had to go to her job. Sounds flowed back and forth like waves through the thin caramel carpets which separated the upstairs flat from the one below and, through the floor, Tuli heard Grace and Mandy's music, their loud talking and sometimes the booming laughter of the friends who came to eat dinner with them. She wondered what they could hear from upstairs: maybe the *Arthur* music on the television before school or Mummy's getting-ready voice?

She liked both the women but she preferred Grace because she once showed her the secret place in the downstairs kitchen where chocolate was kept, hidden away from Mandy. Grace was kind but Mandy was funnier, especially when she spoke in her sing-song voice. Tuli liked to call the two women one name, Grandy. They ruffled her hair and called her strange words like *possum* and *cherub* when she first started saying it; she just liked the convenience of one name instead of two.

Grandy's flat felt like a home. It was different to upstairs: warm, even in the coldest months; a proper kitchen with a bench like the ones in the school playground but pale blue and without the pigeon poo; there was a bathroom with a bathtub and a separate shower which you didn't need to hold up with your hand. Grandy shared a bedroom with one big bed even though they were both grown-ups and the flat was big enough for them to have their own rooms. Tuli guessed they liked to snuggle up in the bed amongst all the bright cushions, just like they sometimes did on the sofa. Their bedroom had glass doors opening up onto a hidden part of the garden with a small round table in the middle and on the side, a broken toilet with big yellow flowers growing out of it. There was another room with a desk in the flat which Mandy called her study; it had almost as many books as the school library. The door to the study was always closed. Mandy said it was *out of bounds* but Tuli kept forgetting to ask what *bounds* were or why it mattered if there wasn't any left.

Tuli never minded going downstairs: Grace and Mandy didn't bother with her much; they just opened the garden door and carried on with whatever they were doing around the flat. At meal times, they sought her out and shooed her towards a bowl of pasta and pesto on the coffee table in front of the TV while they ate their own leafy lunches with glasses of juice at the kitchen bench. Sometimes Grandy looked after her if Mummy was out in the evening too. It didn't happen very often but when it did they gave her books to read and colouring to do while they drank red wine, laughed at the chatty voices on the radio and cooked things which never looked like the food she and Mummy ate.

On weekends, when Grandy were away visiting friends who'd moved to big houses in places away from busy streets, she was allowed to use the garden in return for feeding Hoyden and Pancake, the two fat lady cats who also lived downstairs. These were her favourite weekends. Grace suggested the arrangement when Tuli was still very young and now she was a little older, she and Mummy looked after the cats when Grandy went on long trips to places Mummy called 'posh-people's destinations.' The cat-sitting was in return for babysitting they said, but she wondered how she was still the baby even though she was growing taller all the time and soon she'd be almost as tall as Grace, who wasn't very big for a grown-up. Nevertheless, she thought it was a good plan because when Grandy first went on a long holiday, Mummy left the downstairs flat door unlocked, made dinners in Grandy's big kitchen and ate them with Tuli on the comfy sofa in Grandy's living room. She loved that time, pretending she lived in a whole house like some of the other children at school, running upstairs to use the toilet and bouncing back down to watch television. Best of all, she could go in the garden as often as she liked, so long as it wasn't raining or dark. But Mummy didn't like the cats: they never did as they were told and she hated cleaning the stinking trays where they hid poo. Worst of all they made her eyes puffy and red, like when she'd been crying for days, and if they came close it made her sneeze and cough so badly it was a real sickness, so the game of pretending came to an end too quickly.

When Tuli heard the shower buzz into life along the landing she lifted the curtain again and looked out to the back of the garden. Just a few days earlier, Mandy had knocked on their door to tell Mummy about an old car which had been left in the path leading to the empty space where the pottery shed was going to be.

'I've emailed the council about it,' Mandy said as Tuli watched from the top of the stairs. 'And left a voicemail for Mr Makrides. Apparently the police won't do anything about it as it's private land but Mr Makrides won't want an abandoned vehicle on his property for too long.'

Mummy shrugged her shoulders like she always did when she didn't feel like talking.

'You know, Ebele, you don't need to be so rude. You could just say thanks or something, just to be polite even if you don't give a shit.'

Mandy was always using bad words, just like Mummy, but they were allowed because they were grown-ups. When Tuli once said the 'shit' word at school, children around her laughed and when the teacher shouted at her, the children laughed even louder.

She wondered whether the noise she'd heard in the night was the council people pulling the car away or whether another car had crashed into the one which was already there. From the corner of her eye she noticed how the thick shards of broken glass embedded in the concrete rim of the neighbour's wall gleamed in the morning sunshine, dancing a pattern of shimmering light across the bricks. She liked the zigzag the glass made and how it looked like the stickleback dinosaur she'd painted at school which was now stuck to the fridge door with a magnet. She sang along to the dancing patterns and forgot why she was looking out of the window in the first place when suddenly there was a movement and a raggedy thing appeared from the bashed up car. She stopped singing and stared at the odd-looking creature, who was a bit like a real man. He looked familiar. *Is it my daddy come home to see me?* The words were in her head and held there so they wouldn't fall onto her tongue and tumble out in front of Mummy. But this man looked too strange to be a daddy.

'Maybe he's in my books,' she whispered out loud. 'Maybe it's a storyman only I can see.'

'Tuli, Tuli are you dressed yet? C'mon, I can't be late again.' Mummy's shouting voice was near to the bedroom door. Tuli jumped away from the window and looked for her favourite purple jeans amongst the pile of clothes in the corner of her room.

'Not those,' Mummy said from the doorway. 'They're dirty.'

'Mummy,' Tuli said. 'Living in a broken-up car can only be in story worlds, can't it?'

This time the words did come out, but they may as well not have because her mother didn't answer. Instead, she pulled Tuli's worst trousers with silly flowers and no pockets out of the drawer and handed them over. Tuli let the trousers fall to the floor. She tried to hold back words but they came pouring out:

'Glass was smashed. He would bleed and then everything would be red and sticky.'

'What are you talking about?' Mummy said.

'Blood would pour out like a river. It would be messy and he would be dead like children in schools in America on the news.'

'This doesn't sound like a good game, Tuli. Stop it! Stop saying those things. I'll be late for work. We'll talk about this later.'

Mummy left the room but the words kept coming.

Cold wind will bite him at night. He'll shiver too much, and shake all night long like on snow days and he won't be able to sleep because of the shaking and shivering. Real people don't live in smashed-up cars. And now, how will the real car people drive all over the place to their jobs and to hospitals and take their children to far-away schools?

She peered out of the window again. The storyman was still there but she didn't feel frightened of him, not with daylight all around and Mummy calling down the landing like she did every morning. The man put his finger to his lips in the same way Mrs Enisuoh did to shut the children up before the learning could begin at school. Tuli knew what the finger to the lips meant. She carried on staring and then she waved with a tiny flicker of her raised hand, not like the big waves children gave parents waiting for them at the school gates at the end of the day; her wave was quiet. Sometimes she waved this way to the people waiting at the bus-stop opposite the front of the house and sometimes someone waved back; perhaps the storyman would too. Once, when she waved, a bus stop boy stuck two fingers up towards her then shook his fist as if he wanted to punch her face. She was frightened so she hid behind her hands and looked through a gap in her fingers only to see the boy laughing with his friends and pointing at her. Mostly though, the bus-stop people just smiled and looked away. She wondered what the storyman would do with her wave; she hoped he wouldn't stick up two fingers. She wanted to keep looking but she knew it was wrong to stare. He looked funny, not like real life: his hair was matted like the doll Mummy bought home from the second-hand shop near where she worked. The doll's black hair was too knotted to comb through so Tuli had taken the scissors from the kitchen and chopped half of it off, but it never grew back and she was sorry. No one had chopped off the man's hair yet and he needed a haircut even more than the doll. Suddenly he waved back; it was a small wave like hers, hardly a movement at all. She didn't know what to do so she bent low until the window was above her and she slid along the floor on her stomach, across to the other side of the room. Then she stood up and pulled on the flowery trousers, tugged her sweater over her head and ran down the landing.

Mummy slept on a sofa-bed in the living room. She only started to do that when Jamal Daddy lived with them but she carried on after he left. Before Jamal Daddy, Tuli always slept by Mummy, just the two of them. These days the sofa stayed out all day and if she wanted to watch *Arthur* or *Deadly 60* on TV she would do so stretched out on the bed with her head just a foot or two away from the screen. At dinner time she watched television propped up on Mummy's pillows with her plate on her lap instead of at the dining table. She liked it best this way, with Mummy next to her. And she liked the living-room: the wide windows let light dance in on sunny days, brightening the grubby walls and making the room glow. But she liked the room even when the sun wasn't shining because it overlooked Black Horse Lane, busy with comings and goings and, when the window was open, she could hear the babble of older children and other people at the bus stop. Behind the bus stop was Hazelwood Park and she liked to daydream she was old enough to cross the busy road herself and disappear into the trees for adventures. In stories, there was always magic in trees. In front of the trees was a wide stretch of grass where big boys played football and beyond that a playground with a slide covered in swear words. Mummy often complained the playground was meant to be for smaller children but growling teenagers took up all the space, standing around in clumps or dangling their gangly legs over the climbing frame, smoking. Both the swings in the playground were broken. Mummy didn't like the park but Tuli missed the little sandpit she used to go to with Jamal

Daddy. It was shaped like a wooden boat with a steering wheel and dials and she liked to pretend she was sailing through a sky-blue sea to cloud islands made of cotton wool and snow. On one side of the playground was an overgrown section of the park which Mummy was afraid of. Children at school with older brothers and sisters called it Dogger's End but there were dogs everywhere in the park; Mummy said they made the name up to confuse the younger ones.

Her mother followed her into the living room, holding out a bowl of Cheerios.

'Eat this, little one,' she said, stretching the bowl towards her.

Tuli moved in closer. She wanted a cuddle but Mummy just stroked her cheek and walked away, out of reach. Tuli grabbed her soft toy from the floor next to Mummy's bed and squeezed it.

'There you are, Froggy,' she said. 'I was looking for you at bedtime, you cheeky thing.' She sat the toy on her lap as she scooped a spoonful of Cheerios into her mouth, dripping splashes of milk and soggy hoops onto Froggy's head.

After Jamal Daddy had gone, Tuli and Mummy spent days and days in the living room on the sofa-bed, sleeping late and wearing pyjamas the whole time. They watched boring television about fancy food and other people's houses and ate cream crackers and Cheerios for breakfast, lunch and dinner. When the Cheerios ran out, Mummy told her she had to go back to school because Mrs Enisuoh kept phoning to see where she was and if she didn't go, other people might start calling too and they might not be as friendly as her headteacher.

When Mummy walked her to school after those few days, she wore sunglasses in the rain which made her look like a bumble bee. She left Tuli at the school gates, alone amongst a roundabout of people and noise. When all the other parents had gone and the children lined up outside the entrance, a boy called Finn prodded her chest and said he'd heard her dad was dead. She knew it couldn't be true: Jamal Daddy's parents would have come from the place she only remembered as a smell and a colour on the other side of the big sky. They would have wept more than they did when she sat on Jamal Daddy's lap and he waved them goodbye from the dusty bus window while she and Mummy looked on. A hushed chant of *'dead dad, dead dad, you've got a dead dad'* followed her around the school and when the chanting wouldn't stop, she stood in a square of chalked hopscotch at playtime and screamed as loudly as she could until her breath ran out. Some of the bigger children with phones took pictures and flashed the screens back at her so she could see her own face all swollen and red. She crumpled like dirty washing, sobbing into the tarmac until Mrs Enisuoh came and sat with her on the hard ground. They stayed there until rain splashed down then Tuli sat up and wiped her face with her sleeve while Mrs Enisuoh sat quietly next to her.

Mummy was cross because she had to leave Mr Makrides' shop early on her first day back at work after the school called and told her what had happened.

'Jamal Daddy isn't dead,' she said. 'He just disappeared into the trees. We won't see him again but he is somewhere, alive and well and probably having a great time.'

'Maybe he got stuck in a different world, like in The Faraway Tree, and he doesn't know how to get back to us,' Tuli said.

'I doubt it. Don't be thinking he's coming back, Tuli. They never come back.'

Mummy said Tuli should ignore Finn and his friends so, when the bell rang for playtime, instead of running out with the other children she waited by the coat racks until a grown-up escorted her out and then she stayed as close to them as she could. The children soon got bored, even Finn, who found a boy who didn't speak English to make cry instead.

Tuli was glad this day wasn't a school day and when it was almost time to leave, she sat on the top step sliding from one side to the other, bouncing between wall and bannister, waiting for her mother to find lost things.

'Can I just go downstairs now, Mummy?' Tuli said.

'No, wait for me. I have things to say to that Mandy.'

So Tuli waited and waited and when she got bored of sliding, she stretched out her legs and arms like a starfish. She wanted to see the storyman again, close up this time, and check if he was real or just for her to see, like the cotton wool islands in the sky. But she didn't say *hurry up* even though Mummy said it to her all the time. Hurry Up was something only grown-ups were allowed to say.

4. JIMMY

Jimmy had walked for almost five hours without stopping, following signs towards places Betwa had mentioned. Eventually he'd emerged through vast iron park gates leading to a bustling high street. He headed for the section called Grand Parade; it was the place she'd called home. The Parade was teeming: people with plastic bags overflowing with produce he didn't recognise. Shabby buildings shrouded in faded splendour lined the main drag. A small child stood behind the glass front of a newsagent's gripping her mother's hand; she caught Jimmy's eye but quickly turned away. He didn't blame the kid; he saw what she saw in the reflection: a wild and stooping *Skellig* from his youth staring blankly ahead.

Grand Parade was familiar, like deja vu. It was just as Betwa described. A mixture of odours crammed the brittle air: a sour undertone overpowered by the aroma of roast lamb. It was like an Easter Sunday in his youth, sat around the table waiting in hushed anticipation for Nan to bring in the dinner while Frank, Jimmy's father, irascible as ever, sat at the head, poised to find fault. For Jimmy, the smell brought Anthony to mind most clearly: his brother Ant before the skag, still healthy, grinning at the thought of his big dinner and only half-an-hour out of his pit. Such a long time ago. He pushed the memory away but it was hard to shift. The next thing he noticed about the place was the clamour of it; no different to south of the river but more compacted somehow. Discordant ringtones and people engrossed in one-sided conversations through imperceptible microphones, shouting into the ether, fighting to be heard against an angry growl of stuck traffic. There were other sounds too: other-worldly tunes floating out on a waft of garlic from Indika's Curry House and the wedged-open door of a jam-packed Turkish restaurant. Beyond the more subtle sounds was the loud repetitive pump-pump-pump of grime music from car windows wound down, pushing the rhythm into the faces of passers-by. The wide street was a tumble of noise and smell, and colour too: bunches of parsley, coriander, dill, mint piled up in crates next to bright mounds of tomatoes, peppers, apples and trays of marbled watermelon, split with machetes to reveal succulent pink flesh dotted with beady eyes. It was life at full throttle, overflowing.

Jimmy edged his way towards the centre of the throng. The rumble in his stomach became a hollow nausea as he passed a line of stinking industrial bins; a bloodied sanitary towel and a withered piece of maggoty fruit lay side by side in his path. He turned away and tried to make out specific places Betwa had spoken about. An ornate Victorian pub on the corner with embellished bottle-green tile-work was easy to spot. It was topped by a majestic cupola which loomed over the bookmakers and bakery on the same block. He tried to enter the pub but a man stood in his way.

'I've got beer money. That's the rule isn't it?' Jimmy said. He expected disgust but the man spoke in a way which threw him.

'Sit in a booth, back there,' the doorman said pointing. 'The manager won't kick off then.'

'What?'

'If the regular punters can't see you, it won't bother them. The barman will pretend he hasn't noticed you and so will I. We're not supposed to let you in.'

'You don't know me.'

'People like you.'

'People like me?' *Flotsam, scum.*

The booth was hidden behind the large wooden doorway. Jimmy sank into burgundy velvet and eyed the other drinkers.

The majority were men in suits: collars loosened, top buttons undone, jackets strewn across bar stools and backs of chairs. They perched alongside small mixed groups of weary folk drinking their pints far too quickly. Teachers perhaps. They looked like teachers. He imagined Betwa amongst the clientele, sipping her vodka and coke, getting ready for an evening stretching ahead of her, full of possibility. A song he vaguely recognised began to play out and he strained to hear it above the crackle of voices. The doorman appeared a moment later with a pint of cider and a copy of the evening edition of the city paper. He placed both on the table. Jimmy nodded a thank-you. He hated cider, a whoosie's drink, his brother used to say, *only whoosies and low lifes drink that shite.*

'People like us are people like you too,' Jimmy said as the doorman turned to leave. The man hesitated.

'I know mate, I didn't mean anything by it.' He spoke in the jangly mishmash accent of the city. He told Jimmy to put the sleeping bag under the table so people couldn't see it. The doorman was similar to him in years, maybe a little older, perhaps nearer Ant's age. He was clean shaven with black hair cut short, close to his head. He wore a small gold sleeper in one ear; the edge of a tattoo peeked out from under his shirtsleeve.

'What's that then?' Jimmy pointed at the tattoo, conscious of his own clunky Northern twang.

The doorman stretched out his right arm and pulled the sleeve to his elbow, revealing a string of daffodils snaking up his skin.

'Strange choice.' Jimmy said mockingly. 'You don't seem like a Welshman.'

'They don't have exclusive rights.' The doorman broadened his chest. 'It connects me to my ancestors,' he said.

Jimmy laughed before he could stop himself. He apologised. 'My ancestors are the kind you want to forget about.'

'No worries, mate. Did it for my mum, she likes it. She's got them too.'

'What, an old woman with tattoos?'

'She's not so old. Anyway, it's tradition where we're from. Even my grandma has them.' He pointed to his forehead. 'Across here,' he said.

'You sound like you're from these parts to me,' Jimmy said. The man looked like many others in the area: Mediterranean, Turkish possibly, Egyptian perhaps. He couldn't tell; he hadn't spent enough time with people from other places to be able to distinguish between them. In his town almost everyone was white: all of them keeping their heads above the parapet, just about; all of them dirt poor just the same.

The doorman said, 'I am from here but we're all from somewhere else originally, even you, I bet.'

Jimmy shrugged, irritated. He hadn't meant anything by the comment; it was just the doorman seemed to belong to this place more than he felt he'd ever belonged anywhere. He bent over his pint.

'My folks are from a country high up in mountains, practically above the clouds,' the doorman said good-naturedly. 'It's one of those invisible places, trying its hardest to exist against all odds. It's a long way from here.' Jimmy relaxed. He wanted to know more, what he meant exactly by *trying to exist*; the phrase resonated with him, but a scuffle at the bar diverted the doorman's attention and he was gone. He returned fifteen minutes later and told Jimmy someone had complained about him.

'Sorry, mate. These people think they're better than the rest of us. Pair of hipsters, the sort who call this place a village. You know the type, always after craft ale and flowery gin, in a boozer like this for fucks sake.'

Jimmy stared into the distance; the things the man spoke about had no place in his world.

'They seem to be moving in around here recently. They think they're so alternative with their ear tunnels and silly beards, but all they seem to talk about is house prices.'

The doorman carried on speaking as he ushered Jimmy out into the dusk by the side door, pointing him onwards and mumbling something about grace and god.

'You what?' Jimmy said.

'Just something my mum says when she sees someone, you know, down and out like you. You could be any of us. I could be in your place. Any of us could.'

'Your god not prepared to give me a bit of grace then?' Jimmy said as he adjusted his rucksack.

The man looked embarrassed. 'I didn't mean that.'

'Thanks for the drink.' Jimmy turned to walk away but the doorman laid his hand on his shoulder; the touch rippled through him.

'I'm Daban, by the way,' the doorman said. 'Listen, there's a hostel on the high street, up there.' He pointed north. 'Maybe check it out. It's getting bitter at night.' Daban took a cigarette from behind his ear and handed it over.

'Ta very much,' Jimmy said and when asked, he told the man his name. 'Jimmy absolutely no-one,' he mumbled with half a smile as he walked away.

Just past the pub, a woman stumbled into Jimmy. She clung onto a small child with one hand and a plastic bag with the other. The little girl smiled and Jimmy recognised her as the same kid from the newsagent's earlier; her long soft curls made her distinctive. The woman dropped her bag of shopping in the collision and a tin of spaghetti hoops rolled out. He bent to pick it up.

'Leave it,' she said firmly without meeting his eye. She grabbed the tin, stuffed it into the bag and dragged the child away, pulling her past people on the pavement. The little girl glanced over her shoulder and raised her eyebrows. Jimmy smiled.

That night, he slept in a wide doorway of an old-fashioned furniture shop near to the pub. Before unrolling his sleeping bag he laid down sheets of newspaper across the concrete step beneath a small canopy. In the pub he'd skimmed through the paper, fixing on an article about a new housing development on the edge of the river where tobacco workers and slum dwellers were once the only residents. He tore out the page and placed it where he planned to lay his head. The article overshadowed another shorter piece: it told of a body spotted bobbing near a mossy bankside by an auxiliary nurse, stretching his legs after a long night at a nearby hospital. The body, a young woman, shoulder-length hair, was dragged from the water at six o'clock one morning the previous week. Paramedics covered her up quickly before school children and day-jobbers caught a glimpse. It was a pointless death; a bedraggled obstacle nudged out of the way by a man in a sharp suit with a butcher's boy look about him, high after payday, caught on CCTV staggering along the wayside. The ruddy-faced man didn't notice the woman lose her footing, or hear the splash and the short but desperate struggle to keep her head above water. He just swayed away, oblivious. Jimmy didn't notice the story as he laid his things over the sheets of newspaper.

Sleep was elusive even after the long walk. It was hard to settle with the noise of the new place. Long after the shoppers, families and tourists had gone home, another set of inhabitants populated the local concerns. Restaurants emptied and the street became one of deals between young men who jiggled about on corners with hands dug deep into pockets until cars with tinted windows pulled up alongside them. Older men filled the cafes, replacing the family get-togethers with card games and bottles of whiskey and Raki. The only women about were one or two in uniform, dog-tired, shuffling home after late work shifts, and those who hung about in the shadows, waiting for customers to buy the only thing they had to sell. As night deepened, the pervading smell became burnt meat and heady skunk, which reminded Jimmy of bus shelters and dilapidated out-houses back home. Since talking with Betwa, random memories were more fluid, freed like flies disentangled from gossamer-thin webs. That night in the shop doorway when sleep finally took hold, he dreamt of the only holiday he'd ever been on; of warm sand cascading through his fingers.

'Nan took us away to give us all a break,' he'd told Betwa just days before. 'She used up all her pay-off money. Frank said she was a fool to waste it on us. I was just fourteen. It was the best time ever, away from him. The sea was so blue, not like the mudflats up at Formby. This was something else: rocks, seaweed, visible beneath the waves. And fish, scooting about your feet, hundreds of the buggers. You had to stand dead still in the water mind, for that to happen.'

Dreaming wasn't clearly defined these days. He cherished the good ones, of being on holiday, the caresses of his mother; moments of fleeting joy, rare and transitory. Too often, dreams shifted into the realm of reality as daily nightmares, fuzzied by alcohol and insomnia. He understood why so many like him favoured unconsciousness to get through. Sometimes it was hard to know what was real and what was imagined; days were muffled between sleepless nights. Now, on the harsh ground in his sleeping bag, he slipped in and out of consciousness. The holiday dream dripped through him: Nan reading *My Weekly* while he splashed in the waves with Ant; his sister Jenny's sunburnt skin, red raw and blistering.

He was woken by a sudden thwack to his shin. A voice from his dream shouted at him.

'Get out of here, Get off my property or I will call the police.'

The man's accent was thick, syrupy. Jimmy rubbed his eyes. It took a moment to work out if the man or the dream came first. His shin was a drumbeat.

'This is my property. Get off it now,' the man repeated. 'I have a shop to open. No customer will come if you are sleeping there.'

People stood at a bus stop just a couple of feet away. They ate pastries from white paper bags and stared at their phones. No-one said *you can't kick a man. It's not right to just kick a man.* No-one until a small Indian woman in a blue coat and a sari the same rainy-day silver as the hair tied neatly away from her creased face. The woman looked quizzically from Jimmy to the shopkeeper. She shook her head and muttered something inaudible.

'None of your business,' the shopkeeper said to her. He raised his foot, poised for another kick but lowered it when the woman spoke again, much louder.

'May your god forgive you Nikos Makrides. Your uncle would be ashamed.'

She pronounced the shopkeeper's name with certainty. People at the bus-stop glanced over but quickly returned to their phones. Nikos Makrides, not so different in age from the woman who reprimanded him, paused for just a second, glaring directly at her, as tiny glimmers of recognition swam across his face. He shoved his wide foot against the sleeping bag, rolling it over Jimmy as if he were a football.

'Get off my property, I have furniture to sell and I don't need a filthy dog making my shop smell bad.'

'You can't just kick a man,' Jimmy said. He curled up, raising his knees to his chest as he watched the old woman disappear down the high street. The shopkeeper stepped over him, fumbling with keys.

'Two minutes to take your rubbish away or I will kick you again.'

Betwa's description of the area had been in fine detail: there was a school nearby, around the corner from the Victorian pub, opposite a much smaller park than the one with the iron gates, close to an old hospital. Jimmy hobbled in that direction with the sleeping bag slung over his shoulder. He walked until he found the unkempt *Hazelwood Recreation Ground* beyond row upon row of mainly scruffy terraces. Through a gap in the railings he made his way towards a small cafe in a shack halfway up a path, where people sat alone at formica tables behind steamy windows. He nudged open the door with his elbow and poked his head around. A woman with a baby in a buggy next to her caught his eye; she quickly looked away. A sprawling middle-aged man in paint-splattered overalls glanced up briefly. He took a bite of the sandwich held between his doughy fingers; ketchup oozed onto the image of a naked girl in his newspaper.

'At least it hasn't spoilt her tits,' he said, looking directly at Jimmy with a dirty grin. Masticated bacon fell from his lips onto the page; he scooped it up with a fat finger. Jimmy looked over the man towards a woman in a headscarf behind the counter.

'Got anything going?' he called across to her. She beckoned him in and he watched as she wrapped up a ham roll and an iced bun.

'Any chance of a hot drink?' he said. She nodded without speaking, poured coffee from the urn into a cardboard cup and slid the items across the glass counter.

'Thank you.' Jimmy said.

'No worries, love. You take care of yourself.'

Her thick accent reminded him of home. He turned away quickly, careful to avoid the young mother bent over her tea near the exit.

Outside, a dog tied up at the railings yelped as it pulled against its lead. Jimmy jumped, scorching his leg with spilt coffee and he yelped too. He was terrified of dogs and this one looked just like the vicious bugger who'd bitten his face one Saturday morning when he was nine years old. At the time his father said it was his own fault for playing with the filthy tinker kids camped with their feral animals near the Hardwick estate. When Ant came in from football practice almost an hour later, Jimmy was still sniffling in the corner with blood streaked across his cheek while Frank washed dishes at the sink with his back to his sons.

'Why isn't he in the hospital?' Ant demanded.

'He doesn't need a hospital, it's a scratch.'

Ant asked Jimmy if the wound had been cleaned.

'It's a frigging scratch, Anthony. Stop fussing about him like a girl. I told him to wash it but he hasn't,' Frank said.

'Is Nan still at the shop, Jimmy?'

Jimmy nodded, his eyes bloodshot and wet.

'Jimmy,' Ant said gently. 'I'll take you to the hospital. C'mon, the number 7 goes there. There'll be one at quarter to.'

Frank said nothing, They all knew he couldn't bear to go near a hospital, not since their mother.

Ant pulled Jimmy up by his hand. 'Great dad you are,' he said.

Frank dropped the plate into the washing up bowl. 'He'll be fine. It's shameful to be blocking up A&E,' he said quietly. 'There'll be real emergencies, you'll be in the way. It's just a bit of a scratch from a puppy dog. It'll toughen him up a bit. You need to be tough in this world.'

Jimmy clutched his cheek as Ant pushed him out of the front door towards the bus-stop. He remembered lying in his bed that night, running his fingers over the ridge of stitches, listening to Ant's rhythmic breathing and the muffled sounds of Frank moving about the house.

By the time Jimmy reached the opposite side of Hazelwood park, far from the dog at the railings and the cafe shack, the recollections began to dissipate but the residue of how Frank had been back then was difficult to clear. He couldn't understand why his father never put him or Ant or Jenny above his own misery. He found a bench behind a large weeping-willow tree and sat for a while, sipping the remainder of the hot coffee and eating the crusty bap before laying his head on his rucksack. He closed his eyes and listened to the soundtrack of the laughter of children in the distance. He woke not knowing how long he'd slept except by the sky, which had altered from a blank grey to a glorious iridescent palette of blood-orange, soft lilac and inky blue, the layers of colour blurring as they merged. It was only since sleeping rough he'd noticed the beauty of October sunsets.

Shifnal Road was middle-of-the-night quiet when Jimmy arrived for the first time. The only sign of life was at the far end near the hospital where a couple of teenagers slunk about, and a fox, brazen, sniffed around a wheelie-bin. At the bottom of the road, a small alleyway jutted off to the left, separating the houses on the corner of Black Horse Lane from those leading towards Atherley Street. It wasn't a cut-through; it led to a disused patch of land the size of a small courtyard, once a part of the old Hazelwood Depot where twenty heavy horses lived, he learnt later. Now it was a place of occasional deals, and where joyriders dumped cars. He saw a glint of silver, the body of such a car in the glow of street lamps, bonnet crushed against a wall under a canopy of ivy and overgrown privet. He prised open the back door, smashing glass in the process, and climbed in, knowing it had to be better than damp ground under park trees where dogs shat and school kids recoiled further from him than from the steaming piles dotted about the grass. He slept, catatonic, hunched up on the back seat of the Audi 400, hidden out of view.

When daylight streamed in through the windows, he woke with a stiff and aching body, eased himself out of his sleeping bag, pushed open the car door and stepped into morning dew, stretching his fingertips up to the sky, bending from side to side. He was surrounded by houses on all sides and he imagined activities of normality behind the facades: people preparing morning coffee while others lay in warm beds with thumping heads and blurry eyes, desperately trying to ignore their full bladders and parched mouths; new babies howling for spare attention from knackered parents; older children sighing with relief at the absence of weekday alarm bells, rapidly sliding back into unfinished dreams; young people buried under duvets in recent but heavy slumber after dancing, imbibing, feeling each other. The devout would be preparing for worship in a bid to aid salvation and, on this street in this city just like every other street in every other city, more than a few souls would be waking up, alone like him or in company, wishing the day would end before it had begun. He looked around and quickly noticed two pairs of eyes in windows next door to each other staring straight at him. He put his hands over his face.

When he was young, Jimmy played a game with Ant, teasing their little sister by pretending they couldn't see her, that she'd disappeared, become invisible if she put her hands over her face. He would say,

'Where's little Jen gone, our Ant?'

Ant would reply, 'Why I'll be damned if I know, Jimbo, my son.'

Jimmy pictured himself lying across stairs on the mouse-coloured carpet in his family's front room, reading *Match* magazine as Ant spread his *NME* across the settee, both of them ignoring Jenny until she giggled and shushed herself as if it was the giggle which would give her away, the whole while standing in the middle of the room with her hands over her face, fidgeting until eventually a gap appeared between her fingers.

'Am I still invisible, Ant? Jimmy? Am I?' she'd say.

'Not now you've looked, our kid. Not anymore you're not.'

Her body would quiver into a tiny rage.

'I didn't mean to look, Ant. Honest I didn't. I want to be invisible again. Why can't I be?' Then she'd strut off, crimson-faced, eyes streaming. Five minutes later she'd come back and lie on the floor with her small face propped up in the palms of her hands and her legs bent upwards, kicking her feet in a scissor motion, mirroring Jimmy on the carpet. She'd put on a baby-voice and plead with her brothers.

'Please let me be invisible again. Go on boys, don't be meanies,' and Ant or Jimmy would start tickling her and then there would be laughter and it would slice through the regular gloom of the house.

Jimmy tried to blink away strobe memory but his cupped hands only added a bloody filter. He lowered them and looked up. One pair of the staring eyes belonged to a little girl, about the age his sister was when she was still able to create light even in the darkest places. The child in the window gave a small wave and he waved back, forgetting for just a moment how he might appear. He wondered whether she could make out his ragged clothes or the scar which zipped across his cheek. She didn't seem frightened; he was glad. Jenny would have been terrified if she'd seen a man who looked as he did now, but Jenny was terrified of most things, which was no surprise to any of them. The second pair of eyes belonged to an old woman. Her window was pushed open and her silver hair hung loose, dancing around her face. When Jimmy waved at the child, the old woman stepped out of view. He closed his eyes and covered his face with his hands again. When he looked through a gap between his fingers both the woman and the child had disappeared.

When he'd first arrived in Shifnal Road, the car in the alleyway, hidden off the main road and obscured by foliage, seemed like a gift. Now, so close to the backs of houses, he wondered if it was such a good idea after all. He tried to focus on why he was there in the first place; what it was Betwa said which drew him to this part of the city.

'Autumn's only just arrived and it's already bloody freezing; fuck knows what it'll be like in proper winter,' he'd said to her.

'Winter is a lifetime away,' Betwa replied, and instead of talking about the cold and where they might find food that day, she suggested they each describe the exact route they would have walked most in their young lives. For Jimmy, it was from the cramped railway cottage where he grew up to the old Edwardian public library in the centre of town where he went instead of school. There he'd hide amongst fusty bookshelves, teaching himself the things he didn't know. In the library, he told her, he'd learnt how the tales told by old Blues singers were the same stories of prejudice as those of the hard-up Oakies and hillbillies; poor folk all over the world found ways to share their shit through song, he said. She told him that when he spoke about music it was like listening to poetry. It was the most beautiful thing anyone had ever said to him and, when a tear escaped, she put her arms around him, kissed his forehead and laughed gently.

For her journey, Betwa drew the way the roads ran from the station to her house on a scrap of paper.

'If I disappear, this is where home is,' she said, pointing to the middle of her sketch.

'You won't disappear, not with me around to look after you.' He felt daft for saying it out loud, for sounding like James Stewart in an old film he'd watched with Ant one rainy Sunday long ago. But he knew people disappeared from the streets all the time. Some simply moved on to a different street in a different area of the city, anonymous, away from familiar faces. The city was big enough to do that; every section was like a small town itself, with its own unique air of flagrant wealth or the sad reek of poverty. Some chose to disappear, needing to be lost, afraid of being found. Others just faded away until they became invisible, whether in plain view or hidden away in hovels for which they were meant to be grateful. Mostly, they disappeared in a completely different way, into themselves with no hope of anyone ever finding them. And, every week, more than a few disappeared out of life altogether.

When Jimmy was twelve, he and Ant lay in their beds side by side and talked about how they would disappear one day.

'I'll just go without saying anything when I'm supposed to be coming home straight from school.'

'Don't be a prick, Jimmy,' Ant said. 'Running away is for cowards. You leave others behind. Anyway, the police will just pick you up and bring you straight back here and then you'll be in for it.'

'Well, smart-arse, what do you suggest?'

'I'll wait until I can get a decent job far away from here and then, with the money, I'll buy one of those big houses which needs a bit of doing up so it's cheap, like – one in the middle of nowhere, way past Skem, up in the Lakes or something. It'll be a proper house, not a shitty old slum like this. My place will be

44

properly warm, and light with big windows looking over fields and hills – a house built for masters not servants, Jimbo, my lad. Miles from the din of those friggin trains. I'll send a car to pick you lot up, you and Jen and Nan. He can stay here with his black dog. We'll go when he's at work and then the four of us can fix the house, make it nice and I'll pay with my wages.'

'You've got it all sorted haven't you? Been thinking about this for a while, Ant?'

'We can but dream, Jimbo. We can but dream.'

'Well you're gonna need more than your Saturday job at HMV to make that dream come true.'

'I friggin' know that, Jimmy. I'll get a job with loads of money like in a bank or somewhere.'

'Or I could get spotted scoring a killer goal out on the field at the back of Naylor Park.'

'Yeah, Jimmy, you could do but let's face it, there's more chance of me shitting gold.'

They both knew it was all pure fantasy but they drifted to sleep thinking about the pretty house with its long driveway and a garage where Ant would play guitar and Jimmy and Jen would keep the shiny new bikes which would be waiting for them when they arrived. Jimmy was three years younger than Ant and Jenny was another four below him. Nan often said Ant was sent from heaven in preparation to help her with the younger ones after their mother died. Jimmy thought this too. The house in the hills was dreaming, but nevertheless he couldn't help believing that somehow Ant would rescue them all one day. When the lights went out and they were too tired for any more conversation, Ant clicked on the CD player just as he always did

'Give it a rest, Ant. We've got school tomorrow.'

But Jimmy knew if the music was turned down they'd hear the grunting from along the landing so he never complained if Ant turned it straight up again.

Jimmy spent the morning wandering around the Shifnal Road area, memorising the names of the streets and the route back to the car, trying to recall the scrawled map on a scrap of paper which had long disappeared. But each street looked just the same, jutting up in a ladder from Grand Parade.

'It's one of those places where the immigrants end up,' Betwa had said. 'You know, when they first arrive and need to settle somewhere they're welcome, so they end up huddled together because it feels safer. Just like now for us.'

He could see she was right as soon as he'd arrived: everyone was from somewhere else.

'It's an amazing place: you can hear meat sizzling on the ocakbasi through open doorways and smell it all mixed in with fried samosas and jerk chicken. And there's music everywhere, different kinds of music. You'd like it, Jimmy.'

'What the hell is an ocakbasi?' Jimmy wanted to ask. He made a mental note to look it up in a library sometime, to teach himself what this strange word meant, just as he'd taught himself the other things. Instead he said, 'Where I'm from it's all pasties and barm cakes. Boring really but what I wouldn't do for a Henshaw's steak 'n kidney right now!'

'What?' Betwa said and he laughed.

It was hard to talk about food. It was hard to even think of it. Any joy associated with it was intangible, like remote satellites high in the sky. Food-talk became disassociated from the act of eating – the hurried chomping-down of cold leftovers from shops or cafes or the slurp of lukewarm offerings from soup kitchens; food-talk was dreaming. Eating now was a function, like pissing up against walls or shitting behind bins in the absence of a public toilet.

Jimmy couldn't control what he ate but he vowed to himself to try and keep some semblance of cleanliness, as far as he was able. His clothes stank and his hair was filthy and matted but he carried around a toothbrush with splayed bristles. It did nothing to shift the nicotine stains off his teeth or prevent new chips and gaps appearing. *Not enough calcium,* a medic at a drop-in centre once told him, but he missed the appointment to see the once-a-month dentist and they wouldn't give him the tablets without the appointment. He washed his hands with soap and water whenever he could and he always went to the toilet away from where he was sleeping. He'd heard stories about older people, the ones who had been on the streets forever, unable to peel off layers of clothing which had disintegrated and melded with their skin over decades. These guys pissed and shat into their clothes, they had no choice. He was determined he would never be one of them but once, in desperation, he'd let warm piss trickle down his thighs for a bit of heat. He hated the putrid smell on himself and the damp lasted far longer than any momentary warmth; he would never do it again. Even on the streets there was a hierarchy, and the men who slept and ate and walked around in their own mess, making passers-by gag, were at the bottom of the pile. For Jimmy, being young and eating so infrequently, it wasn't always an ordeal to wait, to hang around a drop-in centre or a project at certain times of the day at least to wash his face, clean his teeth and shit on a bowl.

When he returned to the car, he picked up a stick from the ground and thrashed away nettles which blocked the path at the far end of the alleyway. He managed to clear a small pathway and discovered there was a clearing about twice the size of the backyard at the railway cottage. The clearing was empty except for discarded bottles and what looked like a torn pair of lady's pants. In the middle of the plot was a half built brick wall around a concrete floor in the shape of a perfect square. He sat in the middle and closed his eyes. Somewhere in the distance there was music, a saxophone, and beyond that, the sound of children playing. Thoughts of Betwa wrestled with long-forgotten memories; he remembered the times he and Ant took Jen to the park instead of delivering her to the junior school as they were supposed to.

'Sod school!' Ant said, 'Let's have some fun instead, kiddies.'

After the park, Ant bought greasy chips from a van on the roadside near the playground, winking at the girl behind the counter as he asked for extras. He always made Jen swear on Nan's life she wouldn't tell and, at eight years old, even she had enough sense of the precariousness of life not to blab. Once, after such a day, when Ant and Jimmy were alone, Ant said half jokingly, 'I should have made her swear on my life, or maybe on your miserable little existence, Jimbo. It wasn't fair to do it on Nan's.'

Back in the car, Jimmy dozed off, daydreaming of steaming hot chips. A gentle tapping on the driver's side window woke him. He bolted upright. Light outside was fading and he realized the day had disappeared again. He wiped dribble from his mouth and shook himself awake, expecting to see a policeman on the other side of the window; instead it was the old woman from the house next to the kid's. She held a Tupperware container, a package wrapped in silver foil and a bottle of water towards him. He opened the window.

'How do?' he said.

The woman passed over the offerings without speaking. The food smelt of ginger. He held the tub up to his nose and breathed in the spicy aroma. The silver foil contained flatbreads and a metal spoon. Before he could thank the woman she was already on her way out of the alleyway.

'Hey, lady, thanks,' he shouted after her. She carried on walking; her lilac shawl billowed in the wind, trailing behind her like a ghost.

He devoured the food, breaking pieces of flatbread to scoop up the rich sauce, quickly discarding the spoon which clunked against his teeth. He licked up the remnants of the sauce with his tongue, leaned back on the seat, licking his lips. The empty container lay discarded on the passenger seat, but after a moment he picked it up and dug out dry crusts of the curry from the ridges with his dirty fingernail.

5. EBELE

Ebele Mangaroo loathed Nikos Makrides. She hated the smell of vinegar and stale tobacco on his breath, and the way the old man moved like a sloth across the shop floor, minutely adjusting cushions and bedspreads and sweeping away dust from the table-tops with the heel of his palm. The sight of blue veins protruding from his salmon-coloured scalp, visible between diminishing strands of hair, made her skin crawl. She hated his drooping jowls and the way his words spat at her through a reservoir of phlegm.

Each work day she dragged herself along Black Horse Lane, up St Ann's Road past the big old pub on the corner to the fusty furniture shop where she worked. Makrides was always waiting, staring at the old-fashioned clock on the wall when she stumbled in, tutting, looking her up and down as if she was something a dog had pulled from an undergrowth.

'You're late again, Mangaroo,' and then, always after a short pause, always the same threat, 'You know, I can find better staff than you.'

'Why don't you then?' she muttered under her breath. And, even though she knew he couldn't hear her, he'd say,

'If this happens again, I will replace you straightaway.'

Then he'd reel out a list of tasks which always began with wiping down the furniture before any rare customer arrived.

Ebele's little girl, Tuli, was almost two when they first moved into the flat owned by Nikos Makrides. They'd been thrown out of the last place when Tuli's father disappeared one night without warning. He left with his guitar slung over his shoulder, off to a gig at the Tramshed, and she expected him home past midnight but this time he didn't show at all. After twenty-four hours she thought about reporting him missing. Anything could happen in a big city; she'd once heard of a man being pushed into a canal at night; a man who, like Tuli's dad, looked like he'd come from somewhere else even though he was born just over the river. She tried to call him but his phone went straight to voicemail. She rang all the people she knew; there weren't very many of them, not now she had Tuli. She called the Tramshed and put a message on Facebook, and then he blocked her and she knew he was alive but just a bastard like other men she'd known in her young life. Tuli stopped looking for her father two days later and, after the crying and the vodka ran out, Ebele decided to follow her tiny daughter's example. She couldn't pay the rent on her own, not with a part-time job in Iceland and the costs of the childminder. The landlord wouldn't accept the benefits she now had to depend on so she took what was on offer in a part of the city she knew nothing about.

Makrides' flat was cheaper but bigger than the previous place; it was obvious why. Powdery mildew teetered up from the skirting boards like a medieval disease. When she first moved in, she scraped away the mildew and washed infected parts of the wall with water and bleach but it kept coming back. She complained to Makrides again and again and each time he told her a man would be around to deal with it but no-one ever came. She slept with windows slightly ajar, even in the depths of winter, so the air would circulate and stop Tuli from getting a cough. The window in the kitchen was partially obscured by shelves filled with pots and pans and dried foods so it was difficult to open and cooking smells accumulated, permeating the flat with an undertone of rotten grease. She guessed that before the house was split in two the kitchen had been a third bedroom, big enough for a single bed and not much more. The bathroom was small too, with just enough room for a bathtub, toilet and sink and just enough floor space to stand on to brush teeth or hair in front of the mirror. But the flat was home regardless of its shortcomings, and the rent was manageable with her shop wages and tax credits and other bits and pieces she could cobble together. Iceland relocated her to Grand Parade but when it closed down and became yet another betting shop, it was Mrs Makrides who suggested her husband give Ebele a job at the store,

'She has the little one to care for all by herself – we should show some kindness.' She spoke in their own language but Ebele got the gist and was grateful. The job was part-time; Mrs Makrides set the rules at first, and it was flexible around the holidays once Tuli started school and it kept the DWP off her back. Ebele found ways to make it work.

A pretty man called Jamal lived downstairs with a tall Swedish woman called Abi and a big man Ebele only ever knew of as K. Brightly coloured block-print cotton sheets hung in their windows. Old-Skool hip-hop and the musky smells of incense and marijuana seeped into her flat from below late at night, reminding her of a time when she wasn't so alone and her head was less cluttered. She liked having them down there. One evening, as Tuli drifted off to sleep to the sound of Ebele's soft singing, she caught Jamal standing in the garden, smoking, looking up at the window of the bedroom where she slept in a single bed with her daughter in a cot beside her. He blew her an unexpected kiss and she quickly closed the curtains and turned her back on him. Two weeks later he was lying naked on the sofa bed in her front room and three days after that Abi stood in the middle of the street with her trolley bag and rucksack, yelling at him in Swedish and mouthing expletives in English when Ebele caught her eye from where she stood watching behind the window upstairs. Along the street, blinds flickered and curtains twitched as Abi continued to bawl while K tried to calm everyone down. K disappeared the next day and Jamal moved his things upstairs. A week later Makrides put the downstairs flat up for sale and it wasn't long before the makeshift curtains were replaced with white plantation shutters and the stuck-up couple, who still lived there now, moved in with their cats and their enormous coffee machine. Jamal stayed until Tuli was six and then he, like Tuli's father before him, went without warning. This time Ebele watched him walking across the park and into the trees, fading into the distance. Later, she heard he was in Sweden and then in Tunisia but by then she'd stopped caring about anything except Tuli; some days even that was an effort.

When Ebele rushed in through the double doors, Makrides glanced at the clock and then at her as she expected he would.

'Clean the front entrance, Mangaroo,' he said without looking up from the newspaper in front of him. 'Use something strong. There is still the stench of a filthy goat who was sleeping there yesterday. The customers will think this bad odour is from my furniture.'

'I'm not the cleaner,' Ebele said, making her way across the shop-floor. 'I'm supposed to be the shop assistant.'

'You do whatever I tell you to. I am the boss, remember. And if you don't earn money you can't pay to live in my flat.'

'Stupid old git!' She mouthed the words silently with her back to Makrides as she filled the mop bucket. She hated the way he took any opportunity to remind her she was beholden to him; that her home and her means to pay for it were dependent on him.

As the bucket filled at the sink, she stared out onto Grand Parade. It was as frenetic as it always was in the morning: cars crawled along, parping at stationary buses and weaving cyclists; younger people rushed by, distracted by the phones they held in front of their faces; older people stooped over heavy shopping bags, stumbling across obstacles in their way. At the bus-stop near the shop, mothers battled to push buggies to the front of the line in time to stake their claim on the approaching bus. Directly across the road, the sprawling bakery was crowded with people buying steaming gozleme, lahmacun and borek. Ebele watched as customers jostled one another, crowding the counter with armfuls of fresh olive bread and packets of pita. They were the anonymous melee of people she walked past everyday; people she lived beside, whose lives ran parallel to hers; people who meant nothing to her and to whom she meant nothing. It was just the same with the people in the cars, on bicycles, in cafes – she knew no-one and no-one knew her. There were those she had to negotiate around each day: Grace and Mandy, the couple who'd bought the flat below her; Makrides and his drivers who came and went; people who drifted in and out of her life as inconsequential to her as she was to them. A splash of water on the thigh jolted her out of her daze. She turned off the tap and lowered the bucket to the floor as a dull pang of hunger reverberated through her body; in the rush to leave the house she'd forgotten to eat breakfast

'Give the man the paperwork and then clean the entrance. Get rid of that bloody smell.' Makrides was shouting across to her. Ebele hadn't noticed a driver come in. He stood at the counter watching her. She wiped her hands on a grubby tea towel and made her way to where the two men were standing

'Hello,' the driver said, holding out his hand.

She ignored him and began to fill in the paperwork; she couldn't be bothered with niceties so early in the morning however genial he seemed.

'I think I've seen you somewhere,' he said.

She shrugged her shoulders; the man was attractive but she wasn't interested in his chat-up lines. Drivers only ever lasted a week or two, the turnaround was quick, they came and went like buses so there was no point in getting friendly; Makrides always managed to scare them away with his tight-fistedness or his tetchiness. Ebele, on the other hand, had worked at the shop for almost two years, though Makrides still called her the new girl. She knew there was no real danger of him getting rid of her, he found it hard to retain staff. The driver carried on talking.

'Yeah, I know where it is, you live on Shifnal Road, next door to Mr and Mrs Banu on the corner, don't you? I used to care for the old man in my last job.'

Ebele looked up; the man actually did know something about her.

'I don't know any old couple,' she said.

'They live right next to you. The old guy is in a bad way, you know, paralysed. Tubes coming out from all over him so you won't have seen much of him for quite a while I guess. But Mrs Banu, she is in and out these days. You must have seen her?'

'No,' she said abruptly. 'Never seen either of them.'

'What, you never see your neighbours? She's nice, the old lady. Sort of traditional, you know, in how she dresses and stuff but she has quite a brain. I suppose he must've too once. Lots of books around their place. It's nice. And photos of when they were younger. They were obviously happy. She's kind of sad looking now, lonely I expect.'

Ebele ignored him and returned to the paperwork, ticking and crossing boxes on the form. The driver was already over-familiar; she didn't want him to think she was interested in what he had to say.

'Here you go,' she said, pushing paper across the counter. 'Leonard Avenue. Should take about forty minutes. It's just a couple of chairs.'

The driver left the paperwork where it was and grinned. 'You ever a bit more friendly?' he asked.

'You should mind your own business and get on with the job you're paid to do,' she replied curtly.

'Just making conversation. You know, like people who work together do.'

'Well I don't have time for friendliness, thanks. I'd never get the shitty job done if I did.'

'Mangaroo!' Makrides shouted across the shopfloor.

The driver smiled. 'I like your straight-talking, Mangeroo. Makes a change.'

'I don't pay you to chat to one another,' Makrides yelled. 'Take the docket and go, Driver. Time is money.'

Ebele picked up the paperwork and waved it in the driver's face.

'See you around, tough-girl,' he said, taking it from her hand, and as he neared the door, he looked across, gave her a small salute and smiled broadly. The driver's good humour floated across the shop as the door swung shut behind him. After he left, she shuffled the paperwork on the counter into order while skim-reading headlines on the open page of Makrides' newspaper. One briefly caught her eye, about a young woman without an identity, trawled up from the river a few days earlier. No-one had claimed the body. The thought of the poor girl, unnamed and all alone unsettled her. She quickly closed the paper and shoved it aside.

Later, as she eddied the mop around the concrete doorstep, she caught the driver's eye as he stood amongst the lunchtime hordes behind the glass window of the bakery opposite. He waved and pointed to the paper bag he held in his hand with a questioning shrug. She shook her head; she didn't want to accept any favours from men she'd only just met, even if her hunger was nauseating. She tilted the bucket with her foot until soapy water slopped into a small puddle onto the step then she ushered it towards the kerb with the mop in a zigzag rhythm.

After work, Ebele collected Tuli from the downstairs flat and closed the door on Grace and Mandy. Their voices added to the clangour of the day and rang in her ears. She dumped her shopping bags on the kitchen floor, kicked off her shoes and slumped drowsily onto the unmade bed in the living room. Her head throbbed. Being in the presence of Makrides made her feel more diminished than she already was. Before the work day had ended he'd said, 'It is no wonder you don't have a husband, Mangaroo. No man would want to come home to your miserable face each day. I am paying you to be cheerful in front of customers, not to scowl at them like an old witch.'

The new driver heard him and, as she collected her things and prepared to leave, he whispered, 'Wow, he's quite something isn't he? Ignore him, I'm sure he didn't mean it.'

'He's a mean old bastard.' She replied loudly so Makrides would be certain to hear. She slammed through the door on the way out.

At home, as she lay on her bed, she listened to Tuli singing to her toys down the landing: *When I was one, I sucked my thumb, the day I went to sea... a bottle of rum to fill my tum...* Her daughter's sweet voice washed away the echoes of Makrides' scathing remarks and her fists slowly unfurled as her body sank into the soft mattress. It was dark outside when she woke. Tuli was standing over her.

'I think Storyman is sad,' the child said.

'What?' Ebele rubbed her eyes.

'The Storyman is sad. He doesn't have any friends.'

'Oh Tuli. I'm sorry. We can read a happy story after food. I got eggs. You must be starving. Sorry Mummy fell asleep, but now we can have scrambled-up eggs.'

'No Mummy. It isn't made up, it's the storything man. He did signs to me, like talking in a different language. But it's not a game, Mummy. It's a real storyman.' Tuli's bottom lip hung down as she spoke.

'What are you talking about, Tuli?' Ebele sat up,

Tuli raised her finger to her pursed lips. 'Ssh. It's a secret, Mummy. But Storyman will be cold at night and shivering too much.'

'What? Is this something you're reading?' Ebele tried to control the impatience in her voice. Tuli was an imaginative child but sometimes her ramblings were just too much. She knew it wasn't healthy. Jamal had once said so too and they'd argued about it.

'Look,' she said, steering Tuli onto her lap. She pulled her in close, nestling her nose into her curls. 'Let's talk about something real, Tuli. Mummy is too tired for stories today.'

Tuli began crying. She wriggled into a more rigid position and put her thumb into her mouth. Ebele softened her voice.

'It's okay, baby. I'm not telling you off. Did a story frighten you? Was it one of the books Grace gave you? Why don't you get it and we can read it together.'

'It was just a storything,' Tuli said between sobs.

''A story thing? You mean it's made up in your head, Tuli?'

'It's just a storything, Mummy. Honest'

'Okay, Tuli. Is it a story about a monster?'

'It isn't a monster, just a storything man. Sorry Mummy.'

Ebele pulled Tuli towards her again and held onto her tightly.

'I'm sorry too, baby. C'mon, let's make eggs. You must be starving. You can sit on the worktop and scramble. You like doing that.'

After dinner, Ebele suggested they have a bath together and Tuli cheered up quickly at the idea. As she splashed about in the water, Tuli said, 'How come, Mummy, I'm like Hoyden and you are Pancake?'

It took Ebele a few seconds to figure out what she was talking about.

'We're not cats, Tuli,' she said.

Tuli laughed, 'I know we're not cats, Mummy. That would be silly. Grace says cats don't even like water so they would never even have a bath with their mummy.'

'You're a funny girl sometimes.' Ebele dabbed a handful of bubbles on Tuli's head and the child giggled.

'I mean, Mummy I'm the same brown as Hoydon and you're more like Pancake. How come, Mummy? Mummies and babies are supposed to be the same colour aren't they?'

'Not always, Tuli. I'm actually more like my daddy than my mummy and so are you. But, you're even more like Papa than I am.'

'But, Mummy. I haven't ever seen your papa-daddy so how come I can be like him?'

Ebele ran the tap, fished a plastic beaker from under the bubbles and poured clean water over her daughter's head. Tuli squealed and wiped her eyes.

'You don't have to have known your grandparents to be like them, Tuli. We are all a mixture of our ancestors.'

'Really? So am I like Papa and Real Daddy and you and Jamal Daddy too? And maybe all my other grandmas and grandpas too even though I've never even met them?'

'Sort of, Tuli. Not all of them but most of them. What does it matter anyway? Everyone is different, especially around here. Not like the place where I was a little girl.'

'Why, Mummy? What was it like in that place?'

'There weren't many children who looked like me. People used to call me horrible names, even teachers sometimes. Here it doesn't matter if you're not the same colour as your mummy or your daddy or your grandparents.'

'But the children at school say bad things about me as well,' Tuli said. 'Finn says I look like poo.'

Ebele sat upright; she stretched her legs around Tuli's hips, causing dollops of water to splash over the side of the bath.

'Did you tell Mrs Enisuoh he said those nasty things?' she said. Tuli shook her lowered head. 'Don't listen to stupid children. You're beautiful, Tuli. My beautiful girl. Okay?'

Tuli nodded quietly.

'When I was little, there was one teacher who used to twirl my hair like this.' Ebele twisted her finger around one of Tuli's ringlets. 'She said she'd never seen hair like mine before, not close up, only on the television or newspapers. Can you imagine that?'

'Really, Mummy? That's silly. Maybe she must have lived on the moon before?'

'Not the moon, just a very small town. This is a big city where people's families are from all over the world so not everyone is the same, but where I grew up it wasn't like here. I think some people thought *we* were from the moon. When Papa died I was little like you; it was hard being the only one who looked different then.' Ebele reclined into the warm water. She closed her eyes.

Tuli played with the plastic beaker, filling and pouring out frothy water from different heights. Ebele listened and thought about her own mother: her lily-white skin; how she'd once heard Papa describing it as beautiful like the white-caps of Caribbean waves. Ebele hadn't been to the sea and she hated not knowing things which made her parents smile in their secret way. She hated it too when her mother wore tan-coloured foundation over her pale skin. Soon after Papa died, Ebele tried to scrub away the constellation of freckles dotting her own sandy face with a scourer and washing-powder, scrubbing in the detergent until it scalded like hot oil from the chip-pan. That night, her mother dabbed baby-pink Calamine across her cheeks to calm the flames and in the dark Ebele prayed she would wake and be the colour of the dried-on lotion forever so people in the street wouldn't shout *wog-lover* at her mother or *jungle-bunny* at her.

'Mandy comes from the upside down of the world?' Tuli said as she moved the bath water with the backs of her hands to make small waves for the beaker to sail on. Ebele had to remind herself what they were talking about.

'They call it Down Under, Tuli,' she said. 'But yes, people live here from all over the world like Mandy, I suppose.'

'But Mandy isn't brown,' Tuli said.

'People in other countries can also be white, and other white people don't seem to mind them as much,' she added.

Tuli thought for a while.

'But you said I was born in the hospital near our old house. That isn't a different country so why should people like Mandy more than they like me?'

'It's complicated, Tuli,' Ebele said. 'It's a problem with the world, with history, not with you; you're perfect. Hopefully by the time you're all grown up it'll all be different.'

'But, Mummy,' Tuli said after a moment, 'Storyman has white skin and I don't think anyone is going to like him to be here in this city's country. It's not fair is it, Mummy?'

Tuli crossed her arms like a grown up and kicked her feet in the water.

'Don't do that,' Ebele said. 'The water will go through the floor and leak into downstairs.'

'But you didn't answer my question.'

'Not now, Tuli. I thought we weren't going to talk about your stories. Anyway, the bath is getting cold.'

Ebele felt a headache beginning to form. Tuli's chattering was too much. She stood up, grabbed her towel from the hook on the back of the door and stepped out of the bath. She wrapped the towel around her damp body, grabbed the other one and held it open. 'Come on, Tuli, time to get out,' she said.

Tuli yawned like a cat and stretched her arms into the air as Ebele lifted her out of the bath. Ebele yawned too. It was not yet eight o'clock but her eyelids were drooping.

Ebele liked to watch her daughter sleep. Often at the end of each day before she climbed into the lumpy sofa bed, she crept into Tuli's bedroom and sat in the dark, listening to the rise and fall of her breathing. This day she did the same and when she was sure Tuli was properly asleep, she crept out of the room and slipped downstairs in her pyjamas to talk to Grace.

'I don't know which book it's from,' Grace said. 'I'll take a look. It's not one I know about.'

As Ebele turned to go upstairs, Grace said, 'By the way, Mandy saw a bloke hanging about in the alley by that abandoned car. We think he may be sleeping rough there. We'll get on to one of the charities about it Monday but just thought I'd mention it in case you hear anything odd.'

Ebele's skin prickled. 'Charities, what the fuck, Grace?' she said. 'I don't want some tramp living at the backs of our houses. If he's still there in the morning I'm phoning the police.'

'That's a bit of an over-reaction isn't it? Probably just someone passing through. I doubt he'll be there in the morning. He's probably gone already. I wouldn't worry about it too much. It's not like we've got the flat on the market or anything.'

'What? You are kidding, aren't you?' Some strange man is hanging around and that's the first thing you think about?'

'You're getting carried away, Ebele. It's just a kid, sleeping rough. There's loads of them these days. He's probably not even there anymore.'

Mandy appeared in the doorway behind Grace, 'Ebele, getting carried away, what's this strange predilection I hear of, sweet love?'

'Piss off, Mandy, I'll see for myself in the morning,' Ebele said. She closed the door on her neighbours and listened to them talking about her in the hallway.

'Cut her some slack, Mandy. You shouldn't be so hard on her.'

'She's a nutcase, Grace. I know she's your good cause but she really is a piece of work.'

'She has a hard time, Mand. Let her be. It can't be easy bringing up a child on your own. And anyway, you know I'm fond of Tuli; she's a great kid.'

'Well at least the nipper gets to see a bit of functionality if she hangs out with us I suppose.'

Upstairs, Ebele lay on her bed and fell asleep quickly, leaving the dishes and the bath unwashed.

6. NIKOS

On the high street around the corner from Shifnal Road, Nikos Makrides opened the rusty shutters on his cluttered furniture store and prepared for the work day by drinking lukewarm coffee from a tartan flask. He watched the oversized wall-clock above the door as it ticked towards 9am. The shop, obscured behind a sheltered bus-stop serving four different routes, attracted little natural light and even less trade. People passed by, hundreds every day, but few ever came in on a whim and fewer still bought anything beyond a mattress protector or a pillow for an unexpected guest. Despite the lack of daylight in the shop, Nikos insisted on keeping the grubby plastic blinds at a quarter mast to prevent any infrequent rays of sunshine from fading the shiny ornate sofas and cumbersome bedsteads. Each morning, he checked the length of the blinds with a long wooden ruler which he kept stored on a thin frame above the front door, adjusting them in minute pulls and retractions to achieve a perfect height before unbolting the door and twisting the sign to 'Open For Business'. Nikos was particular about many things. He knew some people used different words for it behind his back but he needed the shop to be ordered, and these days he didn't much care for what other people said or thought of him.

Nikos lived in a house further up the high street, long after the shops ended and the road became a tree-lined avenue with detached houses separated from the pavement by driveways, front gardens, gravel paths and ornamental bushes. Here the neighbours only ever heard each other in the summer months when strimmers and lawn mowers broke the peace of Sunday morning lie-ins. He woke automatically at six forty-five every day, including Sundays. It made no difference to him if this was in the deep black of a January morning or to chinks of warm sunlight slipping between heavy green drapes in the midst of a bright summer dawn. His arm stretched out into the empty space beside him in the bed, and then, on the threshold of consciousness, the shock of realisation that his wife Ourania now only existed in dreams. Rituals followed: a shit, a shower, a cigarette and a breakfast of olives, bread, honey and coffee, just the same as he'd eaten every day since his boyhood in the place he still thought of as home.

Nikos Makrides was sixty-three, stooping and large-framed, as tall in feet and inches as he was old in years. His once thick mane of mahogany hair was now without colour and skirted a freckled crown mapped with pale blue rivulets criss-crossing below the surface. His face was sallow, drained of the sun-kissed glow of his childhood spent around the turquoise waters of the Mediterranean. His skin was lined with ridges of despair, etched by the bitterness of a life which was unexpected and disappointing in many ways. People had called him 'old man' since well before he'd passed the markers of middle-age.

The Furniture Store had occupied the same spot on the high street for as long as anyone in the area could remember. It opened its doors in the 1950s when Nikos was a small boy. It had a different name then and was owned by two Scottish brothers from a town called Dull. They ran it until they grew too feeble, hoping to pass it on to sons who had long since run off to join rock 'n' roll bands. They sold it to Nikos' Uncle Kostas. He was the only party interested. Nikos was close to Kostas, who was his godfather as well as his uncle; their ties were multiple. Kostas had left the island of their birth as soon as his military service freed him to escape. He was keen to be part of a bigger, more liberal, world, so he joined the exodus to England. Nikos followed him a few years later, shoved towards the same destination but with far less motivation and absolutely no choice in the matter. For him there was none of the eager excitement of building a life in a new country as conveyed through Kostas' letters. He hated the idea of leaving behind his beloved home on the edge of Europe for a drab land full of pale people and perpetual rain. The only thing he knew instinctively was that England would make his bones and his heart ache.

'This island is no home for a young man like you right now, son,' his father told him as he prepared to leave. 'Trouble is coming, we all know this and now with this accident, it is surely a sign. The wrath of Savvas Savvides may be a worse prospect than the instability of our little country. We are lucky England is calling and we are luckier still to have contacts, to have Kostas there. It can all be sorted quickly.'

A month before that conversation, Nikos had run into the courtyard next door to tell his best friend, Georgios that the record they'd been waiting so long for had finally arrived on the island. After an early breakfast, the two young men rode their bicycles non-stop for an hour and thirty minutes to cover the twenty kilometre distance into Larnaca so they could stake their claim on one of just two available copies of the album. For months, they'd pooled bits of money from odd jobs around local farms, just as they'd done with the previous Cat Stevens record and the Poll one before that. It never crossed their minds there might be a time when they wouldn't be listening to music together, on the Savvides family's red Dansette, the only record player in the neighbourhood.

On the cycle ride home, with their prized possession tucked away in a saddle bag, a rock the size of a small chicken suddenly flew out of the sky towards them and smacked Georgios on the right side of his head. He tumbled off his bike and into the path of a mouflon who stared at them for a moment before skipping off towards the forest. Georgios was out cold for what seemed to Nikos to be an eternity. He shouted for help into the deserted outskirts of the town. No one came to help, and when Georgios regained consciousness he said, 'The wind has come into my ears and blocked all the sound. Make it come back, Nikos, make it come back.'

The trip, which was packed with joyful banter on the way to Larnaca became a very different journey home: slow, laden, anguished. Nikos watched Georgios carefully from the corner of his eye as they walked in silence. Blood was crusted across his friend's face and shirt and he swayed as they pushed their bikes along the rugged ground. Eventually, Georgios said angrily,

'Don't look at me. I'm fine. I can walk straight. I can even ride if I want to.'

'Okay, Nikos replied, 'maybe we should ride then so we can reach home before dark and there'll still be time to call the doctor to check you.'

'When you talk it's as if we are under the water at Mazotos. Don't speak, Nikos. If you shut up perhaps the sound will come back.'

Two hours later, their identical stone houses became visible in the distance, side by side on the up-slope of the road leading to the compact village square. They reached home as the sun fell away and a dusky lilac enveloped the sky.

Georgios's father stomped around the village for two days after the incident, cursing the Turkish devils who'd attacked his son and stolen his hearing.

'Oh no, Uncle Savvas,' said Nikos. 'We didn't see who threw the brick, it could have been anyone.'

'You are a piece of shit, Nikos Makrides,' the older man said. 'You didn't defend my son and instead you defend the devils who did this to him. You are lying to save your own skin.'

All the while, the copy of *Catch A Bull At Four* remained in the saddle bag unopened.

The following weekend Nikos' father said, 'You will go and help Uncle Kostas in the business; a godson is the closest he has to a son. This is the best thing.'

'No, Baba. I can't leave you and Mama. I want to stay here. I don't want to go anywhere else.'

'You can come home again. We aren't talking about forever, son. Your brother Marios is big enough to help your mother with the garden and soon he can come on the boat with me too. And he is still young enough to keep away from trouble. Go, my boy. Please.'

School friends of Nikos' had often discussed going to England, of joining rock bands or revolutionary groups; others talked of making their way to Paris or Hollywood to find fame in the movies or with art. Not Nikos; his dreams were of looking after the family's smallholding on the edge of the little village, providing plump tomatoes and fresh bunches of flat leaf parsley to local tavernas like his mother had done for years, or fishing with his father, as rough and as thankless as it was. This was all he ever wanted from life, that and finding a woman who would love him as much as his mother did. But a new life away from his village was his destiny; a life in a huge ugly city thousands of miles away, where people rarely smiled and the sun hardly shone. Soon the dawn chorus of tinkling goat bells and the sweet scent of calendula was replaced by a constant rumble of traffic and the stink of its fumes and of damp clothes. It was a destiny he couldn't have imagined in his worst nightmares.

Nikos worked in the furniture shop on Grand Parade for well over forty years: for thirty-nine of those he was the manager and for thirty-seven the sole owner, following the untimely demise of his uncle Kostas, unmarried and childless, who fell into his final sleep one cloudless night with an empty bottle of whiskey and sleeping tablets by his side. Nikos was in Cyprus at the time, preparing to marry the girl he loved, unaware he would be back in the village within weeks, accompanying the body of his father's brother. It took some years for him to realise that each return to or from Cyprus was momentous, usually in the most devastating way, marred by the deaths of those he loved. Only his betrothal necessitated return journeys of joy. It was no longer a place he could travel to with the ease of going home; instead, the big shifts in his life were marked as stamps in his passport, each one cementing the distance between his past and his present lives. And now, after more than four decades in a city he'd never loved or longed for, he was as much a part of the fabric of it as he was a part of the furniture in the Makrides' Store.

At five past nine, he stubbed out his third cigarette of the day, waved his hands around to clear the air and took another glance at the clock above the door.

'Bloody girl, always late,' he mumbled as he shuffled paperwork around the cluttered desk. The coffee had left a bad taste in his mouth. The clock approached ten past and there was still no sign of Mangaroo. He'd only given her the job because of the child, and the fact she was paying most of her wages back to him in rent for the upstairs rooms of the home he'd once shared with Uncle Kostas.

The house on Shifnal Road, along with the shop, was bequeathed to him after his uncle died. Eventually, the ground floor was sold, giving him enough to live on without debt but he held onto the upstairs, just in case his sons Dimitri or George ever wanted to return from the far-off place they'd settled in, choosing instead to live near their father in his old age. He knew this wouldn't happen; as the years went by his boys became little more than strangers to him. Occasionally, he got a card from a grandchild he'd hardly met and sometimes a handwritten letter from either Dimitri or George, but the letters soon dropped away, replaced by emails and text messages. He missed holding his sons' letters to his nostrils, searching for minute traces of them amongst the biro smudges and crossing-outs. Instead, each night he kissed photographs of them as young men which sat framed on his bedside table. He had no framed photos of his grandchildren; they only existed ephemerally as fleeting digital images which were hard to envisage as flesh and bone connected to his own.

When the shop-girl stumbled in, he didn't look up.

'You're late,' he said.

'Yeah, I know.'

'No apology?'

The girl ignored him and headed to the small utility area at the back of the shop. He watched, irritated, as she clanked about putting her bag in the cupboard and filling the kettle with water from the sink.

'What are you doing?'

'Making tea.'

'You are already late, there is no time for tea. The driver will be here for the orders. Clean the front entrance and get the papers ready.'

The girl continued to make her drink, squeezing the bag against the side of the cup in a motion which seemed to be extra slow on purpose. She didn't offer him a cup. His face flushed. She made him feel worthless. He wanted to tell her he wasn't, that his wife had loved him and so had his children too once. Instead he said,

'You are pushing me to the limit, Mangaroo. Be careful.'

He left her there, sipping from the mug and staring at him while he stood at the front of the shop, looking up and down the road for customers like a restaurant owner in Cyprus in July.

7. TULI

Tuli sat on Grandy's sofa with her arms folded tight against her stomach. Mandy sat on the other side of the room talking into her phone.

'Can I go in the garden?' Tuli said quietly. Mandy glanced over but didn't answer. 'Can I go in the garden?' Tuli said again. Mandy carried on talking, using long words Tuli didn't understand. The next time Tuli asked she shouted, 'CAN I GO INTO THE GARDEN?'

'I'm so sorry, I'll have to call you back,' Mandy said down the phone. 'I need to open the door for someone. Really sorry. It'll just be a minute. I'll call straight back.' She stood up and walked over to Tuli. 'For god sake, kid,' she said, 'you almost messed up a very important call. You're becoming more and more like your mother everyday.'

Tuli bit her lip. 'I just want to go into the garden,' she whispered.

'Okay, okay,' Mandy said in a softer voice. 'C'mon then.'

Mandy pressed buttons on her phone at the same time as she pushed open the back door, and as Tuli slipped out, she heard her say, 'I'm so sorry about that. Jehovah's Witnesses again.'

As soon as she was outside, Tuli ran down to the bottom of the garden and pressed her ear to the brick wall; she knew the storyman and the car were just behind it.

'Hello,' she said but there was no answer. 'Are you there, Storyman?' She said it a bit louder but not in her loudest voice. There was still no answer. She moved away from the wall and skipped to the secret part of the garden by Grandy's bedroom, past the flowerbeds to the furniture near the glass doors. She grabbed a heavy garden chair and dragged it across the lawn, making deep lines in the grass. She scrambled on to it but still wasn't quite tall enough to see over the wall so she scanned the garden for something to raise her up. When she couldn't see anything she clambered down and ran into the house. Mandy was still talking loudly into the phone, calling out times and dates with her back turned. Tuli looked around the kitchen; there were two squidgy cushions on the bench but she didn't want those. Instead, she nudged open the door to Mandy's study and pulled two large books from the bottom shelf, wobbled down the garden with them hugged to her belly and plonked them on the chair. She stood on the tips of her toes on the books, leaned over the wall and called out. The man was in the car, reading with the door open; it sounded like someone was playing the piano in there too. At first, he didn't see her. When the music paused. she shouted out again and this time he looked up, caught her eye and smiled like the people at the bus stop sometimes did. He stopped the music, put his book down and climbed out of the car.

'Hello.'

'Hello,' she answered. 'Are you real?' The man laughed and she saw his eyes were blue like the crayon skies which ran across the tops of her drawings.

'Yep, as real as real is,' he said.

'Real people don't sleep in cars.'

'Yes they do. People sleep in all sorts of places.'

'No they don't,' she insisted. 'They only sleep in beds. Even in other countries where they live in big huts and tents they still have beds. I learnt it at school. It's why we have bedrooms. Cars aren't bedrooms, so there.'

The man laughed again and she liked the way his beard jumped about on his face; it made her think of Pebble, the gerbil which lived in a cage in her classroom.

'Are you sad to be sleeping in a car and not a bedroom?' she asked.

'Nah, it's not such a sad thing kiddo,' the man said. Tuli liked the way he called her a special name even though she'd only just met him.

'Where's your real bedroom?' she asked.

'I don't have one. I don't have a home. You can't have a bedroom without a home.'

'That's silly – everyone lives somewhere?'

'Nope, not these days.'

'But where do you belong?'

'I don't belong anywhere,' he said.

'Everyone belongs somewhere though. You speak funny. Are you from a different country?'

'Not a different country, just a different world.'

'Then you are a story thing, like in my books. I told Mummy you were a Storyman but she didn't believe me.'

The man stopped laughing and seemed angry now but she didn't know why.

'Listen,' he said. 'Don't you tell anyone I'm here, okay.' He turned his face away so all she could see was the tangled mess of his knotted hair.

'I won't tell anyone,' she said. 'I can keep a secret. Mummy tells me secrets too and I don't tell anyone. Only if it's hurting me. Then I have to tell because it's the rule.'

The man looked at her. 'I wouldn't hurt you. I wouldn't hurt anyone. That's my bloody problem,' he said.

Tuli thought he was going to cry but she knew he wouldn't; big men didn't cry, except Jamal Daddy once. Only little boys at school cried when they weren't included in football games, or when they fell over and their knees got all scratched and bloody.

'Shove off, kiddo,' the man said. 'Go and find someone your own age to play with.'

'My own age people don't play with me,' she said sadly. The man's face softened.

'Why not? You seem like a nice kid,' he said in a gentle voice.

'Because I'm a bad-luck person,' she replied. The chair wobbled beneath her and she clung to the wall to steady herself.

'Hey, be careful, kiddo. What are you standing on behind there?'

When she told the man she was standing on a chair and books, he said, 'Don't you hurt yourself because of me. I'm not worth it.'

'I'm okay,' she said. 'Are you a storyman?'.

'I have a story, if that's what you mean. We all have a story, even you, kid. So, what's all this about bad luck anyway?'

Tuli wished she hadn't said the thing about luck. She hated the way words fell out of her mouth when she didn't want them to. She said, 'Do you have a real name, Storyman?'

'Yep, it's Mr No-one,' he said.

'That's a funny name.'

'Yep but it's my name! Go on, kiddo, tell me what's so unlucky about you.'

Tuli shrugged her shoulders. 'Just!' she said. 'Cos my daddy got lost. I must be a bad-luck person for that to happen. And then Jamal Daddy disappeared into the trees.'

'Ah,' Storyman said. 'I know how you feel, people seem to disappear around me all the time too.'

'But my people disappear because of me, so I am the bad luck,' Tuli said.

'No way, kid. People disappear all the time. I don't think it makes you the bad luck,' the man said kindly. 'More the recipient of the bad luck.' She didn't know what a recipient was so didn't say anything and instead looked at the zigzag line across the man's face which was the same pattern as the broken glass along the top of the wall next door. She wanted to ask about it but something inside told her not to. The man carried on speaking. 'Anyway, if a sweet kid like you is bad luck, imagine what I am – right proper evil luck, I'd say. So, what's your name anyway?'

'Tuli.'

'Short for tulip, like the flower?'

'No, just Tuli, not a flower. Why do you sleep in the smashed up car, Storyman? Is it in your book?'

'There is no book, Tuli. I lost something and came looking for it. The car is the only place I could find to sleep. Don't you get too wrapped up in story stuff. It makes having to live in the real world sort of unbearable.'

'What did you lose? I can help find it,' she said. 'I'm good at finding like in hide and seek.'

'I lost a person. A friend.'

'Wow, that's a very big thing to lose.'

'Tell me about it, kiddo.'

Just then she heard Mandy's voice shouting into the garden.

'Bloody hell, Grace, have you seen what Tuli's doing? The kid is standing on my books, in the garden. Tuli, get down. You could break your bleedin' neck doing that.' Mandy's voice got louder and louder. 'Tuli, TULI, get down now, you bloody stupid kid.'

The storyman put his fingers to his lips in a ssh and Tuli did the same. She carefully climbed off the chair, picked up Mandy's books and staggered towards the house.

When Mummy came home from her job, Mandy was waiting for her at the door.

'You need to teach Tuli how to respect other people's property,' she said.

'I've just come in. Give me a break.' Ebele said, She put down the bags she was carrying and called Tuli to her. Tuli held on to her mother's leg and hid her face behind her bottom as Mandy carried on speaking.

'She went into my study and took my books without permission, and she stood on them. Those academic books cost a bomb.'

'Tuli, is this right?' Ebele said in a flat voice. 'Books are not for standing on. You know that, don't you?'

'At least say it like you mean it,' Mandy said.

'Oh for fuck's sake, Mandy. It's hardly a major crime.'

Mummy was smaller than Mandy but if there was a fight, like in the playground every day, Mummy would definitely win. Mandy was too tall, like a giraffe. She always looked like she was too big to be inside rooms. Grace was short and she was fat too so she definitely wouldn't be good at fighting. Sometimes she looked like there were cushions tucked up under her clothes but Tuli wasn't supposed to say those things out loud. Grace and Mandy were opposites, like people in cartoons.

'Look, Ebele, if you want us to keep an eye on the kid you could teach her a few manners, and perhaps yourself too. You shouldn't swear in front of her all the time,' Mandy said.

'Don't tell me what to do with my own child. I can find someone else to look after her if you don't want to but don't expect us to feed those cats of yours either. This is a two-way street remember?'

Tuli began to shake her head but she was still behind Mummy so no-one could see. She thought about Storyman behind the wall. She didn't want to be looked after by anyone else.

'Oh no,' she whispered into her mother's bottom.

Grace appeared in the doorway. 'Come on now you two. I love having little Tuli round here. She's a good kid, Ebele. Mandy's just upset because she could've hurt herself standing on the books on a chair like that.' Grace put her hand on Mandy's waist and continued to speak, 'She was just playing a game – imaginary friends or something.' Grace bent to look at Tuli. 'You didn't mean to do something wrong, did you?' Tuli shook her head again. 'See,' said Grace.

'Whatever,' Ebele said and she ushered Tuli up the stairs, slamming the door behind them as Grace and Mandy still hovered in the hallway. Tuli ran to her bedroom. She looked out of the window but all was still and Storyman wasn't visible. She wondered what he would have for his dinner without a cooker. Maybe a cheese sandwich. She liked cheese sandwiches.

Mostly though she liked cheese on toast. Cheese on toast was even better than beans on toast, but Storyman would only be able to have a cold sandwich without a cooker.

8. JIMMY

Jimmy blocked the broken window at the back of the car with cardboard he found in a nearby recycling box. He shoved it into the gap before trying to sleep but it was no guard against the freezing rain which beat a rhythm on the car roof throughout the night. He woke up cold. He was always cold. The radio worked though, just about; he'd tried it on the off chance soon after finding the car, expecting the battery to be flat. It was a thrill to hear music, not discordant in a mesh of noise along the high street or in a pub but quietly, alone in a confined space, where he could really listen, soaking up the warmth it radiated. The tuner knob was stuck on an easy listening station which reminded him of Sunday mornings when eleven o'clock mass meant the heft of Frank Noone was lifted temporarily from their home, Frank being the god-fearing man he was. It was the only time music played in the kitchen: love-songs filling the moist air with breeziness while vegetables were peeled and chopped for dinner.

'This is shite music, Nan, proper cheese,' Ant would say teasingly. 'How about a brew and a bit of Primal Scream instead?'

Mass ended at a quarter to; the radio got switched off at half past, just in case Frank was early, though they all knew he would be bang on time. Lunch at one o'clock, first grace then eating under surveillance, snide remarks across the table then out again by two for last orders. Never an offer to help with the washing up, never any gratitude for Nan.

'It's the least I can do,' she said when Ant berated Frank behind his back. 'Your children's children are twice your children, Anthony. Anyway, it's what your mam would have wanted.'

There wasn't a dishwasher in the house; they could have one with Frank's wages for his pen pushing job but he said a dishwasher was a waste of money: indulgent and vulgar, he told them. They could and would do without.

The music on the car radio was cheesy too but it was a small joy to have it. The volume button jammed halfway; Jimmy would have liked it much louder, to really block out the rest of the world but it did him fine; it was better than no music at all. The only thing he could control with ease was the on/off button. He wondered how long the battery would last without recharge and decided to limit it to just ten minutes to mark the beginning and the end of each day, like the music in the subway with Betwa, rationing himself in the way Nan told him they had to do in the war.

'Get off it, Nan. You're not old enough to have been around in the war.' he said once. They both knew he was being nice. She replied,

'I am so, you daft apeth. Mind you, I was much younger than our Jenny when it ended. I don't really remember it, just what my mam told me.'

Back then, Jimmy found it hard to believe the grown-ups around him had been children once. Not a single hint or remnant of childish bliss existed in any of them. He couldn't believe it ever did for Frank, and it had certainly long since been obliterated for Nan.

After the third song, Jimmy switched off the radio and tried to recall the little girl who'd appeared over the back wall like a jack-in-the-box the day before; thoughts of her seeped through him like wine. She was sweet, even in her naive confusion, talking about her stories and books. He liked her. *A slip of a girl*, as Nan would say. Grubby-faced like kids should be. He liked the way she surprised him unexpectedly, like the music. She said things in the same way Jen used to at that age, with a buoyancy which made everything seem okay; it was a way of speaking only really young children had. She had the same look in her eyes as Jen too: curious, darting about as if there was too much to take in all at once. Something about her made him optimistic but he knew he couldn't talk to her again. People like him weren't meant to speak to children.

The old woman came again later in the morning, before the day was fully churned up. She brought tea in a flask and warm toast on a plate covered with foil.

'Somebody must be worried about you,' she said. 'Perhaps your mother or a friend maybe?'

'Nobody's worried about me. You don't need to bother about that.'

'But someone must wonder where you are?'

Jimmy glugged the tea from the flask into the cup, took a sip and wiped his mouth with the back of his hand. The tea was too hot and it was too early to talk.

'Take your time,' the old woman said and he thought she meant with the tea until she added, 'You don't need to tell me anything. It just makes me so sad to see a young man like you living here, like this. Whatever has happened to you, I am sure there is a way to fix it.'

Jimmy looked at her as he gulped down the toast. He wished she would go away.

'Life isn't a fairytale, lady.' His words sounded harsher than he'd meant them to be. More gently he said, 'I'm one of the lucky ones: I've got this car to sleep in and you're bringing me scran.' He was grateful for the food so he worked hard to keep the bitterness out of his voice.

'What about clothes? Do you need blankets? Tell me what you need and I will try to bring it. Me and my husband, we believe in looking after the less fortunate.'

He didn't think of himself in this way. Life happened, fairly or unfairly; he despised the idea of being a charity case. The woman was beginning to irritate him with her cloying concern.

'Fortune is a judgement,' he said. He was fortunate to have met Betwa: he was alone until she came along, and when he found her again his fortune would be restored.

The woman didn't appear to hear him. 'We have many books too. Perhaps a book to read? It must get boring for you sitting in this car all day.'

Jimmy shrugged his shoulders even though he would have loved a different book to read. As the old lady turned to go he said,

'Actually, I do have a friend, a good friend. But she's lost and I need to find her. She's from near here.'

'Where does she live, your friend?'

'If I knew that I'd be round there, wouldn't I?'

The woman looked hurt and Jimmy said, 'Look, sorry, you don't get much sleep out here. It makes you cranky. D'ya know what I mean?' She nodded in a way which made Jimmy think she really did. 'Maybe a blanket would be good. Yes a blanket and a book,' he said. The woman nodded again.

'Okay, yes we have plenty of both.'

'My friend's name is Betwa. She's like you, you know, Indian, your skin colour. About your height, too. Hair up to here,' he said pointing towards his shoulder. 'She has a little gold stud in her nose.'

'There are many people around here who fit your friend's description. I don't know anybody called by this name.'

'It's a river, the name of a river. It's near where her mother was born. It's an unusual name, right?'

'Yes I know the river, I too come from near there. But I don't know too many people here, not now. It's just me and my husband. We keep ourselves to ourselves.'

Jimmy sighed. 'Kids all flown the nest then?'

The woman left without answering. He noticed her face was more crumpled than when she arrived. He shouted as she moved away. 'Thanks for the toast. I haven't had toast in ages. I'd forgotten how good something so simple can be.'

The woman looked over towards him. 'You should let your parents know you are alright,' she said.

'Am I?' he said, far too quietly for her to have heard.

Jimmy got out of the car, stretched his limbs and headed for the places Betwa talked about: the hospital grounds adjacent to the park opposite the cafe where the dog had scared him. Saturday morning liveliness echoed across the wide traffic-filled Black Horse Lane in front of the houses on Shifnal Road. He hesitated before crossing and glanced up to the window where the woman who'd not long since brought his tea and toast was looking out across the park in a daze; she didn't notice him. In the small front garden next door to her house, a large-framed woman in overalls and wellies was pruning the hedge. He watched her as he orientated himself, trying to work out if this was the house where the little girl lived or whether it was further along on the other side of the row. The big woman saw him and said,

'Hey you, I've seen you hanging around the back. We don't need you around here. This is a nice place, or at least it's trying hard to be. Why don't you go home?'

She had an Australian accent. 'Why don't *you* go home?' Jimmy said.

'The bloody cheek of it,' the woman said. 'Listen mate, there's places you can get help, with the drugs and shit. Just move on, go and sort yourself out. Get some rehab and then maybe you'll be able to hold down a job and get a place to live decently. It's not good for this place to have tramps and beggars and stuff.'

He shook his head and crossed the road, trying his best to control the rise the woman stirred up in him. *The bloody cheek of her.*

Immediately behind a bus stop and bottle-green railings, two rough sleepers slumped against a tree whilst a third flopped forward in a stupor, his head lolling like a pendulum. The least catatonic of them saluted Jimmy with a strange grimace. Jimmy returned the gesture and moved on quickly. He asked a young woman with a pram if she knew a girl called Betwa. He wished he had a photo he could whip out of his wallet like they did on the telly. The woman, startled, rushed away without responding. He asked others along the pavement about Betwa: most just walked away; some told him to *piss off* or worse; a youth in a baseball cap spat at him and pushed him out of the way into the road, missing a car by inches. After that, Jimmy walked across the park to the bench behind the willow tree where he'd slept before and lay down, away from the gaze of footballers, pram-pushers and dog walkers but close enough to hear the white noise of normality. The sound of children laughing in the distance was like music. He closed his eyes and let the weak autumn sun warm his face, trying hard to forget who he was. He drifted off to a different place, where the laughter was his own and Ant's as they ran from the corner shop with pockets full of *Pick 'n' Mix* while the shopkeeper waddled after them shouting, *Stop Thieves* to an empty street. The daydream was abruptly interrupted by loud sniggers nearby, and then the sudden sensation of warm liquid trickling down his leg, quickly followed by the acrid stench of piss.

'You fucking cunts,' he shouted as two tall boys in tracksuits ran down the path shrieking; both stuck middle fingers up at him.

He made his way to the toilet block behind the cafe, removed his shoe and peeled off his damp sock. He rinsed his piss-soaked leg under the cold tap. The hand dryer was broken so he attempted to dry himself with paper-towels. Blobs of green paper stuck to the hairs on his leg and when he tried to brush them away he stumbled off balance and fell, bashing his shoulder on the stainless steel sink. He managed to compose himself, squeezed as much water as he could from the fabric, rolled up the trouser leg and stepped outside, one foot still bare, hobbling through the park with his shoe in his hand. Ahead of him, the old woman disappeared into her front door and when he reached the car he realised she'd left him gifts on the driver's seat. He removed his wet trousers and put the thick tartan blanket over his knees before picking up the book she'd left. The title was one he recognised and, as he held it in his hands, he suddenly felt tearful. He stroked the cover. It was a copy of his mother's favourite novel by a Chilean writer whose name he could never pronounce. For years it had sat on Nan's mantelpiece like a family heirloom.

'Your mam thought books were magic,' Nan once said.

When he asked her to tell him more, she told him the story of how his parents first met in the library.

There was a rainstorm late in the afternoon; not everyday drizzle but a deluge, flooding the streets within minutes. People didn't know what hit them. The library was a place to flock to. Linda was already there, after school, unaware of the storm except as a distant rumble. She thought the noise was from the empty belly of the thin fella in the seat beside her. Frank came in for shelter with many others. The library hadn't been so full in ages. He was older than her, ten years exactly, and he wore a suit to his job, not like anyone else we knew. He looked smart, I bet. He was different. On wedding photos, our Linda looked as tiny as a sparrow next to him: paper-white skin and all that beautiful red hair she had, flowing over her shoulders. He must have thought she was an angel from the way he looked at her in those pictures. She was an angel, our Linda. My Linda.

'But why did she love him?' Jimmy asked her. It was easy to see why someone would love his mother but he really couldn't fathom how anyone could love Frank.

'He wasn't always this way, Jimmy. I mean, he was always a bit sombre, you know, inclined to get a bit moody, but it hit him hard when she went. He loved her, that's for sure. She was everything to him. And now he doesn't know how to exist without her. I don't think he had much happiness before your mam came into his life.'

'Yes, but why did she marry him?'

'You'll understand one day, Jimmy. You're too young to know everything just yet.'

He was just eleven at the time. Later, he asked Ant the same question and his brother said, 'Blimey, Jimbo. Birds and bees, facts of life and all that. Don't be a muppet, do the maths. There's only one reason she married old misery guts and it'll be yours truly.' Jimmy goaded him and Ant explained, adding in the graphic detail for effect. Jimmy felt sick at the thought of it but Ant said, 'Sex is everywhere, Jimbo. Wait until you're as old as me and you'll know what I mean. Don't let the thought of him spoil everything.'

As all these thoughts careered through his head, Jimmy sat in the car clutching the book and wiping his dripping nose with the edge of the clean blanket.

9. EBELE

Ebele first fell in love the week the planes crashed into the towers in New York City. She was nine years old. All around her adults were locked in shock: wide-eyed, aghast in front of televisions, glued to the horror as it unfolded in front of them. One minute huge buildings full of office workers existed as normal, the next they disintegrated, collapsing to the ground as the inhabitants of the tower blocks were lost in great plumes of smoke and ash and the world shifted on its axis. She watched people leap through flames from upper floor windows, unsure whether it was the news or a film she was seeing. When her mother realised she was in the room she quickly shoved her into the hallway.

'No child should see this,' she declared.

Instead, Ebele listened with her ear pressed against the door while her mother wailed out her disbeliefs to an empty room. *How can this be? What the hell...? Poor bleedin' sods.*

Over the following days, while her mother continued to be gripped by the news, Ebele spent time after school watching the new boy next door through her bedroom window, concealed behind calico curtains and surrounded by the discarded books and toys she was meant to be occupied with. The boy scrambled around the bushes in the back gardens, retrieving lost balls like a puppy. She watched as his untamed hair accumulated stray leaves and feathery dandelion seeds, becoming speckled in green and white. He looked mythical, like the strange bird in the Trinidadian stories Papa told her, passed down from his own father and his grandfather before that. She watched as the boy delighted in a recovery, throwing his prize into the air and catching it over and over. His hair was the colour of fire and the exact same shade as her father's first car, an old Ford Escort proudly acquired sometime after he first arrived in England. The car was long gone now just like Papa, but both were captured in a photograph hanging in the hallway next to the front door, a reminder of his existence which was once as present in Ebele's world as she was herself.

The boy always played alone. She guessed he was like her, without brothers and sisters. After watching him for two consecutive afternoons, she leaned out the window on her elbows and sucked in air plump with the aroma of fried meat and a sweet scent of the dusty pink roses growing beneath her window, and she waited for the boy to notice her, heart pounding, throat dry. When he didn't look up she heard herself shouting out before she could think twice.

'Is that your new house?'

He jumped and looked around.

'No,' he said when he spotted her. 'It's where my dad lives. I'm only here while my mom's having another babby.'

'Oh,' Ebele said. 'I live with my mom too,' and so concluded their first conversation.

The following Saturday she leaned out the window after breakfast. The day was heavy with moisture and it was hard to catch a breath. The boy told her his name was Michael and asked if she knew how to play football.

'No, but I can play cricket. Papa taught me,' she said.

They took it in turns to bat and bowl. Four days later Michael left.

'I'm going home,' he'd said with a big grin across his face.

'If this was your home we could play cricket together all the time.'

'Nah, I wouldn't like to be here all the time,' he said. 'Home is where my friends are.'

'Aren't I your friend now?' she replied, and when he shook his head she swallowed hard to push away the lump in her throat. Later, she watched as he bundled his bags into the back of his father's white Transit van. When he climbed in she lifted her hand to wave but he was looking the other way. She let it drop down quickly before anyone else saw her. After the van pulled away, she felt her stomach plummet. The last time she felt so bad was the day Papa died by crashing into a wall on the ring-road junction near Kebble Lane, smashing both the car and his own head into an unrecognisable mess.

The night Michael left, Ebele's mother climbed into her bed and patted her hair as she sobbed into the pillow. She eventually fell asleep with her mother's voice whispering in her ear.

'Boys are trouble, Ebele. They come into your life like a whirlwind and then they're gone. You'll forget Michael in a week or so and I'll tell you what, he'll have forgotten all about you in less than half that time. Don't worry, you'll soon find some friends your own age to play with.'

Michael didn't come back to his father's house until the following summer. He was taller, almost as tall as his dad, and he'd developed a shadow of maroon hair above his upper lip which made the edges of his mouth look dirty. She only realised he was back when she saw him sitting on the wall in the garden occupied with something he held in his hands. She skipped out to meet him.

'Wanna play cricket?' she asked, as if she'd seen him the day before.

'Nah, boring. Got this now.' He waved the Gameboy in her face.

By the end of the summer he was taller still, and his voice was different; it squelched like her trainers in the rain; it made her skin prickle like nettle-rash did.

Near the end of the long school holidays, he finally let her have a go on the Gameboy as he stood close behind her looking over her shoulder, his breath hot on her. Then, all of a sudden he shoved his hand down the back of her shorts and into her knickers. She was stunned. She struggled to free herself but he crooked one arm around her neck and groped around her private parts with his other hand. She kicked his shin and managed to wriggle enough to loosen his grip, but before she could escape he grabbed her and pulled her to the ground. He sat with his full weight pressing down on her stomach, moving his snakey hands over the bare skin beneath her vest-top. She screamed as loud as she could manage and, before her mother came running out the back door, Michael jumped up and leaned against the wall, nonchalant, Gameboy in hand, seemingly oblivious to her screaming.

'I don't like boys,' she told her mother later in the day.

'I don't blame you,' her mother said off-hand. Ebele wasn't sure if she was joking or not until she added, 'They always let you down.'

'Papa didn't let you down.'

'He got himself killed by driving his damn car too fast. That was a letdown, for me and for you. You're too young to understand these things. When you're older you'll know what I mean.'

Ebele avoided the garden for the rest of the holidays despite the unbearable stickiness of the long summer days. By the time she turned ten later that year, she and her mother had moved from the estate to a small flat near the big school and she never saw Michael again.

It was some time before she knew what her mother had meant that night after the incident in the garden, and it was only when she sat in the window with Tuli asleep on her lap, watching Jamal as he walked across the park, that she recalled the conversation. She wished she could pick up the phone or send a message and let her mother know she now understood her words but she knew it wouldn't be that simple. The gorge which had developed between them would be hard to narrow; far too much had happened since that summer long ago, and it wasn't only boys who'd let her down.

10. RAYYA

Rayya didn't know the name of the young man in the car. On the second day of feeding him she thought about asking but what did it really matter? Names were not so important. She was hardly ever addressed by her own given name: sometimes people called her Rita or Ruby but she existed beyond and between those monikers. These days, she felt she hardly existed at all. For many years, she'd not been the Rayya her mother shouted for across the mounds of amber rubble and broken glass which were her playgrounds in the neglected Delhi back streets. Then she was Rayya, daughter of Raju, labourer; never daughter of Chitramala, maid. To Satish she was always *darling* when they were not in company, and he was *darling* to her; they were equally treasured. On their wedding night, he made it clear she was not a possession; she belonged only to herself and not to her father nor to him. She trembled with excitement at the thought of her world being shaken up like this; it made her heart soar. She thought Satish brave to be challenging all that had been and continued to be around her. It took her some years to realise his bravery stemmed from her; she made him brave by giving him the reason to be so. Later, after they'd been married for a short time and she was able to have conversations with strangers and read the newspapers and magazine articles by the bedside, she realised his interests in equality extended far beyond their small unit and she loved him all the more for it. He was a proud autodidact and he encouraged her to be one too; together they read about the work of Baba Amte and reforms of Mohan Roy and, on arriving in England, they enrolled in an English language course and attended it religiously, sitting side by side in a blank, soulless classroom before completing the homework soon after in their neat and cozy little house on Shifnal Road. On weekends, they visited the library and within a year were reading Orwell and Steinbeck out loud to one another in the language in which the texts were written, stumbling at odd words and giggling at their own heavy English accents. Evenings were spent drinking beer and talking at length about the student/worker demonstrations in Pakistan and the outcomes of the Liberation War in Bangladesh. They were on the exact same footing in all pursuits of the mind. In the bedroom, Rayya was more spirited, surprising herself as their first fumbled liaisons became less hurried and more satisfying with her coaxing. Beyond the house, she was mostly Mrs Banu, wife of Satish Banu, but they both knew the truth of it; he was her equal, her co-conspirator, her lover, this man who now lay inanimate in the bedroom where once she and he had never felt more alive.

When Satish first became ill, Rayya thought it would pass; a momentary lapse of well-being, a wicked virus which would soon peter out, exhaust itself and disappear as if it never existed. It didn't happen like that: a stagger or a slip soon became a wobble and then a fall; a bruise became a break and then a paralysis. Satish once asked for a cup of tea not realising she'd only just placed one on the table beside him, and then he made the same mistake again and again. When the post office where he worked advised early retirement, the illness took hold very quickly and she knew he couldn't be left alone all day so she too gave up her job in the infant school, leaving behind the laughter of children which gave her so much joy.

It took many months for Satish's illness to be diagnosed. Months quickly became years wherein his quiet deteriorations surfaced as micro-rages, and Rayya's own guilt-ridden irritability became weariness and grief for the man she loved with all her heart but who was fading away in front of her eyes, slipping into a chasm neither knew how to bridge.

On the day the illness was named, she squeezed Satish's hand reassuringly as they walked slowly from the bus stop to the hospital to receive his test results. The GP who'd sent them had known Rayya and Satish for many years but not since the infertility tests decades earlier had they seen him so regularly. Dr Razak was a very young man then, not long qualified and keen to escape the arduous night shifts associated with hospital work. Now he'd been a regular face at the surgery for over thirty years, but only on more recent visits had she noticed how grey his hair had become and how his shoulders had started curving inwards making him seem much smaller than he used to be, He had aged in tandem with her. When he spoke, he didn't tilt his head condescendingly or speak in the wispy tones of forced concern. She always appreciated that.

Before sending them to the specialists, he said, 'It looks like Parkinson's, but I can't be sure.' He handed them a bundle of leaflets. 'To be frank, Satish, the symptoms are not conclusive; the signs could mean a lot of things. I will refer you. Hopefully, whatever the diagnosis, it can be managed effectively.'

'Managed? Not cured?' Satish replied.

'It's just words, my friend. Managed. Treated. Let's see what the test results show.'

The doctor shook Satish's hand. He bowed courteously towards Rayya and ushered them out of the room.

During the consultation, Rayya had noticed a picture of a very young child on the doctor's desk. The photograph perplexed her until she realised it must be a grandchild; this was the age they were at now. Years ago, when it became obvious she would not conceive herself, the photographs of Dr Razak's own children, which once sat proudly on display in his surgery, disappeared from his desk. The void of them upset her more than their presence ever did. She always wanted to tell the doctor this but she could never find the courage. On this latest occasion, as she and Satish were leaving, she said,

'Your grandchild is beautiful, Dr Razak. It makes me very happy to see the photograph of her.'

The hospital they were sent to was anodyne but confusing. Pale green and salmon-pink corridors alternated between sets of heavy double doors. Corridors with direction lines in bright primary colours appeared to lead back to the same starting points and Rayya only realised they were going around in circles when, for the fourth time, they found themselves in front of a wall of naive paintings of seascapes and boats.

'Same damn jolly pictures again. This place is a maze,' Satish complained. She squeezed his hand again.

'Darling, it will be fine,' she said. 'Have faith. They will find out what is causing the eye problems and the falls. It will be a simple thing and will pass like sickness always does.'

'I'm an old man. I lost my faith in medicine many years ago. It's been a long time since faith featured in any equation of mine, Rayya. What is there to have faith in?'

She let go of his hand, steered him by the shoulders to face her and said, 'Have faith in me, darling. Have faith that whatever is going on with your health, I will be by your side to look after you.'

'You are my wife. My comrade, my partner, remember? Not my bloody nursemaid.'

'If you love someone, you can be a comrade and a nursemaid at the same time if that is what is required.'

Then, in a room made smaller by the amount of furniture crammed into it, a tiny bespectacled woman tentatively declared a grand sounding name for the illness and it was if a tiger had been described as an apple.

'We'll call it PSP for short,' the consultant said. The words were directed at Rayya. They held in them a devastating pity which took her back to the day when Dr Razak first told her she was barren.

Ten months after the illness was named, Satish started using a stick for balance. Within the next few months, his speech became slurred and then practically non-existent; he lost the ability to swallow solid food, his eyes stung and his sight became blurred. To communicate, he wrote out short notes with a pen attached by string to a notebook at his side. Rayya dressed and undressed him. She fed him soft foods with a spoon and they both pretended it was normal. Then, when his legs became increasingly faltering and he wasn't able to reach the bathroom in time, the smell of his excrement permeated the whole house. She gagged as she cleaned him, and he cried silent tears from fixed eyes loaded with fear and humiliation.

Each day a little more of him slipped away: the ability to eat, to talk, to move parts of his body, until Rayya's whole existence revolved around the care she gave or managed to secure from a myriad of service providers with the help of Doctor Razak. She was angry with the illness. There was no warning that the man she loved would become trapped inside a closed case of a body, as helpless as a newborn baby. Care-workers came to the house twice a day and soon they arranged for a special bed to be delivered, complete with pulleys and levers. It was put in the centre of the bright front bedroom which they had shared as man and wife for almost five decades. The wardrobe was cleared of clothes to store the cartons of powdered food, bulky packages of incontinence pads, eye drops and other lubricants. She made herself a separate space in the smaller back bedroom at the end of the landing, taking with her a few books from the overstocked shelves of her former bedroom and the resplendent peacock-patterned bedspread which had adorned their marital bed ever since they'd brought it home after a longed-for trip to Jaisalmer, almost two decades earlier. Here she was far enough away from the clinical smells and the hum of machines but close by in case Satish pulled on the bell an inch from his reach or an unexpected sound came through the baby monitor on her bedside table. Then, on the day the boy appeared sleeping in the abandoned car at the back of the gardens so did a letter from a hospice on the outer reaches of the area. It was an invitation to discuss Satish's imminent transition to palliative care, as advised by Doctor Razak and their hospital consultant. She read the letter at the front door, quickly screwed it up and stuffed it into her pocket. Later, she shoved it behind a framed wedding photograph on the mantelpiece, out of sight of the carers.

The carers always came in pairs so they could lift Satish, wash him and change his pads and his tubes together. The task was too much for one person. When they first started coming, Rayya sat in the corner, uncomfortable at the prospect of leaving him alone with strangers, tears trickling down her face as they shifted him about like a corpse. One day, a carer called Daban said, 'We'll be gentle with him Mrs B. Why don't you nip out to the shops? Get yourself a treat or something.'

'No, I'm not leaving him. He wouldn't want me to.'

'Just a few minutes to yourself. It'll do you good, bit of fresh air.' The young man put his hand on his heart and said, 'I promise you Mrs B., we'll take the best care of him.'

For some reason she believed the young man meant what he said, so she tentatively made her way across Black Horse Lane to the corner shop; it was less than a minute's walk away. She teetered on the threshold, looking back towards the house; nothing had changed: no ambulance, no carer running out the front door towards her, so she carried on walking, out of view and around the corner to a bigger shop a little further along. There she bought the toilet roll and milk she needed. It was the first time in a while she'd shopped without having to wait for Satish to be sound asleep so she could dash across the road with the baby monitor in her hand. Less than ten minutes passed by before she returned to the house and the carers were still measuring out boiled water for the powdered food as she entered. Since then, when the carers arrived she'd say to Satish,

'I'll just be ten minutes, maybe fifteen, to get essentials. I promise I won't be any longer.' And she never was.

The carer called Daban was the only one she really trusted with Satish. His face was kind; his smile reminded her of Kostas, and he always talked directly to Satish rather than over him. He explained what was happening as if seeking permission. She always made tea when the carers came but only Daban ever drank it. The others would say yes when she offered but as soon as it was ready they'd say, *Got another chap to see, sorry Mrs Banu,* and off they'd rush. Daban stayed for longer. Once he stayed for an extra hour to help her set up online shopping on her cranky old laptop. He showed her how to create a list of all the things she needed and which buttons to press to make repeat orders. He looked away as she added her debit card details and they laughed together when the first order she made on her own came with twenty tins of minestrone soup instead of the two she'd meant to click. She was surprised at how sad she felt one morning when Daban said,

'Mrs B., I spend too much time in traffic trying to get between appointments. Sometimes it can take an hour to travel from one end of the high street to the other and they don't pay us for that so I figured I might as well earn money from the driving itself.'

She still saw him sometimes but only in passing, sat in the delivery van outside Makrides' Furniture Store or, if she'd nipped out to pick up vegetables or toiletries in the early evening, standing in the doorway of the big Victorian pub where he worked. He would always raise his hand in a salute and ask,

'How's the captain doing? Keeping you busy?'

'He's just the same, Daban. Just the same.'

She never knew why Daban called Satish *captain* but it was far better than 'the client', which was how the other carers referred to him. When Daban stopped visiting, she missed him in a way she couldn't fathom until she realised he was the only other human being she'd been having two-way conversations with for some time. Friends she and Satish had made over the years slipped away at the same rate her husband slipped into his illness: support staff at the school where she worked, couples they'd met at cultural and educational events, the men from the post office who were active in the union, as was Satish. She talked to him of course, but then it was only ever her voice in the room. Now she was having different conversations again, with the boy in the car and when she took food to him on the second evening he said, 'You're very kind,' and began eating while she stood watching.

'Oh it's no problem,' she replied 'I have to cook anyway, for me and my husband. It's no bother to make a little extra.' The lie seeped out with an ease which unsettled her.

'It's delicious. I've never tasted anything like it,' he said as food spluttered on to his beard. His teeth were almost the exact same shade as the turmeric which coloured the dish.

'It's nothing. Just dhal. It's very simple to cook. I'll bring breakfast again too.' The boy nodded, his mouth bulging. 'If you're still here?' He nodded again, staring her in the eye as he chewed. She watched him for a moment longer than was comfortable, then turned and walked away quickly to the house where the carers would be getting ready to leave.

Each evening, Rayya told Satish about the things which occupied her during the day.

'Darling,' she said, when dusk arrived, 'do you remember the first time we cooked masoor dhal? The telephone rang and I forgot to turn down the gas before I answered it. Do you remember? Mummy-ji was talking too much about the new bazaar and the *paan-wallah* knocked over by a bullock in the street. You must remember. Mummy-ji was making me giggle when she described how the bullock ate the *catechu* and it's mouth was so red it looked like Aunty Savita in the lipstick she wore to Cousin Kuldip's wedding. Savita was always a big girl.' She leant over Satish as she spoke and stroked his cheek. 'You didn't realise the flame was so high. You were cutting garlic and the radio was on too loud. And then, when I came back from the telephone, the whole cooker top was covered in yellow foam boiled over from the dhal and the pan was spoiled with burning.' Rayya sighed. 'Well, at least we knew to keep an eye next time, hai na? And now, this poor boy eats my dhal like I've served him the most exquisite dish from the kitchen of the Rashtrapati Bhavan. Such a strange and confused world.'

She straightened Satish's blanket and adjusted his head on the pillow and, before she resumed reading from *Mr Biswas*, she said, 'You don't think I am being a silly old woman do you, darling? Feeding this boy like a proper dadi-ma?'

When streaks of sunset became a dense indigo, she folded the page and set down the book. The main road was momentarily quiet, free of traffic as she drew the curtains. Inside, the only sound was the faint beep of the machine keeping Satish alive. When she slept she dreamt of running for the second time that week.

Rayya Banu ran. As soon as she could walk, she ran. At first she just ran around the tumbledown timber structure where she lived on the west side of Delhi. Then, when she was firmer in her footing she ran around the small backyard, causing chickens to flap and cluck in her wake. Copper dust plumed around her wherever she went and when sheets which had taken a whole day to wash were coated in a film of fine orange, her small legs stung from the slapping she received as a result. On her fifth birthday, she ran out of the front door and way past anywhere she'd run before. She wanted to see what was beyond the criss-cross of alleyways surrounding her little shack and what lay beyond the horizon which appeared as a thin bright blue line across the top of a ramshackle jigsaw of dwellings. She ran without losing her breath: skipping over dank gulleys; skimming the cart of the tea-wallah, causing his steel cups to rattle as she passed by; tripping on a *lauki* from the wobbly vegetable stand, always piled high with mountains of bitter melon and okra. As she ran, she could hear her mother's voice calling for her, echoing across tin rooftops, fading away and then becoming louder as she whirled through the maze of streets. When she'd passed the same tethered goat on the roadside for the third time, she stopped, sat on the kerb on the corner of the crossroads and waited for a sign which would lead her back home. None came so she began to shout, quietly at first then more and more urgently.

'Mama, I'm here. Mama, I want to come home.' Her voice crackled and was so inconsequential not even the goat batted an eyelid. She began to sob. Suddenly, Satish, the boy from the house at the back of her own, was in front of her holding out his hand.

'Come, Rayya, I will lead you home.'

The next time she ran, it was in an unwavering line around the block, past Satish's house, over and over until she collapsed in tiredness twenty minutes later at her own front door. By the time she was seven, Satish always waited for her, waving and clapping as she whizzed by. When she was twelve, he started to blow her kisses; in response, she stuck out her tongue then hid her face in her hands so he couldn't see her grin. By then she already knew the only two things she wanted in life were to run and to marry Satish. When she was fourteen they became betrothed.

'Please arrange it, Pita-ji,' she'd begged.

'Rayya, it's our decision not yours. A marriage is between families not just two emotional children. What if the family is not good enough? You are just a young girl – you don't know about something as important as this.' She knew her father was teasing her. He himself was card-partners with Satish's father. Everyone knew it was the right match but her mother still protested.

'She won't marry while she is a child. Not like I did. India needs to look forwards, not backwards. We need to give our girls the gift of childhood instead of burdening them with babies while they are little more than children themselves.'

So Rayya's wedding day was on her eighteenth birthday and that night she felt as if she and Satish were running as one person, as if their bodies were so inextricably linked they would now always run as one.

11. EBELE

On Saturday, the new van driver at Makrides' persuaded Ebele to have a drink with him after shop hours. She wished she hadn't agreed as soon as she said she would, but the alcohol was a draw and the day had been long.

All morning, Makrides lurked around snapping and mumbling, waiting to catch her dawdling so he could reprimand her as if she were a child. Then, at lunchtime, a middle aged couple came in to inquire about the price of a coffee table in the window; Makrides never displayed the prices explicitly, always open to an offer, just like back home. The woman, thin and timorous, cowered behind the bulk of her husband in a way which made Ebele feel uncomfortable. The man caught her looking at them.

'What are you staring at, girl?' he said from across the shop.

The way he spoke reminded her of Brian, her stepfather. She shuffled papers on the desk and tried to look busy but before the couple left the man pushed his face close to hers and when he spoke she smelled sour milk on his breath.

'You girl, you're not good enough to lick my arse, never mind to stare at me and the missus,' he said.

The offer of a drink was welcome after that and besides, there was an endearing quality about the driver, something about his naive acceptance of the world which made him seem innocuous.

'We could both do with it after a day here,' he said.

'I'm not sure,' she replied even though she was desperate for a vodka.

'Go on, it's not often I get a Saturday night off and it'll be nice to spend it in some decent company. My only other option is the X-Factor and that's no way for a hard-working man to spend his free time.'

Ebele knew he liked the way she looked, even if he hadn't completely declared his motive; men could never hide that kind of thing. It'd been a while since anyone had shown her attention of this kind and he was okay; he seemed gentle in a way not many people were, as far as she could tell. He'd have to pay, of course. She said so straight up. She was long past feeling embarrassed about money.

Nights out were a thing once, before Tuli, and now, at her age, she should still be making the most of the big city but the opportunities and the inclination were long gone. After work, all she wanted was to knock back a large vodka and blot out the day before the evening began.

'Ebele is a nice name,' the driver said as he placed her drink in front of her. 'Where's it from? I've not heard of it before.'

'My dad's from Trinidad. I'm named after a great-grandmother or something,' she said sharply.

The driver sat down and adjusted his seat. He took a sip of his beer.

'What about your mother?'

'What about her?' she said frostily.

'Where's she from?

'She's white! If that's what you mean?

'I didn't mean anything. I'm just making conversation.'

He continued with his chitter-chatter but any ease between them had already quickly fallen away; she knew it would be hard to restore. She looked around the pub. It was like other shabby Victorian drinking houses along the high street: run down and struggling but so far escaping the take over by ubiquitous chain breweries. They would, no doubt, soon come along and paint over the oppressive dark wood panelling with *Skimming Stone* white or *Duck Egg* blue; essentially wash-overs of grey to obscure any nostalgic sense of the bawdy labourers and laundry girls or the cider-swilling punky youths who'd sung and stamped and fought and fallen in love in those dim corners. This pub had a nautical theme: fishing rods and lobster pots. She thought it silly, so far from the coast in the middle of an overcrowded city. The driver said he chose it because it was one of the few drinking holes along the strip where he didn't moonlight as a doorman. He'd done stints at one or other of them over the years and there were at least three where he was still on the books. He didn't like to mix work and pleasure.

The pub wasn't busy, a few couples and some student types in the corner: lank hairdos, bland understated clothes. Soon after she and the driver arrived, a group of girls stumbled in; the student types looked over but quickly returned to their lofty conversations. The girls were dressed for a night on the town: heavily painted faces, low cut tops, unfeasibly high heels; one had a sash across her chest, *21 Today*, and rabbit ears. *Why rabbit ears?* Ebele thought. *Stupid!* The girls' howling laughter bounced off the high-ceilinged room and echoed across the other customers like a car alarm. Ebele didn't want to answer any more of the driver's questions. The stifling atmosphere was beginning to chafe at her skin. Her mouth felt dry. She knocked back the drink.

'Want another?' she said, pointing at the barely touched pint in front of the driver. He shook his head and she was relieved; she only had enough for one.

At the bar, she thought about her stepfather again. The first time he came to their cramped tower-block flat, he cornered her in the living room while her mother fussed about the kitchen.

'Ebele – what the fuck kind of name is that?' he'd rasped at her. 'Paki or nig-nog? It's hard to tell with you.'

She didn't know what to say.

'As long as I'm with your mom you'll have a normal name. From now on you're Ellie. You're not pale enough to pass for one of us but if you sort out that hair it'd be a start.' He moved away quickly when the kettle ceased hissing in the kitchen.

Her mother blustered into the room like an over-excited teenager, carrying a tray of clinking crockery. 'Nice to hear you getting on so well,' she said. Ebele was thirteen at the time.

'He's a bastard,' she told her mother two years later as they applied make-up together in the bedroom of Brian's semi, in preparation for the registry office wedding. The reception to follow would be in his local.

'Well, it's hard to find one who isn't,' her mother replied. It wasn't any kind of revelation; she'd said it many times. 'Look around you though, Ebele. We could never live in a place like this if it was just you and me. Besides, he wants me and right now it's enough. You'll go, you'll disappear off somewhere soon enough, leave me on my own and I won't be able to stand it.'

A few months later she did go, after she awoke one night to find Brian standing over her watching as she slept. At first the scream in her head was frozen. It took a moment to thaw and by the time it came hurtling out, he'd disappeared, down the landing and into the bathroom. He laughed when she told her mother what had happened.

'You're dreaming, girl. I went for a piss, for god's sake, she's bonkers. Why would I want to stand over her? She's a bloody fantasist.'

Her mother didn't believe her, or at least that's what she said in front of Brian as she stood next to him yawning in her cheap pink negligee.

'You probably did dream it, Ebele,' she said. 'You never were a good sleeper.'

Ebele wondered if her mother had actually taken in what she'd been told, whether she was even awake enough to comprehend the magnitude of Ebele's words.

Brian lingered in the darkness for a few seconds after her mother crawled off to bed, and before he left the room he said in a whisper, 'If I want something, I get it. Remember that, Ellie.'

The next day, when Brian left for work, she tried to talk to her mother again, to tell her what really happened.

'You're wrong. You must've just imagined it,' her mother said.

'I didn't. I know what it was. I'm not daft.'

'Please, Ebele, don't spoil everything. He's the best chance I've got. People aren't meant to be alone.'

Ebele found the betrayal beyond forgiveness.

Brian built a wall between her and her mother and she had no idea how to break it down; she guessed her mother didn't either. She avoided both of them for the rest of the day and, before climbing into bed at night, she built up a pile of random items against the door: coat hangers, a tower of books, plastic bags stuffed with dirty washing; a precarious mountain which would alert her with clangs and rustles if anything pushed against it. The next morning, while her mother was downstairs crashing about the kitchen and Brian was on the toilet, she sneaked into their bedroom and grabbed his wallet from the bedside table. She picked up her rucksack, already stuffed with clothes and make-up, tucked the wallet firmly inside it and crept downstairs as quietly as she could. She ignored her mother's shouts from the kitchen about breakfast and front door keys and walked out into the new day. She'd never forgotten that moment. It was a raw spring morning and she inhaled a deep breath of sharp air before scarpering, away from the neat line of 1950's semi-detached houses with their crazy-paved front paths and designated parking spaces, past the small parade of shops at the end of the road and around the corner, out of sight. Fear mixed with an overwhelming sense of freedom was unlike anything she'd ever experienced. She caught the first bus away from the small town, far away from Brian and into the only big city she knew anything about.

When she returned to her seat in the pub with her drink in her hand, the driver said, 'So tell me about yourself, Ebele,' as if the earlier conversation never happened.

'I'm going after this. I've got a kid,' she said.

'Oh I didn't realise.'

'You probably wouldn't have bothered with me if you had,' she said.

'Makes no difference to me,' he replied. 'I like kids. But we've only been here a few minutes.'

'I'll go when I want,' she said abruptly.

'Sure,' he said, unable to conceal what looked like disappointment. 'You're free to do whatever.'

She watched as he slurped a mouthful of beer. He was okay: not too pushy, vaguely handsome. When he smiled his face opened up, but she'd decided long ago open faces were deceiving and such a facade of affability could never be trusted. These days, the only person she was certain was good was Tuli; Tuli and other children who were too young to wear good nature as a deceptive mask. She wanted to leave, she didn't really know why. Discordant noise was closing in on her and she didn't want to explain her name or a history she knew little about to anyone. The inane banter of people in the pub and the superficial conversation with the driver made her feel as if she hardly existed, like a ghost invisibly circumnavigating its way through some liminal state. Sweat broke out across her nose and brow; her hands were clammy. The drinks didn't help, especially on an empty stomach: it was as if she'd stepped outside of herself.

'I told the babysitter I'd be back by half past. That I was working late,' she said.

The driver glanced at his phone; It was five past. 'You should've told them you were out for a drink. Everyone deserves a break. It's Saturday night.'

She tried to steady her breathing. He didn't seem to notice.

'It's a cool name, Ebele. I suppose I'm a sort of mixture too in a way, these days at least.'

She let him speak. His words washed over her. When he paused she said, 'Daban is not exactly normal either, is it?'

'It's pretty normal for where my folks are from. Probably like Ebele where you're from.'

'Just because my dad came from somewhere else doesn't mean I'm not from here.'

She knew she sounded more harsh than she meant to. He was clearly trying hard to rise above her scratchiness. For a moment she felt sorry for him; it would take a lot to rectify her bad mood. Brian's leering face flashed through her head again. The driver smiled and said something she couldn't hear; his words were drowned beneath a crushing wave of sound; she was uncertain whether it was within or around her. Her throat constricted and panic needled up her body, threatening to take hold. It wasn't a new feeling: she thought she'd tamed these attacks some time ago and now here was one arriving out of nowhere. She tried to distract herself by focussing on the movements of the driver's face: how the wrinkles around his mouth creased when he spoke; the way the faux-antique lamps reflected tiny sparkles into his dark eyes. He was animated, gesturing with his hands but it was as though she was watching him on mute. The background music bore in on her, like static on an untuned radio. She heard only fragments of what he said through the fuzz: about his dad who wasn't around, his mum who struggled on her own. It was a familiar story.

'Ebele, are you listening?' His voice cut through the noise. 'I was asking how long you've lived on Shifnal Road?'

She looked across to the birthday party in the corner. The girl with a sash was only a few years younger than she was. She couldn't remember how she celebrated her twenty-first birthday: probably alone, with Tuli asleep nearby, Eastenders on the telly and perhaps a can or two, cold from the fridge, maybe a pizza. No phone calls or cards, not even a text. A day like any other.

When she didn't respond, the driver filled in the gaps in the conversation himself.

'I wasn't born around here but I've been here since I was a baby. It's my manor; know it like the back of my hand. Where were you born, Ebele? You've got a bit of an accent. I had a mate once, from near Birmingham; you speak a bit like him.'

She watched the birthday party girls for a moment longer as they clinked glasses of Prosecco and swigged them like shots. The din made her head and her eyes ache. She needed to get out, to feel cold air on her skin. To breathe. The driver was nice enough but she wished she'd never agreed to the drink and the forced chat which accompanied it. She stood up and steadied herself by holding on to the back of the chair.

'To be honest,' she said, 'I'm knackered. I just want to get home to my child. This whole life story shit isn't for me.'

'It's just a drink,' Daban said. 'I just thought we could be friendly, seeing as we've got to work together.'

'Friendly? Really. I guess it's one way of putting it.'

'Putting what? I like you. God knows why,' he said with a soft smile.

'I know what you're after really,' Ebele said. 'All this small talk is making me nauseous.' She downed the remainder of her drink and grabbed her coat and bag.

'Wow, Ebele. I don't know anything about you but I bet you're not as tough as you make out.' She moved towards the exit. 'Listen,' the driver said gently as she pushed past him, 'I really am just trying to be friendly, that's all. Nothing else.'

'Really!' she said, sarcastically.

He looked exasperated. 'No one has to be alone, You just have to see the good in people,' he said.

'You're right, you know nothing about me,' she replied. 'See you around, driverman.'

On the table beside them, an older couple with the same receding silver-streaked afros stared open-mouthed at her.

'What are you two looking at?' she said. 'Got bored with not having anything to say to each other the past fifty years?' The old man looked wounded but the woman tutted and retorted calmly,

'Perhaps the world would be a bit nicer to you if you showed a bit of kindness, young lady, to yourself as well as to others.'

Ebele rolled her eyes and the woman sucked her teeth so loud other customers turned to look in their direction.

'Sit back down, please,' Daban said, touching her elbow. 'We've only just got here. It's been a bad start. No-one should refuse a friendship.'

Deep down she wished she hadn't been so rude. The panic attack had startled her and she just wanted to escape; she couldn't say any of this to the strangers surrounding her and instead declared her exit.

'I'm off. I've got to get back for my kid.'

From the doorway she looked towards Daban: he sat with his head in his hands, hunched over his half empty glass. She seemed to have developed a habit of pushing people away and she had no idea how to stop it. Next to Daban, the old couple sat in silence, holding hands across the table.

When she picked up Tuli from Grace, her neighbour said,

'Did Mr Makrides say anything about the guy sleeping out back? We've left him a message. I'll try him again tomorrow. We've got guests tonight. It's our turn to host the book group!'

Ebele was angry for not remembering about the tramp and as soon as Tuli was asleep she dialled Makrides' number herself; it went straight to voicemail.

Later, the sound of entertaining rose up through the floor: the cackle of laughter mingled with bassy jazz was grating and Ebele's headache returned as a throb. She poured herself the dregs of a bottle of cheap wine from the fridge and sat on the edge of the sofa bed skimming through images on her phone, trying to ignore the noise. People she'd long lost contact with popped up on the screen with stage-perfect grins against backdrops of beaches and parties, their arms flung around others she'd never met. She clicked away from them and instead hovered over her mother's profile picture. It was always the same, old and grainy, of her as a babe in the arms of her young mother who smiled straight at the camera, proudly showing her off to the world.

She wondered what her mother looked like now, after nearly a decade had passed by: dyed hair, middle-aged spread, the strain showing in an ageing face after years with Brian? She quickly swiped the picture away. There was no access to any others. She changed into her pyjamas, flung her clothes onto a nearby chair and re-dialled Makrides' number. Still voicemail. She climbed into bed and returned to Facebook.

A few minutes later the bell to the downstairs flat rang. It was half past nine. There were voices in the hallway but it was late for arrivals; by now Grace and Mandy's dinner parties were usually in full swing. Then her phone buzzed, it was Grace telling her the visitor was for her; she'd told Mandy not to knock on the door as it may disturb Tuli. She was always the more considerate of the two.

'It's one of your male friends,' Mandy said dismissively as Ebele edged open her door. Mandy grimaced at the sight of her in faded Bart Simpson pyjamas and she grimaced back in return. Mandy's brightly patterned jumper made her look more frumpy than usual. Behind her, Daban was leaning on the frame of the open front door. He held up a bottle of vodka, swinging it close to Mandy's head.

'It's not what you think,' he said, directing the comment to both Mandy and Ebele at the same time. 'I just thought maybe we could have another drink, that you'd be more comfortable at home, knowing your child is okay.'

Mandy looked at Daban suspiciously. 'Keep it down Ebele. You've got a kid up there.'

'Piss off, Mandy. And you keep it down too.'

'One drink!' Ebele said to Daban. 'On the basis you are just being friendly like you say, and then you can piss off as well.'

He laughed.

Ebele watched Daban scan her living room: clothes strewn across furniture and Tuli's supper plate still on the dining table alongside a small puddle of milk. The room was always cluttered and untidy but it wasn't usually dirty. She disappeared into the kitchen for glasses and a dishcloth to wipe up the spill. When she returned, he was standing by the mantlepiece holding a wooden frame; it was Tuli's first school photograph.

'You can sit there,' she said, snatching the photo away. Daban perched awkwardly on the edge of the sofa bed with his elbows on his knees and his hands on his chin.

'Can we put some music on?' he said. 'Quietly so we don't wake your little one I mean.'

Ebele poured vodka into tumblers without answering. She topped them up with juice from a carton and remained standing.

'Cheers!' She knocked the drink back and poured out another.

'You should slow down,' Daban said.

'Thanks for the vodka but maybe this is a bad idea. I've had enough of people telling me what to do. I don't need you to start on me too.'

'Listen, Ebele, we got off to a bad start. I'm sorry. I just think you seem like you could do with the company, nothing more.'

'What makes you think I don't have enough friends already?'

'You said you were on your own. Must be hard with a kid.'

'It's none of your business. I do alright. I survive.'

'We all need a bit more than survival though, don't we? Life has to be more meaningful than just getting through it.'

She couldn't quite work him out and the vodka wasn't helping.

'Oh, I get it, if it's not my body you're after, what is it? God Squad?'

'No!'

'You sound like it.' She sucked her teeth like the old woman in the pub.

'I'm not, okay? My mum's a believer but I gave up that shit long ago. When you walk around these streets and see what's going on it's hard to keep the faith, any faith!'

'It's all bullshit,' she agreed, and the atmosphere warmed a little. The vodka burned in her stomach and made her forget

110

about her headache. Daban smiled. 'Yep,' she continued, 'Even thick-headed, thick-skinned girls like me have enough learning to know what religion is all about.'

'When I was small I used to love it at the mosque, all the ritual and the praying and the camaraderie,' Daban said. 'Even the most skeptical amongst us would find it hard to believe there wasn't something celestial in those places sometimes. But it's not for me.'

Ebele felt her limbs loosen as the driver spoke. When he paused she said, 'You're oversharing. You did it in the pub too. I didn't ask for your whole life story.' This time she said it with a small smile.

'Oversharing? I'm just making conversation. It's what people do when they want to get to know someone.'

'Why? Why do you want to know me?'

'Can't a person just be nice?'

'There's no such thing. Why would someone just be nice for the sake of it? What's in it for them?'

'You need to chill out, Ebele. Not everyone has a bad motive.'

'I don't need to chill out. There's nothing wrong with me. Look, what is it you want?'

'Okay,' Daban said. 'I'll come clean. I don't know why but I just like you. I think there's a lot more to you than a pretty face and the hard-nut mask you wear.'

'What the fuck? You don't know anything about me! What are you, a shrink or something?'

'You're a challenge.'

'Now we're getting to the truth of the matter.'

A frostiness returned to the room. Ebele grabbed her jumper from the back of a chair and cloaked it over her shoulders.

'Truth? What do you mean? It seems like you're always trying to push people away,' Daban said.

'You've only known me five minutes. What do you know about what I'm always doing? You talk like you can see through me or something.'

'The way you spoke to your neighbour. The way you're talking now. The way you speak to Mr Makrides. All of that is about pushing people away.'

'Mr Makrides? What about the way he speaks to me? Have you heard him?' Even the vodka couldn't halt the agitation which bubbled inside her. 'Listen, I didn't ask you to come here. I left the pub because I knew it was a mistake going for a drink with a stranger. You lot are always after something – control or conquest or whatever. I don't need it!'

'Us lot? Really? All men or just men like me?'

'Just men. All of them – makes no difference in my experience. Look, maybe it's time to leave, I don't want Tuli waking up because of all this. It's bad enough with the bloody book group dinner party nonsense downstairs.'

Daban got up. 'Yep, time to go,' he said. 'Life is hard enough, Ebele. Don't always think the worst of people.'

When she heard the front door close, Ebele stuck her head out of the window and blew smoke into the night air as she watched Daban disappear down the street, unsure who she felt most annoyed with, him or herself. He didn't look back towards her. She didn't expect him to but a small part of her felt a pang of disappointment. She leaned out further and took in the city. It wasn't slowing down for the night. It rarely slept the deep sleep needed for proper restoration. Nightmares, she knew, existed regardless, on the streets and behind shabby net curtains and pricey louvre shutters. Traffic which had chuntered frustratingly throughout the day now sped precariously down Black Horse Lane, screeching into the night. Across the road, beyond bottle green railings, the park was a dark oasis in a desert of glaring pollution. A group of teenagers huddled around a bench – it was hard to tell where each ended and the other began. They too blew out wafts of smoke, passing a spliff around the circle. The smell was strong enough to reach her and she breathed in the heavy scent, wishing her cigarette was as potent as theirs. One boy, bloated with puppy-fat, stared directly at her. He exhaled a long whistle of smoke in her direction and smirked a 'fuck you,' glance she recognised as very similar to one of her own. She stubbed out her roll-up on the sill and closed the window. Before climbing into bed, she crept into Tuli's room and lifted the curtain. She couldn't see the abandoned car in the darkness but she knew it was there. She would call Makrides again in the morning.

12. NIKOS

Nikos Makrides sat in the armchair in his wife's favourite room in their house. He looked out to the neat back garden through the frame of wooden doors towards the large fig tree in the centre of the lawn, planted with his two boys when they were both much shorter than him. The figs were over-ripe. He thought about other autumn mornings, when the boys were young enough to press their noses up against the glass and bicker about who would get to eat the first of the fallen fruit. He'd never told them his secret, how he'd always picked the first ripe fig for Ourania and how, when he knew others were ready to drop, he slipped into the garden with his flashlight late at night when the boys were fast asleep and picked two of the plumpest, most delicious looking figs he could see and placed them at the foot of the tree, ready to be discovered in the morning. Surrounding him in the room were Ourania's clothes: dresses, blouses and cardigans, slacks and nightdresses spread out across the furniture with outstretched arms and flattened skirts. Getting rid of them was not an option. The week after she died she came to him in a dream in the blackest part of the night, wearing the yellow dress he liked best, dancing around the fig tree in the summer sun, beckoning him. Within the clothes were minute traces of her life, not just imperceptible flecks of skin or hair but moments they had shared together: their laughter, their sadness, tiny particles of grief and joy. When he awoke to the empty space beside him in the bed after the yellow dress dream, he wept into a pillow which still retained the faintest smell of Ourania's perfume, then he carefully removed each item of her clothing from the wardrobe and laid it across the furniture in the living room. He had left her clothes spread out, undisturbed, ever since. Ourania still existed in that room and he found some comfort in this.

The first time Nikos Makrides saw Ourania it was with wet eyes across mossy stone crosses which lined the sprawling cemetery on the Larnaca road. He'd arrived at the cemetery gates on a hired moped just as Georgios Savvides' body was being lowered into the ground. He switched off his ride only to find the heat of the day as hot as the bike's engine, and its roar replaced by the breathless sighs and high-pitched sobbing of the Savvides women. The noise melded with the low moans of Savvas Savvides which resonated across the valley. The sobbing became a desperate wail as he approached the funeral party and Savvas Savvides turned to see what had diverted the attention of the women. He stared at Nikos as if he were a stranger rather than the boy who'd been in and out of his back yard as often as his own children. Similarly, Uncle Savvas was no longer the ox of a man Nikos remembered; instead he was broken, like a lame horse, unsure of its position in the world. Nikos watched, static, as Uncle Savvas scattered the first handful of dust over the wooden box, looking decades older than the few years which had passed by. Hestia Makrides, Nikos' mother, lifted her long skirt and ran towards her son as soon as she saw him. She stretched out her arms to embrace him but lowered them quickly when she saw his eyes were on the mourners beyond. Instead, she lightly kissed his cheeks, took his hand and led him to the edge of the small crowd which circled the grave. Nikos' father moved through the gathering towards them, followed by Marios. Mother, father and brother stood close to him; close enough to sense the invisible threads which bound them. He held on to his parents, squeezing each of their hands tightly.

Earlier that month, the phone had disturbed the peace of a bitter English night by ringing way after bedtime. Kostas answered it and by the time Nikos emerged, blurry eyed in crumpled pyjamas, Kostas sat on the leather seat of the telephone bench holding the receiver towards him. Nikos cupped his hand over the mouthpiece so he couldn't be heard on the other end and said shakily,

'Baba?' Uncle Kostas shook his head. Nikos took the phone reluctantly, expecting to hear his mother's voice. Instead it was Marios.

'Marioso, my brother, it's so good to hear your voice but why are you calling at this terrible hour?'

'The sun will be rising here soon Nikos and I didn't want Mama or Baba to wake with the dread of telling you the horrible news we bear so I got up before them. They already weep each time you are mentioned. We miss you so much, my brother.'

'Marioso, what is it? What's happened?'

'It is Georgios.'

'Georgios? What has he done now? Left the feta in the sunshine to go sour again?' Nikos forced out an awkward laugh.

'No, Nikos. It's not good news. It is beyond bad. Let me tell you first how Angeliki, his sister and I have been seeing something of each other.'

'Little Angeliki? Marioso, you devil. How old is that child?"

'She's nineteen years old, same as me and not far from the age you were when you left us. We're not children anymore.'

'Nineteen. Already? My goodness.'

'This isn't important. Listen Nikos, she ran to me last night, one hour after Mama and Baba went to bed. Her banging woke them up and when I opened the door she fell into me, crying like a baby.'

Marios stopped speaking and after a moment, Nikos said, 'What happened, Marioso? What's happened to Georgios?' Kostas stood up and guided Nikos to the bench seat. Marios began speaking again.

'He's dead, Nikos. Georgios is dead!'

Nikos felt the blood drain from his face. 'What happened?' he whispered; he didn't want to know the answer. He began to shake uncontrollably.

'Angeliki found him in the old shed. He was inside Uncle Savvas' truck with a hosepipe through the window.'

'I don't understand.'

'It was his birthday, twenty-three years old. They had loukoumades for his celebration. Remember how the two of you used to eat them all before us younger ones could get to them? Mama Savvides always made the best loukoumades,' Marios paused again. 'Georgios said he was going to get some air and then, when he didn't come back by midnight, Angeliki went looking around for him in the land at the back of the house and Uncle Savvas did the same at the front. The pipe was attached to the exhaust. Georgios had seen someone do it this way in a film at the Attikon.'

'He killed himself?'

'He was unhappy. We all knew this but there was going to be a specialist, new hearing aids. He had so much to look forward to.'

'But why?' It was all Nikos could think to ask.

'He was miserable. Who knows why? Sometimes people are born with it. Two days before his birthday he smashed all the records you collected and all the others in the house too. Who knows why someone does such a thing? Perhaps all the change, you going, the noises in his ears.'

'It's my fault,' Nikos said. He slumped over with the phone held to his ear, still shaking. Kostas lay a hand on his shoulder and he was glad his uncle was next to him.

'It's nobody's fault.' Marios sounded like the older brother. 'Who can know what goes through another person's head? Angeliki was crying – it was hard to make sense of her. She kept saying he may not be able to have a proper funeral. Baba says Uncle Savvas must ask the doctor if perhaps it was an accident? Maybe he hadn't meant to do this dreadful thing. I couldn't make sense of it all. She was crying and crying like a baby. It was just a few hours ago, Nikos. All I can say for certain is Georgios is no more.'

Nikos couldn't speak.

'Are you sure, Marios?' he said eventually. 'That this isn't my fault, I mean. The rock came from the sky, from nowhere but perhaps I should have seen it and pushed Georgios out of the way. I should have stayed with him until he was fully recovered, until he saw the specialists, but Baba said I had to come here, because of the trouble. Will I never see Georgios again? This can't be true. Was it my fault, Marios? Tell me the truth.'

He didn't sleep the rest of the night and first thing the next morning he got the bus to Brighton Road where Uncle Kostas had friends with a travel agency.

On the day of Georgios's funeral, Ourania Dimitriou was tending a grave on the opposite side of the cemetery when she caught Nikos' attention. He stood holding on to his parents' hands as the priest said prayers over the casket, when she appeared in his eyeline. He was transfixed by the way her ebony hair fell from beneath her headscarf and cascaded over her shoulders. *It is God's will. So be it,* he heard his mother whisper next to him and for a split second he thought she was talking about the girl. He shuddered, sleep-deprived and heady from the journey, and, when the burial ended, instead of attending the *Makaria* in the village hall, he made excuses and drove down the hill alone until he reached the little stone house on the up-slope to the village. He parked the moped and sat for a while, taking in his surroundings, allowing the intense afternoon heat to absorb into him, and the smells and sights of home to overpower the hangover of being away; only then was he able to enter his home and collapse onto his old bed as if he'd never left. He closed his eyes and plummeted into an exhausted sleep, dreaming in fragments: Georgios strumming his old guitar, the two of them discussing who might be the prettiest girl in the district like they often did; snatches of dream-memory floating away like cherry blossom on a sea breeze. When he woke, he thought of the conversations about pretty girls and decided, without a doubt, the answer was concluded this very day at the cemetery. He knew Georgios would agree; like music, their taste in women was fairly close to identical. Later that evening, he asked his mother about the girl.

'Why, it's little Ouranoulla from the watermelon farm outside Anafotia. You know her, you went to school together.' And later, after the others had gone to bed, his mother kissed him on his forehead and said softly, 'Ourania Dimitriou would be a fine match for you, Nikolaki mou. A fine match.'

The next morning, he discarded the noisy moped, dusted off his rusty bicycle and made the short but wobbly journey uphill to Anafotia. He cycled around the small village in the bright sunshine, asking questions about the girl and the watermelon farm until he got the information he wanted. Some people shrugged their shoulders, others nodded in a general direction across parched fields and olive groves towards the mountains beyond. Eventually, the chef at the Adamos Taverna said the Dimitrious' were relatives of his sister-in-law. An hour later, Nikos leant his bicycle against a giant plane tree and watched the girl from a distance. She moved across her decked veranda with a broom sweeping up a mist of red dust which accumulated around her ankles; it was as if she was floating on air. She didn't notice him at first and when he caught her eye she turned away shyly. He approached the farmstead tentatively, his stomach twisted in somersaults.

'Excuse me miss,' he said when he was close enough to be heard. 'I hope you don't mind but I would like to introduce myself. I am Nikos Makrides.'

'My father is away on family business,' she replied without turning to face him. 'If you've come about work, I am afraid you'll have to come back another day.'

'Please,' Nikos replied. 'I've come to speak to you.'

She stopped sweeping, wiped away beads of sweat from her forehead with the tips of her fingers and looked at him quizzically.

'I'm afraid you are mistaken,' she said. 'It's my father you will need to speak to, about whatever it is you are here for. Please come back another time.'

'Okay,' Nikos said apprehensively. 'I'll return tomorrow at this same time but I hope your father will still be away as it is you I will be coming to see.'

The girl blushed, lowered her eyes and resumed her sweeping as Nikos walked backwards towards his bicycle with the hot sun on his face, watching as the dust rose up around her again.

'Let me write to you from England,' he begged, and after the third day of pleading, she consented.

'Perhaps,' she said eventually. 'But I don't promise to reply; I am not so good with words as you appear to be. Now please go away before people start to talk.'

That afternoon, Nikos skipped away from the little wooden farmstead with a smile so broad it made his face ache.

He packed his bags ready for the flight to Luton, leaving just enough time to visit the Savvides' house next door but when Uncle Savvas refused to speak to him, Mama Savvides spoke firmly through her streaming tears.

'Our boy loved this boy. Georgios could not accept the life he was given but this is not the fault of anyone. Let the boy go in peace with his conscience at rest. Let us all go in peace.'

Nikos wrote the first letter to Ourania on the bus from Luton airport.

Dear Miss Dimitriou
I am the boy who came to your farm just a few days ago. I am not a stranger so please do not be fearful of me – my mother tells me we played as small children and we once cracked our red Easter eggs together. I hope you will permit me to call you Ourania?

Do you like music, Ourania? Cat Stevens is my favourite but here in England where I now find myself (temporarily I hope) there is so much music everywhere: so many radio stations and always music on television too. This music is not always like the music I listened to at home but perhaps a little more angry, and maybe these people have more to be angry about; it is such an ugly, sunless place. When I first arrived here three years ago it was boys who looked like girls making music; boys in make-up with sequins. Now the musicians (boys and girls) are beginning to look like creatures from a different world – crazy, torn clothes and stupid coloured hairstyles. Near where I live there is a bar called Oasis. where bands play and sometimes I go with my uncle to hear the music I like – Leonard Cohen, Bob Dylan – not the real people of course but pretenders, men on stools with guitars. Some are very good. I too would like to play guitar one day.

Perhaps this is boring for you if you don't like music? Apologies but it is something which makes England bearable for me. England is so dull, I have to say. The sun shines for such a short time and the winters are cruel and long. From September to June it rains. Sometimes it rains until August. Luckily, the sun shone for a few weeks last July but the country nearly ran out of water so I suppose it is just as well it rains so much. Can you imagine sunshine for only four weeks of the year, and then only if you are lucky?

One good thing, in the area where I live there are many Cypriots and I have made some acquaintances amongst them; we play cards and discuss football of course. There are also many Turks but not so many Greeks from the mainland. I suppose they didn't need to leave. The Turks keep themselves to themselves. There are fewer of them than us but, to be honest, they are young men like me mostly, yearning for home, and they probably miss their families just as I do. If I stand side by side with some of the Turks my age, we could be brothers.

I miss Cyprus too much. I can't wait to be there again. When I saw you for the first time we were burying my best friend,

Georgios and I realised it wasn't just him I was crying for. I miss home so much sometimes it is as if my whole body aches for it. Can you understand this? Perhaps not. You are lucky to still be there in our beautiful country. Am I making any sense, Ourania?

Please write to me. Please tell me about yourself. I know nothing except you broke my egg and you are from a family of watermelon growers, the sweetest watermelons in the whole of the island, Mama says. I see your beautiful face in my sleep. I am brave enough to tell you this because there are so many miles between us. Distance makes it easier sometimes, to say what it may take many months to say face to face, I realise this as I write to you. Mama told me you were the winner when we hit our eggs against each other so now please allow me a little hope that one day we can play a return match of egg-cracking.

I hope you don't find my long letter a nuisance. I know I have said more than I should already but I want to talk to you and get to know you. I wish I could have cycled out to your farm again on my trip so we could have sat under the trees and talked a little more but I was home for such a short time with many duties. And I was sad, so sad about my friend Georgios but seeing you was such a bright light in such a dark time. I know you must be thinking I am taking liberties writing to you like this, you who I know nothing about, who may not even remember me, but, with Georgios dying so young, so pointlessly, I feel compelled to act on what is in my heart.

Please write back, Ourania, even if it is just to tell you me you have received my letter.

Kind regards
Nikos Makrides

Three weeks later Kostas handed Nikos an airmail letter with a Larnaca postmark. It said,

Dear Nikos Makrides,

Thank you for your very informative letter. I know very little about music and even less about England but I am glad to be informed on both counts.

I remember the egg competition but not you. It was the first time I ever won at anything.

You may write to me again and I permit you to call me Ourania.

From
Ourania Dimitriou

Nikos read the short letter again and again, running his fingertips over the pale blue paper and raising it to his face in the hope of detecting some lingering aroma of Ourania on it. He searched for words between lines of ink, imagining wistful sentences drifting through her mind only to be curtailed before reaching paper. For the whole of the day he walked with a skip in his step, smiling at strangers between Shifnal Road and the store on Grand Parade and, at lunchtime, he ate a hearty lunch of Turkish gozleme and rice-stuffed vine leaves. When Kostas returned from the wholesalers later in the afternoon, he said to Nikos,

'One little note from a girl over two thousand miles away and you're behaving like you've won gold at the Olympic Games.'

Nikos replied jokingly, 'Uncle, shall I ask her if she has a friend for you? Maybe a spinster aunt or some other old maid in Anafotia?'

'No thank you, I can sort out my own love-life,' Kostas said with good grace, but when Nikos began whistling along to some jangly pop-song on the radio, he snapped. 'Shut up, Nikos! For goodness sake, all this cheerfulness is giving me a headache.'

'Maybe you should marry one of these 'loves' of your life, Uncle and then I can have a little nephew or niece to run around after, to take my mind off Ourania.'

'Be quiet, Nikos. Don't behave like a donkey. I don't need you to take on the role of some interfering hag back home. I came to this country to escape this kind of talk and to keep my private life private. It has nothing to do with you who I see or spend time with. We don't all want to marry village girls who know nothing of the wider world.'

Kostas was generally a genial man and Nikos was taken aback by his outburst. He stopped whistling and didn't mention Ourania or the letter for the rest of the day. Instead, he spent the time daydreaming about the girl, imagining her going about her village in her pale yellow cotton dress. Later, over supper, Kostas said, 'I'm sorry, Nikos. I am tired. It's been a busy time. You be happy, my boy. Love is a strange and unexpected thing. Sometimes it happens in places we least want it to and other times, like you, right on our doorstep. You have such a strong feeling for this girl so you must act on it, and if you can find a way to make her love you back then you are a lucky man. Good luck, nephew.'

Nikos wrote to Ourania almost every day after this. He started a new letter each Sunday and by the time Friday came the letters were five or six pages long and ready to post. He'd spent less than twenty minutes talking face to face with her but somehow this didn't matter. He told her everything in the letters: names of songs he discovered for the first time; articles or books he read (often as recommendations from Kostas) and how they made him feel: sad, amused, angry, perplexed or just plain bored. He told her about Indian food which made his mouth erupt like a volcano and about football hooligans who threw bricks through the windows of restaurants where they served such food; he told of the stern woman everyone disliked but who was certain to become the next Prime Minister of the country. He described the wide pathways and huge trees in the park at the end of Grand Parade, and his walks to the big glass palace on the hill where television was first broadcast. He told her about streets teeming with rubbish and jostling crowds of scowling people at bus stops and stations, and how he longed to sit quietly under an olive tree and listen to goat bells in the distance instead of the wailing sirens and the growl of traffic which swamped him in the city. He told her about fish-fingers and cotton wool bread which tasted of nothing but air, and salads with no oregano, lemon juice or even olive oil. He told her how people were poorer here than he could have imagined and how they all looked under their seats on buses and in bars in case there were bombs beneath them. He told her that even in the middle of this dirty brown smokey city there were beautiful gardens as green as the flat leaf parsley which grew in abundance back home.

Ourania wrote back occasionally; once or twice a month a new letter arrived at the house on Shifnal Road and he savoured it as if he were sipping some fine wine or eating the most exquisite *kataifi*. Her letters were short and to the point: about the workings of the watermelon farm, the tasks lined up for the week, whether she'd been to the beach near Mazotos or shopping in Larnaca. As his letters became even longer and less inhibited, eventually hers did too. He began to address her as Nia and then, on his twenty-fifth birthday he wrote her a letter in a drunken haze whilst listening to Kostas' cassette of sensual songs by a woman called Summer.

'This will get you in the mood for dancing,' Kostas said in English. 'Everyone should dance on their birthday.'

But Nikos wanted to write to Ourania instead so he slipped out of the room leaving Uncle Kostas to pour more ouzo into the glasses of his Indian friends from next door. Their laughter trickled through the house, seeping into the coldest corners and the warmth this generated, together with the red wine consumed over his special birthday dinner, helped to loosen his pen and propel him to express things he may otherwise never have written. The letter was short, just two pages. At the end of it he said,

'I think of you all the time. I know I shouldn't be saying these things. I know it isn't right or decent but when I think of you I imagine holding you close to me, feeling your skin next to mine, your lips on mine, our bodies entwined. I need you here beside me, next to me. I dream about you in the day but it is the dreams under the cover of night which make me yearn for you the most.

He sealed and posted the letter whilst it was still his birthday, before he had a change of heart, and then he slept deeply without dreaming. The following week, he received a typically succinct reply, in which Ourania said she would like to see him and maybe he should find a way to come to Cyprus so they could talk about the future. He wrote a rushed scrawl to his mother.

Dear Mama
I want to make the girl from Anafotia my wife. Please tell me what I should do to make this happen.

Your loving son, Nikos.

Ten days later there was a phone call.

'Nikolaki mou, come home,' Mama said. 'See her father, ask him for permission and we will make the arrangement.'

By the time Nikos made it back to Cyprus, his twenty-sixth birthday had been and gone.

In the living room, surrounded by Ourania's clothes, he picked up a photo album which sat on a nearby shelf and allowed memories to transport him back to those times. The shrill ringtone of his mobile startled him from his reverie. He aborted the call without checking the number. It rang again a moment later and dragged him firmly back to a stark present. This time he looked at the contact, It was the shop-girl, Ebele Mangaroo, on the other end.

'What is it?' he said. 'Don't you know it's Sunday?'

'Yes, but it makes no difference,' she said. Her words were garbled and he found it hard to keep up. 'You need to do something about the man on your land. It's dangerous having someone like that around children. It's your fault for not removing the car. If anything happens to my daughter, you'll be to blame,'

'What the bloody hell are you talking about, Mangaroo? This will have to wait – it's early and I'm busy. Tell me tomorrow, whatever this nonsense is.'

He silenced the phone and pushed it into his pocket. The photo album lay on his lap, open at a page which captured the last visit he made to Cyprus with his wife by his side. It was a year before she died in his arms in the same hospital where she'd given birth to both their sons. *Let me go, agape mou* were her last words before she closed her eyes for the final time. A quiet nurse put her hand on his shoulder and told him Ourania had gone, but then his wife's body jerked in a spasm which startled them both.

'No,' he insisted, 'she is moving. She is trying to stay alive. Can't you see this, you silly woman?'

A dreadful moan emanated from Ourania's limp body which, had he not been holding her at the time, he would have sworn was not of this earth. Nikos fell to his knees muttering, *zoe mou, zoe mou,* until the nurse got down beside him and allowed him to rest his head on her bony shoulder.

Ourania's deathly wail haunted Nikos deep at night when he was alone in their bed. At first he tried to block out the noise, burying his head under the covers, imagining she was still on the other side of the sheets. He tried to conjure up some remnant of her clinging to the duvet: a smell, a crease, a trace of her make-up but as fear subsided he gave in, embracing the terrors, reassuring himself – *It is just my Ourania letting me know she is waiting for me.*

In the photographs, Ourania's hair was speckled grey and she wore the dowdy beige of an old woman but her eyes sparkled out from the page, as bright as the first day Nikos saw her, across the sombre graveyard. He welled up, just as the phone in his pocket began to vibrate.

13. TULI

On Sunday morning before Mummy woke up, Tuli drew a picture of Real Daddy and Jamal Daddy holding hands with Storyman in front of the broken car, but she didn't know what colour to make Real Daddy's hair so she screwed up the paper and threw it under her bed.

She couldn't remember Real Daddy. Mostly he was a smell of beer and stinky cigarettes. Sometimes he was a tiptoe across her bedroom late at night when he came to kiss the top of her head, or he was a noise of shouting across the landing when she was half-asleep in her cot. He left two days after she toddled across the room and into his arms for the first time without falling over. At least this was what she'd heard Mummy tell Grace when she wasn't supposed to be listening. Real Daddy was just a made-up picture in her head, like the ones she drew with crayons or felt tips of stick people in bright triangular clothes. Mummy didn't show her photographs; she said there weren't any but she was always looking at people on her phone so Real Daddy must have been in there somewhere. The only thing she remembered properly was sometimes there would be singing and the guitar would play, when the day was disappearing and she was falling into dreams. Mummy's singing wasn't good but Real Daddy's was soft like warm blankets; it made her fly through clouds. One day she asked Jamal Daddy to play the guitar and do the soft singing which gave her wings but he didn't know what she meant and Mummy said, 'Jamal isn't a musician, Tuli. You must have imagined something.'

When Jamal Daddy left the room, her mother said,

'Don't talk about the guitar and singing. It's just a dream from a different time, Tuli. That Daddy doesn't exist anymore.'

'Jamal Daddy isn't the music daddy?' Tuli asked, just to be sure.

'No,' Mummy said. 'The music daddy has gone.' And it was the last they spoke of him. *Like ice-cream melted away.* It didn't matter much. She liked Jamal Daddy: his growly voice was like the bear on CBeebies and the way he tickled her made laughter shake through her body. On her birthday, he baked chocolate cake with a number five made of Smarties across the top. As a present he gave her a Buckaroo game like the one he had when he was a little boy.

Mummy asked if she wanted to invite some of the other children from school to watch her blow out the candles and play with the Buckaroo but Tuli knew they wouldn't come. Jamal Daddy was her friend and he would play the game with her. Mostly now, she remembered she was sad on her birthday because Jamal Daddy and Mummy shouted at each other when they thought she couldn't hear.

'It's not right for a child to have no friends. It's strange. She's too quiet – it's no wonder the other kids don't play with her.'

I am strange, Tuli knew this already, it was what the other children told her.

'She's not strange, Jamal! Don't call Tuli strange,' her mother said.

'I didn't say *she* was strange; I said it is strange. It's not normal to always be locked in your own head like she is. She should be across the road in the park running about with other kids, skipping and stuff. You talk to her like she's an adult. She's your child, Ebele, not your emotional prop.'

Tuli put her hands over her ears but it didn't block the shouting.

'You're a construction worker, Jamal, not a fucking psychologist. You're not even a parent so don't tell me about my own child. She's normal.'

'Well there you go! You never really let me in do you? I love that kid but you never let anybody in. What are you scared of? That you might actually begin to give a shit about someone?'

'You're not her dad, Jamal. She's mine. I choose what's right or wrong for her. I'm all she needs. Other people just let you down anyway.'

'Jesus, Ebele. You just block them out. Don't teach her to do it too. It's not healthy. We all need other people, even you.'

'Fuck off with your sermon, Jamal. Children can be cruel. Really cruel. I'm just protecting her. Life is cruel enough already.'

Tuli didn't know what it meant when Mummy told Jamal Daddy he wasn't her father. She hated this kind of grown-up talking where nothing made sense and people said mean things to each other. She didn't want them to be angry with each other because of her. Mummy would cry later, as soon as Jamal Daddy went out the door with a loud slam. It was what always happened after this kind of shouting. It wasn't a happy birthday.

Being five seemed to bring more sadness into her world. Jamal Daddy and Mummy weren't very good friends anymore, except when they were cuddling in the middle of the night. Sometimes she needed a cuddle at night too, when bad dreams came to scare her but they shouted at her in one voice if she disturbed them. She kept Froggy close in case she was frightened at night: she didn't want to make her parents more grumpy with each other than they already were. She'd noticed they'd stopped laughing together too since her birthday. She wondered why five made everything different. Even the tickling stopped and she missed rolling like a ball on the carpet while Jamal Daddy giggled until his shoulders shook. By the time her sixth birthday arrived he wasn't there at all.

She remembered the night before she saw Jamal Daddy for the last time. He read the final chapter of her Sophie book. Sophie and she were the same age, they even looked a bit like each other except Sophie's skin was white and freckled, but Sophie had a pony and that wasn't very fair; Tuli didn't even

131

have a dog or a cat. Jamal Daddy was a good reader; he never yawned in the middle of a chapter and his reading voice made her sleepy in the way she remembered Real Daddy's singing did. Jamal Daddy didn't say goodnight that last evening, just *see you later, little Tuls*. In the morning, Mummy's eyes were as red as Froggy's scarf but she wouldn't tell where Jamal Daddy was or when he was coming back. It was the first day they watched grown-up telly all day in pyjamas, even though it wasn't a weekend. On her sixth birthday it was just her and Mummy, and the cake was from Tesco and looked just like the ones Grandy gave her on days which weren't even birthdays. She wondered if Jamal was making a chocolate cake with Smarties for a different little girl now. Mummy bought her another Sophie book as a present but when she opened it, it said To Rosa on the inside. Mummy got red eyes again when Tuli said she didn't want it. She didn't say it was because it was really Rosa's book. She left it on the floor next to the torn up rainbow wrapping paper.

When it was properly light, Tuli stopped drawing and looked for Storyman through the window. She couldn't see him but the door to the car was open so she knew he must be still there. She wanted to talk to him again. She wanted to ask him which book he was from but Mummy was home all morning, lying on the sofa bed in pyjamas.

Usually Sundays were Tuli's favourite time, when they woke up late and ate breakfast and lunch in one go and Mummy read stories without looking at the clock. Sometimes, they walked to the big park for fresh air and ate doughnuts on the way home. Today Mummy didn't want fresh air: she said all she wanted to do was stay in, but if Tuli really wanted to go out she'd put her coat over her pyjamas and they could go to Hazelwood across the road for a short while. Tuli said *no thank you* because really she just wanted to be in Grandy's garden, but Grandy were out with their friends and they didn't leave keys because Mandy was still angry about the books on the chair and the way Mummy spoke to her.

Tuli didn't speak to her mother about Storyman again; Mummy hardly ever read books these days so she wouldn't know he was a story thing and not a stranger or the dirty tramp she'd heard her talking about. Sometimes, Grandy gave Mummy books as presents but she threw them under her bed, preferring to look at pictures of people on her phone. She couldn't understand why Mummy wanted to look inside other people's houses or their dogs and dinners all the time instead of reading stories. Even at six, she knew books were more interesting; they let you go to places without having to get on a bus or an aeroplane. Phone pictures just made Mummy grumpy. After breakfast, Tuli saw Storyman standing next to the car-house and she jumped up and down to try and make him notice her in the window. Once or twice he looked up at the house next door but he didn't seem to see her and she wondered if she'd become invisible. She got the blue stool from under the bathroom sink, stood on it and waved at him until her arm hurt. Froggy waved too but Storyman still didn't wave back. When she heard Mummy in the kitchen, she quickly climbed down and pretended to read her book to Froggy. It was about a strong girl called Pippi who lived in a big house without grown-ups. Tuli couldn't read all the big words but she liked Pippi and she liked the pictures too. She wondered if Storyman knew Pippi, whether all the story people from books had assemblies like at school so they could get claps and gold stars for being the best.

Later, when she was eating her lunch in front of the television, Mummy said there was only going to be one more day before the end of the half-term holiday.

'It's a special Inset day for teachers so they can get everything ready for all the children.'

Tuli pictured Mrs Enisuoh and the other teachers standing on the big cushioned chairs in the staff room and screaming about all the creepy crawlies in the same way Mummy screamed when there was a spider in the bath.

'Can't there be more Insect days?' Tuli said, pushing her gloopy food around the plate 'I don't want to go back to school.'

'Don't play with the food, Tuli, just eat it or you'll be hungry later.'

'I don't like it.'

'Yes you do. You love macaroni cheese. You always eat it.

'I don't want to go to school.'

'It's okay,' Mummy said putting on her soft voice. 'That horrible Finn won't be there anymore, he left, remember? And you can see all your friends again.'

'I don't have any friends, Mummy. I don't want to go back.'

'Tuli, eat your mac cheese before it goes cold.'

'I don't like it. It tastes like soap. It's not nice, Mummy.' She tried hard not to cry but failed.

Mummy picked up the plates and went to the kitchen. She came back with custard creams in her hand.

'Come on, baby,' she said. 'It's not so bad. I need to work and if I do more hours at my job we'll have more money and I can take you for pizza.'

Tuli took a biscuit and nestled into her mother's lap; she smelled of warm bed even though it was the middle of the day and she felt bad for wishing Mummy was at her job.

'Don't worry, Tuli. There's still one more holiday left and that means school will only be for four days this week. And, I'm not at work tomorrow so I can take you to the big park with the boats on the pond and we can get doughnuts on the way home. How about that?'

Tuli wanted to say *no thank you*; she definitely had to see Storyman tomorrow or he would be waiting for her all day when she was back at school, not knowing where she was. She needed to tell him she wouldn't be able to talk to him until after school from now on. She bit her bottom lip and nodded at Mummy.

14. EBELE

Ebele often slept badly; it was no different on Saturday night. At first it was the new driver, *Driverman, Daban* who filled her dreams but his face quickly melded into that of her stepfather, Brian, and then into Michael, the boy who once pinned her down in the damp grass and put his grimy hands all over her childish body. Both were frequent spectres, appearing in the dismal recesses of sleep. This night they came disguised as people she loved: her mother, pushing her over a cliff edge into an implacable sea; Papa, holding his hand over her mouth, preventing her from screaming out; and worst of all, Tuli, lurking behind doors with a kitchen knife in her hand. She called to her mother to save her but she never came, not even in dreams. Ebele woke drenched in heavy sweat. These night panics were not unfamiliar. Soon after Tuli was born, they began to creep up into waking hours too: on short walks pushing the buggy through quiet streets; in innocuous places like the library or the hairdressers, in the supermarket buying Marmite or toothpaste; pushing Tuli on park swings; a trip to the post office. The panic took a grip, possessing her until she was no longer in control: throat tight, mouth dry, her tongue a foreign object, obstructing breath; palms clammy; flames raging beneath taut skin. In those moments it was hard to hold on to who she was, even though she'd long been aware this stalker was meshed within her own being, manifesting itself in a deep and sudden anguish, roused by a smell or a sound, a throwaway comment or a half-seen headline. To cope, she restricted how far she would travel across the city alone, conscious the stalker might take hold, paralyse her and keep her from getting back to Tuli. She developed other strategies too: vodka to blot it all out; weed to calm her racing heart. For years she managed to keep it from drowning her completely. Eventually, bad dreams faded into the background, and, for a short time, the crippling anxiety abated.

After Jamal left, she was adrift again, barely treading water. Some mornings she wished the day was over before it began, even with Tuli asleep down the landing. It was hard to get out of bed, to dress or eat. The pounding in her chest was constant, blocking out all other sounds. Neither she nor Tuli left the house for several days, wearing the same pyjamas until one night she forgot to lift her child onto the potty and she wet the bed. The smell of soiled sheets hung about the flat until Tuli dragged them out of her washing basket and into the bathtub where she squirted bubble-bath on them and started the taps running. Ebele was ashamed. Soon the school secretary began calling and threatening to get the local authority involved so she finally made an appointment to see Doctor Razak.

The doctor was happy to give her pills but told her they wouldn't work on their own and she'd have to speak to someone too. He arranged for a therapist called Tessa to call when Tuli was settled back at school but it was weeks before the first call came. The initial conversations were awkward and Ebele decided it was a waste of time, but Tessa was patient and said it was often like this to begin with, and when she called a third time, Ebele felt like a dam had burst in her head. She told Tessa about the way Michael touched her and how she couldn't wash the stain of him off her body; how Brian stood over her at night and threatened her with his eyes and his rasping voice. The more she spoke, the more she realised it wasn't just Brian or Michael who haunted her but something else too, way back in the far reaches of her memory. They talked about the car containing Papa and how it crashed into a wall and into her childhood at the same time.

'They all disappear in the end. Why would anyone want to stay?' she said in one of the calls.

'Including you?' Tessa said.

'What?'

'You left your mother. Disappeared from her life. Ran away.'

Ebele was stunned. No-one had ever said this before. She knew instinctively the Tessa woman shouldn't have mis-spoken but it was said and couldn't now be unsaid, and it was said without judgement, a statement of fact. She imagined the blank face of the prim middle-aged woman whose image she'd searched online taking notes on the other end of the phone. At exactly half past the hour, Tessa said,

'We have to leave it there for now. Time's up.'

When the call ended, Ebele sank to the floor and sobbed until she was wrung dry. With her back against the wall, she held her knees to her chest and rocked, calling out for her mother, wishing her world could be like it was before Brian, before Papa's accident, before life happened. She stayed on the floor until her phone alarm beeped then searched in her handbag for her sunglasses and dragged herself to get ready to fetch Tuli from school.

Tessa called every Tuesday morning for the next seven weeks and, as each call ended, Ebele cried without expecting to. As the sessions progressed, Michael was shoved from the conversation, pushed away to the edges along with Jamal and Tuli's father; even Brian became less significant, mentioned only in passing. On week seven, she sat and waited for the phone to ring, holding on to a photograph of her father from just before she was born. It was the only one she had. He stood proudly in the back garden of their little terraced house with his hand on her mother's swollen belly, both of them partially dappled in the intermittent shade of a sprawling silver birch which stretched above them. She peered closely at the picture, focussing on her mother for the first time; she was smiling broadly, looking not at the camera but at Papa, her face lit up with speckles of sunshine. The final conversations with Tessa focussed on a different time, after Papa but before Brian, when it was just her and her mother, like it was with her and Tuli now. After the eighth and final session, she searched out her mother's Facebook page and discovered the image of herself as a baby in her arms. She guessed it must've been Papa behind the camera. Eventually, going out became easier, to the pharmacy to pick up her prescriptions, and to the job centre to present them with the letter from Dr Razak, only to have them roll their eyes and shove it away in a drawer. The panic attacks started to ease again, occurring less often in streets she was used to. She managed to arrange her life to avoid crowded stations and shopping centres but the school playground was another matter; it was harder to avoid the perfectly made-up women who grouped together at the gates with their backs towards her. They were a daily reminder of demons which could resurface at any moment.

Early on Sunday morning, Ebele crept into Tuli's bedroom and whispered into the darkness.

'Stay in bed Tuli. Don't get out until I'm back. I'm just going to get milk. I'll be two minutes.'

Tuli rolled over and pulled the duvet over her head. Ebele slipped on her trainers and grabbed the door keys. It was cold outside and daylight struggled to break through leaden clouds. She tightened the belt of her coat around her pyjamas and headed to the alleyway to see for herself whether there was someone in the abandoned car.

The alleyway was unlit and all she could hear was the sound of her own breathing, loud against the faint tread of her feet in mud and leaves.

She saw the broken window plugged with cardboard first. She peered in through the back windscreen: there was a bulk in a sleeping bag curled across the seats. She held her breath and walked to the front to get a better view. The sleeping bag, pulled up, covered the lower part of a face, a woollen hat, pulled down, covered the top. Only the middle was visible, obscured by a thick beard. A scar linked the woollen hat to the rim of the sleeping bag like a zip. Ebele covered her nose and mouth with a cupped hand and stepped backwards. She rushed towards the road and leaned on a wall near the entrance, trying to regulate her breathing in the way Tessa had taught her to over the phone. She looked around. Curtains were open in a house across the road and a dishevelled man stumbled from the front door, tugging an arching toddler in a buggy out behind him. She wanted to say something to the man but she couldn't catch his eye. She wanted to tell him: *He's too close to our children, close enough to touch them, What are you going to do about it? How can you carry on as normal?*

Back in the flat, Makrides' number went straight to voicemail. She dialed again, still no answer. She glanced at the clock, it was almost eight now; a decent enough hour even for a Sunday. On the third attempt she left a message:

If you don't get back to me soon I'm going to call the police. There is a man in the car on your land. He can see into my daughter's bedroom. He could be a pervert or a murderer. What are you going to do about it?

Makrides didn't call back.

She washed the breakfast dishes whilst planning what to say to the police or the council or whoever else might force the man away. Sunday meant the council offices were closed and if she phoned the police they would only say it wasn't an emergency, as though a strange man hanging around the backs of houses where little girls lived wasn't urgent! She couldn't understand why Grace and Mandy and other neighbours weren't alarmed as she was. He could be surveying the houses, checking when they were in or out, watching Tuli move around her bedroom. She picked up a soapy mug from the bowl and rinsed it under the running tap for far longer than necessary.

Tuli came out of her bedroom.

'I'm bored, Mummy. Can I ask Grandy about playing in the garden?'

'No!' Ebele said abruptly.

'Please, Mummy.'

'Don't whine, Tuli. We're staying in, just you and me. It's an inside playing day.'

'But you went out this morning already. Without me. That's not fair. I want to go outside too.'

Tuli sloped off down the landing with her arms hanging limp by her sides. Ebele ignored her. She wished her daughter didn't have it within her small body to demonstrate defeat so clearly. She finished the washing up, dried her hands on her thighs, pulled her phone from her back pocket and dialled Makrides' number again.

At midday, rain came hurtling down without warning. Ebele was relieved.

'See Tuli, I knew it would be wet today.' she said, peering into her daughter's bedroom. Tuli didn't look up; she was pulling at the knots of an old doll with a comb. 'Be careful, Tuli. Do it gently like I do yours, you don't want to hurt the dolly.'

Tuli put the doll down and grabbed a book from the floor. She looked up at her mother briefly,

'Please go away, Mummy. I want to read my book, alone,' she said.

'That's not very kind, Tuli.'

'I said please.'

'Okay but you need to say sorry too, for speaking in an angry voice to me.'

'I learn angry from you, Mummy.'

Tuli bent her head low and stuck her thumb in her mouth. Ebele left the room and moved around the flat checking each window, assessing viewpoints and distances. From the front bay, she watched people dash across the park, trying to escape great slants of rain. She returned to Tuli's room and peered through the window towards the space at the back of the houses. The haze of the day made it impossible to see anything so she stood with her back to the window and watched her daughter for a moment.

'Tuli,' she said, 'put your book down for a minute, I need to talk to you.' Tuli did as she was told without looking up. 'Have you seen anything at the back of the house?' Tuli shook her lowered head. 'Well don't look out of the window, okay?' Ebele said as she pulled the curtains closed.

Tuli said, 'It's daytime, Mummy. Why are you making it all dark?'

'So no-one can look in and disturb you,' she said.

Tuli mumbled something about her story. Her voice was so quiet, Ebele couldn't quite make out the words. She kissed the top of Tuli's head.

'You just read your story and keep away from the window.'

Ebele tried Makrides a fourth and fifth time. Straight to answerphone. She left another message, and another: *Mr Makrides, please call me back. I'll be phoning the police at five o'clock.* She wiped the moist handset on her pyjama top and pushed it into her pocket.

In the middle of the afternoon, there was a loud knock on the door. She ignored it. It would only be Grace or Mandy complaining about the music, on loud to block out thoughts of the man in the car. She turned the volume up: lyrics about swimming pools full of liquor blasted out. The knock became persistent. Eventually, she paused the track and shouted down the stairs,

'Go away!'

The booming response made her jump.

'Mangaroo, what is this nonsense?'

It was Makrides; he'd let himself in with his landlord's key. His sonorous voice irritated her before she'd edged open her door.

'All these phone calls one after the other like some insane kind of person.'

Nikos Makrides pushed past her, up the stairs and into her flat. He looked her up and down disapprovingly as she crossed her arms over Bart Simpson. Toys, books and shoes dotted the narrow landing and damp towels were hung to dry across the bannister. The door to the front room was open, exposing the unmade sofa bed. A muddy anorak was slung on the balustrade. Makrides rolled his eyes.

'You should clean up, Mangaroo, it's not healthy to be living in such filth.'

She said, 'Why don't you fix the mouldy wall in the living room? That's not healthy!'

Makrides changed the subject.

'Why are you disturbing my one day of rest in the week, Mangaroo?'

She tried to explain about the man in the car but the presence of Makrides in her space unsettled her.

'It's your responsibility Mr Makrides. We can't have someone like that so close to where we live.'

'You call me twenty times for this nonsense? Pah, you are ridiculous. I will get rid of this thing in five minutes if I want to. Why do you have to panic in this stupid way? Don't phone me again on a Sunday, Mangaroo. Do you hear me? I will get rid of this beggar in my own time.'

'Do it now, Mr Makrides. It's dangerous. I have a child. He might hurt her.'

'Don't you order me around. Remember who I am. Speak to me with respect.'

She felt like shoving the old man down the stairs but instead she held her breath, exhaled slowly and said,

'The man shouldn't be there. It is your duty to get rid of him.'

'How do I even know there's a man there? Only you have seen this creature. Everyone knows this is my land, why haven't they told me?'

'I don't know why other people haven't told you. Maybe because you never answer your phone; but he's there. I saw him this morning, asleep in the car. An abandoned car which has, by the way, been an eyesore behind the gardens for weeks now. You should've removed it ages ago then we wouldn't have this problem. I have to protect Tuli.'

'Protect? You are overreacting, Mangaroo. These people are vermin like rats but they go as quickly as they appear; it is the nature of these gypsies, always moving around. You are making too much fuss; typical of you. I soon got rid of the beggar sleeping in the shop doorway. I will do the same here but you need to stop making up crazy things in your head, Mangaroo. Why should he hurt your child? What proof do you have?'

'I'm not saying he will.' She caught a glimpse of Tuli in the slit in the doorway behind Makrides. 'Tuli, shut the door please,' she shouted. Tuli did as she was told.

Makrides said, 'I will go and see what he is doing and tell him to get off my land but don't call me again and spoil the only peace I get in the whole week away from you.'

'I don't want him here. Not with Tuli being so young.'

'Don't be late tomorrow, Mangaroo. You have already ruined my weekend. Don't spoil the new week too.'

'It's my day off tomorrow,' Ebele said.

'Good. I get a day off from you. Don't be late on Tuesday and don't call me again. I don't want to hear your voice until then.'

When Makrides left, she told Tuli to go into the front room, handing her the remaining custard creams. She switched on the television and closed the door. From Tuli's bedroom, she watched the alleyway through a gap in the curtains, waiting for Makrides to come into view. It was just a two or three minute walk to the space but after ten minutes there was no sign of him. She was about to move away from the window when there was movement around the car. She opened the curtains to get a better view. The tramp stuck his head out of the side window. He was a mess of hair. She waited; still no sign of Makrides but the man appeared to be talking to someone. Suddenly, a smaller figure came into view, shielded by a pink and white polka dot umbrella. The person handed over a bag which the tramp pulled into the car. The figure glided away. Ebele was stunned: there was more than one person lurking behind the houses, just metres away from where Tuli slept. She rubbed her eyes, wondering if the whole scene was shapes thrown up by rain, an illusion. She checked the window was firmly locked and pulled the curtains across so they overlapped.

15. NIKOS

The day Dimitri was born was the happiest day of Nikos' life. Ourania woke him gently as a rose gold dawn glowed across a tranquil sky.

'Nikos, it's time,' she said calmly as he fell out of bed and reached around in semi-darkness for his clothes.

Ourania, meanwhile, switched on the bedside lamp and raised herself out of bed by pushing both her palms onto the mattress. A peach-coloured stain across the bed sheets and down the back of her white cotton nightdress shocked him.

Are you sure? Are you absolutely sure?' he said.

'Yes. I'm certain,' she replied firmly and Nikos gulped.

Ourania put her hands on her hips, bent towards the floor and let out a succession of slow sharp breaths.

'Are you okay, my love?' He tripped over his trousers as he tried to pull them on.

'Yes,' she said abruptly, straightening herself up. She placed one hand against the wall. 'We need to hurry. I can feel him pushing down. He's impatient.'

'He?' Nikos said with a big grin. It was the first time she'd assigned the baby a sex. For eight months, it was the neutral *moraki: Moraki has hiccups; Moraki is hungry, Moraki wants Baba to sing.*

'You think it's a boy, Nia?' He could hardly contain his excitement.

'He, she, it, whatever. Get me to the hospital now, Nikos. We don't have time for this chit-chat.'

Nikos helped Ourania into the car and rushed around to the driver's seat. His hands shook on the steering wheel as he weaved through the back roads, avoiding the high street which he knew would be clogged with traffic even though it was still some time before rush-hour.

'Soon be there. Hold on moraki mou, hold on, little baby,' he said as Ourania opened the window, stuck her face into the crisp morning air and panted.

Six hours later, he held a tiny squirming pink bundle with a mop of black hair, and a swell of ecstasy careered through his body.

'I knew it would be a boy,' he said to Ourania. She smiled weakly and closed her eyes. Her hair was as black as the baby's; strands stuck to the side of her bloodless face. Nikos pushed them clear with his lips while holding his baby in his arms.

'We'll call him Dimitri,' Ourania said. Her voice was tiny but assertive. 'After my father and my brother.'

'Okay,' Nikos said. And then, to the baby, 'Kali-mera, Dimitri, my boy.'

George came just a little less than eighteen months later, arriving one lunchtime, three weeks early while Nikos was fiddling about with a delivery of waterproof mattress protectors at the shop. When he heard the news, he ran down Grand Parade nudging people out the way as sweat dripped from his forehead into his eyes; damp spread in huge patches beneath his armpits. At home he was met by Doctor Razak at the front gate followed closely by a midwife he'd never seen before. The doctor slapped him on the back,

'All is well, Nikos. Your wife is as strong as a bull. Congratulations, my friend. Two fine sons. It's more than most people could even wish for.'

Inside, he found Ourania sitting up in bed with a tiny new boy at her breast and Dimitri crawling around his playpen in the corner. Two women from the church fussed around the room but quickly disappeared when he entered and soon the sound of them clanking around in the kitchen rose up through the floorboards. He lifted Dimitri and sat him on his knee next to Ourania.

'Dimitri,' he said. 'Meet your brother Georgios. George. You will be lifelong friends, my boy. Nothing will come between you: not women, not money, not war. You'll love each other as brothers should.'

He kissed Ourania and the new baby on the tops of their heads while Dimitri wiggled free and crawled along the floor towards the playpen. The new baby let go of Ourania's nipple and howled as she tried to reposition him. Nikos laughed.

'It seems like our little George is even more impatient than his brother. We'll have our hands full with these young men.' Ourania smiled and Nikos said, 'Thank you, my love. Thank you.'

The boys were always healthy: the usual coughs and colds as infants and then, as teenagers, a broken limb here and a sprained or twisted joint there, but on the whole they both thrived. Things only began to fall apart when, one evening, a young ruddy-faced police officer knocked on the front door, disturbing Nikos and Ourania as they ate pork stew with Dimitri, fed up of waiting for George to return from his football match or his snooker game or wherever he was.

'Goodness me, Nikos,' Ourania said when he returned to the table. 'You're as pale as milk.'

'He's been arrested,' Nikos said, shaking. 'It is ridiculous: they say he was stopped with some kind of drug in his possession. I don't understand. I need to go to the police station with his passport and other things. Come with me Dimitri.'

Less than six months later, Nikos stood in the airport terminal with his arm around Ourania's shoulders as she wept into his handkerchief; Dimitri stood beside them and all three waved twenty-one-year-old George off to board a plane on his own for the first time.

'Cousin Andreas has a successful fashion business in the middle of the best shopping centre in Toronto. Canada is a good place,' Nikos had told them all just a few days after the incident with the police. 'I will make arrangements. There are opportunities there. He will train George up, keep him away from troublemakers. This city is too full of temptation. It's difficult even for boys like ours, good boys from good families. It's the right decision, Nia.'

'Please no, Nikos,' Ourania pleaded. 'He needs to be here, with us. This is his home.'

'He'll come back, my love. It is just for a short time, to keep him out of trouble, away from the bad crowd he's become mixed up in. I promise you, Ourania, he will be home before we know it. And then he can help Dimitri in the store here, and together they can grow our little business into an empire.'

But George didn't come home. He found a girl in Toronto whose parents weren't even Greek. Two years later, Dimitri joined him across the pond, at first for a holiday to spend time with his brother, but then as a permanent arrangement, and both sons lived a few miles apart from each other but thousands of miles away from Nikos and Ourania.

'But why do you want to settle in that place, Dimitri?' Nikos said, when his firstborn broke the news. 'If you stay there it is encouraging George to stay too. You will break your mother's heart.'

'It's better there, Baba. For us, I mean. Canada is safe from all the terrorism and bank problems. We have prospects. I need to do more than just be a shopkeeper forever. There are opportunities there; it's what you told us when George left, remember?'

'Maybe we too can emigrate,' Ourania said often. 'I want to be near my grandchildren when they come along.'

But Nikos had the business to consider and Canada was much too far from Cyprus; it was inconceivable. The boys came to visit every two or three years and he and Ourania made the long-haul journey each time a new grandchild was born. They stayed for as long as they could manage but it was never long enough for Ourania and always too long for Nikos.

'Please come for one month, Mama,' Dimitri said when his second child was born. 'Baba can return earlier for the shop but you can stay longer, can't you? You can take care of Alyssa while Charline looks after the baby.'

'I'm not sure,' Ourania said pensively. 'You know I don't like to travel alone and your father can't shut the shop for any longer than two weeks.'

'Nia, my love,' Nikos said when she came off the phone. 'Of course you should stay with our boy. He needs you. I cannot think of anything which would make you happier.'

They phoned Dimitri together that night and Nikos smiled at Ourania's excitement as she left a garbled message on his answerphone.

'It's all arranged,' she said. 'Your baba is pretending he can survive easily without me for a little while so we should give him the chance to prove it. I can spend time with you and I will see Georgios every day too. And I will fill your freezers with kolokotes and flaounes, so even when I am gone you will think of Mama.'

The next day, when Dimitri's number showed up on the phone display, Ourania put it straight to speakerphone so both she and Nikos could discuss the plan with their son.

'Hey, Mama,' Dimitri said. 'I've been talking to Charley about the idea of you staying for the whole month, and she says it's too much to expect you to look after us for that long, that I was being a little selfish and shouldn't have asked you.'

'Nonsense, Dimitri. I'm your mother, I long to care for you and I cannot wait to hold little Lyssie in my arms again; she must be getting so big now. If I stay for one month there will be time to teach her the numbers in Greek.'

'Listen Mama,' Dimitri said more adamantly. 'Charley says I shouldn't have asked you, and she's right, not without discussing it with her first.'

'What are you saying, Dimitri?' Nikos shouted from where he stood behind Ourania.

'Well, to be honest, there isn't really the room and Charley's mother is just down the street so she will be popping in and out all the time. It'll be too much to have you here too, for so long I mean.' Nikos watched helpless as Ourania's face crumpled. There was a pause before Dimitri said buoyantly, 'But hey, a week or two is good. You'll still get plenty of time with Alyssa. By the way, Mama, Charley doesn't like her being called Lyssie; she thinks it sounds weird, and we prefer to call her Ali for short.'

Over dinner, Nikos watched Ourania pick at her meal in silence and, as he gathered up the plates from the table, she said quietly, 'If they had married nice Greek girls things would be so different; I wouldn't be a stranger to my grandchildren and my heart would still be in one piece.'

It was the first thing she'd said since the phone call an hour earlier.

Over time the calls and Skype messages dwindled and soon the boys only rang on birthdays, Easter and Christmas until Easter slipped off the list and then, one year both Dimitri and George forgot to call on their mother's birthday.

George broke his foot in a skiing accident two days before Ourania died. He wasn't able to make it to the funeral.

'You're an oaf, George,' Nikos told his son in a text message. 'It's because of you your mother's heart first shattered all those years ago. She has never been the same since you got mixed up with those drug dealers and hooligans.'

George didn't reply.

Dimitri stayed for just a day after the rituals were done.

'They only give you a week off for this kind of thing,' he told his father.

'What thing is the same kind of thing as the death of your mother?' Nikos said.

On the day of his departure, Dimitri waited by the window, looking out for his taxi and glancing intermittently at his watch. When the cab arrived, he tentatively touched Nikos on the elbow and said,

'Take care of yourself, Dad. I'll call you when I get home.'

'Baba,' Nikos declared as his son rushed out of the door. 'I am your Baba,' he shouted as the taxi pulled away.

Nikos picked up a nearby framed photograph of his two sons as toddlers in which they both clung on to their mother's skirt. He hugged it close to his chest and walked around the house into each empty room calling out Ourania's name, as if she might suddenly emerge from some shadowy corner into his arms.

16. JIMMY

Each time he caught a glimpse of himself in a mirror, Jimmy was reminded of the person he most wanted to forget. Frank Noone was a miserable bastard. He never smiled or laughed in the way normal people did. Frank's miserable bastard face was part of Jimmy's own face and there was no escaping it. On Sunday morning, it took Jimmy by surprise when he saw his father's bastard face staring back at him through the cloudy mirror above the steel basin in the toilet block at Hazelwood. Lack of sleep and a gauntness developed on the streets transformed his boyishness, making him more like his father than ever before. He flung scoops of cold tap water over his head to try and wash Frank away but he was still there. Jimmy knew his beard reeked but it partly obscured the look of Frank and he was glad of it. At the drop-in centre near the subway they sometimes offered shaves and showers. He gladly accepted showers, even with the knowledge that it was hard to get completely dry with threadbare towels and there were only filthy clothes to put onto his newly washed skin, but he never took up the offer of the shave. He didn't want to be reminded of his father any more than he already was and, as far as he knew, Frank had never had a beard. This was the problem, he knew very little about his father; Frank never let them in. He never showed them any kind of affection; it was as if they lost both their mother and their father all those years ago. Frank lived behind a wall of ice and it was his detachment which was the cruelty. Not once had he said a soft word to any of them; not once had he showed them he cared. Jimmy threw water at his reflection and walked out of the toilet block into the day.

Sunday in the area was only slightly less busy than other days from what he could tell: people were up early, off to worship or Sunday-league matches played by those who cared more for sport than they did for lie-ins, just like his brother did. Across the park in the playground a little girl laughed loudly as she was being pushed on the swings by a man with dishevelled hair. There was a song about Sunday mornings, climb downs or come downs or some such thing: little kids on swings being pushed by proper dads; some old fella looking on with a hangover, alone and lonely. The old song wormed its way around Jimmy's head as he crossed the park; it was hard to get rid of. Ant really hated that song. Frank used to play it on an old tape cassette, over and over on Sunday afternoons after the pub, when Nan had gone home for the night. He'd shove them out of the living room so he could be on his own when he listened to it.

'I wish he'd give that friggin' country-shite a rest, or piss off to wherever it is those whining bastards are going on about. He belongs in their world,' Ant said once.

Frank rarely listened to music; the joy of it didn't seem to penetrate him but *Sunday Morning Coming Down* was an exception and Jimmy wondered if there was something in the song which flicked a switch.

Ant said, 'Nah, he just listens to it because it's the only tape he's got, and because he knows we hate it. He plays it to wind us up. Everything is to wind us up, Jimbo.'

Jimmy hated the song as much as Ant, or so he thought. But, as songs often did, it came to him in dreams, echoing its truth and its clemency and when it did, it was always a soundtrack with Frank centre stage. Now, this Sunday morning in the middle of a strange town, surrounded by people who looked straight through him, it occurred to him the song didn't just belong to Frank but to him too, right there in the park with the kid on the swings laughing in the background. Jimmy looked around and wondered which direction he should take in his search for Betwa. He glanced at the cafe and thought about popping his head through the door to ask if they knew her, but there were dogs tied up against the railings again and they snarled like before.

When he and Betwa had walked up alongside the river towards the festival just weeks earlier, she'd said,

'You should get a dog, Jimmy. Keep you warm, and it's company.'

'Nah, hate them. Anyway, I'd rather you kept me warm; you're much nicer than a scuzzy old mutt.'

She laughed awkwardly. 'Thanks,' she said.

He apologised. He knew it was too much to say out loud. She became all serious.

'You hardly know me, Jimmy. It's only been a few weeks. It was you who said we shouldn't get too attached to things out here. People too.'

'Sorry. It was a naff thing to say. I just meant it's nice, you know, to have a friend out here, to not be alone.'

'You're never completely alone out here.'

'Everyone is your friend and no one is your friend, so you're always alone,' he said.

'Including you, Jimmy?'

'Until you came along I suppose. But, this, it's something else. Something normal, like before.'

'Don't say that, Jimmy.'

The festival was close by then. The bright lights and traffic drowned out their conversation.

Jimmy turned from the cafe and walked across Hazelwood towards the streets beyond. He needed to move around the area more. He wished the bloody rain would hold off for a bit longer. His plan was to walk back to the station at the far end of the high street and trace the exact route Betwa had described. He tried to remember the direction of the scrawls on her map but the image in his head was fuzzy. She'd talked about a little green bookshop, tucked down a side road off the high street where she sometimes hid behind shelves in the same way he did at the library. He aimed for where he guessed she meant it to be. When he reached the main road, the man called Daban was outside the big bakery. Jimmy lowered his head and shuffled past, expecting to be invisible but Daban reached out and laid a hand on his shoulder.

'Hey man, how are you? Remember me from the other day? Did you find the hostel?'

Jimmy tried to jerk himself free but Daban's grip was firm. A child near to them said, 'Why is that man so smelly?' and his mother put her hand over his mouth and shoved him through the bakery doorway.

'Hey, let me buy you a cup of something.' Daban said, offering Jimmy a Danish pastry.

'This'll do,' he said, biting into it.' Apricot jam oozed, dripping onto his beard.

'Please, let me get you a coffee or something.'

'Is the pub open?' Jimmy said.

'It's not even ten o'clock. It's Sunday. The pubs around here won't be open yet.'

'Not even Wetherspoons?'

Daban laughed, 'Not yet.'

'No thanks then,' Jimmy said.

Daban shrugged. 'Have you got a phone, Jimmy?'

'You remembered my name.'

'Don't you remember mine?

'People come and people go. I don't have room for names.' He pointed to his forehead. 'There's too much other shit in there.'

'Well, do you?'

'What? Remember your name? Nope.'

'I meant do you have a phone?'

'What do you think? Yeah, I have a phone. Just not on me right now. It's on the bedside cabinet next to the Rolex, charging so I have it for when I go to the theatre later.'

'I just thought you might, that I could give you my number, help you get sorted.'

Jimmy looked at the man suspiciously. No man had wanted to help him for a long time. Sometimes women stopped, usually old women like the one who was bringing food to the car but men, especially those of a similar age to him, only ever looked on with disgust.

'I had one once but I lost it. It didn't have any credit.' He was more conciliatory now.

'I'll write my number down for you anyway,' Daban said, pulling a notebook out of his pocket. 'You got a pen?'

'A pen? I'd love a pen,' Jimmy said without thinking. 'But I left that next to the Rolex too,' he added smiling.

Daban stopped a passerby. The young woman pulled a pen from her tote bag and handed it over. 'Keep it,' she said as she strolled off. He wrote his number and his name in block capitals on some paper torn from the notebook and gave it to Jimmy. He handed over the pen too.

'Have it,' he said.

'Ta.' Jimmy said with a nod. He stuck it behind his ear and walked towards the station. Daban caught up with him and handed over the notebook.

'I've pulled out the used pages,' he said, waving a bunch of torn sheets at Jimmy. 'Writing stuff down is good.'

'Thanks. Bouncer Counsellor.' Jimmy sniggered.

'Just trying to be decent. It's not always easy but it's a choice. Listen, just find a way to call me if you need anything. There's still a phone box here and there. You can reverse the charges. Do you know what that means?'

'I'm not thirteen.'

'I bet you've not got ten on that,' Daban said.

'Almost exactly!' Jimmy said. 'You're alright, you.'

'Glad to hear it. See you around, Jimmy.'

Daban walked away. Jimmy hesitated then shouted after him.

'Actually, maybe you can help. I'm looking for someone. A friend. Someone I've lost.'

'I'll ask around,' Daban said when he'd described Betwa. 'Listen, I'm in there sometimes.' He pointed to Makrides' Furniture Store. 'I work as a driver for the geezer who owns it. Come and find me if you need to. I'll ask about your girl.'

'I'm not going anywhere near that fucking lunatic,' Jimmy said.

'Ah, you already met our Mr Makrides then?'

'I met the back of his shoe.'

'What? He kicked you? Shit, he's an old bloke. Wouldn't think he had it in him. I mean his tongue is sharp but I didn't have him down as the type to kick a man.'

'You'd be surprised. Some people think we're nothing more than a bit of rubbish. Kicking isn't the worst of it.'

'There's gotta be a better way for you to survive, Jimmy. Why don't you go back home?'

'Home? Yeah right.'

Daban took Jimmy's hand and shook it. 'Gotta go man. See you, Jim. Find me, in the shop or anywhere along here. I'm always around this place. Take care of yourself.'

After he left, Jimmy thought hard about what made Daban different to other men he'd come across. He realised part of it was the way he looked directly into his eyes when he spoke. People stopped to throw coins sometimes. Others asked if he was alright but rarely stayed long enough to hear the words behind the answer. Some left shop-bought sandwiches or hot coffee, a woolly hat or an old coat. He was grateful for it all, it kept him alive, but no-one really looked him in the eye. Once, when he first arrived in the city, a young woman left a copy of a classic paperback novel with a ten pound note tucked between the pages, so as not to embarrass either of them. He wanted to thank her properly but she'd already disappeared by the time he saw the money. He bought biscuits, bananas and vodka from Lidl. They made the next few days bearable. The book was good and he read it twice; it took him to a different place and he was grateful for that too. Until he arrived at Shifnal Road, it was the nicest thing anyone had done for him for as long as he could remember.

At midday it started drizzling and by then Jimmy had walked the length of the high street, up and down twice: past the pub where Daban had bought him cider; past the bakery and the restaurants and the furniture shop full of ornate tat. On a narrow side street off Grand Parade, he found the little bookshop but it was closed so he couldn't ask about Betwa. He headed back to the car, hoping the old woman had been. She, like Daban, was a rarity.

The rain was belting by the time he reached Shifnal Road. His clothes were soaked through and his bones ached in the way they did in the dead of night: pain gnawing into him until he had to sit up and stretch the stiffness away. He was used to rain, he'd grown up with it, coming as he did from the wettest part of the country. He knew warmth had no chance of penetrating waterlogged clothes. Once, when the television news told of a great storm in Brighton – waves crashing against stony beaches and over iron railings as people ran into the wind with out-turned umbrellas – Frank said, 'We'd never get out up here if we behaved like those bloody southerners when there's a bit of weather. Look at them, poofters.'

But the rain in the small town up north was close to home. Wet clothes could be replaced with warm pyjamas or trackies and hung out to dry in airing cupboards and on radiators. In this place it rained less often, and it was a blessing of sorts, but Jimmy was still angry with himself for getting drenched. He grew up learning to predict the weather like all the people did in his town. He knew how to read clouds, judging each shift or change, assessing the likelihood of downpours. He should have returned to the car earlier. He should have known better. Now he'd have to walk around soaked for days, spreading the damp to the car and the sleeping bag and the blanket. There were no dry clothes. Wet shoes were the worst of all. They'd take ages to dry. When Jimmy first started sleeping out, the man called Alan talked about trench foot as they sat around a bin fire. The street veterans were full of horror stories.

'Your feet turn into stinking gristle, lumps like burnt meat, fucking excruciating. But at least we don't have to dodge bullets like the other trench-footers, Jimboy. Not yet at least. Give 'em time though. It'll be government policy soon enough the way things are going.'

When Jimmy approached the Audi in the alleyway he was grateful for his dismal haven, despite the wet clothes. He slipped into the back, removed his jacket, shoes and socks and spread them on the parcel shelf above the seat. He took off his trousers and hung them over the headrest of the front passenger seat, switched on the radio, pulled his sleeping bag over his bare legs up to his shoulders and listened to the sound of the rain drumming against the car roof as the song about umbrellas faded away and the DJ made an obvious joke about the weather. A different song came to mind and suddenly, like deja vu, he understood what the singer meant when she sang of feeling as if it were raining all over the world.

The old woman came eventually. He guessed it was around three, long past lunchtime.

'I was waiting for the rain to pass,' she said apologetically as her spotty umbrella blew about in the squall. 'I was waiting but it wasn't going to stop so here I am anyway.' She glanced at the wet clothes as she handed a bag of food through the window.

'It's just tinned soup, and a sandwich too. I'm sorry it is boring food. Minestrone,' she said as Jimmy took the bag. 'I will make a proper dinner later for you.'

'Thank you,' he said. 'This is great. Honest.' He meant it.

The woman dashed away but returned less than an hour later with another bag. She handed it over and Jimmy peered inside, reaching in for the small hand towel which lay at the top of the other contents. He put it over his head, sucking in the aroma of mothballs and lavender. The bag contained a set of garments; trousers, an old-fashioned vest, underwear, several pairs of socks, a tee-shirt and a clean but faded blue fleece; it looked warm. Beneath the clothes was a pair of old brogues, scuffed and worn in; bigger than his usual size. He pulled out the bundle and placed it on his lap, running his fingers over the pile as if he were stroking a pet.

'They're my husband's,' the woman said quietly. 'Used things. He doesn't wear them anymore. He is not so tall as you but you are so thin, I think they will fit. Trousers may be a little short perhaps but there are long socks to cover ankles. You can tuck in the trousers to prevent this part of your leg becoming cold. My husband also wore them like this when he was riding his bicycle.'

Jimmy didn't know what to say. He continued to stroke the clothes, running his hands over the clean dry fabric. When he looked up to thank the woman she was gone.

17. RAYYA

Clothes worn by Satish once occupied the wardrobe next to Rayya's own things. His sky-blue shirts and grey slacks hung on thin metal hangers next to her ivory coloured blouses, brightly-coloured kameez tunics and pastel saris. His muted V neck sweaters sat next to her pink and emerald cardigans in a neat pile on top of a set of drawers hidden behind wardrobe doors. Wafts of washing powder drifted out of the wardrobe when she emptied it to make room for the boxes of incontinence pads and powdered food. Mingled with the scent of clean washing was the subtle undertone of majmua oil from her perfume and beauty products. Together, she realised, it was the smell of them, her and Satish, combined in one aroma. She moved her own things to the smaller in-built cupboard in the back bedroom then removed each item of Satish's with care, folding and placing them in a large green suitcase until the only garments to remain were six sets of men's pyjamas, 100% cotton, navy with light blue piping. She didn't tell Satish what she was doing. Instead, to reassure him about the disruption, she said in a steady voice,

'Time for a spring clean, darling. This is what the English do and now we have lived here for many more years than anywhere else, we too can claim this ritual.'

The suitcase was zipped up and dragged into the small middle bedroom which had served as Satish's study. There the case remained for over a year, pushed up against the wall behind the closed door.

The study lay between the large airy front bedroom and the bright bathroom, and each time Rayya passed it she imagined

Satish at his desk, surrounded by precarious piles of books and paperwork, spectacles slipping down his nose as he concentrated on whatever he was absorbed in under the light of the Anglepoise. In her head he was still there, full of spirit as he often was in that room, fired up over some newly discovered work of fiction or a political article with which he felt closely aligned or fervently in disagreement. Regardless of how deeply he was absorbed, he'd never show any irritation at being disturbed by Rayya if she crept in to place a cup of tea next to him. Instead, he would squeeze her hand without taking his eyes off the page, and she would rub his shoulders or kiss the top of his head. She kept the door to the study tightly closed to keep him alive behind it.

It was a damp Sunday when she nudged open the door for the first time in over a year. Before entering, she stood outside preparing herself, breathing in deeply before peeping into the darkness reluctantly. The musty smell of neglected paper was palpable but it was the absence of Satish which was overwhelming. She stepped back, pulled the door shut and returned to the front bedroom where she slumped into her chair next to the bed. She placed her hand upon Satish's but it was sometime before she spoke.

'Darling,' she said gently. 'Do you know it has rained so much already today it reminds me of *baarish* back at home. Remember when I was running and you caught me as I slipped? It was after marriage was arranged but I was still shy of you. I am sure you already know the time I am talking about, when the monsoon rains came so suddenly. Silly me didn't check the clouds and before I knew it, rickshaws and the cars were floating like boats and Tilak Nagar became the Yamuna river. You ran to me and lifted me up high above your head so I wouldn't drown. I think this was when love really happened, when you lifted me up, Satish. My body was suddenly so full of Diwali explosions.'

She stood up and stroked Satish's cheek before walking across the room to the fireplace where photographs in cheap plastic frames were displayed. Still images captured moments of their life together: Rayya's head thrown back in laughter as she leaned against a wall on the bottom step of Qutub Minar; the two of them stiff in overcoats outside Buckingham Palace. In the centre of the display was a large grainy monochrome image taken on the day they were married, on a makeshift stage behind the ramshackle dwellings which lined the streets where they grew up. It was the only wedding photo they possessed.

'Can you believe it, darling?' she said, in the most buoyant tone she could muster. 'The paths in our little Hazelwood are flowing with brown waters just like the Ganges now. Good job we are cosy inside, my darling.' She patted his arm and tried to gulp down the lump which blocked her throat.

Later, Rayya looked at her face in the bathroom mirror. Her eyes were red and puffed, surrounded by indigo rings resembling the colour of fresh bruises, and deep lines which stretched from the edges of her eyelids to her hairline. Wrinkles seemed to have multiplied since she last looked so closely. Her steely hair was swept back into a ponytail; it showed no hint of her natural charcoal colour. *I am an old woman, older than my own parents ever were.* She wondered if her mother had ever looked at her own reflection in a mirror, expecting to see a cascade of dark hair and a face free from the creases of time; shocked to see instead a shrivelled face staring back. Life, she now realised, happened rapidly and moments of pure bliss were only ever transitory, to be snatched away by disappointment and despair. She let the tap run, and with both hands she scooped and splashed ice-cold water onto her face before drying it with the hand towel, then she sat on the edge of the tub and breathed in long slow breaths, exhaling audibly in the way she used to with Satish when their mornings began with yoga on the bright kilim rug in the living room.

Rayya put her freshly brewed mug of tea on the table in the room where Satish lay.

'There will be a little noise, nothing to worry about,' she said sighing.

The hefty green suitcase was a dark shape against the wall of the study and, without switching on the light, she dragged it from its resting place onto the landing and into the front room.

'Just me sorting things out. You know I like to be organised.'

She sat for a moment, preparing herself for the jolt she knew was coming.

'Sorry about the disturbance, my darling,' she said.

She swept the train of her sari across her forehead, mopping up beads of sweat with it, and when her breathing settled she said, more calmly,

'Satish, I know your answer even before I ask you this question because this is how we are, isn't it? Our two bodies sometimes have just one mind. It's the young man I told you about. I don't know his name. That is a funny thing, right? For three days I have been feeding him as if he is a *rishtedari*, one of our own family, and yet I don't even know this boy's name. Well anyway, he will be soaking today in this weather, sleeping outside without a home. Not like the rooftops in Delhi, eh? That was when sleeping outside was something else indeed, isn't it so, my love?'

She squeezed his hand again, remembering a distant night when as teenagers they sneaked onto the flat roof of the Bata shoe shop at the end of the gulley, long after the proprietor left for his big *kothi* on the other side of town. There they fell asleep hand in hand on a discarded jute bed until bright moonlight woke them and Rayya, terrified of repercussions, ran down the stairwell and sprinted home before Satish managed to shake away his sleepiness. She told Papa-ji she'd got lost after accidently straying away from the criss-cross weave of back streets she knew and, instead of scolding her as expected, he hugged her tightly, told her how precious she was but how she was no longer a child so must never stray too far. She smiled at the memory of her father. It came with a familiar yearning she'd held for over forty years, ever since he dropped dead one afternoon as he wiped okra with a damp tea towel just a few months after she'd left for England. He was forty-nine years old.

'The question I want to ask, Satish,' Rayya said as she pushed the suitcase flat onto the floor, 'Is whether it is okay for me to give this boy some of the things you don't wear anymore? Not your best things of course, but just some dry clothes. He will be soaking wet in all this rain.'

She knelt next to the suitcase. Held her breath and opened it. On top lay a mustard-coloured sweater she'd knitted for Satish. Together they'd laughed at the misshapen neckline and sleeves which dangled way beyond the tips of his fingers but he refused to throw it away, or allow her to unravel the wool and start again. He treasured it, he said, as if it were made of gold. She lifted it up and buried her nose into the bobbled wool then set it aside. She pulled out a shop-bought sweatshirt which he wore at the weekends when there were household jobs to be done. She held it up towards the light.

'You never really liked this one did you? Just a cheap thing from the supermarket. You don't mind if I give it to the boy?' She placed the sweatshirt in a separate pile and added other items. First was a Chicago Bulls tee shirt which appeared amongst Satish's clothes some years ago. She teased him at the time, mockingly suggesting it might be a present from an admirer at the post office.

'Don't be ridiculous,' he'd responded. 'I would never accept such a gift and therefore encourage the attention of someone who would assume I'd desire such a garment.'

They decided the tee shirt was a mix-up from the launderette but it was still well worn on summer days, in the garden, drinking Coca-Cola on an old bedspread as they flicked through weekend newspapers together.

'When you're better we can get new things for you.' Rayya said as she continued sorting through the clothes. Her voice wavered as she spoke. 'He is very skinny this boy but you will also be thinner so you will need new things. It will be a good excuse. I know you hate shopping but we can try more of this internet thing. I'll need you to help me of course. I can just about get the groceries but clothes shopping is another thing altogether, hai na?'

She added a pair of slacks and a belt to the pile plus three pairs of sports socks and finally a thick fleece, not the waterproof one she was searching for but warm enough, and the extra layers would always come in handy, she had no doubt about this. When she was sure she'd selected the right items she re-zipped the suitcase ready to haul back to the study.

'You don't mind do you?' she said again, holding up each selected item in turn to the direction of Satish's fixed stare. 'Goodness knows he needs them. And maybe I should take your old shoes? They too can be replaced, my darling.'

From the front garden, Rayya looked back at her house before she took the bag of dry clothes around the corner. It looked dreary in the rain and it was too big. Even before Satish became ill, she knew it was more than they needed. Three or maybe four years earlier, he'd said,

'Space is such a luxury here, Rayya. Maybe we should sell it and move to a smaller house, somewhere on the edge of the city and then we will have money to go back and forth to India.'

'Perhaps,' she said. She knew he was broaching a difficult subject.

The plan was never to have space for the sake of it or for the status symbol property had become in the city, but rather to have a house large enough to grow into as they became a family. The neutral walls were meant to consist of seeped-in memories, permeating the plaster and brickwork with echoes of sleepless children crying into the nights, rocked in loving arms, consoled with lullabies, and the laughter which should have buoyed the house, turning ordered spaces into chaos and merriment. The attic space should by now be crammed full of stories, jigsaw puzzles and board games, ready to be discarded by the grandchildren as they were by the children, in favour of more modern things with beeps and flashes. There would be boxes piled high with felt-tip drawings, old school books, certificates, diaries, and photographs, so many photographs, printed in the old fashioned way and collated in albums, one for each child and another for each grandchild. Instead, over the years, she and Satish learnt how to fill the empty spaces themselves with their chat and their rituals. In the early days, Kostas and other friends visited often and more of the space was occupied but after Kostas died, and the other young couples they became acquainted with had children, people drifted away. Even so, the kitchen was filled with the sounds of Rayya and Satish cooking together, humming along to old tunes on Indian radio stations. The small dining room was used for more serious music and long meandering conversations over food; the cosy living room was for political programmes on television and Rayya's dramas on Zee TV. Shelves filled the alcoves on either side of a beige art-deco fireplace and were lined with books, photographs, Indian ornaments and films they liked to watch over and over. Both of them were experts in Satyajit Ray and Ritwik Ghatak but also in the works of Kurosawa, Bergman and Billy Wilder. Thick curtains protected the windows from draughts and, when there was film watching to be done, served the dual purpose of blocking chinks of light which might reduce the cinematic effect. Since the illness, Rayya moved around the downstairs of the house shrouded in a heavy silence, like a trespassing stranger.

When Satish talked of selling up, she made an effort to respond pragmatically. 'Perhaps we should wait until retirement,' she said. 'And then we can just go home. There is nothing for us here we can't have there, so long as we are together. We can live near Panji Bobbi or your sister, see our nephews and nieces, and become something important in their lives and those of their children too. Perhaps there life will have new meaning for us.'

'Rayya, you are all the meaning I need, but yes, one day soon we will sell this place and go home like you say and there we can live as we please with the sun beating down, warming our old bones, eh.'

So that became the dream to which they clung as they trudged through monotonous weeks and grey years. But then Satish became ill and the dream was rendered meaningless like dreams always are in the stark light of day.

When she returned home after delivering the small bag of dry clothes to the boy in the car, Rayya checked on Satish again and then, when all was quiet in the bedroom, she slipped past empty rooms towards the long galley kitchen at the back of the house and began to gather together stray vegetables from the wire rack on the worktop and the plastic drawer at the bottom of the fridge. Within minutes the only sound was the hiss of the gas cooker and the *chud chud chud* of the knife against her wooden chopping board.

18. NIKOS

T he last time Nikos entered the alleyway behind Shifnal Road was when Ourania was still alive. Since then nearly a year had dragged by, bloated with silent mornings and long empty evenings. Throughout her last summer, he spent all spare and snatched hours on the small patch of land connected to the alleyway, working under placid light on a secret construction project; a surprise for Ourania. To justify his late homecomings he told her he was sorting out a backlog of orders or meeting suppliers over beer or cake to keep them sweet. Sometimes, he said he merely fancied going for a long walk, stretching out his aging limbs in the way he once stretched the restless limbs of youth in the hills above Larnaca. Dusty overalls were tucked away out of sight and when a thin layer of rubble-dust coated his strands of wispy hair, he washed swiftly at the utility sink in the back of the store before the day's final lock up. He hated lying to Ourania but for this he felt justified. The surprise was to be a small but sturdy brick-built outhouse which would one day contain a kiln and a potter's wheel. It would be Ourania's pottery shed: a haven out of sight of prying eyes; her own piece of land in a city where it was the most sought after commodity money could buy. There'd been offers for the wasteland from would-be purchasers, mostly keen-eyed developers with visions of big bucks for tiny homes, smart on the outside but held together with little more than string and glue. Nikos refused them all. This would be for Ourania alone and, while he was busy at the shop, she could replicate the ceramics of home and be the artist he always knew she was. His plan was to fit a gate with a lock at the roadside end so only she could access the land, keeping out undesirables.

He would give her a large key in a velvet-laid box on their next anniversary and this would be the first she would know about the studio. But Ourania died, unexpectedly, three months before the anniversary arrived, while the studio was still little more than crude foundations and one half-built wall now obscured by brambles and weeds. He couldn't bear to revisit; the place reminded him of lost hours wasted on a folly which could have been spent by the side of his beloved.

Rain eased but still spat on Nikos as he walked to confront the stranger in the alleyway on Sunday afternoon. Getting past the bashed-up car was difficult to manoeuvre, making the path to the pottery shed inaccessible, and he was glad. He peered through the driver's side window of the Audi. The passenger seat was covered in a pile of sloppy clothes. He held his nose and tried to get a good view of the back seat where, curled in a sleeping bag like a baby, was a body. Only a mess of black hair visible just above the grubby rim of the bag indicated human life. The overwhelming stench made him retch. He gathered himself and shouted into the car,

'Oi, get up you filthy pig.' The body in the backseat stirred but remained beneath the sleeping bag. Nikos shouted again, louder this time, 'You in the car, sleeping in a place you don't belong, get up.'

The bag stretched, arching like a gigantic caterpillar. The specimen inside sat up slowly, revealing himself. Nikos rubbed his eyes. It was hard to tell where the creature's beard began and head hair ended. He was relieved to see the man was clothed beneath the bag.

'You, filthy pig, you are trespassing on my property,' he said.

The man peered back. He sat up. 'My name is Jimmy, I have a name. I'm not a frigging animal, I am a man like you.'

'Get out here,' Nikos said. 'Get your things and go from my property. People like you do not belong here.'

The man sniggered. 'I know you,' he said. 'You're the bully from the shitty furniture shop, the one who kicked me. What kind of man kicks another while they are lying down? What would your mother say if she knew what you'd turned into? You should be ashamed of yourself kicking someone like that.'

'You are nothing,' Nikos replied. 'Not good enough to lick my boots. You have no right to conjure up my mother.'

'What difference does it make to you if I sleep in this car? No-one wants it. No-one owns it. It's not yours. All I'm trying to do is shelter here while I search for a friend. Hardly a crime. Where's your humanity, for fuck's sake?'

Nikos was taken aback by the man's speech. He expected expletives but nothing more. 'You are committing a crime being here,' he said in response. 'This land is private property. You are frightening the people who live here.'

'What people?'

'Children are frightened when they see you, looking like some brother of Gorgon. There have been complaints.'

'Get me removed then. See if the police bother. I'm not begging, I'm not littering or being a nuisance. You'll need a court order to move me. '

'I will get this car removed with you inside it and both can be destroyed together. This is my land. Not some bloody resting place for filthy gypsies.'

'Well good luck, grandad. Do you think the police care any more about your shitty property than they do about me? You're a nobody, just the same as me. You might own a tatty old shop but what else? You have no power, nobody cares about a disused strip of land in the back streets.'

The man in the car was out of his sleeping bag now and he'd pulled on his shoes. Nikos could see he was young; thin like a stick but still with youth on his side. He glanced around. This part of the alleyway was out of view, and even if it wasn't, there was hardly anyone about: the rain had sent them all scurrying away. The back door of the car swung open and Nikos instinctively stepped backwards, slipping on wet mud. He fell on his backside and when he tried to push himself up his large hands sunk into the sodden earth and he slipped again. Cold moisture seeped through his trousers until the skin beneath was damp. He tried again to lift himself but floundered in the mud, writhing until the whole of his underside was caked. The young man climbed out of the car and loomed over him. Nikos tried to look over his shoulder towards the entry but it was difficult with his face so close to the ground. He recoiled, sinking further into wet earth as his limbs shivered uncontrollably, blinking dirty rain away from his eyes.

'Don't hit me,' he pleaded to the young man. 'It would not be good to hit a man on the ground, especially an old one like me.'

'It's not good to hit anyone, on the ground or not, mate. You should remember that.'

The younger man stretched out his hand and Nikos flinched.

'We're not all mean bastards you know,' the young man said. 'C'mon grandad.' He clasped both his hands onto Nikos and pulled him up to standing. 'You'd better get yourself back to your cosy house and into the bath before you catch a cold. There's nothing worse than being in wet clothes.'

Nikos leaned on the car to steady himself. He watched as the man climbed into the driver's seat and then something, a tiny unexpected thing made him think of Georgios: perhaps it was the sight of the awkward lankiness of the man's body, suspended somewhere between youth and manhood. Or maybe it was the wild raven hair. Whatever it was it unlocked memories which soared through his mind like arrows. He tried to push them away but Georgios' face became interchanged with the young man's, one minute sitting in the car reading sleeve notes to *Tea For The Tillerman,* the next lying slumped across the seats, hair matted with dried blood. Nikos shook his head like a wet dog but the images wouldn't shift. His legs wouldn't stop shaking either; his whole body juddered. He wanted to be at home, surrounded by the essence of Ourania but his knees buckled when he moved. After a moment, the young man poked his head out of the window.

'What is it, grandad? You okay?'

'I'm fine. Mind your own business.'

'Not got a home to go to after all, old fella?'

'I will give you twenty-four hours to move away from this place. Go home, go back to your mother. This is no life for a man.'

By the time Nikos showered and changed into his pyjamas and dressing gown it was dark outside. He walked through the house, drawing the curtains in each of the empty rooms before making his way to the kitchen to open a tin of pre-prepared *gigantes plaki*. He scraped the beans and sauce into a bowl and heated it up in the microwave. When it was ready, he squeezed half a fresh lemon over the dish, pulled a chunk of bread from the village loaf which lasted him all week and placed it on top of the bowl. He poured out a large ouzo and carried his tray of supper into the room where Ourania's clothes lay spread out. The pungent smell of the plaki permeated the room. He ate in silence, wondering what his sons might be doing that very moment in the place they now called home thousands of miles away from him. Mostly, he thought of the way the young man in the car called him *grandad*; the word made his heart sink in a way no other word did. When he settled enough to raise the first spoonful of food to his mouth, it tasted only of wet salt.

19. JIMMY

Rain was a fine spray across a colourless sky as the old woman approached with dinner on Sunday night. She brushed the back of her hand across her damp face, forcing a small smile as she handed the warm container through the car window. It had taken Jimmy a short while to notice how each time she arrived with food, she left behind a trail of sadness in her wake which he couldn't quite put his finger on. At first he thought it was pity but soon realised it had little to do with him. It was something she wore about her presence unaware, a kind of melancholy cloak, invisible yet distinct.

'Your kids are lucky,' he said. 'You've gotta be one of the best cooks around here.'

She didn't speak.

'I always liked a curry when I was a kid. Not that we had one very often. It's oven chips and chicken nuggets where I'm from. And curry from the chippie or from a tin, nothing like this.'

He knew he was jabbering.

'My nan could cook too but she could just do the English stuff, you know, hotpot and a roast and stuff.'

It was the most he'd said to the woman. She stared directly at the fleece he was wearing. He stroked his own arm.

'It feels so good to be wearing dry clothes,' he said. 'And clean ones at that. Thank you.'

Something akin to distress moved across her face and he wondered if she regretted giving him the clothes, whether her husband had searched for them and complained about their absence. For a second he thought she might ask for them back.

Her lip quivered almost imperceptibly before she spoke. He knew what it looked like to be holding back tears.

'When I first married my husband we could hardly eat the food I cooked. His was no better,' she said. 'But, as an Indian woman, I was told it was my duty to feed my husband so I had to learn. He didn't mind if I was not such a good cook. He is a modern man and didn't want me to be his servant. We learnt together and cooking became a pleasure for us.'

The woman was from a different world and Jimmy was slowly beginning to realise how much he had to learn about other people. When he was young, people around him were all the same, poor and Catholic; the younger ones were disaffected, the older ones, disappointed. There were only two children at school who weren't white. Once, he'd pushed one of them aside when the lad strayed into his path along a school corridor. The boy fell onto the floor and cried out while a small crowd of jeering kids watched on. Jimmy didn't think twice about the incident at the time, ambling on without a backwards glance. When he heard the boy's wrist had been fractured in the fall, he shrugged and walked off. It was no big deal: he'd broken two bones himself and Ant at least three, possibly more. It occurred to him that this old woman could be related to the boy at school.

The woman seemed to look at something way beyond him and he watched how her eyes crinkled as she fixed into the distance. Her skin was smooth across her forehead; he tried to imagine how she'd looked as a younger woman. There was a quiet beauty about her face.

'We all cooked in my gaff,' he said, aware he was disrupting some sort of daydream. 'We had to or we'd have no dinner.' He didn't know what else to say.

'Yes, this was the way it was for us too,' the woman said distractedly.

'Well tell your fella he's a lucky man and I said so, for what it's worth.'

The woman breathed in and when she exhaled it was carried on a deep sigh.

'Have you found your friend?' she said. He shook his head. 'Will you stay until you do?'

He hadn't thought that far ahead. 'I suppose I'll stay as long as it takes or until the big bloke shifts me off his land.'

'Nikos Makrides?'

'Maybe, the Greek fella. He came around today. He said there'd been complaints.'

'Some people like to complain about everything. He did not kick you again I hope.'

The incident in the doorway of Makrides' shop was just days earlier but already seemed a lifetime ago. The woman lingered. She didn't seem to want to leave but she didn't seem to want to stay either.

'Well, you've been very kind,' Jimmy said. 'They must be proud of you, your family. Your husband and kids.' He placed the container on the seat and stuck his hand through the window. 'My name's Jimmy, by the way.'

She took a small step backwards. Jimmy looked at his hand: dirt embedded into the skin like ink, thick in the spaces around his fingernails. He retracted it quickly.

The woman said, 'Jimmy, you should go to your family. Someone will be missing you. Children, even grown up ones, are precious. You should go home.'

He wiped his hands on his trousers but the dirt remained unshifted.

'If you need money for train fare, I can help you. Just ask me.'

The woman walked away. When she neared the entrance, he shouted after her.

'My mum died. My dad's a waste of space. There's no family waiting for me.'

She stopped in her tracks, She didn't turn to face him but instead looked up to the sky and he watched from the shelter of the car as the spray of rain reverted to great splotches which belted down on her.

Before Jimmy met Betwa, he hadn't spoken about his family to anyone for a very long time. At first he found it hard to listen to her talking about her own mother without mentioning his; he felt the anguish written across her face. But she wasn't like him really. She was running away and he knew she'd find her way back. When he finally spoke of his mother, he said,

'She was too young to go and we were too young to be left.'

'Sorry,' was all Betwa could say. There were no other words and besides, he knew she meant it. She was sorry for the things he'd lost but she couldn't know that by speaking of them he was handing over something broken, in hope of some kind of salvation. Really it was respite he wanted, not repair: if she could carry his pain for just a moment it would be made lighter, and when it was delivered back to him, with another person's touch upon it, he'd know it was okay not to be completely fixed. Being broken didn't mean he couldn't be pulled up if he'd somehow fallen behind.

In the car, after the old woman left, he ate the biriyani from the Tupperware and thought about all of this as best he could. The car was the first space he'd had to himself in a long time and the thick mist in his brain cleared a little as he spent time there. When the tub was empty, he leaned back in the driver's seat and thought about what he'd told Betwa on the walk up to the festival all those days ago.

One minute Mam was there, the next she was gone and we had Jenny instead. No one ever spoke about it. I didn't know what'd happened to her 'til years later. I just missed her. I used to call out for her in the night and Ant would climb in my bed and hold me. He was only a little kid himself. Nan stayed for a few weeks and came whenever she could but it must've been hard for her; it was her daughter after all. Sometimes she'd take Jenny away for a night or two but Frank always wanted her back by the weekend. He said she belonged to him even though he didn't really know what to do with her.

By the time they'd reached the river, he'd told Betwa the bulk of it. He wanted to tell her more. He needed someone to know he didn't blame Ant for what happened later. At the time, he'd made his brother feel bad about going and now there was no way to make it better.

'Don't go, Ant. Don't leave us behind,' he'd said when Ant told him he was moving out.

Ant said, 'I've got to, Jimmy. I can't be around here any longer. I've done my stint. Besides, there's some space in a squat near the blue bridge, close to the garage so I'll always be on time for work. I'm a grown man and I've got to start living for myself.'

'You're abandoning us.'

'I'm not, Jimbo. I promise. I'm just abandoning this place. It's suffocating me. If I don't get out now, I never will. I need to start living a little. Anyway, when I've got some money saved I'll search for our house in the Lakes and you and me and Jenny will be together again. And Nan if she wants.'

Then, just a couple of months later, Jimmy's mobile rang in the middle of the night as he slept next to Ant's empty bed and he knew before he answered that his brother was gone for good too. Jenny wouldn't listen when he crept into her bedroom to tell her; she put her hands over her ears and screamed. Frank came in to see what all the wailing was about and when Jimmy told him, he watched his father leave the room without uttering a sound. Soon after, Jen moved in with Nan and refused to see both Frank and him.

'Give her time, son,' Nan said. 'We all grieve in different ways. She'll come round. You're all she's got now. '

'She's got you, Nan,' he said.

'Oh Jimmy, you've both got me. I wish I could take you in too but you know I don't have the room.'

He did know; the flat was Council and as tiny as a shoebox.

'Anyway, your father needs you more than ever. One day you'll understand. It's one thing to lose your wife, but losing a child is something else altogether. As for Jenny, don't give up on her, Jimmy lad. You're going to need each other one day. I'm not going to be around forever.'

He really wished he'd had a chance to tell all those things to Betwa that day on the way to the festival, but the small boy appeared sobbing by the tree and she'd run ahead towards him.

20. NIKOS

Ourania had never thrown a pot. She'd never even sat at a potter's wheel until Stella, one of the regular congregation at St Barnabas, invited her to a taster class at the school around the corner from the Orthodox church. The woman's husband suggested it, Ourania told Nikos one morning as he sipped bitter coffee on the patio while she pruned the lilac buddleia which lined the edge of the lawn.

'What does an ugly old goat need a chaperone for?' he replied. 'You are too easily fooled. It's so she can park in our driveway and pretend she associates with us.'

'Really, Nikos, sometimes you are unnecessarily hard. Stella is ten years younger than me, at least. She is not at all like a goat. Anyway, it was her husband, Yannis' idea for her to ask me. Perhaps he thinks she needs friends. Perhaps they both do. Their youngest child has recently gone to live in Athens.'

'Pah! Exactly. Her husband is a buzzard. These people are nobody.'

'We should be kind to them. Their children, like ours, have flown away. We know more than most how heartbreaking this is. Perhaps Stella is missing them and the pottery class is her way of trying to fill her life with new things, new people. So many her age still have their children with them. She is lonely. So what if they want to park for free? We are lucky to live in such a street. They are not so fortunate. Perhaps I too need something more to fill the gap. Why don't we invite them to eat with us one Sunday after church? Perhaps you and Yannis can also become friends?'

'These mainland people look down on us. We don't need them. You are my life, and I yours, and Dimitri and George. They will come to visit soon and then there'll be no gap inside you. Besides, it's not so long since they last left; you'll get used to it. And we can visit in the summer again, as soon as I find a good manager for the shop. Anyway, we don't need friends. Friends become a burden.'

'Perhaps,' Ourania said but he knew she was a long way from being convinced. He would prove it to her.

'Only you, my sweet, never let me down.' he said.

Ourania stroked the side of his hair just above his ear. 'Sometimes you are a funny man, Nikos. I love you but you know better than many that no-one should be lonely. I will go to the class with Stella and I will allow her to park on our drive and, if she wants to be friends, I will invite her and her buzzard husband for coffee and baklava.'

Soon pottery became a part of Ourania's life. Every Tuesday, Stella pulled up on the drive and the two women walked around the corner to the little school where the classes took place. Whenever Nikos was at home, Ourania always waved as she and Stella were about to disappear out of sight and he was always ready to wave back, standing at the window or the front door, watching her walk away with her friend, to pursue a hobby she was coming to love. At the end of her first term, she brought home an ashtray painted in the copper colour of the island flag and decorated in a pattern of deep green olive leaves which snaked the rim like a wreath.

Well into the fifth year of classes, Nikos returned late from work expecting to see Stella's red Polo parked badly on the driveway, leaving him little room to manoeuvre in his own car. But there was no Polo on the drive and when he entered the house, Ourania was alone in their living room, sitting on the settee with her head resting on the palms of her hands staring into space. The muted television was switched on to an old episode of *Escape To The Sun*.

'What's wrong? Why aren't you in your class?' he said. She didn't answer. He sat next to her and put his arm around her shoulders. She laid her head on his chest and started to cry, silently at first but then loud like a baby, sobbing into his shirt and vest.

'What is it, my love?' he repeated gently.

'She is leaving. There will be no more pottery class.'

'Oh, is that all?' Nikos said with a sigh of relief. In his mind all sorts of disasters had befallen them. He wanted to say, *thank God nothing has happened to Dimitri or George.* Instead he said, more flippantly than intended, 'The teacher? That's no big thing, they will easily find a replacement.'

'No, it is Stella who is leaving.' Ourania replied and he sighed with relief yet again.

'Ah, then you can still go to your class. It's not so bad if you can still make your pots.' And in that exact moment he decided he would build her a place to do her pottery whenever she wished.

It was Kostas who'd suggested they buy the few square metres of land when it first came up for sale. *Let's make a motorbike park, Nikos. Or a music studio* he'd said. *Or perhaps we can plant trees and make the space a secret garden with a back gate leading to it for all those children you will have as soon as your little Ourania comes to stay, eh godson!' We have the money. Let's use it to make something of beauty in this ugly world.* Nikos never forgot the conversation and vowed to hold on to the land, fulfilling Kostas' dream of a space to do something creative, liberated, unexpected. Now he'd decided, it would be a special place where Ourania could find freedom and peace.

'You don't understand, Nikos,' she said. 'Stella is leaving. My friend is leaving. Yannis too. Our friends. Their youngest daughter is having a child, in Athens. They are going home, to support their child, to be near their grandchildren, to be part of their lives as they grow up. She won't be coming back here with so much to look forward to. She says it will just be for a year but who ever comes back? Why would they? There is nothing so attractive here.'

He listened quietly, all the time wondering how he would build the surprise without her finding out so he could present her with the key on their anniversary. He thought about what a pottery shed might contain and how he would get hold of such equipment. After a short pause he said, 'Okay, my love, I understand.'

Stella and Yannis left one icy February morning with four bulky suitcases stuffed with teddy bears, blankets and romper suits from Mothercare, jars of Marmite in bubble-wrap and a small bowl decorated with yellow sunflowers, made by Ourania in their last term of pottery class together. Nikos began working on the pottery shed as soon as the weather was more clement. In snatched hours over the summer months, he dug the foundations and built up the first few layers of brick but by autumn Ourania was dead, all of a sudden after just a week of illness, no warning, no chance to prepare, no chance to ask her how he should live the rest of his life without her by his side. She was gone in a cruel instant and the shed remained as a reminder of their curtailed life, as a pile of bricks and rubble hidden behind a path of weeds.

21. EBELE

Ebele knocked on Grace and Mandy's door. There was no answer. Piano music seeped from within the flat; it was epic, rising in volume. She knocked again, this time hammering loudly. She held a scrawled note in her hand; block capitals, child-like handwriting. When the door swung open, she flipped over the note so the words were visible and she held it across her chest. It said, *GO AWAY. WE DON'T WANT YOU HERE*

'What the fuck?'

'It's not actually for you, Mandy, although you can take it if you want.' Ebele looked at the glass of wine in Mandy's hand. She longed for a drink; the vodka was almost gone and payday was still days away. 'Disturbing you, am I?' she said.

'Jeez, Ebele, you get crazier by the day. And yes, we were watching a movie.'

Grace appeared. 'What is it, Ebele?' she asked gently.

'The man you thought it was okay to ignore is still lurking there, looking up at Tuli's room; watching her window.'

'What?'

'The tramp in the car at the back of your garden. He's there. Looking at us. Watching us.'

'Don't be ridiculous,' Mandy said. Grace nudged her aside.

'I didn't say to ignore him, Ebele. I said we'd deal with it in the morning. You know, on a work day when the right services are open.'

'The police are open all the time.'

Grace and Mandy glanced at each other.

'What exactly are you worried about?' Mandy said.

'Are you serious, Mandy? There's a strange bloke watching our houses at night. Aren't you worried? Also, I think there may be more than one person in the car. Two, possibly three. Is that okay too? I've seen another person going to and fro – a woman. It's like they've set up home.'

She knew she was being over-dramatic but she didn't care. Her chest was tight but she did her best to keep her voice steady.

Mandy looked at her incredulously.

'What are you talking about? It's just a bloke sleeping rough. He'll be gone tomorrow.'

'What if tomorrow is too late, Mandy? I've looked online and half of these so-called homeless people aren't homeless at all – they just do it to get money, you know, making people feel sorry for them because they're too damn lazy to do anything else. Sometimes they even have nice houses to go back to.'

'Don't be ridiculous,' Mandy repeated.

'Actually, Mandy, it's not ridiculous; it says on one website that most of them have been to prison. He could be a murderer for all we know. And some people do anything to get to children. They're everywhere, these people.'

'Jesus!'

'What if he hurts someone in the night?'

'She's off her fucking rocker, Grace. I told you she was. She spends too much time in her virtual reality and not enough time in the real world. Maybe actually, Ebele, the poor bugger has just found himself in the shit without a paddle.'

'Mandy, ssh. Go inside, I'll deal with it.' Grace said.

'I don't need dealing with, and I'm not off my fucking rocker, Mandy. And I've hit rock bottom before but I've not ended up living in a broken up old car, staring at little kids through their bedroom windows.'

'Bloody hell, Ebele, you don't think much of your fellow man, do you?'

'That bloke is nothing to me,' Ebele said.

When Mandy stomped back into their flat, Grace said, 'Calm yourself down, Ebele, you are being a bit over the top. It's probably nothing like you imagine. We've left a message for Mr Makrides already and I'm sure he'll evict the fella if he's even still there tomorrow.'

'I've told Makrides too; he's been round to mine already today but he's too cowardly to do anything about it so I'll have to deal with it myself. Anyway, I'm just here to ask you to keep an ear out for Tuli. She's flat out asleep upstairs.'

'Why? Where are you going?'

'I'm going to tell him to sling his hook, of course. I can't sleep knowing he is out there.'

'Why don't you ask your new boyfriend to sort it out?' Mandy shouted from inside the flat. 'He looks like he can handle himself if things get messy.'

'I don't need a man to look after me, or my child, thanks Mandy. And, he's not my boyfriend, just someone I work with, that's all.'

Asking Daban to evict the tramp wasn't such a bad idea though; he was a bouncer in another job after all. She tucked the thought away.

'Keep a listen out for Tuli, will you please, Grace?' she said in a softer voice.

'Don't be silly, Ebele. Just leave it until the morning can't you? What are you going to achieve by going out now in the rain?'

'Tuli will be fine if you can't be bothered though, Grace. She's fast asleep and I'll only be a few minutes. Go on, get back to your cosy film night and your fancy wine.'

'Honestly, Ebele, can't you just leave it?'

'No! I can't relax in front of the telly with him there, watching us. I'm not asking you to do anything. Just keep an ear out, that's all. Please.'

'She's a nutcase, Grace. Let's finish the film,' Mandy hollered from within.

'No,' Grace said. 'I'll wait here in case Tuli calls.' She took a large gulp of wine and added, 'Ebele, if you're not back in a few minutes, I'll come and get you.'

'I can handle myself,' Ebele replied, quietly grateful for the back-up.

She walked into the night shivering. She'd left home without a coat and to compensate she wrapped her arms tight around her body. Across Black Horse Lane, Hazelwood undulated with elongated silhouettes; inky figures dancing beneath a sepia sky. A wave of drizzle blustered towards her; she wiped her face with the damp sleeve of her hoodie and pushed the note into her back pocket. In the alleyway, the smell of rotten foliage was overbearing, festering on the air. The only sound was the thump of her feet on wet ground. It was difficult to see. She fumbled for her phone and switched on the torch, but the beam created a shower of blurred light which ricocheted off raindrops, making visibility more difficult. Bramble brushed against her cheek, making her jump. She walked tentatively towards the car and when she was close enough, she shone the torch through the back windscreen. There was no sign of the man but his belongings were there: sleeping bag rolled up on the front passenger seat and clothes laid out across the back seat and parcel shelf above it. The cardboard box which blocked the broken window was soggy. She pushed it through and poked her head into the empty gap, shining light around the interior to make sure the man wasn't concealed in the shadows. There was an overpowering odour of dank cloth so she pulled her hoodie up over her mouth and nose and sucked in the scent of her own body. She took the note out of her pocket and flattened it across the driver's seat but before walking away she hesitated for a moment, opened the back door, covered her hand with her sleeve and reached in, grabbing wet clothes from where they lay. She threw each item onto the muddy ground, pushing it further into the earth with a twist of her foot.

'I just left the note, He wasn't there,' she said to Grace when she returned to the house.

'He has probably left, like I said. You'd better get changed before you catch a cold.'

'Yep.'

'Hope you are happy now,' her neighbour added as she closed her door to her flat.

Ebele checked on Tuli then poured out the last measure of vodka and stared at her own glowering face in the mirror above the bathroom sink. She thought about the clothes in the mud and the man returning to find them and wondered when she'd become so hard; when the scowl across her face had become so rigid. Deep down she knew it was a build-up of layer upon layer of her life's hardships: disappointment lain across rejection lain across grief, stacked up, one on top of the other, stuck fast so even when she laughed the scowl was there. She opened her mouth wide and raised her eyebrows as far as she could, attempting to stretch away the lines which made her appear perpetually angry with life. When she relaxed her face, the lines were still there, deep-set between her eyebrows, across her forehead and around the edges of her mouth. Thoughts of her father began to collect as she looked into the mirror. She wondered if he too would have developed such a scowl after years of trying to exist in adversity? He had, from what she had gleaned, always been a genial man, even in the evenings when he drank rum and played dominoes with two or three compatriots he'd managed to seek out in the town. She wondered how much she actually looked like him; it was hard to tell from one photograph and a long-faded memory. Her skin was a shade or so lighter but her hair just as dark; her eyes the same deep mahogany – a stark contrast to the cornflower blue of her mother's. Thoughts of her father had drifted further and further away as she struggled through life but there were fragments of him embedded so inextricably within her they had actually become part of her fabric. Phrases he'd used and little snatches of songs he'd sung came unexpectedly in reveries and dreams. She couldn't picture him in her world but lost memory resurfaced frequently since her sessions with Tessa. She remembered times he'd sat her down and spoken to her in earnest, away from the earshot of her mother, like on the day she'd just started junior school and an older boy teased her about her freckled skin and coiled hair. It was the first time her father had taken her aside in this way, speaking to her as if she was much older: *You have to show them they can't beat you,* he said. *Even if you feel scared to death. We people have to learn to be extra strong. They mustn't see we are weak even if inside it feels like everything is crumbling. We are a long way from home, you and me, Bel-Bel, but we can never let them know we are frightened, okay?* Ebele asked him who 'they' were and he told her it didn't matter. Had he still been alive he would be firmly into middle age now and she wondered how her life would have turned out if he'd been there to steer her through it. Would he be proud of the way she'd turned out? She thought of the clothes she'd just trodden into the mud and she was glad she hadn't told Grace what she'd done; they already thought she was unstable, perhaps they were right. She continued to scrutinise herself in the mirror, pressing her fingers into her face as if the act might remould her features, reshape her existence. She applied more and more pressure until her cheeks became bloodless and sore. Slowly the thoughts of her father switched from grief to anger. She remembered the way her mother collapsed when the message came that he'd crashed his car into a tree, *just like Marc Bolan* she'd spluttered, explaining through her tears how Papa and Marc Bolan were the only men she'd ever loved. Ebele didn't know who Marc Bolan was at the time; she still hardly knew who her father was. She stepped away from the mirror and shook her face until colour came flooding back, then she climbed into the bath, ducked her head beneath the hot·soapy water and lay there submerged until she was forced up for air.

It was long past eleven when she phoned Daban. He answered straight away.

'I didn't expect to hear from you,' he said.

'I'm sorry it's so late.'

'What can I do for you, Ebele?'

'Nothing. I don't need you to do anything for me.' She tried to sound neutral.

'Okay then, to what do I owe the pleasure?' He sounded exasperated.

'As you say, we've got to work together so I wanted to let you know it won't be awkward or anything at work. I mean, you know, perhaps I overreacted the other night.'

'Sure. Okay. Thanks. But it would have been fine at work. It is fine. Couldn't this have waited until the morning?'

'Am I disturbing you? Do you have company or something?'

'No. Not exactly. Not really your business anyway. Bye Ebele.'

Before he had a chance to hang up, she said, 'Look, I'm sorry, okay? Let me say my piece; you're very honoured to get an apology from me so take it in the spirit it's meant.' Daban laughed and she relaxed a little. 'I've had a bad few days that's all. Actually, I've had a bad few years. I'm not really as tough as you seem to think and, well, I'm not usually such a bitch.' She tried to sound frivolous.

'Apology taken,' he said lightly.

In the background, a woman's voice called out his name and he shouted a response in a language Ebele didn't understand

'Oh! There is someone there. I'll leave you to it. Sorry.'

'It's my mum.' Daban said quickly. 'We're watching a film. We do it every Sunday, like a routine. We always have, since I was a boy.'

'You better get back to it then.' Ebele was unexpectedly relieved by the information.

'She likes Bollywood but, to be honest, I'm quite happy to escape all the crazy singing and dancing for a few minutes. It can get a bit much sometimes, plus having to read the subtitles.

Not that you need them; the plotlines are all pretty similar. Have you ever watched an Indian film, Ebele?'

'Not really. My father used to watch them when I was young. His family were partly Indian I think, but I never met my grandparents on that side. My mother hated them, the films I mean.'

'Does he still watch them? I could pass on which ones to avoid.'

'He's dead,' Ebele said abruptly.

'I'm sorry to hear that. When?'

'Years ago. I was a kid.'

'That must have been hard; he couldn't have been very old. Is your mother still around?'

'Probably. I don't see her anymore.'

'What do you mean?'

'I mean I left, we fell out. It was ages ago. I don't know where she is. It doesn't really matter. It's history.'

'Of course it matters; she's your mum. They don't become history – they are too much a part of us. Doesn't she live in the same house anymore?'

'I don't know. Maybe. We've lost touch.'

'How can you lose touch with your mum? Does she know she has a granddaughter?

'You're prying again,' Ebele said. 'Tuli doesn't need anyone else. She has me,' she added bluntly.

'My mother is always talking about grandchildren. I've told her it'll be a while yet.' He spoke light-heartedly now, ignoring her reprimand. 'You should reconnect with her. Before it's too late. It's easy to let shit fester and then suddenly years slip by and people disappear completely.'

'Why do you always jump into the deep end, Daban? I don't want to talk about my parents.'

'Look, I won't pry if that's what you think it is. But, just so you know, I decided long ago I would get to know people for who they really are and the only way to do so is to have proper conversations. I have no time for photoshopped lives.'

'There's nothing photoshopped about my life.'

'And, if we are going to be friends then that's the deal. And whatever you say, I know you need a friend. I can tell loneliness when I see it. It's nothing to be ashamed of.'

'See you around, Daban,' she said but she didn't hang up.

'As you want, Ebele. See you around, but you know what, you call me if you ever want to have a proper chat. or if you need help with anything. My phone is always on.'

That night, Ebele tossed and turned in her bed, thinking about the car just a few metres away from Tuli's bedroom window.

22. TULI

Nothing happened on Monday. Not enough was allowed to happen as far as Tuli was concerned. Partly it was because of the rain but really it was Mummy who made the rules about staying in and keeping dry even though she'd promised a day out with boats on the pond and doughnuts on the way home. Tuli didn't mind the rain, not usually. It made patterns on the window which sparkled magic light through the drops when she shone her torch on them. She didn't understand why her mother wouldn't find their kagoules so they could go out like other people. After all, if everyone stayed in when it rained, there'd be no milk to buy in shops, and probably no shops open in the first place to buy anything at all; and children wouldn't skip to school and teachers would have no one to teach (but actually even the teachers wouldn't be there so school would be locked, which wouldn't be such a bad thing). But school was always open if it rained; only snow closed school down, and holidays. It didn't make any sense not to go out in the rain. Sometimes grown-ups made stupid decisions. Mummy's decisions were often stupid, like when she argued with Jamal Daddy and it pushed him away. If everybody stayed in on a rainy day, hospitals would have to close too. And what would happen if she fell down and cut her knee so badly that blood flowed like a river down her leg? They'd be no smiling nurse to stick it back together with special tape. What would happen then if it was a rainy day and no-one was supposed to go out?

Pencil scribbles across a grey sky made it difficult to see but she could just about make out people in Hazelwood park, walking quickly with hands in pockets and collars turned up, sheltering under trees while their wet dogs ran about shaking, creating showers of smelly water. It seemed only the old people had remembered to bring out umbrellas but there were plenty of people around nevertheless. Tuli wanted to tell Mummy this. To say the world didn't need to stop because of the rain. When she was bored of looking at people, she shuffled up and down the landing with her head slung low.

'Give it a rest, can't you Tuli? Stomping about the flat isn't going to make the rain go away.'

'I can't be stomping, Mummy. I don't even know what stomping is. There's nothing to do inside. I'm bored.'

'Read one of your books or watch telly or something. Can't you just keep yourself busy? We can't help the weather but it does mean we'll have to stay in, for now at least. As soon as it stops, we'll go out. I promise.'

'But I like rain. Why can't I go outside now? I can just go to the garden and splash, and it's close enough to change my clothes if I get wet.'

'Don't be silly, Tuli. Go and play in your room?.

'I want to play outside. You don't have to come. Grandy can open the garden for me.'

'Mandy won't want you walking through her kitchen all wet and muddy. We'll go out when the rain stops.'

'Can I play on your phone?'

'No. You're too young for phones, we've been through this before. Anyway, I need to make some calls.'

'But it was a park day, together, before the rain kept coming. You're always busy; too busy for me.'

'Don't be cheeky, Tuli.'

Tuli skulked to her bedroom and closed the door. When she came out to go to the toilet, Mummy was putting school clothes over the radiator in the hallway. She ran back into her room with her hands over her eyes, shaking her head and trying hard to hold in the wee. She picked up a book from the floor but the words were too close together and the pictures were all the same so she threw it across the room. It landed beneath the bed. She could hear her mother's voice shouting into her phone at the man called Makrides, the boss of Mummy's work and the boss of their home too. He was ugly and bald and had yellow crooked teeth but Tuli felt a little sorry for him; he always looked sad, like he would cry as soon as no-one was looking. Mummy was always being mean about him, just like Finn was mean to her at school. It was no wonder Mr Makrides was sad. She picked up Froggy from the floor and looked out of the window to see if she could see Storyman through the rain yet.

The next morning, the reflection of raindrops on her carpet was replaced by an oblong of light in the middle of the bedroom floor. She wanted to sit in it and feel warm sunshine on her skin but her mother was calling so she pulled the covers over her head and pretended to be invisible.

'Tuli get up,'

The thought of going to school made her upset; she started crying.

'What's wrong, baby?' Her mother knelt at the side of her bed. Tuli found it hard to speak through her tears.

'I don't want to go. I want to stay here. The children at school are horrible. I have friends here, Froggy and you know, story friends.'

'Oh Tuli, we can't go through this every time, not again. Sometimes we need to learn to play with real friends, not imaginary ones. You have to go to school or I'll get letters telling me I'm not looking after you properly.'

'Nothing is worse than school.'

'Yes it is. School is the least worst thing in life. Come on sweetheart, get up or I'll be late for work. I'll take you all the way in if you want me to, I won't just leave you at the gates, I promise.'

Tuli wanted to say, you promised we could go out to the park yesterday but she held her tongue. She didn't want to be angry.

Her mother had enough anger for both of them. Instead, she popped her head over the covers and sat up, rubbing her sore eyes with her knuckles.

'Do I have to go to after school club? It's the worst bit, Mummy.'

Ebele paused. Tell you what,' she said after a moment. 'I'll see if Grace has any meetings after school today. Perhaps she'll bring you home with her. How about that? But, no messing with Mandy's things and you'll have to say sorry about taking her books the other day, okay?'

Tuli nodded as her mother handed over a pile of clothes, still warm from the radiator. She pulled them on under the covers while Mummy opened the curtains and looked around for what seemed to be a very long time. Tuli held her breath and prayed Storyman was well hidden.

'Right Tuli, two minutes to breakfast,' Mummy said as she left the room. Tuli jumped out of bed, filled her cheeks with air and peered through the window. When there was no sign of Storyman in the car, she exhaled with a loud sigh.

When her mother shouted again, Tuli twirled around but quickly returned to the window for another look.

'Tuli. Come on, we'll be late.'

Just as she was about to give up hope of seeing him, the car door swung open and Storyman appeared. She let out a small squeal and began to wave. *Storyman, Storyman, look this way.* She was careful to keep her words silent. She jumped up and down with her arms above her head but still he didn't look. When she heard her mother's footsteps coming towards her down the landing she jumped away from the window and onto her bed just in time.

'What's all the thumping about? You should be getting ready for school.'

'Nothing. Just playing. With Froggy.'

'Okay but this isn't the time for playing: you're going to be late for school. Please Tuli, get a move on.'

She was glad Mummy didn't look out of the window .

Tuli was made to sit next to a new boy at school. He smelled of fried onions. She hated onions and just wanted the day to end so she could go home with Grace and speak to Storyman. When the teacher said *Tuli, it's your job to show Victor around. You can be buddies,* she shook her head but nobody took any notice. She didn't want to be anyone's buddy but everywhere she went that morning the boy was right behind her. When playtime came and the teacher said *show Victor where to put his coat; show Victor our work drawers; show Victor the way to the school hall,* Tuli hid in the toilets instead. At lunchtime, she stood behind the bushes near the school gates and watched as he sat on the 'Friendly' bench with his chin in his hands, swinging his skinny legs.

The school day went slowly, even slower than the long rainy day before it but, other than the new boy, no one bothered her too much and she was grateful. When Grace came to meet her soon after the school bell rang she flung her arms around her legs before she realised what she was doing.

'Hey, Tuli Wuli, everything alright?'

She nodded and squeezed Grace tighter. 'Can I play in the garden when we get back?'

'Sure you can. Tell you what, maybe we can go to the playground instead of going straight home. I'm sure your mum won't mind if we do. I'll text her.'

'Oh no. Not the park. Just the garden. Just Grandy's garden please. I promise I won't stand on the books.'

Grace laughed and ruffled her hair. 'You're a sweet little thing for sure. But all the other kids are going to the park by the looks of it. Wouldn't you rather be with your friends? You haven't seen them all half-term.'

'Just the garden please.' Tuli said.

'Okay Tuli-Wuli.'

Back at the house, Tuli used the metal chair to scramble up on the small apple tree which stretched from next door into Grandy's garden. She sat in the lower branches looking over the wall towards the abandoned car. She'd always wanted to climb the tree but was never brave enough. Now, she reckoned, if Storyman was brave enough to stay outside all night, she was brave enough to climb the tree. She wanted Storyman to see what a big girl she was. Perhaps then he might be her friend.

She couldn't tell if Storyman was in his car-house or not from the tree. She called over but there was no response. She pulled a handful of crispy leaves from above her head and threw them over the wall. The leaves drifted down, some blew onto the windscreen, others landed on top of a pile of rags near to the car but still Storyman didn't appear. She grabbed another handful from branches above her head, holding onto the knobbly bark to steady herself as the tree shook. She called out again but nothing happened. She didn't want to shout too loud, aware that Grace might hear and tell on her and she'd no longer be allowed in the garden. Mummy didn't like men, not since Jamal Daddy went away. She might think Storyman was real and dangerous like the men she'd once warned Tuli about.

'But what about all the daddies? Daddies bring children to school on their own sometimes without mummies there to stop them being dangerous,' Tuli had said.

'Sometimes even daddies hurt children.'

'But Mummy,' she said, 'your daddy didn't hurt you. You said he loved you. Loving isn't hurting.'

'No, he was a good daddy but not all daddies are kind all the time. Papa died when I was around your age, Tuli, and then my stepfather wasn't so good.'

'But children love their daddies, Mummy. In books, I mean. Daddies are always nice in stories. '

'I'm talking about real life, Tuli. Don't ever go too close to a strange man, or a big boy on your own. Okay? They can hurt you.'

'In fighting?'

'In lots of ways, You're too young for this conversation. We'll talk about it when you're older.'

Tuli was confused. Lots of things grown-ups said didn't make sense, like the time Jamal Daddy was tickling her and her mother told him he shouldn't play in that way, it wasn't right for a grown man to do those things. After that, every time he read her a bedtime story, Mummy would stand in the doorway and watch and when Tuli was pretending to be asleep, she heard them shouting at each other outside her bedroom.

'What the fuck?' Jamal Daddy said. 'What the hell is going through your head?'

'Nothing,' Ebele said, but even Tuli knew she was lying.

'Why are you monitoring every minute I spend with Tuli all of a sudden?'

'I'm not!'

'Yes you are. You hover around us every time I read her a story or play with her. What's going on?'

'Nothing. I just think it's not appropriate. You're not really her dad.'

'I love Tuli. I'm not pretending to be her dad but I have the right to have a fatherly relationship with her. I've been around since she was tiny, remember? What's not appropriate about that?'

'She's getting older. She's growing up. Kids grow up fast and I just think you can't keep playing with her like that. People will say things.'

'For fuck's sake. She's five years old! I'm playing with her as if she's a five year old I've known since she was less than two. You're out of order, Ebele.'

'She's almost six. She'll be six in just a few weeks.'

'Fucking hell, Ebele. What are you saying? What the hell is going through your head?' Whatever it is, it isn't right.'

'I'm just saying you're not her dad. People will think it's weird if someone who isn't a kid's dad is all, you know, physical with them.'

'For fuck's sake, Ebele. You're sick.'

The fight was a few days before Jamal Daddy disappeared forever. Tuli knew it was because of the things Mummy said, and also the things she didn't say.

There was no-way she could tell her mother about Storyman! She kicked her legs and waited for him to appear. Time went even slower than it did at school. When she got fed up with waiting she jumped from the tree and landed on the small patch of lawn. She dragged her feet across the soft grass making tracks in the damp ground.

Grace sat at the kitchen table with a pile of exercise books spread out around her.

'You okay, Tuli?' she said when Tuli tramped back into the house. 'You want a snack? Get too cold in the garden, did it? I knew it would.' She spoke without looking up. 'There's chocolate in the drawer. Don't take too much though, your mother will be annoyed with me if you don't eat your dinner later.'

'Chocolate, yes please,' Tuli said gleefully. She'd had an idea! She opened the sweet drawer and quickly stuffed three Penguin bars into her fleece pocket before grabbing one more bar which she held in her hand as she ran from the room, shouting 'I'm going to watch telly.'

'Hey, slow down. Don't run in the house,' Grace said, glancing up for just a second. 'And take your shoes off, Tuli. And just CBeebies, okay? And close this door. I'm working.'

Tuli switched on the TV and flicked through the channels before settling on a programme about farmyard animals but it wasn't very interesting. She climbed down from the sofa, checked the chocolate bars were still in her pocket then quietly slipped out of the room. She stood still for a moment, listening to the blare of the TV and the sound of the kettle boiling in the kitchen. She edged open the door of the flat, stood in the small shared entrance and stared at the front door. The latch was high up and she stretched her hand above her head to see if she might be able to reach it. All she wanted to do was let Storyman know she was going to be in the garden again, that he could talk to her and tell her things about his world like he did last time. She could give him the chocolate biscuits so he wouldn't be so hungry-looking. She'd run back quickly and Grace wouldn't know anything about it. She walked her fingertips up the door towards the lock. It was slightly out of reach so she jumped up to try and nudge it. Eventually, the front door swung open and a blast of air pushed her backwards into the narrow hallway. She managed to grab the door before it slammed against the wall and pulled it quietly behind her until it was slightly ajar. She teetered on the doorstep looking out over Black Horse Lane.

23. RAYYA

On days when the carers arrived early, Rayya slipped into the living room downstairs and sat with the curtains drawn. The rows of DVDs and old video cassettes were gathering dust on shelves built many years earlier by Kostas. In the dark, she imagined Satish reclining on the settee beside her: his body curled around hers, a bowl of *farsan* between them, watching Rajasthani deserts flicker across the screen in Technicolor. The squeak of a door or footsteps above always dragged her back to reality, empty and overwhelmed with yearning for the minutiae of her everyday life with her healthy husband: shopping for groceries together, cups of tea in bed, disagreements over which film to watch. Neither she nor Satish ever cared much for British television, with its chintzy game shows and stream of cookery programmes, but now, when the presence of the carers disturbed her in the darkness, she switched between channels searching for distraction. Occasionally, the banality of travel programmes transported her but never for long enough, and in those tiny moments of respite questions surfaced to nag at her: *how has my life become so disrupted? Why should my Satish be this way? Hasn't there already been enough cruelty?* The ask varied but the sentiment was clear: *Why us? Why me?* Once, in the presence of Daban, the pleasant young man who helped her with computer things, a 'Why Me?' almost slipped out and she was horrified. She held her tongue just in time. What would this hard-working young man think of her, surrounded by holiday photographs, a comfortable house, things many people his age no longer had a chance of acquiring in their lifetimes?

Shame inched through her body until Daban threw a curve ball, announcing he would no longer be caring for Satish, and the shame was rapidly replaced by profound sadness. Later, she lay in bed berating herself for not making more of the opportunities to converse with Daban. She tried to summon up a more transcendental connection in a bid to feel less alone but, as hard as she tried, mantras were inconsequential and prayers would not come.

Years ago, soon after they made the long journey to England, Rayya and Satish agreed together they could no longer justify a belief in the gods they'd grown up with. This eventually extended to religion as a whole. It wasn't the book learning which convinced them, rather the journey itself and the reasons they'd wanted to escape their impoverished lives in the first place. Satish was bright and managed to win a scholarship to attend school past the age of puberty, unlike many of his peers, but this also meant travelling on foot across the dusty Delhi streets for over an hour twice a day. His mother insisted he took up the school place; it offered a chance of earning more money in the future.

'It's the only way to stop this cycle. Labouring in the heat will continue to be the cause of death for all men in my family for decades to come if we don't put a stop to it now,' she said, and eventually Satish's father gave permission.

For Rayya, as a young woman from a lower caste there was no such opportunity. Her destiny was set out before her. At best she would be a maid like her mother, washing grubby underwear and sweeping the dirty floors of a Brahmin family in a nicer part of the city. And, if she rallied against a life in servitude, her only other option would be scavenging like countless hordes of other children her age, rifling through rubbish tips for glints of metal and old rags which could be transformed into utensil holders or dishcloths. There was no chance of a better life for a young woman of Rayya's standing: like the Victorian governesses and scullery maids she read about as an adult, her trajectory was still very much dependent on the men in her world. Satish couldn't bear the idea of his beautiful Rayya being looked down upon by some rat who in actuality only had a surname to flaunt as a sign of superiority. At nineteen, he secured a job as an assistant to a travel agent and he and Rayya began to carve out a different destiny, transforming their dreams into reality with the help of Satish's *Employee Discount Benefit* and his discipline in putting aside one or two rupees from his scant wage packet each week. It took three years to save the money, by which time they were married and England beckoned. God did not fit in with the political and intellectual bent they aligned themselves with, at least this is how Satish once presented it.

'There is no God, Rayya, my darling. If there was, I would thank him for you and you alone. As far as I can tell, this is the only tangible evidence of his holiness. The rest we have done for ourselves, fighting all the way. He has not helped us one bit; if anything, he has held us back.'

'Oh Satish, you shouldn't put me on such a pedestal,' she said at the time. But beneath the flattery she knew he was convinced in his rejection of God, and she more or less agreed. She never told him she still avoided washing her hair on a Thursday and rarely, if ever, could bring herself to cook meat on a Tuesday; those rituals were harder to dismiss. Sometimes, she still tried to summon up a distant god so she could ask the questions which tormented her, and if some such deity were to manifest itself, to reprimand it for the unfair hand she'd been dealt.

These days, Rayya had different rituals on weekdays. After the carers left in the morning, she stood by the window in the room where Satish lay and watched little children snake down the road towards the primary school on the corner. In particular, she waited for the beautiful girl from next door to emerge with her mother and watched as they strolled down the pavement, hand in hand, describing each scene to Satish.

'Today she is wearing those stripy dungarees. The blue and white ones which make her look so sweet, like a baby's toy. And her jumper is yellow like a lemon.'

She wanted Satish to picture the girl: her carefree skip, and the way she swung her arms like a pendulum when she walked, and her striking hair, long curls the colour of cloves and cinnamon. She wanted him to grasp the living, a world which would continue to flourish long after they had departed it. She acquired some comfort in the idea that whilst a harsh winter was crushing down on the two of them, for others spring blossomed, bringing with it lighter air and a fresh scent of renewal; she longed for Satish to gain such comfort too.

Afternoons were less predictable, as far as the next door child was concerned, and Rayya always felt her own heart soar a little if she unexpectedly caught a glimpse of her running ahead of her mother on the way home from school. Sometimes the child came home with her downstairs neighbour and occasionally she played out in the garden, in school holidays and weekend mornings.

On this afternoon, Rayya read from *Mr Biswas* until she was tired, then she took off her glasses and laid them on top of the book, apologising.

'My eyes hurt, darling. I don't know why, perhaps because the light is changing so rapidly these days. You don't mind, do you? I will read again later, after a little rest. Perhaps after feeding the boy in the car. He wasn't there yesterday, Satish. Did I tell you this? I only went once because the weather was so terrible but I think he will be back. His sleeping bag and other items are still there. Some of his clothes had fallen out of the car. I thought about picking them out of the mud and washing them but I didn't want him to think they'd been stolen. Anyway, I think it will be better to give him more of your old things instead. Is this okay, Satish?'

She looked for signs of accord in his eyes. There were none.

'If he still isn't there later,' she continued, 'perhaps it's because he's found his friend, this girl he seems to have fallen in love with. I think she is *apna*; certainly from the way he described her she seems like one of our own, and her name is of our magnificent Betwa. Or maybe it is just modern parents; so many English take on our pretty names these days. I wonder if he dreams about this Betwa. Sometimes when we lose someone, the only place for them is in dreams. Poor boy.'

She stopped speaking when she heard an unusual noise in the street; a person yelling in a way which set it apart from the usual hollers and shouts in the park. This sound was urgent; more a scream than a call. There was a desperation to it.

'Someone is upset,' she said to Satish and she rose to see what was happening.

Across the road, children ran around swings and balls. The park was busy but all appeared normal for the time of day. The noise was close by but she still couldn't see the cause of it. She pushed open the window and stuck her head out. Almost immediately below, the small dark woman from next door was clearly distraught but her piercing voice was muffled by the roar of traffic making it hard to work out exactly what she was shouting.

'TULI! Tuuuliii! Where the heck are you?'

It took a moment for Rayya to realise the cry was the unusual name of the little girl next door, the name she sometimes heard being called out in quiet moments through her upstairs walls. She quickly closed the window and ran down the stairs, grabbed her front door key, flung open the door, hitched up her long skirts and ran to her neighbour. The woman was shaking, tears streamed from swollen eyes as she spoke words which made no sense. Rayya placed both her hands on her shoulders and tried to steady her.

'Where is the little girl?' she asked.

The woman's answer was carried on breathless sobs. 'She was inside. Watching TV. I went to see if she was okay but she's gone. She's disappeared. I can't find her. She's disappeared.'

'How is she disappeared?' Rayya asked as calmly as she was able.

'The front door was open. I heard it bang and went to look. She's a tiny thing, just an ankle biter really. But the door was open.' Distress shrouded the woman's face. 'Tuli. Tuli. Where the heck are you?' she shouted again.

'Perhaps she is with her mother?' Rayya offered. 'Maybe you can telephone the mother?'

'No. Her mum's at work. She'll kill me. Ebele will kill me. I was only supposed to have her for an hour or so. Oh shit, where the fuck is she? What if she's lost? What if someone's got her?'

Rayya looked across to the park. It was teeming with football games and small children running rings around their adults. She looked for a gap in the traffic. When one appeared, she ran across the road, lifting up her sari as the screaming of the neighbour was drowned by the screech of a lorry. On the other side of the road, she tucked her sari hems into her petticoat so it was knee length then began to pick up speed. People along the pathways of the park stared at her, watching as she darted past, but she was oblivious to the onlookers. She scanned clusters of children for Tuli but there was no sign of her. On her second lap, sweat dripped from her forehead blurring her vision. Her feet hurt and she realised she was still wearing her house slippers, now damp and covered in filth. She looked towards where she'd left her neighbour crying out, but her view was obscured by whizzing traffic. The sound of her own thumping heartbeat cancelled out all other noise. She headed across the grass, slowing her sprint to a jog, attempting to steady her breathing. A line of six, possibly seven people stood outside the cafe and clapped as she ran past.

'Way to go, grandma,' someone shouted, but Rayya didn't care for their comments. She stumbled over a stray football and kicked it back towards a teenager a few feet away. As she composed herself she heard a familiar voice.

'Wow, Mrs B. I had to rub my eyes. I thought it was Mo Farah running past me.'

'Daban, hello. I cannot stop to talk to you. Someone is missing. A baby. A child.' The words came out in short bursts.

'What? Hey, slow down Mrs B. Let me help.'

'I can't see her, Daban. She might be in danger. She is so small and there is so much traffic.'

'Who are you talking about?'

'A child.'

'What child? What do you mean missing? Have you called the police? Ease up Mrs B. Tell me what's going on. Maybe I can help.'

'The small child of my neighbour. The sweet girl who sings to her toys. She is missing. Lost by the babysitter.'

'Ebele's girl?'

Rayya took in a deep breath.

'I don't know the mother's name. I see her sometimes but I don't think she sees me. The girl is lost. We have to find her before she gets hurt.'

'Okay. Calm down Mrs B. Let's slow down. All this running isn't going to help.'

Daban took her elbow and guided her slowly across the park. He carried on speaking as they walked. The familiarity of his voice helped her to settle.

'You're okay now. We'll find her. Don't worry. Kids find all sorts of hiding places. She's probably in the house.'

'I hope so,' Rayya said. 'You know her? The mother I mean.'

'Yep. I know Ebele. We work together.' He paused, then added, 'We're friends, sort of. Look, I should phone her. She needs to know her child is missing. Perhaps there's a place they go to. You know what kids are like. I'll phone her.'

Rayya nodded. 'It will be dark soon,' she said to herself as much as to him.

They stopped by a bench while he made the phone call. As soon as it connected, his tone switched from alarm to mollification; he spoke soothingly down the receiver. He rushed away, his voice trailing off, still speaking to the mother, seeming to forget Rayya was left behind until he shouted over an apology. His walk became a run and he became a blur in the distance. Rayya stood fixed by the bench. Games and laughter continued around her. She willed the little girl to suddenly appear through the clump of trees nearby. She did not.

24. JIMMY

An old fella who'd been sleeping under the wide awning of a butcher's shop at the top end of the high street told Jimmy he'd heard mention of a girl like Betwa; *injun,* he said, like a cowboy. The talk of the girl was from a group of men camped out in a graveyard; it was unusual to see someone like her near their hangouts. Jimmy followed the old fella's directions and found the raggle-taggle gang huddled around a bin-fire next to the Greek Othodox church. When he spoke of Betwa, they stared, eyes blank, bloodshot, shaking their heads, poking at flames with sticks. One held out a pill in the palm of his hand. Jimmy pulled himself away. She would be looking for him too, he was sure of that. He had her jacket tucked away at the bottom of his rucksack, safe from rain and dirt. She'd need it now winter was properly settling in.

When he got bored of walking past the same shop fronts and street signs, he sat dozing on a bench in the park, watching as people passed him by. He looked out for faces which bore resemblance to Betwa: the same skin tone and hair colour; a cousin or an aunt perhaps. He could ask them if they knew her, and they'd be able to say, *oh yes, I know the girl you mean.* But the people of the area were as diverse as his town was bland. All of them and none of them could know Betwa. Everyone looked as if they might be from somewhere else but it was he who was the real stranger here. Each one of them was connected to some bigger world, some community he had no idea about, and it seemed there were as many accents around him in the local streets as there were shades of orange on the autumn trees. His only community was in dream states, and in memory which ebbed and flowed like the sea at Crosby Beach.

Jimmy didn't see his clothes in the mud when he returned to the car; it was too dark. He knew they were missing as soon as he'd opened the door but his sleeping bag and his rucksack were still there. He rifled through to check if anything of any worth was gone. Betwa's jacket and his two books were safe so he tore up the handwritten note left by the vandals and slept until well past dawn.

The new day started quietly and Jimmy resigned himself to it by listening to short bursts of music on the radio until drizzle dissipated and a watery sun emerged through a break in the cloud. It was then he saw his clothes strewn about outside the car. Part of him wanted to leave them there, to fester into sodden earth but once he mustered up some energy, he lifted each item off the ground and flattened it against the body of the car. He tried to sleep again, wishing the day away but the old woman arrived with a sandwich, closely followed by the man from the furniture store warning him away.

Later, Jimmy headed to the local library on the other side of the park for some peace and quiet, and to Google Betwa's name and check directories and local registers. As he arrived, a group of school children were just leaving. Their high-pitched chatter danced on the air like birdsong and he guessed they must have been on a trip, and now liberated from the shushes and whispers of the library they were letting their little voices fly. He moved to a nearby tree and stood behind it, out of sight so as not to alarm them and watched as they jiggled about, waiting for the teachers to lead the way. The less animated children loitered at the edges, standing apart from the others with lowered heads. When the teacher shouted instructions and the children started to move away, he went into the library. The heat inside was even more overpowering than the heavy silence and he soaked up the familiar strangeness of a hushed room in the middle of a noisy city. He slumped into a cushioned chair, straining to hang on to the echo of children's voices as it faded into the distance. He closed his eyes, planning to rest for a moment but when he opened them hours had somehow slipped by and the library was preparing to close. He stepped outside to a low-slung sun and a fresh chill in the air.

Ahead of him across the park, he saw the man called Daban with the old woman who bought him food. He stopped still, watching them for a moment, wondering how they knew each other, whether the woman told of how she fed him. He rubbed his eyes. They were locked in conversation. It was obvious they weren't just randomly standing together as he first thought. Even from a distance he could see the woman's face was puffy and red. She wiped sweat from her forehead with the back of her hand in the same way he'd seen her do before. Neither of them noticed him. Daban walked with his hand on the woman's elbow, as if he were helping an older relative across a busy street. Jimmy thought of Nan, and Jen, and for a brief second he longed to be in the front room at home, lying across the stained carpet reading his magazine, his sister pleading with him to play games with her while Nan clanked about the kitchen. He moved through the park quickly, hoping to thwart the chasm deepening within him. Across the road on the pavement near the corner of Shifnal Road, a woman was hysterical; her wailing added to the clamour. Strangers walked by, some in headphones, all seemingly unperturbed. Jimmy shuffled past, towards the abandoned car, away from the melee of the day.

25. NIKOS

'The council won't take the car away,' Nikos told Ebele. 'Not yet anyway, these things take time. Don't you think I have the sense to find this out already?'

The shop-girl ruined his weekend and he had no time for her nonsense now. He closed his eyes and tried to imagine a different sound, the gentle lapping of the Mediterranean Sea or the loud chirping of cicadas at siesta time.

'It's your responsibility.' The shop-girl droned on. She was more belligerent than usual.

'I have no responsibility except to myself,' he told her. 'Anyway, your neighbour said the boy is gone. You scared him away all by yourself, Mangaroo, so you are doing a fine job already.'

'I'm not talking about him, I'm talking about the car.'

'Why are you worrying about a broken up car?'

'If you don't get rid of it, he'll come back, or someone like him. These people are everywhere these days.'

'Just ignore this man if he comes back. He is nobody. And nobody can live in an old car forever. You women worry too much. Always worrying about unnecessary things.'

'If you had a young child, you'd be worried too. Don't you read the news? Don't you know what goes on in the world? Most of these people are completely crazy. Some of them could be even worse: criminals, drug addicts, paedophiles. It's not safe to have them near where we live, near our children. They're outcasts for a reason. They're not lost, they're in hiding, from the lives they've left behind. They don't belong here and the longer the car's there, the more likely it is the bloke will come back. It's your responsibility to move it.'

'Yes, yes, you keep saying the same things. I know what my responsibility is in this life. Stop telling me, Mangaroo. I'm losing my patience with you. I can't physically remove this car. There is a process.'

'If it was your grandchild living nearby you'd think differently. It's always the way with you rich folk, you don't care how the rest of us live, what we have to put up with. Your money makes you blind.'

Nikos walked away. She knew nothing about him; she had no respect and seemed to be holding her tongue less and less as time went on. She was very close to crossing the line. He flung open the shop doors wide, hoping for fresh air to dispel Ebele's bluster but stuck traffic coughed at him and fumes itched his nostrils. He sneezed and the girl tutted in disgust. She hadn't stopped talking the whole time.

'Surely you can just pay someone to take it away? It's not too much to ask is it?'

'For goodness sake, Mangaroo, shut up and get on with the paperwork. You drive me crazy with your noise all the time. I can get quieter staff than you, you know?'.

He couldn't bear the way she sneered at him, as if he were shit on her shoe. Only out of loyalty to Ourania did he keep her on. He remained in the doorway, facing the street, watching stationary drivers glare irritatedly at the pedestrians and cyclists weaving their way through the din and stink of Grand Parade.

'I'll be quiet when the car is removed,' Ebele said behind him

'Please shut up, Mangaroo. You are causing me to have a headache, I will sort out this piece of junk in my own time. Right now I am going for a walk and a cigarette, away from you and your nonsense. Concentrate on your work, not on imaginings of things which are not real. There is more peace and quiet out there than here with you, talking, talking all the time.'

Nikos rarely left the shop during opening hours. He rarely walked further than the few feet to and from his car outside his house or in his designated parking space behind the shop. This day he walked without purpose, aware only of a slight ache in his right leg: a nagging pain behind the knee where it twisted when he fell in the mud in the alleyway. He lit his cigarette and thought about what Mangaroo had said, about people hiding from reality. Kostas had said something similar once, just days before he faded away into a final sleep.

'We are lost, you and I, Nikos. We're away from our true homes but we haven't yet found a place to be ourselves, to belong. Just like our beautiful neighbours, we're lost and we are hiding from this truth. Some of us will be hiding for as long as we live.'

At the time, Nikos didn't know what all this meant. He was too busy waiting for Ourania to arrive, to be by his side, this would be his belonging. Cyprus was slowly ebbing away, and his profound yearning for it was transitioning into a gentle nostalgia, less burdensome, except in the depths of night when it appeared as a siren in the waves, beckoning him home. He shrugged off his uncle's words as he often did; after all, Kostas wrote poetry, he sang songs about birds and freedom, he was a dreamer, a different kind of man to Nikos. But now, with Mangaroo's words clanging about his head, he felt a small pang of regret for the way he'd kicked the tramp who slept in his doorway and now squatted on his land.

Nikos only realised he'd walked in the direction of Shifnal Road when he stopped to light a second cigarette. He stood at the top end of the road looking down towards the small park on the far side, shaken up by unexpected memory which flooded his mind: the shock of the drab city, his first few years, filled with homesickness and longing for Ourania; and his years with Kostas, whose free yet troubled spirit existed in the fabric of the house on the corner like layers of wallpaper and paint. He thought about the euphoria of marriage, with his *zoe mou*, his life, and the sons she gave him whom he loved so intensely it was hard to imagine a greater sensation, yet somehow that love managed to swell with each passing day. He recalled journeys along those pavements, to the furniture store, the music bars, supermarkets, pharmacies, schools, parks, until his bank balance became big enough for their home to become too small and he moved his family to a detached property just over a mile away, with a driveway and a paved front garden but without the history or the soul of the cluttered little house on Shifnal Road. He glanced over his shoulder in the direction of the furniture shop, aware he ought to be going back, but somehow his feet kept moving forwards, towards the space where Ourania's pottery shed should have been.

A fug of stale air confronted Nikos as he reached the car. Clothes caked in dirt lay across the body of it, giving the impression of a mud hut. He peered inside; the tramp was slumped over the steering wheel, appearing dead. He sucked in a huge breath and held it, wondering what to do. But suddenly there was a movement and the tramp sat up and stretched. Nikos exhaled sharply. He broadened his shoulders and rapped on the window.

'Oi aliti,' he shouted into the front window.

The car door swung open, bashing his bad knee. He stumbled but steadied himself by the wall, determined to be in control of the situation this time.

'It's Jimmy!' the tramp said. 'How many times do I have to say it? My name is Jimmy – not that word you keep calling me.'

'What is all this filth on the car?' Nikos said.

'My things. Someone trod them into the mud. Was it you?'

Nikos disregarded the question. He tried to say Jimmy but the word stuck in the back of his throat. Instead, he pointed at the house where he once lived.

'The people who live there, you are disturbing them. You need to leave this place before I call the police.'

'The police won't do anything, grandad. I told you already. I'm not hurting anyone.' He fiddled with the knob of the car stereo as he spoke. Music came seeping out.

'The radio? It works without the engine?' Nikos said, unable to hide his surprise.

'Yeah, good isn't it?'

'The battery is not dead?'

'Nah. It's beginning to fade away but I just listen for a few minutes each day. A song or two, that's all. It makes everything different for a while. You know what I mean? We all need to be somewhere different sometimes, eh, grandad?'

Nikos nodded along to the beat without thinking. He thought of the small red record player from his youth, of himself and Georgios swaying in time to some rhythm, turning up the volume to drown out the clucking of chickens in the backyard.

'You like music, grandad? What's it like where you come from? Zorba, smashing plates? The fat guy in the dress, Demis whatshisname? I've seen him on the old music shows on the telly. Not quite rock n roll though is it?'

Nikos sniggered. This was all anybody seemed to know about his culture. And the food of course.

'Why are you such a stubborn boy? Why don't you go back to your home?'

'Listen, old man, I don't have a home to go to. Do you think I'd be here if I did? We're not all as crazy as you.'

'I'm not crazy, and I'm not so old as you think, Mr Jimmy. I am sixty-three, probably younger than your father. I too have a name. Nikos. Nikos Makrides.'

'Oh yes, a fancy name like your fancy furniture shop. And your fancy house, no doubt, with your fancy children and your fancy wife.'

'Don't you dare speak of my wife. You have no right to. You are already trespassing on her space.'

'Her space?'

Nikos stared at Jimmy's hair. It looked like the old rags on the end of the mop Ourania used to swish across the kitchen floor. He softened his voice.

'Why do you sleep in this old car? What kind of life is this? Why don't you go to your family? They will be worrying about you.'

'I can't!'

'Why not? Everyone wants to go home.'

'Not me, grandad.'

Beneath the long beard and the filth, Jimmy was younger than he looked; much younger than either of Nikos' own boys.

'Anyway, I'm looking for my friend. She's from around here,' Jimmy said.

'Ah, always a woman is mixed up in these things. So aliti, you think your girlfriend will be happy with you sleeping like a dog in a dirty car?

'Stop calling me that bloody name. What the hell is it anyway?' Jimmy said.

'Vagabond, you say here. Tramp perhaps. Alitis is the word we use in my country.'

'Cyprus?'

'How do you know this about me?'

'Everything about you says where you're from,' Jimmy said.

'You know my country?' Nikos moved closer to the car and pulled out his cigarettes, offering the packet to Jimmy. The boy came and stood beside him and took two, placing one between his lips and the other behind his ear. 'How do you know?' Nikos repeated.

'Holiday. Only time I've been abroad.'

'Where did you go?

The boy couldn't recall the name of the place.

'Paphos? Limassol?' Nikos offered helpfully.

'Nah, said the boy. 'Don't really remember. We flew to a place called Larnaca. Stayed in a little town near there.'

'Larnaca? Larnaca,' Nikos repeated the word over and over before saying, excitedly, 'Larnaca is my home. I am from very close to this place. You have visited my home.'

'Maybe,' Jimmy said, clearly bemused. 'It's nice,' he added.

'Yes it is!'

'Why are you in this shithole and not there?' Jimmy said.

Nikos repeated the boy's words back at him. 'Why are you in this shithole?'

The boy laughed. 'I am the shithole,' he said.

Nikos could see the young man might be handsome if he were clean shaven and perhaps a little better fed. What kind of father would allow his child to descend to such depths? He'd hardly spoken to Dimitri or George since their mother was buried all those months ago but he would never allow such a fate to befall them. Before he left the alleyway, he said,

'You should find a way to go back to wherever it is you are from. People everywhere are scared of strangers, anyone who isn't like them. We need to be around those who know us. Even other strangers are wary of strangers. Soon the car will be dragged away. I have to make this happen. This is my land and people complain.'

The young man shrugged his shoulders and Nikos felt an impulse to touch him, to place a fatherly hand on his arm or shoulder. He stepped away.

'I've already called the necessary people to remove this car. I'm on a list. They'll email me when my turn is near.'

Jimmy stared into space. 'How long?' he asked.

'I am already waiting some time for this information. I'll come and warn you of the day it will happen but please make your plans soon. It could be tomorrow, it could be in one week.'

The boy was back in the car and had switched the radio on again and by the time Nikos started to walk away, it was to the melancholy lament of Otis Redding, a song Kostas used to play often. It lingered in Nikos' head all the way up the Grand Parade. When he reached his shop he just continued walking, around the corner to his car where he sat for ten minutes in the driver's seat before calling the shop-girl and telling her he had to be elsewhere. He spent the rest of the day sitting amongst Ourania's things, watching the remaining leaves on the branches of the fig tree fluttering in the afternoon breeze.

26. TULI

Outside Grandy's flat it was really noisy. Dogs barked in the park and roaring cars made it difficult for Tuli to hear her own thoughts. She put her hands over her ears; everything became muffled in the way it did when she talked to Froggy under the pillow so no-one could hear their secrets. When she lowered her hands, everything seemed even louder. She stood behind the wooden gate at the end of the front garden, not sure whether to open it or not. Sometimes, on a nice day, if Grandy weren't at home, her mother kept the front door wide open with a brick while she sat on the stairs playing with her phone, allowing Tuli to chalk on the paving stones or play with her skipping rope. This was the first time she was outside all by herself. It was cold but she was burning hot like the time she had to stay in bed all weekend while Mummy put wet flannels on her head and fed her pink medicine and brown soup. She edged open the gate, looking back at the house. She opened it a bit wider, stepped onto the pavement and tried to stop her legs from shaking.

Two big boys on skateboards slid by, almost crashing into her.

'Out the fucking way,' one of them shouted and she pushed up against a wall and hid behind her hands. When she looked through a gap in her fingers, the boys had disappeared so she ran and didn't stop until she reached the alleyway.

A ginger cat crawled across the tops of walls, checking her out in the same way children in the playground did, rolling eyes up and down her faded purple hoodie, pausing at the frayed pull cord, the overly long sleeves and the paint stain on the pocket. The cat only jumped away when the wall became the zigzag of broken glass she could see from her bedroom window. When she realised she was not too far from home she felt less scared but she still couldn't stop her body from melting. She dug her hands into her pockets; the chocolate bars were still there. Storyman would definitely want to be her friend if she had chocolate. But her feet stuck like glue to the ground and the car was too far for him to know she was there. She'd never been this far from her grown-ups before; even in the park she could always see her mother or Grace in the distance and she knew they could always see her. Now, all she could see was the broken car. It was covered in bushes and weeds but mostly it was covered in raggy clothes which looked like her jeans after she'd jumped in a puddle and splashed muddy water all the way up her legs. She held her breath and crept towards the car until she was close enough to touch it. She remembered the time Jamal Daddy took her on a train for the first time, into town to the shop full of teddies. They'd waited at the station while trains shot past and she'd started crying because she didn't want to go on anything which moved so fast it became a blur. She didn't know how to stop crying but Jamal Daddy said she could sit on his lap for the whole journey and he held her tight so she didn't fall. She wished Jamal Daddy was with her now. She gripped a chocolate bar in her hand until it became soft.

The car smelled as bad as the bins in the school playground near the dinner hall but inside it looked the same as all the other cars on Shifnal Road: crisp wrappers and empty drink cans on the floor, dirt smeared across seats. She was disappointed. She'd expected a Storyman's home to have a different inside, maybe like Justin's House on CBeebies, bright colours and bold patterns. Storyman wasn't even there and she was sort of glad the car was empty but didn't know why because she really did want to be friends with him. She wondered where to leave the bars of chocolate for him to find easily. She opened the car door and tried to wave away smells which spilled out. Suddenly there was a voice behind her.

'Go away, kiddo.'

She jumped and a chocolate bar fell out of her hand into the dirt.

Storyman was taller than he seemed from the bedroom window. He looked like there was a bird's nest on his face and on his head.

'I bought you chocolate biscuits.' Her voice was smaller than she wanted it to be.

'That's very nice of you, Tulip, but I can't take them. People will say stuff.'

'What stuff?' Is it bad for storythings to eat chocolate, like dogs?' she said. 'My teacher said her dog ate Easter eggs once and was sick with vomiting all over her carpet so she was late for school because she had to clean it and it was really smelly, like the worst smelly thing ever, until your car-house.'

Storyman laughed. She kept on talking. She didn't know how to stop.

'I love chocolate. I'm glad I'm not a dog. Anyway, it's just Tuli not tulip. Not the flower. Everyone always thinks it's the flower.'

Storyman laughed again and her legs stopped shaking.

'Wow, you don't half talk for a tiny kid,' he said.

'I'm six. I'm in Yellow Class now, not reception.' He laughed again and the nest on his face wiggled. 'I thought we were going to be friends,' she said.

'Listen, kiddo, you can't be friends with me.'

'Why not?'

'It's not right for me to be friends with kids. I'll get into trouble.'

'Why? What's wrong with us? Weren't you a little kid once?' She rubbed her chin. 'Or maybe were you just always grown-up? That can happen in stories, can't it?'

'Look kiddo, thanks for the chocolate but I reckon you need to go. Get back to your books and stuff. There'll be people looking for you; your mam won't be best pleased if she doesn't know where you are.'

'Mummy's at work, in the shop selling beds and crappy tables.'

'Crappy tables?' Storyman laughed again and she was glad.

'It's what Mummy calls them.'

'Maybe that's what they are then.'

'How do you make dinner, Storyman? I looked but there isn't a cooker in your car house.'

Storyman was suddenly grumpy again.

'Listen Tuli,' he said. 'You're a nice kid but get lost now will you, before someone sees you here and I get accused of something or other. It's not right for blokes like me to be hanging around with kids. Your dad definitely won't be wanting you out here talking to a strange bloke. If I had a kid I would want them to be safe at home, not wandering about the streets on their own talking to strangers.'

Tuli swallowed the lump in her throat. She didn't want Storyman to see her crying like a baby.

'There aren't any daddies anymore; not Real Daddy or Jamal Daddy. They disappeared. I told you before, remember?' she said.

'Well that's a shame, kiddo but daddies aren't so important. Now scoot, people out will be getting worried about where you are.'

'Do you have a daddy, Storyman?'

'What is all this storyman rubbish? Why are people always calling me stupid names? This isn't any kind of story, kiddo. You don't get people like me in stories.'

She didn't believe him.

'Mr Stink is in a story. He's like you but a hundred years older.'

The man laughed with his eyes but not his mouth. She held out one of the other bars of chocolate on the flat of her hand.

'You have to have it because it's for you and Mummy says my teeth will be rotten if I eat any more.'

He reached over and took the chocolate. She wiped her empty hand on her trouser leg and watched as he tore off the wrapper and shoved the whole bar into his mouth. Chocolate leaked from the sides of his lips and into his beard. He wiped it with a dirty sleeve.

'Is your daddy dead?' Tuli asked. 'I think mine is but I don't really know. Children at school say he's dead but Mummy says he just disappeared into the trees.'

The storything man didn't answer. He'd climbed into the car, closed the door and fiddled with a knob next to the driving wheel. Suddenly there were singing voices all around him. He closed his eyes and leaned back in his seat

'I have to go now,' she said quietly. But the singing voices were louder than her voice and he didn't seem to hear.

She pushed both her hands into her pockets. There was another chocolate bar in one of them. She pulled it out and tapped on the car window. He didn't look up or open the door to take the chocolate so she pushed it back into her pocket and waved at the car.

'I'll be in the garden, just there,' she said pointing to the back of the wall.

When she reached the edge of the alleyway there was a screaming sound which was louder than all the other outside noises including the barking dogs and the singing. Sometimes she heard noises like this at night and her mother told her it was foxes in the park. The noise was horrible and she wanted it to stop. It took her a few moments to realise what she was actually hearing wasn't foxes but her mother, calling her name, over and over. She froze. Maybe it was a nightmare? Maybe she was imagining too much, like Mummy always said she did. Storyman was still inside the car with the door shut. Perhaps he could lift her over the wall and she could sneak back into Grandy's house through the back door and sit on the sofa and watch telly and everyone would think she was always there. Tears came and wouldn't stop. Even if he put her over the wall, she would drop down on the other side and cut her knees or break her bones. She didn't know what to do so she sat on the muddy ground near the car and waited until her eyes stung with soreness and snot trickled into her mouth.

27. RAYYA

The mother fell on her knees near the corner of Shifnal Road. She hammered at her thighs with clenched fists. Daban was next to her, resting his hands on her shoulders, rooting her to the ground as she screamed out the name of her daughter. Both Daban and the mother were dressed in black puffer coats, dark jeans and as Rayya crossed the road towards them she thought they looked like one entity extended across two bodies. The other woman, the neighbour, was statue-still: eyes swollen, mouth fixed in a solid straight line; her only movement a quick swipe across dripping snot with the back of her thumb. Rayya brushed past them; only Daban noticed. He raised his eyebrows and the gesture restored a hint of colour to his face. She quietly slipped through her front door and stood with her back against it, waiting for her racing heart to settle. It took a few moments.

Upstairs, Rayya adjusted Satish's blanket and stroked his hair. She checked the time – it was still a while before the carers arrived. From the window she watched Daban talking calmly into his phone, one hand still on the mother's shoulder as she kneeled beside him: head bent, face in palms. The neighbour was out of view. Rayya thought of the little girl alone somewhere. Disappeared. She turned to Satish.

'I have never forgotten how it felt to be lost all those years ago, Satish. It may have been just for a moment but some feelings stay with us forever, as a reminder that our lives exist on a tightrope, to warn us to be careful so we don't fall off. I don't know what would have become of me if you hadn't found me and led me home to my mother that day. Being lost is a terrible

227

thing. The child will be frightened. I haven't done enough to find her.'

Outside it was bitter. The day was on the turn. The mother was standing now. She rested her head on Daban's chest and he comforted her. Rayya was glad the young woman was not on her own. The neighbour had moved, across the road towards the park and was calling out Tuli's name; her voice shaky but with renewed clarity and resolution. Rayya inhaled, trying to gather some energy to summon up her own determination. She was unsure of where to look or how to find the child.

After walking the length of Shifnal Road, checking down side streets, behind bins, over front walls, she wondered whether to carry on walking, along St Ann's up to Grand Parade. Instead she went around the block, past the primary school, returning to the corner of her street where Daban and the mother stood in breathless silence, staring at a police car which snaked through busy traffic towards them. Rayya headed to the alleyway, annoyed with herself for not thinking of looking there first; it was a clear hiding place. She wondered if the boy was in his car. At the very least, he may have spotted the child going by? Perhaps he could help in the search – he would be more agile than she was; he was thin but he was young. At the alleyway entrance she heard a voice. It was Jimmy.

'Don't cry, kiddo. It'll be okay. You won't be in trouble. You can tell them you were just playing a game or something. They'll just be happy to see you,' he said kindly.

Rayya took in a huge breath and as she exhaled, the muscles around her neck relaxed. *Shukar hai, thank goodness* she said out loud as she watched Jimmy put his arm around the little girl's shoulders and gently coax her towards the entrance.

'Go on,' he said, guiding her towards Rayya. 'Your mam needs to know you're safe.'

'Anything could have happened if you weren't here, Jimmy. The mother will be grateful beyond belief. I'll take her now,' Rayya said. She squeezed his arm.

The boy smiled. 'Probably best,' he said.

Before he walked back to the car, he patted the little girl on the head and said, 'I kind of think you're a good luck person, Tuli. Your mam's definitely lucky to have a nice kid like you.'

Rayya took the child's small hand in her own and led her onto the street. She cleared her throat and shouted as loudly as she could over the thunder of noise.

'I've found her. She is right here. She is alright. Everything is alright.'

The mother ran towards them and flung her arms around Tuli.

'Please don't cry, Mummy,' Tuli stuttered, biting her lip. Rayya stepped aside as the mother and child wept into each other.

'Looks like a false alarm. All in hand now,' Daban said to the police woman who'd just arrived on the scene. He gave Rayya a small salute as she walked away.

That evening, Rayya didn't feel like talking too much. She briefly told Satish the child had been found, was safe and unharmed, then she kissed his cheek, administered his eyedrops and sat quietly by his side until the room yielded to the night. Before she retired for bed she said,

'Do you remember how I used to run, Satish? I thought my body had forgotten but suddenly it has remembered again.'

28. EBELE

Ebele woke in darkness. Somewhere far off a fox screamed into the night but it wasn't the noise which woke her. A child was trapped in a box: a little girl shouting, *Mummy, Mummy*, but her voice was stolen away by thick walls and the screams were silenced. It was sweat trickling on to her dry lips which woke her. She wiped her face with the corner of the duvet, kicked off the covers and lay rigid until the flame searing through her body receded and the residue of the nightmare dispersed. She needed to speak the dream to dispel it but there was no-one to listen. Daban had said to call anytime, but a bad dream was not enough of a reason, not at this time in the morning; he was still little more than a stranger.

When she was a small child, Ebele's favourite toy was a golden heart-shaped cushion with her name embroidered across the middle in turquoise silk. The cushion was a present from the grandmother she'd never met but was told to call *Biji* down crackly phone calls to a place so far off it was hard to imagine the sounds or smells of it. Biji said she should whisper her dreams to the cushion, in the note which arrived with the parcel. *Good and bad, give the dreams to the cushion and it will take them, send them to the spirits and free you of them.* Papa said it was silly but her own mother had a feathery dream-catcher above the bed. Ebele loved the cushion; it made tangible the invisible bonds between her and Biji. But when the shattered windscreen severed Papa's jugular vein so too did it cut through the threads which linked her to the land of his birth; rendering the little island nation beyond the clouds unbidden in her world. Phone calls and emails stopped when he stopped. No more birthday cards from across the oceans, no more gifts of cotton dresses in bold Indian prints or handmade rag-dolls clad in the offcuts from the bright cotton. And, when her mother moved them to the estate near the big school it was the end of Biji completely; there was no point keeping the old woman hanging on, her mother said. It was cruel to give people false hope; Ebele couldn't be the grandchild she wanted, not from such a distance, not now Papa was gone. Sometimes, Ebele wondered if Biji was a figment of her imagination, in the same way Tuli found it hard to separate truth from fiction. The dream cushion was lost long ago, in moves from hostels to bedsits to flats, but something made her recall Biji in those early hours and it helped push away the nightmares.

A fiery dawn illuminated the room and Ebele reached for her phone to check the time. It was close to seven but still too early to call Daban. Instead, she scrolled through a newsfeed and checked headlines about the young woman whose story she'd been loosely following. The news outlets used the headline, *The Body in the River* and showed a mock-up of how the girl might look if the water hadn't sucked the life from her. There was something familiar about her face but Ebele couldn't place it. They (whoever made a living of such things) estimated the girl's age as being the age she was when she had Tuli. She tossed the phone onto the floor.

After breakfast, she knelt behind Tuli on the rug in front of her bedroom window, looking out beyond the garden towards the roof of the abandoned car which glinted in weak autumn sunlight. She pulled long spikes of the comb through Tuli's hair as gently as she was able and said,

'We need to talk about what happened.'

'No thank you,' Tuli said quietly and Ebele felt her daughter shudder.

'I thought you were lost.' Ebele's voice became softer as her own tears welled. She put the comb down and wrapped her arms around Tuli, pulling her close.

Tuli said, 'I don't want to go to school, Mummy. Not today. Please say I don't need to.'

Ebele held on tight. 'You have to go,' she said. And to after-school club too. I can't have more time off.'

'No Mummy. Please.'

'Yes! You have to go. It's the only safe place for you when you're not with me.'

The phone rang. Ebele loosened her grip and reached over to the bed to retrieve it as Tuli slipped out of her arms and ran from the room. The bathroom door slammed.

The voice on the other end said, 'Hey, how you doing?'

She was glad it was Daban.

'Okay,' she said. 'I was going to call you. To say thanks for helping out yesterday.'

'No worries. How's your kid? She okay? Must've been frightening for her, all the commotion. Poor thing.'

'She's fine.'

'You going to be at Makrides' today?'

'If I can get Tuli to school. She doesn't want to go.'

'Fair enough. It must've been a shock. Don't be too hard on the little thing.'

Ebele felt the hairs on the back of her neck prickle.

'I think I know how to deal with my own child,' she said, and almost immediately she wished she could recover the words before they reached Daban. He laughed, in the way she sometimes laughed when Tuli strutted around the flat with her lip drooping and her arms hanging limp.

'Sure thing,' he said. 'See you later. Look forward to it. Hope little Tuli is okay,' With that he was gone.

Ebele couldn't stop thinking about him after the call ended: the soothing way he spoke when Tuli was missing, comforting her when she was going under; the way he laid his hand on her shoulder, keeping her steady. She shook her head – his kindness was bound to be a delusion, kindness usually was. Instead, she stood outside the bathroom and waited for Tuli to come out.

Ebele was late to the shop and Makrides huffed around her. Tuli had only been lost for a few moments but the aftermath was difficult to shift and, as with all hangovers, the next morning was a struggle. Makrides never made anything easy, so when he reprimanded her for abandoning the shop in his absence the previous day she couldn't summon up the energy to explain what had happened.

'It's not my fault you weren't here,' she told him, and it was obvious to both of them there would be no apology.'

Later he said, 'As well as your lack of manners, you are also really a very stupid girl, Mangaroo.'

'I beg your pardon.'

'I was too busy with important business to tell you yesterday, but I have been dealing with this matter you are so concerned about.'

'What?'

'The trampman you are so worried about, well he is harmless, totally harmless I tell you and I have dealt with him.'

Ebele's heart raced; her palms became clammy and her breathing shallow. Makrides continued to brag.

'He is just a young boy and so, you see, you are scared of something which is nothing. On the surface perhaps he looks like a bad thing but he is just lost, far away from home with no family in this city. Soon he will be gone. I have told him this. Don't you worry. I've dealt with everything this morning.'

'What are you talking about?'

'You see, you are very stupid, Mangaroo. Very stupid indeed. It was you who spoilt my whole weekend with this matter and now already you've forgotten? I am talking about the boy squatting on my land, in the crashed car.'

'But he left days ago. Didn't he?'

Just then Daban walked into the shop. He nodded at Makrides.

'You're late,' the older man said, pointing at the wall clock.

'Here now,' Daban replied breezily. He smiled at Ebele but she was too preoccupied to acknowledge him.

'What are you saying? The tramp is still lurking behind our house, watching me and Tuli! Fucking hell.'

'What's going on?' Daban asked.

'There is nothing going on.' Makrides answered before Ebele could. 'This silly girl is overreacting to something which is nothing. I'm in control, Get back to working. I don't pay you to stand around chatting about local gossip.'

Makrides stood by the shop entrance, looking out for customers in the way he always did, like an over enthusiastic waiter. Ebele felt the blood draining from her face.

'What's wrong ?' Daban asked.

'I thought he'd gone,' she said, as much to herself as to him.

'Who?'

'What if he'd got hold of Tuli when she was lost? What if it was him who told her to leave the house? Fuck! All this story stuff in her head. Shit! I'm a bloody idiot.'

'Ebele, you're not making sense. Calm down, tell me what's happening.'

Daban seemed genuinely concerned. She blurted about the car and the man living in it and how it was Makrides' fault for not getting the vehicle removed weeks earlier.

'He watches us, I'm sure of it. He can see straight into Tuli's bedroom. We can see him so he must be able to see us.' She chewed at her thumb nail as she spoke.

'Why would he be watching you?'

'Who knows?' she said.

'Have you actually seen this man?'

'I've seen the car. And he has friends. I've seen others come and go. It's not right.'

She thought of the man's stinking clothes in the mud. 'What if he caught Tuli when she was missing?' she said.

'Caught? What do you mean?' Daban put his hand on her arm.

'You could go and see him,' she said after a pause.

'What?'

'Do what Makrides is supposed to have done. You know, tell him to piss off away from our homes.'

'I dunno. Didn't Mr Makrides say he's dealt with it?'

'He's a coward. I've been at him for weeks about getting the car removed. If the car wasn't there this never would have happened.'

'Perhaps.'

'And the old woman next door you seem so friendly with, she can't like it either. She's on her own isn't she? Rattling about in the house, it isn't safe having some dosser hanging around.'

'She's not completely on her own, she has a husband but he's in a sort of coma, but perhaps you're right.'

'Please, Daban. I'd appreciate it.' The words felt awkward in her mouth; she hated asking anyone for anything.

'I could have a look, if it'll make you feel more at ease,' he said and she relaxed a little.

'Today?'

'Tell you what, why don't we go together? What time do you take lunch?'

'Lunch-break is half an hour only.' Makrides shouted from across the shop.

'I dunno,' Ebele said, hunching her shoulders.

'Well, it's up to you. I'll be back from the delivery around one-ish. If you want, we can go then.'

All morning she found it hard to concentrate on the emails she was meant to be responding to. The week had been a difficult one; it was catching up on her. At five to one, Daban guided her towards the entrance while Makrides looked on.

'C'mon, we'll drive around in the van to save time. He's alright about it, Mr Makrides. I said it was something to do with your daughter. I reckon he's got a soft spot for little ones. Probably got grandkids of his own somewhere.'

'He's never said.'

'He's a private sort of person.'

'He's a bloody lunatic, if you ask me.'

She climbed into the passenger seat, watching Daban as he manoeuvred the van through heavy traffic. His skin glistened; his hair was the exact same shade as hers. As he drove, he reached into the drawer on the dashboard and retrieved a packet of tobacco.

'Can you roll?'

'What do you think!'

He smiled. 'Do one for yourself too.'

She wasn't used to doing things for anyone except herself, and Tuli. When she'd finished rolling the first cigarette, she placed it between her lips and lit it before handing it over to Daban. They smoked in unison in the stationary traffic.

It took over twenty minutes to reach the alleyway. They pulled up onto the pavement alongside it.

'We could have walked faster,' Ebele said.

'Perhaps. We're here now though. You coming?'

She disembarked feeling tense. It didn't feel right to be walking behind this man she hardly knew to confront another man she'd barely seen. After Jamal left, she'd promised herself no man was going to control the shape of her life again, but here she was surrounded by them: Nikos, Daban, the stranger in the alleyway. She wondered how all of a sudden these men were able to disrupt her life, why she had allowed it to happen, again. She blew a plume of smoke into the air and tossed the end of the cigarette to the pavement. Daban didn't seem in the least bit agitated. As they walked down the alleyway she saw the garments she'd trodden into the mud flattened over the car, stiffening in the air like cardboard cut-outs.

Daban looked around, exploring like a child. 'I've never even noticed this place,' he said.

'It's something to do with Makrides,' she said dismissively. 'He was going to build a shed for his wife, for making stuff in, but she died.' She stopped speaking as they neared the vehicle. 'Shit!' she said. 'He's still there!' A body laid across the seat. 'Oh fuck, he's dead.' She gagged, gulping hard to suppress the urge to throw up. Daban steered her away from the car window and moved in front of her.

'Sshh,' he said calmly. 'He's definitely not dead. I think he's asleep. Look, you can see him breathing.'

She didn't want to look.

'Tell him to piss off, Daban. I'm going.'

'Ebele, be quiet. It's just some poor sod, that's all. He's just sleeping rough. Probably got nowhere else to go. We've all fallen behind at some point. I'm sure even you must have.'

An image of the dingy bus station in her home town flashed through her mind; the anxiety as she waited for the coach to arrive and rescue her from her dead-end life.

'I think he's waking up,' Daban said. He tapped lightly on the window and the man jolted upright.

'Jimmy!' Daban exclaimed.

'What the fuck, Daban? You know him?'

The car door swung open and the man eased himself out. Ebele recoiled and watched, stunned as Daban embraced him, hugging him like a brother.

'I kind of guessed it might be you, my friend, when Ebele here told me about this whole situation.'

The man glanced over. 'How do,' he said. She shook her head in disgust.

'Ebele,' Daban said, 'This is Jimmy. He's passing through, isn't that right, Jimmy? Searching for a lost friend.'

She didn't know what to say. The silence was loaded.

'Ebele, did you hear me?'

'For fuck's sake, tell him to piss off, Daban. We don't want him around here. Watching us.'

'I can hear you, you know. I am here. You don't need to talk about me like I don't exist.' The man looked directly into her face. She tried not to meet his eye. Beneath the beard and the muck, he was young; probably younger than she was.

'Oh I know you exist alright,' she said. 'I can smell you a mile off.' She started to walk away.

'Don't be so rude, Ebele,' Daban said.

'Hey,' the tramp said. 'I'm just trying to survive. I'm not hurting anyone. We don't all have your privilege.'

Daban's tone changed; he was more familiar with the man called Jimmy than he was with her. She was astonished at the weird conviviality which existed so naturally between them.

'Don't take offence, Jimmy. She's having a rough ride of things,' he said softly.

'She's not the only one,' Jimmy said.

'So,' Daban said more cheerfully. 'This is where you've been hanging out then? Any luck with finding Betty?'

'Betwa, no. not yet.'

Ebele listened to their conversation with her back to them. She was angry at how she so suddenly was made to feel superfluous; invisible.

'Well, listen, Jimmy,' Daban said. 'I've been looking out for you, around and about. I had no idea you were hiding back here.'

'Looking for me?' Jimmy said. 'What for?'

'I did a bit of searching, on Facebook, local notice boards and stuff, for missing persons. No real luck but maybe a lead; someone I work with said he may know something.'

'What? Really? What does he know?'

'Don't get your hopes up, Jimmy-mate. It's just a guy in a pub but he'd heard the name. Someone he's working with at the Railway Tavern, a place a mile or so away from here. This girl, she's small, shoulder length black hair, like you described.'

'Where is she? Take me there, Daban. Let's go now. Please.'

'Jimmy, slow down. Loads of people look like that around here. It might not be her. I'll do some more digging and I'll come back later and take you there if it sounds real. I promise. Please stay calm. This is a massive city with a lot of folk in it.'

'Jimmy mate?' Ebele repeated under her breath. She had no idea what they were talking about. 'Fucking hell,' she repeated, loud enough for all of them to hear. She addressed Daban directly. 'You know this person! You know people he knows!' The sentences were statements rather than questions.

Daban ignored her, talking reassuringly to Jimmy instead. She stomped away, on to Shifnal Road, past the works van and towards the furniture shop on Grand Parade. She was already late.

When Daban returned to the shop, he said, 'He's just a person, Ebele. Like me, and you. A person with a past and hopefully some kind of future. This is just the shit bit for him, the bit where everything is broken. We've all been there, or will be at some point. I know you have. You need to remember those times. What it felt like.'

'I have to think about Tuli,' she said quietly, dusting a large ornate chest of drawers which lurked neglected in a far corner.

That evening, as she stood by Tuli's window she saw Daban sitting on the bonnet of the Audi with the tramp, smoking roll-ups and swigging from beer cans like a pair of sixth formers. She pulled out her phone and pressed on his number but aborted the call before it could connect.

29. JIMMY

'Why do you only call him Frank?' Betwa had asked Jimmy one night in the subway.

'He was only ever Frank to us for as long as I can remember,' he told her. 'I spoke more to the man in the corner shop.'

He didn't tell her how sometimes, unexpectedly, formless memory, gossamer-thin, snuck in from nowhere. It was hard to speak about something which existed so delicately it hardly existed at all. Those memories made no sense to him: big hands tickling his belly, and booming laughter, foghorns filling in all blank spaces around him. Sometimes those same hands lifted him up high to the sky so the grass was above his head and he was a bird, swirling, while Anthony jumped around in the background, yelling, *What about me? Is it my turn next?* A residue remained from those visions: an inarticulate yearning which he was never able to fathom.

At the age of twelve, he asked his brother about Frank.

'What was he like, you know, before Jenny arrived?'

It was before school, Ant was sat cross legged on the bed opposite, picking at an old guitar which seemed to have been around the house forever although, as far as they knew, neither of their parents had ever played.

'I was young too, Jimbo. I don't remember,' Ant said.

'You were bigger than me. You must remember something. You remember Mam. I don't. Not really, only from photographs and the stories Nan tells us. I wish I could really remember her.'

'Sometimes it's better not to.'

'Go on, Ant, tell me. What was it like then? You're the only one who knows.'

'Nan knows. And him. He knows.'

Jimmy sat up in bed, shifted his pillow to the wall and sat with his back against it. He pulled the covers over his knees, up to his chest and said, 'You know I can't ask him.'

'You were a chubby little bastard,' Ant said eventually. He twanged a guitar string as he spoke. 'You stole my thunder, Jimbo. It was all about me before you came along.'

He knew his brother was joking. They were in it together; from the beginning it was the two of them, him and Ant always, despite the years which separated them. He followed his brother about like a shadow and if he got too far behind, Ant would be there, waiting for him to catch up.

Ant stared into the space above Jimmy's head, at the poster of Steven Gerrard on the wall. It was next to an old framed picture of Kevin Keegan, which had probably hung there since Frank was half the age Jimmy was then.

'He used to make us dens under the dinner table, with blankets and cushions. You loved them. You begged for him to make a den.'

Jimmy couldn't remember. 'Really?' he said. 'What else?'

'Shut up now, Jim, will you?' Ant said.

There was never a right time to ask Nan about it. To talk about Frank would be to talk about Mam and Jimmy knew she didn't like to do that in front of Jenny.

'It'd be cruel to the poor child. At least you boys knew her. At least you got to feel her love for you. Poor wee Jenny.'

'I never did really, Nan. I was just a baby myself,' Jimmy said once.

'Aw, shush now. You were three, almost four years old. They're the most important years, so they are. They form you, those years. You were surrounded by love then, Jimmy.'

When he tried to disagree again, she changed the subject. She was set in her ways; no different from Frank really. In actuality, she was less different in age to Frank than her own daughter who'd married him. Sometimes Jimmy wondered if everyone of their generation was like that or whether it was just his family. Nan closed down the conversation abruptly.

'One day I'll tell her everything, mind, when she's old enough. Not yet, so don't be asking any more questions and prying about things you can't understand, son.'

Almost two years passed by before he was able to broach the subject again.

'Why is he so sour all the time, Nan?' he asked.

He was on a sick day from school but he was up and dressed and sipping the instant coffee Ant had made him by the time Nan appeared at the door at eight o'clock sharp. From the top of the stairs, he listened to her talking to Ant in the hallway.

'I'm not happy about him being on his own all day when he's feeling down as he is, Anthony,' she said.

Ant was trying to push past her. 'I've got to go, Nan,' he said. 'It's only the first week of the apprenticeship still and I don't want to be late. I've got to get all the way over to the blue bridge by eight-thirty. I can't stop here chatting about our Jimmy.'

'Let's just hope it's not the same as your father's sickness. You're old enough to know about these things. It's in the blood, Anthony, so we have to make sure none of you children let it get a grip on you. It's not good to be in all day, alone in the house, not at his age.'

'I'll miss the bus, Nan.'

'Okay, Anthony. You get off and I'll make myself busy about the place.'

She stepped out of the way and as Ant disappeared through the door, he said, 'Jimmy's a big boy now, Nan. He'll be fine. He'll have to learn to be. We can't be here to look after him forever.'

Later that morning, Jimmy sat on the rim of the bath and watched as Nan brushed bleach around the toilet bowl.

'Why is he always such a grim bastard, Nan?'

'Language please, James.'

'But why? It's not fair on us to be around it all the time.'

'He's had a lot of sadness to contend with.'

'There's plenty of sad people in the world. Most of them don't take it out on their kids.'

'He isn't taking it out on you, Jimmy. He's just not doing the opposite either. He pays the bills. He does the shopping. He makes your dinners when he can. Or at least he makes sure there's things in the house you can cook for yourselves. He does all that, doesn't he?'

'He grunts at us. It's as good as taking it out on us. It's not our fault she died. It's not even Jenny's fault, even though she thinks it is.'

'I certainly hope she does not,' Nan said sternly. 'She must never think such a thing. I've made it clear to your father. Poor wee girl.'

'Jimmy banged his foot against the side of the bath beating out a rhythm – *thud, thud, thud-thud thud-thud.*

'Stop now, Jimmy,' Nan said. 'It's so irritating. Why don't you go off to your room and do something useful; you must have some homework to be getting on with. Or tell you what, why don't you make the two of us a nice cup of tea?'

'I will, Nan, but first tell me something about him. No-one tells us anything. It's some big bloody secret you all keep from us. It's like all the heaviness he carries around him isn't any of our business but we still have to live with it. We have to look at his miserable face and wonder why he doesn't love us like other dads love their kids.'

Nan rested the toilet brush in the pan, allowing the bristles to soak in the bleachy water. She sat on the edge of the bath next to him, pulled off one of her rubber gloves and put her arm around his shoulder.

'Listen here,' she said. 'Even before your mam died, he was sad. People who knew him before they met say she brought happiness to him, and any he already had in him he projected onto her. There's none left for anyone else.'

'But we're part of her.'

'I think that's the problem, Jimmy my love.'

'I don't understand, Nan. Our Jen is just a kid. It's not fair for him to hate us.'

'Love is a funny thing, Jimmy. It doesn't always come in the form we expect it to. He doesn't hate you. He loves you. Perhaps he loves you a little too much, like he loved your mam.'

'What? So much it feels as if he hates us.'

'He is a man of few words, Jimmy and even though he keeps the curtains drawn when the sunlight should be streaming in, it doesn't mean he doesn't want to open them, or that he won't be able to one day. Don't forget he is your father.'

'I think those chemicals are getting to your brain, Nan.' Jimmy said, scratching his head. He left the bathroom for the bedroom he shared with Ant, closed the door and switched on the CD player. The Arctic Monkeys boomed out around him.

The day Jimmy left his town was the day of Ant's funeral. Frank stood alone in the untidy living room, glancing from wall clock to window as the air loaded up with unspoken things. Jimmy watched his father from the threshold for a moment before walking out of the front door and down the road with music blasting in his ears. Ant's old sleeping bag was tied to his rucksack and bounced against the small of his back, annoying him. When he reached the corner, he saw the hearse approaching. He crossed the road quickly before he could see the coffin.

At the end of his MegaBus journey almost six hours later, he stepped from the dim station forecourt into a glare of artificial light: back-lit shop signs, theatre displays, bus headlights, Belisha Beacons, illuminated office windows and the flashing lights of ambulances. Towering above the buildings were red beams atop two gigantic cranes, throwing parallel lines across the dark sky. When his eyes adjusted, he felt for his phone and scrolled for the number of Big Bob, an old school friend of Ant's who'd left for the city years earlier with an open invitation attached. He rang the number and strained to hear the voice on the other end with the din of the city around him.

Big Bob said, 'Nah mate, don't recall a fella of that name. Nope, not the school I went to. I think you're mistaking yourself. You'll have to find somewhere else to stay. I can't just let any stranger kip in my gaff.'

'But Bob you were in the team with our Ant. You were in the same class. Your sister worked with him at the record shop.'

The phone went dead. Jimmy rang back; straight to voicemail *Robert Braithwaite here*, the same accent as his own but clipped around the edges. It was Big Bob.

He searched out the nearest YMCA and spent the bulk of his few quid on a couple of nights in a room with five other men he didn't know, none of them in the mood to make conversation. He used the days to seek out paid work. He asked in pubs and restaurants but there was nothing going so he moved on to building sites where there seemed to be a bit of activity. Workers directed him to foremen who looked him up and down and then told him there was nothing available there either. A man on a market stall gave him forty quid to stand behind a great mound of potatoes for eight hours but the man didn't speak much recognisable English and when Jimmy turned up bright-eyed, ready for a second day of work, the man and his stall had disappeared. Cash started to run out so the YMCA was swapped for a park bench. After the first night sleeping outside, Jimmy phoned Nan.

'I'm alright, Nan. How's our Jen?'

'Same, Jimmy. Doesn't speak much. Comes out for her dinner. Always on her phone. God knows what she's looking at. She won't even come to church although I know it would do her good. It'd do her good to see you too; it would do us all good, Jimmy. Why don't you come round?'

'No Nan, I can't.'

'I know you've been hiding away. And I know it's probably what you need to do so I haven't bothered with you but you can't stay locked away in your room forever. You could come for your tea one day soon at least, Jimmy?'

'I'm not there anymore, Nan.'

'Not where? What do you mean, son?

'I've left, Nan. I'm away. Down south.'

'Oh no, Jimmy. Your father didn't say owt. I asked how you were at the church, you know, for Anthony. I assumed you just couldn't face it all; it's a wonder any of us could. He didn't say anything, just walked away, quiet like he always is. Oh no, Jimmy. Oh poor Frank.'

'I just wanted you to know I'm okay, Nan. Tell our kid I'm alright if she asks. Will you, Nan?'

'Where are you, son? Come home. You can have my room. I'll go in with Jenny. Don't be on your own Jimmy. Being alone isn't the answer to anything. You can't know anyone down there, Jimmy. Oh it's such a big place to be on your own. It'll eat you up, son. Can't you just come home, now?'

'I can't come back, Nan.'

He held the phone away from his ear. Her voice faded away but her words lingered.

'I'll say a prayer for you, Jimmy. For all of you. I'll pray for you to come home.'

He cut the call without saying goodbye. That night, as he slept with his rucksack under his head, both his phone and his wallet disappeared. He didn't know Nan's number off by heart. He didn't know any numbers off by heart except the landline in the railway cottage which was once his home.

He'd told Betwa he never knew a dad or a daddy, and he could hardly bring himself to say father, just as Frank never called either him or Ant 'son'. In the days after Ant died, alone in a squalid bedsit on a damp mattress with a syringe by his side, Frank took to chain-smoking in a tumble-down shed at the bottom of their small backyard. He stood out there for hours blowing smoke towards the sky, whatever the weather, leaving Jimmy alone with the ghosts in the empty house. When he told Betwa all this, she pressed her mouth against his cold hands and held him in her arms until sleep blotted out the day.

30. RAYYA

Rayya woke to a thunderstorm. It came crashing through the sky, strobe lights illuminating ethereal ghosts. Her first thought was of the little girl next door, lying rigid in her bed as the world shook around them, but the little girl had a mother who would be there to scoop her up, hold her close in the dark. Her next thought was of the boy in the car, exposed. He always seemed to be shivering, his bones rattling, She gasped when she realised that in all the commotion around the little girl, she'd forgotten to cook dinner for him, instead falling asleep with *Mr Biswas* open on her lap. She felt sick with guilt. She had not gone hungry. She'd been distracted by Daban who'd knocked on the door to check how she was after all the stress of the missing child.

'I'm okay. Thank you for asking me,' she'd said, touched by his concern. She didn't want him to leave, not straight away. 'Come and have tea with me, Daban.' It was the least she could do after he'd shown such kindness.

'Actually, go on then,' he said. 'Have you got biscuits? Shall I nip across the road for some?'

'Oh no,' she replied, and quickly added, 'But I have bread. We shall have tea and toast like the English people we are.'

Daban laughed and, for the first time in as long as she could remember, she laughed too.

While Daban made tea and buttered hot toast, she wiped down the table in the dining room and opened the French doors to allow a strong breeze to clear the stale air. And, while they ate, he chatted to her as though her life was normal. They talked about his driving jobs across the city, to places which only existed on maps and local news reports for her, even though they were on the doorstep. Then he talked of his boss, Mr Makrides, the nephew and godson of gentle Kostas, who'd been like a brother to her. She didn't mention how well she'd once known Nikos: how they'd shared wine on his birthdays and celebrated his engagement with a glorious cake baked by his uncle, decorated in hand-piped pink rose-buds; how she'd drunk tea with Nikos' wife as little Dimitri Makrides crawled around their ankles and pulled at his mother's skirts; how Nikos and Ourania, like other couples she knew, drifted away soon after babies arrived; and how she now found it hard to recall exchanging more than a single word with him these last few months, possibly even years. Daban made gentle fun of Mr Makrides, the way he fumbled around customers, presenting outdated pieces of furniture as though they were top of the range designs from the unaffordable 'lifestyle' stores up town. He told her about the mother of the little girl, how he liked her but he didn't think she wanted to be liked so it was a difficult job to get to know her. He stayed for over an hour until the evening carers arrived, and while he was there Rayya ate two whole pieces of toast with jam; it was the most she'd eaten in one sitting in such a long time. It was no wonder she'd forgotten about Jimmy. When the thunder woke her, she lay in bed and listened to the storm, thinking about these two men, young enough to be her children, possibly her grandchildren. Great slants of rain bashed against the windows and somewhere, not too far away, a car alarm sounded – its wail cutting through yet another squally night. It was only then Satish popped into her head. He was an afterthought and she was horrified. She checked the baby monitor; it was working fine; the soft whirr of machines down the landing could be heard clearly, even against the storm. She stretched stiff limbs and reached around the bed for her dressing gown.

For well over sixty years, Satish had been Rayya's first and last waking thought. To begin with, he was an imaginary friend, someone she talked to late at night with bed sheets pulled over her head so her family, who all slept in the same room, couldn't hear her whispering. Then, when he led her home on the day she got lost as a child, she couldn't stop chatting and it was if they'd always been friends. She told him how far she'd run and the things she'd seen on the way: the rickshaw wallah who stole oranges from the juice-wallah as he turned his back to fetch clean glasses; the huddle of old ladies outside the temple who shouted at her when she stuck out her tongue. Years later, when he blew kisses to her as she sprinted past, he occupied all her thoughts, awake and asleep and, when she developed small mounds beneath her tunics and hair grew in unexpected places, thoughts of him careered through her body as well as her mind. In the days before their wedding, it was as if she held a coiled firework within her, sizzling but tempered, and it wasn't until a week into their marriage, she found it could explode without destroying either herself or him. She began to take control in the night, gently steering him, guiding his shy hands across her body, growing in confidence as she moved across his. But as months became years, their lovemaking became charged with a different kind of expectation, one which only ever ended in disappointment, manifested every four or five weeks by vermilion trickling into the pan. As they got older, her body still longed for him despite the fruitlessness of the act. Sometimes she reached in the dark and placed her hand on his belly, waiting for the beat within him to quicken. Visits to Doctor Razak and the spiral of appointments tired him out more than the early days of his illness and, as time went by, instead of placing her hand on his belly at night, she put her arm around his shoulders so he could lay his head on her breast. She stroked his hair and kissed the top of his head while he sobbed silently, dampening the cotton of her nightclothes with his tears.

As the storm raged, she pulled her dressing gown tight around her nightdress and dashed down the landing.

'Oh my darling, I am so sorry I left you for so long with this horrible noise all around,' she said.

She switched on the table lamp and sat on the wooden armrest of the chair beside him. His lips were dry and cracked.

'Oh my goodness, Satish. It's no wonder you couldn't sleep, not only with all this banging everywhere but, silly me, I forgot to prepare you for bedtime.' She gently opened each eyelid with the tip of her finger, lubricated it with eye drops and closed it again, then she swabbed his lips and the inside of his mouth with water. 'Perhaps now you can drift off, and I will sit by you while you do,' she said.

She looked around for her reading glasses and picked up *Mr Biswas* which had fallen to the floor. She flicked through the pages, trying to find where they'd got to.

'Shall I read to you, Satish?' She said. 'Or maybe we can just talk, like we used to in bed at night. Is this a good idea? Perhaps it will help you to sleep. We could say anything to each other in the dark. Do you remember? It was as though you could see into my soul, and I into yours.' She paused. 'Am I babbling on? Do you want to sleep? I don't mind but I want to be here with you tonight. I want to be close by.'

A huge bolt of lightning illuminated the room. It was followed instantly by a huge crash of thunder.

'The weather is very fierce tonight, darling. It disturbed my sleep. I expect it disturbed you too. I'm so sorry for not coming sooner, darling.'

She sank into the chair and closed her eyes, but continued to speak through the drowsiness.

'You see, so much happened yesterday. I must have been exhausted by it. I am sorry.' It was hard to believe how much could happen in a day. 'I wish I could tell you it all but I am so tired now.'

She switched on a table lamp and a soft glow warmed the room. It was full of the remnants of the life she and Satish shared: a small map of India, framed in gilt and hung next to a shelf of novels, all gifts from her to him and he to her. She scanned the spines: A*nna Karenina, The God of Small Things, Love in the Time of Cholera*; books they cherished, books which had them both sobbing, holding on to each other for solace, laughing through tears at their own mawkishness. They loved all of these books, separately and together, in a weak reflection of the way she guessed perhaps parents loved their children, totally immersed and then slowly mourning as their lives drifted further and further away. She thought about the letter from the hospice, concealed behind a large framed photograph on the mantelpiece.

'At least the little girl was safe, hai na?' she said after a moment.

'But I am bad, Satish; I neglected the boy in the car. You see, so much commotion and it isn't just you I forget about. Oh Satish, if you could speak, what would you say? What would you tell me to do? Would you say it is time to let you free, my love?'

She reeled at her own words.

'I want to go backwards not forwards, darling,' she said. 'What I wouldn't sacrifice for us to be twelve and fourteen again, for you to be waiting for me as I sprint past. I wish we were there in Tilak Nagar with nothing but our lives ahead of us, instead of stuck in this dreadful place where this cruel sickness has stolen you from me. I wonder if we would do it differently, knowing what fate had in store for us? Maybe we would've spent less time crying for the things we couldn't have.'

She opened her eyes and held onto her husband's arm, squeezing it with a gentle pressure.

'There is something I need to ask,' she said. 'What do you want me to do? If you give me a sign, I will do whatever it is you need me to.'

An ambulance screeched past. Rayya closed her eyes again, and, as if waking from a dream, she said, 'The darkness is wicked. It makes us believe we are free but we are not.' She leaned back in the chair and yielded to the drag of sleep.

The buzz of the doorbell woke her with a start. She looked around; the table lamp still glowed but daylight flooded in through uncovered windows. It took her a moment to realise she'd slept half the night in the chair.

'Oh Satish, I am a bad person,' she said again as she slowly rose. She lifted his lids and picked up her conversation from hours earlier. 'It was so bad to leave the boy without dinner. Now I will make paratha for breakfast. Surely this will make it up to him. Yes, paratha with radish. Your favourite, Satish. Remember when we last ate mooli paratha together? You had to wipe the butter away from my chin. Such messy food. Such joy to eat only with fingers. To eat as if we were children. Yes, this is what I'll cook for the boy.'

The doorbell buzzed a second time and she glanced at the clock on the mantelpiece. She rapped on the window to let the carer know she'd be down soon and he raised a hand, nervously looking up and down the street for his back-up.

'Another new one,' she said, turning from the window with a sigh. 'Let's hope this one doesn't also speak to us as if we are imbeciles.'

31. JIMMY

Daban returned to the car in the evening as promised and Jimmy was pleased to see him. He'd bought beers and insisted they drank one before they set off.

'You need to be chilled,' he said. 'If it's her or not, either way you need to be chill.'

They sat on the front of the car, leaning onto the cold windscreen, swigging the beer and smoking in silence while Jimmy tried to still his shaking legs.

'There can't be more than one Betwa – it's not a common name,' he said.

'I suppose it's unusual even for round here,' Daban replied.

'It's a river' Jimmy flicked ash into a small pile on the bonnet. 'Her name, I mean. It's the name of a river. I'd never heard of it until she told me.'

'There's millions of rivers in the world, Jimmy. No-one's heard of all of them.' Daban's eyes followed a ginger cat teetering on the wall above them.

Jimmy tried to picture Betwa, in the subway just a few weeks earlier with her head against the green and blue wall with the music playing out around her, but her face was blurred, slipping away like dreams in the morning. He could picture the shape of her, huddled up against concrete painted with sharp images of kingfishers and lorikeets.

Together the two men walked the length of Shifnal Road and on to busy Grand Parade, past the sprawling bakery which still teemed with people and smelled of freshly baked bread in the neon glow of the city nightscape. Jimmy tried to imagine the lives of people who dashed by clutching shopping: last minute frozen pizzas, milk, bottles of red wine; rushing home to warm rooms, hot food, company. He thought of the car: stinking and damp. Daban walked in front, able to move with ease through the tumult. People stepped aside to let him pass.

'C'mon Jimmy, get a move on.' Daban's yell was the exact same tone Ant used to rush him along to school. He could never keep up; his legs were weaker now.

The walk up Station Way was longer than he'd expected. *Just up the road* but it was another area, away from the shops with boxes of tomatoes and green peppers cascading onto slate grey pavements. Rows of checked tables in busy cafes began to fall away as they approached a wide junction. Then a different kind of street emerged, more like the ones he was used to: dull generic stores, glaring cut-price offers, boarded up boutiques and sacks of discarded jumble outside a Save the Children shop. The few people around walked purposefully away from the place.

'Wow,' Jimmy said. It was the first time he'd spoken since they left Shifnal road. 'It's like we've entered another world.'

'Yeah, well Grand Parade is special,' Daban said. 'We could be anywhere now though, right? Bet it's just the same as your town. Where is that exactly?'

Jimmy only half heard what Daban was saying. Betwa could be within metres, within minutes of where they were. He looked into Poundland: 3-4-1 cans of *Monster* drink were stacked up as pyramid towers; a backdrop to a Halloween display of cotton wool spider webs and garish plastic pumpkin-faces. He turned away. Halloween wasn't an occasion he'd thought about for many years. Mostly it came and went, not like when he was young. The last Halloween he remembered with any clarity was when he was a teenager and Ant, dressed in a bin liner, threw the Sunday-best tablecloth over little Jen and pushed her in a shopping trolley up and down the long drives of Orchard Avenue. He turned away from the display.

'How far is it?' he asked, heart thumping against his ribcage.

'Not far, just up ahead.'

'I need to wash my face,' Jimmy said anxiously and Daban disappeared into a newsagents and emerged a minute later with a packet of Kleenex and a bottle of water. Jimmy splashed the icy water on to his face and shook his head, directing the spray away from Daban.

They continued up the high street past an old man slumped in a doorway, partially obscured by an overflowing bin. Jimmy raised his hand in the way men did when they spotted someone wearing the same football shirt. He wondered if the terrible smell which hung about the old guy was the same as others smelt on him. Further up the road, a different smell filled the air: teenage boys huddled around a bench, hoodies and baseball caps pulled up and down over heads and faces, hands shoved deep into pockets. One of them waved and Daban waved back.

'Do you know everyone around here?' Jimmy asked.

'Just about,' Daban replied. 'Carlo's my neighbour. Those kids are part of this place.'

Jimmy breathed in deeply. He'd stopped listening and was looking past the boys towards a scruffy-looking pub on a corner up ahead.

'That's the boozer,' Daban said, pointing to it.

Jimmy's heart pounded. 'Will they let me in?' he said.

'I'll go in first. I'll see if she's there,' Daban said.

'I'm scared.' Jimmy said. He only realised he'd spoken when Daban's hand was on his arm.

'What have you got to be scared of Jimmy, mate?'

'Everything,' he replied. It was more than he intended to say.

They carried on walking, up towards the pub, stopping briefly while Daban searched his pockets for coins to throw into the hat of a young busker with an old voice strumming 'A Simple Twist of Fate' on a guitar with a broken string.

'My brother loved this song,' Jimmy said.

'Not really my kind of thing,' Daban replied.

Ten minutes later, Jimmy stood a few feet from Daban outside The Railway Tavern, staring at the ground as a train chuntered past on the tracks beside them.

'I'm sorry,' Daban was saying. 'I should have checked it out myself before leading you to a dead end.'

Jimmy shrugged and stared at the uneven paving stones beneath his feet.

'Bettina. It's a similar sounding name,' Daban said apologetically. 'An easy mistake. I'm sorry Jimmy mate. I really am. I'll keep asking.'

Jimmy had no words.

Later, after Daban had taken his leave, Jimmy lay on the car bonnet with his blanket wrapped around him, looking up at the sky, hoping for tiny glints of starlight to break through thick clouds. The busker's song looped around his head. He tried to picture Betwa again, to remember her face but he couldn't quite see her. Instead, it was his brother who came, sat next to him on the bonnet, close enough to hear his breath, heads touching, swigging from the cans Daban left behind, whispering into the night about the music which had always managed to rescue them. But Ant, he knew, could never really be anywhere again so he closed his eyes and let the liquid seep through him, filling up empty ravines in the way only alcohol could.

32. NIKOS

The summer Nikos was eighteen, he and Georgios slept out most Friday nights on the hillside above the village overlooking the sea.

'Why do you want to sleep on the hard ground, amongst beetles and the excrement of goats, when you have perfectly good beds at home?' Nikos' father asked them.

'Let them be,' his mother replied. 'Were you never young once? Is this not what boys do?'

She'd prepared packages of koulouri bread, chunks of cucumber, hard cheese, plump tomatoes, stuffed grape leaves and cold slices of roast lamb. The food quickly became sticky in their bags with syrup oozing from Mama Savvides' freshly baked samali cake. The boys didn't care: any food was delicious in the moonlight. They sneaked bottles of Keo from the shed behind Georgios' house and covered them with blankets to wrap around their shoulders later, when the temperature dipped in the early hours. The boys clunked through farms and orchards on their bicycles until they found the right place, always the same spot, coaxed by the beauty of it: a small meadow clearing between sprawling olive groves and dense pine woods staggering up towards the sky. They settled next to a cluster of cypress trees, where grass was more plentiful than scrub-land and views were uninterrupted to the lapis sea ahead and stony mountains behind.

On one such night, at the tail end of summer, the boys lay on their backs and stared at the velvet sky, hoping for shooting stars. Nikos blew a succession of smoke rings towards the slim moon, goading Georgios to compete with him, but his friend was lost in thought and blew his cigarette smoke in one direct trail.

'Sometimes I think it is the beginning and the end of the world in this place,' Georgios said,

'What do you mean?' Nikos asked, rolling onto his stomach.

'It's a feeling, I don't know. It's like the land and the sky are calling me. Like I am falling into them both at the same time. When I lie here I know I won't be going anywhere else. You will travel, see the world, see new things, meet new people. Me, well time will stand still and this land will swallow me up one day soon. I can feel it in my bones. Something, I don't know what, comes to me in dreams out here, pulling me towards it.'

'Have you been listening to The Doors again, Georgios?'

'Oh shut up, Nikos,' Georgios said, changing his tone. 'You're too much of a donkey to understand.'

'Maybe, because you don't know what you are talking about yourself.' Nikos said, teasingly. 'If it's not The Doors, then it must be those hippy books you brought home from Larnaca.' He yawned. The beer made his head light and his eyelids heavy; neither was conducive to philosophical conversation.

'Go to sleep, Nikos. In the morning we can talk about the shape of Stephania's backside and Elena's breasts and the other earth-shattering things which occupy you.'

'Ah, Elena's breasts,' Nikos said. 'This will be what I dream of tonight. Meanwhile you enjoy your date with Socrates.'

'Go to hell,' Georgios said and Nikos knew his friend was angry with him. He would apologise for his facetiousness in the morning.

Georgios woke early the next day, while the peachy sun still lingered on the horizon. He sat up and launched into a different conversation.

'Who is the more superior, Nikos, as a lyricist I mean, forget about the individual songs, Dylan or Stevens?'

'It's too early, Georgios. Go back to sleep.' Nikos said.

'Come on. You're pretending to sleep just because you don't know the answer.'

'They are too different, Georgios. You can't compare an olive with an aubergine.' He stretched, yawned and rubbed away pollen from his eyes then sat up. 'How can you just launch into conversation as if the day has been open for business for hours? One minute you are keeping me awake with some heavy shit talk and now you are stopping me sleeping with your insubstantial musical observations.'

'Of course, neither is quite the poet of Cohen,' Georgios continued, ignoring Nikos. He rolled up his blanket and walked a few feet away to relieve himself against the bark of the nearest tree, shouting over the splash of his urine.

'Dylan too is a poet, but of a different school of course.'

'Shut up, Georgios. It is still night,' Nikos curled himself into a ball and pulled the blanket over his head. Through the muffle of wool he could still hear Georgios.

'Well there you are wrong my friend. Look, the sun has a different idea, you lazy goat. Get up and enjoy the day, we never know how long we've got on this beautiful earth.'

It was less than a full year later when the chicken sized rock flew out of the sky and hit Georgios on the temple.

Nikos recalled the night on the hillside as he sipped his coffee, looking out at the russet-tipped leaves of the fig tree in the garden. After days of rain, weak sunshine crackled through the clouds and lit up the earth in a new way. It was a very particular kind of light, made up of tiny shimmering dew drops nestled amongst blades of grass, resting on the surfaces of autumn foliage. He thought about the song which had played out from the car and the young man who slept there and had a look of Georgios; it was this combination of music and light which drew out the most reticent memory.

Georgios always wanted to talk with him about music in a way no one else ever did, before or since. This was one of the gaps he'd left. Ourania could take or leave music. She hummed along to show tunes and pop songs on the radio, and she danced with him after retsina if he played records on Kostas' old turntable. But her eyes only really sparkled if the music was bouzouki accompanying *tatsia* or *syrto* dancing in the church hall on celebration days and that was a different kind of music altogether. Kostas loved music too but he had his own tastes: often more flamboyant than Nikos was used to – glamorous and confusing. Other times, Kostas liked to listen to the laments of torch singers; songs which sounded like weeping for voids which could never be filled. Nikos' own more troubadour tastes had aligned most perfectly with those of Georgios.

When only coffee dregs remained, he walked across the room to the turntable which sat on a small cabinet below a bookshelf. He ran his finger across a layer of dust on the transparent lid and paused before pulling out an album at random from the stack below. When he realised it was *Catch A Bull At Four* he quickly shoved it back into place but it was too late: the words of Georgios's last letter swam around his head.

'Nikos, my friend, how I long to hear music with you again. Perhaps one day soon it will happen. Baba says there will be new hearing aids from America arriving at a special clinic in Athens. We have an appointment, provisional at the moment; the news came last week but the cost is expensive, and there will be boat fare on top. Baba is planning to sell the old van and there are some savings so it will be a birthday gift, or perhaps Christmas. They are very hopeful, and then, once they fix this thing, you can come over and we can open Catch A Bull together; it's still in its wrapper my friend. I am waiting for you before I can listen.'

Two months after sending that final letter, Georgios was no more.

Nikos stood with his back against the door bracing himself for the chores of the day. Then, as he washed his coffee cup and breakfast dishes at the sink, his phone beeped in his pocket. It was a text message to say the abandoned car would be removed the following day, to be disposed of. Twenty minutes later, he parked his own car behind the furniture shop and walked towards Shifnal Road. As he turned the corner into the alleyway, Mrs Banu, Rayya who was once his neighbour was heading towards him, hitching up her long skirts as she walked across muddy ground. She nodded at him, as though it was perfectly normal for her to be on his land.

'What is this?' he said as she brushed past.

She rushed by without responding.

'Stay off my land, old lady. You have no business here,' Nikos shouted after her. Mrs Banu stopped and turned towards him. She repeated the words she'd said outside the shop in front of the people at the bus stop.

'Your uncle would be ashamed of you, Nikos Makrides.' She paused for a moment, softened her voice and said, 'And your wife too, she can't like this man you've become. You are such a hard fellow now, Nikos. You used to be such a sweet boy once.'

He froze, 'Don't speak of my wife,' he said. 'You know nothing of her.'

'Your memory is short. You always treat me like a stranger. Have we not shared meals together? And your wife, she and I took tea often when we were neighbours. I hardly see her since you moved away.'

His stomach sank; he didn't want this woman to speak of his Ourania.

'She is not here,' he said.

'Where is she? Has she gone home to Cyprus? Or perhaps to be with your sons in Canada? Do you have grandchildren, Nikos? I know so little about you these days.'

His breathing quickened.

'Yes, she has gone home,' he said softly. 'Goodbye Mrs Banu. Rayya.'

'Goodbye, Nikos. Give her my regards,' Mrs Banu said. Then she added, 'Don't be too hard on the boy, Jimmy. He is just a lost soul.'

Jimmy was eating when Nikos reached the car. The food looked fresh. Steaming flatbreads like the gozleme of the Turks. Between mouthfuls, the young man said, 'Alright, grandad? Is it time to go?'

'Yes,' Nikos said. 'They are coming tomorrow daytime. You need to find somewhere else to sleep. Perhaps you should go home?' The boy stopped eating for a moment and stared at him.

'Perhaps,' he said.

Nikos reached into his pocket and pulled out the notes he'd placed there before he'd left the house. He handed them to Jimmy.

'There is enough, to get the train home I mean. Back to your family. One hundred pounds. Perhaps it is also enough to go to a hotel first. Take a shower, eat some breakfast then make the journey refreshed, clean. Please, go home. No-one should live like this.'

After work, Nikos took a tea towel from the kitchen drawer and with the dampened edge he wiped the turntable lid then flicked through the albums beneath it until, eventually, he came to the one he was searching for, *Teaser and the Firecat*: the record he and Georgios had loved together. He put the needle on the first groove and stood listening to the whole of 'The Wind' without moving. Then, as 'Ruby Love' began to play out he folded each item of Ourania's clothing and piled them up on the chair she most liked to sit in, looking towards her fig tree. He placed the yellow dress neatly on the top of the pile and sat down on the nearest chair with *Catch A Bull at Four* on his knees.

As the evening closed in, he switched on the laptop which had lain dormant in the corner of the room for many months and composed an email to his sons.

Just a few weeks ago it was the anniversary of your mother leaving this earth to go to a better place. One day, before we know it, I will be joining her but before that day comes I want us all to be together again to honour her memory, in the place of her birth on the day which marks that momentous occasion. I will send money for tickets. I need you to be with me so she knows we are all together, and this will give her peace, and me too.

At nine o'clock he pressed send with a sigh of relief. Ten minutes later the laptop pinged with a new message.

Sure, Pops. That's a great idea. I'll speak to Karin to see what we can arrange. We could sure do with a holiday and it'll be good for the kids to go to the old country with their grandpa. I'll call Dimitri later when I'm home from work. Good to hear from you Dad, Gx

Before he went to bed, Nikos sent a text to Marios. It said,

Marios, I hope you are well. I'm coming home soon. I will telephone you tomorrow. Your brother, Nikos.

33. RAYYA

'Why are you so kind to me?' the boy in the car asked when Rayya came to collect the Tupperware.

'I'm doing what anyone would do,' she replied. She started to walk away but the boy spoke and his words made her pause.

'Most people aren't kind,' he said.

'Sometimes it is hard to show kindness but it doesn't mean people are bad. Me and my husband, we try to see the good even though it isn't always apparent.'

'Perhaps,' the boy said. 'I don't even know your name. I told you mine, Jimmy, remember? You never told me yours.'

Rayya smiled. 'I am Mrs Banu,' she said.

'Who were you before you were Mrs Banu?'

Rayya laughed. 'I have always been Mrs Banu in one way or another. It isn't a constraint for me to be his wife; it's what liberated me, in fact. Me and my husband are what you might call soulmates, ever since we were children. Mrs Rayya Banu. This is who I am.'

'Have you told him about me? That you feed me, I mean?'

'We tell each other everything. Absolutely everything. I am fortunate to have a good marriage. Did your parents have a good marriage?'

Jimmy clenched his fists and she knew her question had scratched an old wound.

'What about brothers and sisters? Do you have those, Jimmy? You told me once of your nanny; about her cooking. She must miss you.'

His shoulders dropped, his hands unfurled.

'I do have a nan,' he said. 'She brought us up. Mam died when I was three, my brother was just seven. They couldn't stop the bleeding when she had our sister. She wanted to do it at home but it got complicated and she had to be rushed to hospital halfway through. Something went wrong. They couldn't save her. Me and Ant, we never got to say goodbye. Little Jenny never even got to say hello.'

Rayya gasped. She didn't mean for it to be so audible. Her knees buckled and she steadied herself by leaning on the side of the car. Jimmy climbed out and took her arm. He guided her to the driver's seat and she sat side saddle with her feet in the mud.

'I'm sorry about the stink,' he said.

Stink was an under-statement. The smell was intense, like the gulleys in Tilak Nagar: the overbearing stench of stagnant water, unwashed bodies and decay.

'Thank you for the seat, Jimmy,' she said, trying hard not to gag. 'I'm sorry to hear about your mother. No child should be motherless.'

'It's okay. I don't really remember her to be honest. Sometimes I dream about her but I guess I'm just dreaming of stories.'

'I dream about my unborn children,' Rayya said abruptly. She quickly clasped her hand over her mouth. The boy was startled and she was sorry she'd burdened him with such an intimate thing. It was something she'd only ever discussed with Satish before, and Doctor Razak.

'You don't have any children?'

She bit her lip and shook her head. 'We could not. I have got used to it over the years, like you've got used to being without a mother. We had a happy life, me and Satish. We found things to fulfil us. Fate can be cruel but we have to accept it; there is no choice. I learnt this early on but it isn't easy sometimes.'

'Had?' Jimmy asked. 'Your husband is still alive though? You said he knew about me.'

Rayya climbed out of the car and gestured for Jimmy to retake his seat. He refused. Instead they stood together in the damp, side by side, leaning against the car. The boy was silent, leaving space open for her to speak, and when she did she couldn't stop. She told him about Satish, about their childhood in Tilak Nagar, where food and other comforts were scarce but they had their families and an ineradicable longing for one another to keep them going.

'It was our destiny; we belonged together,' she said. 'I knew this from the moment he first took my hand when we were children.'

'I don't believe in destiny,' Jimmy said. 'It implies there's no responsibility for all the shit that happens. Like we deserve to have a bad time because it's all mapped out.'

'No,' Rayya said. 'It just means we should see what is in front of us and not always be looking elsewhere for something better.'

She told him about moving to England to escape the limitations of being from a lower caste family only to find hostility and prejudice awaiting them across the oceans.

'It got better over the years. We worked. We made some friends,' she said.

She told him of the years spent trying for a family, the medical interventions and the illness which devoured Satish and devastated both their lives. When she finished speaking, she used the corner of her sari to wipe her eyes and inhaled slowly and deeply, filling her lungs with new air, then she put her hand on Jimmy's arm and said,

'Thank you, Jimmy. Thank you for listening to my story.'

Jimmy looked worn out. He put his hand on top of hers and they stood in silence.

Before she left, Rayya said, 'Your father must be very sad to have lost you. Your brother and sister too and your nanny. They must miss you, Jimmy. You are a good boy. Go back to them.'

'My brother's dead, Mrs Banu. He died just before I came here, to this city. And my dad, well, he can't see beyond his own grief. It's hard to break through that wall. There isn't room for me in his world.'

'Oh your poor, poor father,' Rayya said. 'To lose your mother and now his first-born child; to have so much tragedy is too difficult to bear. But your sister, she will need you most of all, Jimmy. Go home *beta*, go and help them get through this and it will help you too. No-one should be alone.'

'I need to find Betwa.'

'You need to see your family, Jimmy. You are lucky to have such a thing. This girl will find you if she can, if it is your destiny. People aren't difficult to find these days. Even an old woman like me knows this. Go home, Jimmy.'

In the afternoon, before it got dark, Rayya knocked on the door of her neighbour's house. The large Australian woman answered the door.

'I am enquiring about the mother of the little girl. Is she okay after the shock of the other day?' Rayya asked.

'Oh she's fine. Hard as nails. Probably won't ever forgive Grace though, although it's the kid to blame in all honesty. What was she thinking, sneaking off like that? Gave poor Gracey the fright of her life. Like mother like daughter, I'd say. Anyway, see for yourself.' The woman banged on the adjacent door in the short hallway. Within a few seconds the girl's mother appeared,

'What?' she said bluntly, but when she saw Rayya standing in the doorway, she softened. 'Oh, it's you,' she said. 'I was going to come and thank you.'

'As if,' the neighbour said.

The little girl's mother ignored her and continued to speak directly to Rayya. 'Daban told me how you ran around the park looking for Tuli. Thank you for finding her. I won't be letting her out of my sight again.'

'Your neighbour, not this lady but the other one, she was very upset,' Rayya said.

'You mean Grace? Well, she should have looked after Tuli better. What if she'd been knocked over? Or been abducted or something? Luckily she's fine. I've told her never to do anything like that again but she's a dreamer, always in her own world, always imagining things; I expect she just wandered off in a daze but Grace should've been keeping an eye. I'll just have to make sure I don't leave her again.'

'You work for Mr Makrides don't you?' Rayya said.

The woman nodded. She looked Rayya up and down suspiciously.

'If you have to work, I can help with looking after your daughter. I'm just next door. I have to stay nearby to look after my husband anyway. He is very sick.' The words stuck in her throat but Rayya forced them out. 'He is confined to bed. I am his carer.'

'Oh, that's hard. I'm sorry to hear about it,' the girl's mother said. Her face was gentle now and she sounded as if she meant it.

'It's okay. It is what it is,' Rayya said. 'It means I have some time but I need to stay close by. I can collect from school even; it's okay to leave him for a few minutes, ten or fifteen perhaps, and I can teach her to cook or help with homework. I probably look like I know nothing but I know many things.' She patted down the pleats of her sari as she spoke. 'Perhaps between us, me and your downstairs neighbour, not this one but the other, we can help you. I imagine raising a child alone is very difficult.'

The young woman shrugged her shoulders.

'And Daban is a friend of us both, yes? He can be a reference for me. I used to work in the infant school, dinner lady and assistant in the classroom. I will be happy to help.' She paused, then added, 'Of course, I don't need payment. Having such a lovely child for company will be more than enough.'

'Really?' the mother said. Just then the little girl appeared behind her on the stairs.

'Yes please, Mummy. I promise I won't go out of the front door, not never ever.' The child grinned at Rayya and the mother smiled too. Rayya noticed how alike they looked.

She told Satish all about it as soon as she got home. She found it hard to contain her excitement.

'Imagine a child, here in our house? It will certainly brighten things up, hai na?'

She didn't tell him of her conversation with Jimmy though; that was just for her to know about.

When it was time to prepare Satish for the night, she gently closed his eyelids and kissed his forehead. She retrieved the letter from the hospice and re-read it, careful not to disturb the peace of the room with the rustling of the paper. She slipped it back into its envelope and propped it up against their wedding photo. Before she left the room, she whispered to Satish,

'Thank you my darling, thank you for loving me.'

34. EBELE

'Apology accepted,' Daban had said when Ebele called him the next day.

'I keep thinking about your friend, Jimmy,' she said. 'I don't like it, him hanging about at the back of our houses, but maybe I was a bit harsh.'

'It's fine. I expect he's used to it. Can I go back to sleep now please?'

'I thought it was morning,' she said. 'Sorry.' She paused, 'He seems so young. He should go home; someone will be missing him.'

'Can we talk about it later?' Daban said sleepily. 'It's only just past six and as you know Mr Makrides is a bit hard to take on not enough sleep.'

She checked the time. It was early but a pale blue light had seeped into the room, enough to draw the line under nighttime. It was her favourite time of day – quiet and uncluttered.

'I was going to find out about a hostel or something. Somewhere he can go, away from here. What do you think, Daban?'

'Mr Makrides?'

'No, your friend Jimmy, the tramp. He can't stay in the car forever.'

'Ebele, I'll call you later, when it's properly morning.'

After the call ended she lay on her bed, watching shadows flicker across the room. She knew she should think of practical things: whether Makrides would let her change her hours so she could be at the school gates in time for Tuli each day; the costs of After School Club. She tried to work out the maths on a scrap of paper – extra hours at Club meant extra work; it didn't make sense. She'd never ask Grace again; at least that was certain. Perhaps the Indian lady's suggestion was worth considering. But practicalities were pushed aside by random musings: Jimmy morphed into a child; the baby Ebele in her mother's profile picture; Tuli, sleeping soundly down the landing, murmuring in her dreams. Each thought dissipated quickly. Really it was Daban she wanted to focus on. She found herself wondering about him: how he could be so gentle when everything was so tough. She wanted to talk to him, to ask him what made him happy, what drove him mad. She switched on the radio and lay back on her pillows, allowing thoughts of him to breeze across her mind as smooth jazz drifted across the room.

At seven, she made herself instant coffee as quietly as she could and sat at the dining table, looking out onto the street, watching as the day caught up with itself. Much had happened in the preceding days to drag her down but somehow, something was pulling her a different way, and for the first time in many years, she looked forward to the day ahead. She checked the clock again and again, keeping her mobile close to hand. She would call him at seven-thirty she decided, a decent enough time. But at twenty-five minutes past her phone vibrated across the table and made her jump.

'So Ebele,' Daban said, completely unexpectedly, 'When was the last time you went out properly? I mean to see some music or eat in a restaurant?'

Once again the lightness in his voice surprised her. It was as though he saw through the second-rate version of herself she presented to the world.

'I don't go out. You know I can't. Because of Tuli. Especially now. There's no one to leave her with, not anyone I can trust.'

'Well, maybe we can go for an early dinner, to one of the Turkish places along the Parade, and Tuli can come along too. Those places are full of families.'

Ebele smiled.

'Why are you so patient with me, Daban?' she said. She imagined him on the other side of the line, scratching his head, thinking of what to say. He spoke immediately.

'Life is short. And, as far as I know, there's just one shot at it. I decided long ago to make it the best I could, to see the best in people. We don't have much, people like us, but there's nothing worth having we can't have. And, I like you. I like you a lot, Ebele. I think about you.'

She blushed. She was glad he couldn't see her: hair frizzy and unkempt, yesterday's make-up; a faded tee-shirt for pyjamas, the funk of morning hanging around her.

'Okay,' she said. 'An early dinner with Tuli sometime. But not yet, it's too soon.'

'What about a walk in the park instead? Less pressure.'

'Maybe a walk in the park,' she said. 'I'll see you at work, Daban.'

Ebele was alone in the shop most of the morning. Makrides was out on business and Daban was yet to arrive after an early delivery. There was no sign of any customers, on or offline, so after she wiped down the displays, readjusted bed-covers and sifted through emails, she made herself tea and half-heartedly scanned through the week's copy of the Gazette which lay idle on the counter. Outside, a stationary vehicle blasted out Beyonce's *Single Ladies* as a couple of old women in niqab shuffled by; she smirked at the incongruity of the scene. When she returned to the newspaper something else caught her eye and she stared at the page for a long time, re-reading the headline and looking closely at the image alongside. It declared the *Body in the River Identified*. A girl missing for nearly a month, gone just days after her mother's funeral. There was no father, just a grandmother who'd identified the girl as Betwa Bansal, aged nineteen. The grandmother was devastated. She'd searched for the girl tirelessly. She was traced through letters she'd written to her estranged daughter, Betwa's mother. The letters were discovered in a locked case stowed above a cupboard in a flat on Shifnal Road. Some dated far back, to when Betwa was just a baby. The news article said there was CCTV of a man in a suit who the police wanted to question in connection with the death but as yet no one had come forward. Ebele was shaken by the story. She wondered which end of Shifnal Road the girl lived on and how many times they'd passed each other in the street. She felt sick at the thought of it. She shoved the newspaper into her bag and slipped into the utility area to splash water on her face before anyone came into the shop. When she emerged, Makrides was stumbling through the entrance loaded up with fabric samples.

'Don't just stand there looking at me like I have come from the moon,' he said. 'Come and help me. Take these and put them on the counter. We have a very important customer coming. They are interested in the sofa set. Come on, hurry up. I don't pay you to stand around.'

Later, when Tuli was fast asleep, Ebele lay next to Daban on her bed, listening to the rain and watching dapples of neon light throwing patterns across his naked body.

At midnight, he said, 'I better go. Before the little one wakes up.' Ebele watched silently as he dressed in the dark. 'It's been a good day,' he said as he pulled on his coat. 'Thank you.'

Ebele switched on the bedside lamp and sat up. 'Don't go yet,' she said. 'I need to show you something first. It's to do with your friend, Jimmy. I wasn't sure whether to show you at all, whether it's too much to know, but I don't want to keep it from you. Not now.'

She reached into her bag and pulled out the crumpled newspaper and passed it over. When he finished reading, he sat on the edge of the bed with his face in his hands. She put her arm around him and he rested his head against her.

'I don't know if it would be more cruel to tell him or not to tell him,' Daban said after a few minutes.

'Maybe it's better to let him have some hope; it's not like he has much else. I'm sorry, Daban.' she said.

'It's not your fault, Ebele. It's somebody's fault but not yours.'

The next morning, as Tuli ate breakfast cereal on the floor of her bedroom, Ebele said, 'You've still got a grandma you know,' and she watched her daughter's eyes light up.

'A real one, Mummy? Not a story one?'

'Yes, Tuli. Look.' She held out her phone.

'Am I the baby?'

'No, it's me, silly. She's holding me when I was a baby.'

'Oh Mummy,' Tuli said. 'She has the same face as you but in white.'

Ebele took the phone back and peered at the profile picture. 'Really?' she said. 'Do you think so?'

'Is that grandma lost, Mummy? Why didn't she come to see me already?'

'She's sort of lost. I think I lost her, or she lost me. I can't remember but maybe the time has come to try and find her. She doesn't even know about you yet and it'll be a big surprise.'

'Will I be a good surprise?'

'You'll be a wonderful surprise, Tuli.'

'Mummy, do you think she likes chocolate?'

Tuli hummed and bounced her favourite soft toy on her knee. Ebele kissed her daughter's cheek and peered out of the window to see if Jimmy was there. All was still at the back of the gardens, except for a ginger cat who tiptoed across the wall and jumped when it reached the zigzag of glass.

35. JIMMY

Daban arrived in the early evening with shopping bags. He pulled out beer and crisps, firelighters and kindling and handed over a can to Jimmy.

'I wasn't sure if you were going to stick around or not but I thought I'd give you a send-off either way,' he said. He spent the next ten minutes making a fire in the centre of the concrete floor beyond the tangle of brambles and bushes. When the fire was lit, the two men sat on a half-built wall staring silently into the flames.

'This was going to be a pottery shed for Makrides' wife,' Daban said casually. He tossed a twig into the fire; it hissed and spat sparks towards them. 'It was a present, a surprise for her but she died before he had a chance to finish it. He loved her very much, they say.'

Jimmy watched as firelight glowed across Daban's face. He'd known this man for no more than a few days yet he could hardly imagine not knowing him.

'Things rarely turn out as planned,' he said, and they sat in silence again.

'Don't suppose you know where you're going next?' Daban asked.

Jimmy warmed his hands in front of the fire. For a few moments the only sound was the crackle of the flames.

'Maybe it's time to stop searching,' Daban said after a short while. 'Everyone knows someone who knows someone around here,' he added. 'It's not as big as people think. You would have found her by now if she was around these parts.'

'She's got to be somewhere.'

'You should call home,' Daban said as he passed across another can.

Jimmy opened it and took a long swig,

Daban held out his phone. 'It's unlocked.' When Jimmy didn't take it, Daban laid it on the low wall between them. 'I'm going to go over there,' he said pointing towards the bright window where Jimmy had first seen Tuli. 'It's where my girlfriend lives; that's her daughter's room you can see. I'll be back in twenty.'

Jimmy picked up the phone and turned it over in his hands, running his fingers across the digits until, almost subconsciously he dialled the only number he knew by heart. It connected straightaway and before he could change his mind there was a familiar gruff voice on the other end.

'Who is this? Speak up will you.'

He wanted to throw the phone into the fire but instead he forced out words.

'It's me, it's Jimmy.'

The phone went quiet for a few seconds until a different voice came on the line

'Jimmy, oh my god, Jimmy. We've been searching for you everywhere. We thought you'd gone, like Anthony.'

It was a shock to hear Jenny's voice, even more so than Frank's. He cut the call without responding but the phone rang back immediately and he knew it would be Jenny and not Frank.

'Please come home, Jimmy,' she said. 'Please, it'll be fine, I promise.'

When Daban reappeared, the flames had fizzled out and only embers remained. Jimmy was glad there was so little light.

When day came, Jimmy surveyed the detritus of his recent life sprawled across the back seat of the car: grubby sleeping bag, mud-caked clothes, the tartan wool blanket, relatively clean. Anything of value was already packed away in the rucksack: two paperback books, pages smudged, corners creased, and

Betwa's denim jacket neatly rolled beneath them. That was it, all he owned. He flung the bag over his shoulder and waited as a song playing on the car stereo faded out in the background.

Mrs Banu appeared mid-morning, just as she said she would. She was wrapped in a thick coat, heavier than the one she usually wore.

'Winter has come promptly,' she said. 'Autumn hardly had a chance to thrive and now suddenly it has disappeared.'

'Yep,' he said. He took the coffee and the package of cellophane-wrapped food she offered and pushed it into his bag. 'I'm leaving the blanket,' he said nodding at the back seat. 'But I'd like to keep the flask? I'll replace it one day, I promise.'

'No need,' she said. 'Once, me and Satish took hot tea in a flask every time we went into town or had a little day trip out of the city. Now I have little use for these things.'

'Well, I'll be glad of it later,' he said.

'I hope you have a good journey, Jimmy.'

'Thank you, me too,' he replied.

There was nothing left to say but she hesitated and his urge was to embrace her, like he would Nan. Instead he reached out and put a hand on her shoulder. She looked like she might cry.

'You are a good boy, beta,' she said. 'I hope you find the peace you are looking for.'

'I hope you do too,' he said as she walked away, but she didn't appear to hear.

Before he left the alleyway Jimmy glanced up at Tuli's bedroom window. She was there, framed, with her back to him, dancing with her arms outstretched.

Acknowledgements

The support and encouragement of others has enabled me to write this book. Thank you to all those who have been there along the way and apologies to those not directly mentioned here.

Firstly, thank you Kevin Duffy at Bluemoose Books for publishing this novel. I am proud to be with a publisher who works so passionately on behalf of writers and readers, to make the industry better, fairer, more diverse. Thank you to the wider Bluemoose team behind the scenes too. I am especially grateful for the valuable insights, patience and skills of my editor, Leonora Rustamova, and Hetha Duffy, who I know does more than she ever lets on.

Funding from Arts Council England almost certainly allowed this book to happen. Thank you to them for crucial financial support at a time I needed it most, and also for funding organisations which work tirelessly to develop and champion new writing and writers. On that note, a massive personal thank you to Lesley Wood at New Writing South for providing me with time, space and moral support throughout the writing process. It is appreciated. Thanks also to Writing West Midlands for allowing me to access Room 204 and receive useful feedback from fellow writers as a result; and to The Literary Consultancy, for sending me in the direction of Anna South whose comments on an early draft were instrumental in the development of this story. Thank you to West Dean College of Arts and Conservation for inviting me to be a writer in residence and thereby giving me space to finish, and to Brighton & Hove Libraries, where I spend almost all my writing days.

Many thanks to the Write Process group for peer support, good company and expert writing advice: Laura Wilkinson, Anna Jefferson, Katy Massey, Bridget Whelan, Lou Tondeur, Jules Grant, Rosie Chard and Kate Lee; all brilliant, talented and generous writers. Thanks too, Beth Miller, Mark A Radcliffe and many others who are an important part of my community of writers. In particular, Amy Raphael for comradeship over many years and, in this instance, for being one of my early readers alongside Joe and Ruben.

Thank you to Małgorzata (Gosia) Łapsa-Malawska for letting us use her stunning painting, *The last conversation (why?) Bright sky after the storm* as the cover of this book; it is perfect.

Love and gratitude to: Joe, Milan, Ruben and Varsha, my mother, Brij Bala Duggal, late father, Sarb Jit Duggal, my sisters and brothers and my extended family. And to my friends for their vital companionship and unwavering solidarity. Finally, a special thank you to Stella Boosalis (née Porpaxias) for specific advice and inspiration but especially for unrivalled friendship over almost four entire decades.

the freelance photographer's market handbook 2011

Edited by
John Tracy
& Stewart Gibson

 BFP BOOKS London

Published for the Bureau of Freelance Photographers by BFP Books, Focus House,
497 Green Lanes, London N13 4BP. Typesetting and page layout by BFP Books.
Text set in New Century Schoolbook. Printed in Great Britain by the MPG Books Group.

CONTENTS

PREFACE

The past 12 months has seen economic conditions continuing to restrain growth in the publishing sector and recent sales figures provide unhappy reading for many publishers.

The effects of the recession and competition from the Internet, in a market already saturated with competing titles, continues to hurt many publications.

Over the past decade, overall UK magazine sales have declined by some 25 per cent, though real decline only really set in around five years ago. Inevitably this coincided with the rise of the Internet as a primary source for news and other information.

However, while newspapers and many general magazines have lost sales over recent years, many upmarket or specialist magazines have actually been increasing them.

A major reason would appear to be that these titles have only a limited presence online. Readers have to buy them to read them, and many remain happy to do so.

Print still provides a more rewarding experience for many readers, especially when it comes to high-quality picture display and information for the dedicated enthusiast.

As we write, figures released by the Audit Bureau of Circulations (ABC) gave an indication of an improving outlook for the UK consumer magazine sector.

Total circulation for audited titles in the first half of 2010 increased by 0.3 per cent compared with the same period in 2009. A small increase to be sure, but an increase nonetheless.

Given the economic climate and those continuing pressures from the Internet, this is rather reassuring for print publishers.

The results appear to underline a continued high level of consumer demand for magazines in the face of both economic pressures and the availability of an increasing array of media choices.

Unsurprisingly though, launch activity has remained at a standstill. Publishers are still unprepared to take the risk of chancing a brand-new title in a marketplace that seems to be content with what it already has.

But compared to previous years, significant closures have been remarkably few. Those titles that have managed to survive so far, seem destined to go on doing so.

The picture agency scene also remains subdued. There have been fewer launches, fewer closures and fewer acquisitions than for some time.

One of the more encouraging events of 2010 was the collapse of the attempt by the giant Getty Images – which has been swallowing up rivals large and small for many years – to acquire the old-established Rex Features, one of the UK's most venerable picture agencies. This followed a referral of the proposed deal to the Competition Commission by the Office of Fair Trading.

If this event signals an end to the reduction of competition and the consequent forcing down of fees paid by picture buyers, then it can only be beneficial as far as both the independent agency and the freelance contributor are concerned.

Overall it remains true that despite the many ups and downs of the past several years, the market for freelance photography continues to expand, both online and off.

ABOUT THE BFP

Founded in 1965, the Bureau of Freelance Photographers is today the major body for the freelance photographer. It has a worldwide membership, comprising not only full-time freelances, but also serious amateur and semi-professional photographers. Being primarily a service organisation, membership of the Bureau is open to anyone with an interest in freelance photography.

The most important service offered to members is the *Market Newsletter*, a confidential monthly report on the state of the freelance market. A well-researched and highly authoritative publication, the *Newsletter* keeps freelances in touch with the market for freelance work, mainly by giving information on the type of photography currently being sought by a wide range of publications and other outlets. It gives full details of new magazines and their editorial requirements, and generally reports on what is happening in the publishing world and how this is likely to affect the freelance photographer.

The *Newsletter* also includes in-depth interviews with editors, profiles of successful freelances, examples of successful pictures, and other general features to help freelances in understanding and approaching the marketplace.

The *Newsletter* is considered essential reading for the freelance and aspiring freelance photographer, and because it pinpoints launches and changes in the marketplace as they occur, it also acts as a useful supplement to the *Handbook*. The *Handbook* itself is an integral part of BFP membership services; members paying the full annual fee automatically receive a copy every year as it is published.

Other services provided to members for the modest annual subscription include:

● Advisory Service. Individual advice on all aspects of freelancing is available to members.

● Mediation Service. The Bureau tries to protect its members' interests in every way it can. In particular, it is often able to assist individual members in recovering unpaid fees and in settling copyright or other disputes.

● Exclusive items and special offers. The Bureau regularly offers books and other useful items to members, usually at discount prices.

● In the Services section of this *Handbook* can be found a number of companies providing special discounts to BFP members on production of a current membership card. Amongst various services members can obtain comprehensive photographic insurance cover at competitive rates.

For further details and an application form, write to Bureau of Freelance Photographers, Focus House, 497 Green Lanes, London N13 4BP, telephone 020 8882 3315, e-mail mail@thebfp.com, or visit the BFP website at www.thebfp.info. Or if you wish to join right away, you'll find an application form at the back of this book, after the main index.

HOW TO USE THIS BOOK

Anyone with the ability to use a camera correctly has the potential to make money from their pictures. Taking saleable photographs isn't difficult; the difficulty lies in finding the market. It isn't enough for you, the photographer in search of a sale, to find what you think *might* be a suitable market; rather you must find *exactly* the right magazine, publisher, agency or whatever for your particular type of work. Many a sale is lost when work which is, in itself, technically perfect fails to fulfil the total requirements of the buyer.

The Freelance Photographer's Market Handbook has been designed to help resolve these difficulties. It puts you in touch with major markets for your work, telling you exactly what each is looking for, together with hints and tips on how to sell to them and, wherever possible, an idea of the rates they pay.

The *Handbook* covers five big markets for your pictures: magazines (by far the largest), newspapers, book publishers, picture agencies, and companies producing cards, calendars, posters and other print products. There are three ways of using the book, depending on the way you need or wish to work:

1. If you are out to sell to magazines and you can offer coverage on a theme particularly applicable to a certain type of publication (eg gardening, angling, sport) turn to the magazine section and look for the subject. The magazines are listed under 36 categories, each of which has a broad heading covering specific magazines. The categories are in alphabetical order, as are the magazines within those categories. You need only read through them to discover which is best for your type of work.

2. If you have a set of pictures that fall into a specific photographic category (landscapes, children, celebrities etc), turn to the subject index on page 21.

11

Look up your chosen subject and there you will find a list of all the magazines with a strong interest in that particular type of picture. You then have only to look up each one mentioned in the appropriate section for precise details of their requirements. (If in doubt as to where to find a particular magazine consult the general index at the back of the book.) There are separate subject indexes for book publishers and agencies on pages 152 and 175 respectively.

3. If you are looking for the requirements of a specific magazine, book publisher, agency, card or calendar publisher, whose name is already known to you, simply refer to the general index at the back of the book.

Some points to remember

With this wealth of information open to you, and with those three options for finding the right market, there is no reason why you shouldn't immediately start earning good cash from your camera. But before you rush off to submit your images, here are some points worth bearing in mind and which will help you to more successful sales:

1. The golden rule of freelancing: don't send people pictures they don't want. Read the requirements listed in the various parts of this directory and obey them. When, for instance, a Scottish magazine says they want pictures of all things Scottish with the exception of kilts and haggis, you can be sure they are over-stocked with these subjects. They are not going to make an exception just for you, however good you think your pictures might be.

2. Digital images supplied on disc are the norm nowadays, but always check preferred image file format and size with your chosen market in advance. Small selections of low-resolution files may be sent as initial samples via e-mail, but e-mail is rarely an acceptable method of submission for larger files or batches of material intended for publication. If still working with colour film, and unless the listing states otherwise, always supply transparencies rather than prints.

3. When submitting pictures, make sure they are accompanied by detailed captions. And don't forget to put your own name and address on each photograph/CD.

4. If you have an idea for a picture or feature for a particular publication, don't

be afraid to telephone or e-mail first to discuss what you have in mind. Nearly every editor or picture buyer approached when the *Handbook* was being compiled said they would much prefer to hear from potential freelances in advance, rather than have inappropriate pictures or words landing on their desks.

5. If seeking commissions, always begin by making an appointment with the appropriate person in order to show your portfolio and/or cuttings. Do not turn up at a busy editor's office unannounced and expect to be met with open arms.

6. Enclose a stamped addressed envelope if you want a posted submission returned if unsuccessful.

APPROACHING THE MARKET

You've chosen your market, taken the pictures and written the captions. Full of hope and expectation, you put your work in the post. A week later, it comes back with a formal rejection slip. Why? Where did you go wrong?

You have only to look through the pages of this book to see that there are a lot of markets open to the freelance photographer, yet the sad fact remains that a great many of those who try their hand at editorial freelancing fail the first few times, and many never succeed at all. That isn't meant to be as discouraging as it might sound. On the contrary, because so many freelances fail, *you*, with the inside knowledge gleaned from these pages, stand a better chance of success than most. What's more you can gain from the experience of others.

So let's take a look at some of the areas where the inexperienced freelance goes wrong. Knowing the common mistakes, you can avoid them and consequently stand the best chance of success with your own work.

The first big mistake made by the novice is in the actual form of the pictures they supply.

Images taken with digital cameras are acceptable to all markets, but really need to be produced on a well-specified digital SLR in order to provide the quality parameters necessary for high-quality reproduction. For submission to picture markets they must also be of a suitable high resolution (usually 300dpi) and large file size. Picture buyers will expect the images to be submitted on CD or DVD, not via e-mail.

In the case of film, high-quality prints or slides may still be acceptable to some markets. But if you are shooting on film, bear in mind that most buyers in the publishing world will prefer to receive digital files scanned from your slides or negatives, not original film material.

Most publications are all-colour, but a number of smaller magazines still use some black and white, while many up-market titles like to use a proportion of high-quality monochrome imagery. In this case, high-quality black and white digital files or prints will usually be required.

A few markets – such as calendars and greetings cards, or certain specialist magazines and picture libraries – do continue to favour film, often in the form of larger format transparencies for ultimate reproduction quality.

The quality of your work must be first class. Images should be pin-sharp and perfectly exposed to give strong, saturated colours. Slight under-exposure of around one-third to half a stop may be acceptable, but over-exposure never. *Never* send over-exposed, washed-out pictures.

While all markets now accept images in digital form, each will have specific technical requirements or preferences that should be ascertained before submission. File format and image size preferences do vary, so always check with your chosen market for their precise requirements in each case.

Unless otherwise stated in an individual entry, it can be assumed that all the markets listed here accept both digital and film submissions.

So much for picture format, but what of the actual subject of your pictures? Here again, a lot of fundamental mistakes are made. The oldest rule in the freelancing book is this: don't take pictures, then look for markets; find a market first and then shoot your pictures specifically with that market in mind.

Every would-be freelance knows that rule; yet the many who ignore it is frankly staggering. Remember that rule and act accordingly. First find your market, analyse it to see the sort of pictures it uses, then go all out to take *exactly* the right type of picture.

Editors see a lot of pictures every day, and the vast majority are totally unsuited to their market. Of those that are suited, many are still rejected because, despite being the right *type* of pictures, the subjects are still uninspiring. They are subjects the editor has seen over and over again; and the type that the magazine will already have on file. So once again, the work gets rejected.

Remember this and learn from it. Most of the pictures that fall on an editor's desk are pretty ordinary. If you want to make yours sell, you have to show them something different. It might be a fairly straightforward view of an unusual subject, or it might be a more common subject, seen and photographed from a new angle. Either way, it will be different.

So when you set out to take your pictures, really look at your subject and, even before you press the shutter, ask yourself, why am I taking this picture? Why will an editor want to buy it? What's so different or unusual about it? How can I make a few changes here and now to give it a better chance of success?

Good, traditional picture composition also plays a part in a picture's chances. Many would-be freelances submit pictures of people in which the principal subject is far too small and surrounded by a wealth of unwanted, distracting detail. So make a point, whenever you shoot, of moving in close and really filling the viewfinder with your subject.

Many potentially saleable landscapes are ruined by a flat perspective. So watch out for, and try to include, foreground interest in such pictures.

People at work on a craft or a hobby can be good sellers, but a good many pictures depicting such subjects are shot candidly without the necessary thought needed to really show the subject to its best. Always pose pictures like these before you take them.

Finally, a word about presentation. It's true that a good picture can often find a sale, no matter how badly it is presented; but it is equally true that bad presentation can have a negative influence on an editor or picture buyer and so ruin your chances of success. So why make things difficult for yourself?

When you send prints or CDs, make sure they are stiffly packed between thick card or in cardboard envelopes. Present any slides in plastic filing wallets and make them easy to view with the minimum of fuss.

With digital submissions, an editor will always appreciate a print-out of thumbnail images for quick reference.

If you are sending words – either captions to pictures or a full-blown article – always submit a "hard copy" print-out as well as including your text and/or caption files on the CD.

Send your submission with a brief covering letter, not with pages of explanations about the work. The sale will stand or fall by your pictures and/or words, never by the excuses you offer as to why certain pictures might not be too good. If they're not good enough, they won't sell.

Give your editors what they want. Give them originality and sparkle, and present the whole package in the best way you can. Learn the rules and you'll be on your way to a good many picture sales.

But don't think that anyone is going to break those rules just for you. If your pictures don't measure up to what is required, there will always be another submission right behind full of pictures that do. And there are no prizes for guessing which submission is going to make the sale.

MAGAZINES

The British magazine market is vast. Anyone who doubts that has only to look at the racks of periodicals in any major newsagent. And this is only the tip of the iceberg, the largest section of the consumer press. Beneath the surface there is the trade press, controlled circulation magazines and many smaller publications that are never seen on general sale. At the last count more than 8,000 magazines were being published on a regular basis in Britain.

In this section you will find detailed listings of magazines which are looking for freelances. Some pay a lot, others are less generous, but all have one thing in common – they are here because they need freelance contributions on a regular basis and they are willing to pay for them.

When you come to start looking at these listings in detail, you might be surprised by the number of magazines of which you have never heard. Don't let that put you off. What the newcomer to freelancing often fails to realise is that there are as many, if not more, trade magazines or small specialist titles as there are major consumer publications, and very few of these are ever seen on general sale.

Trade magazines, as the term implies, are aimed at people whose business is making money from the particular subject concerned. As such, their requirements are usually totally different to their consumer counterparts.

As an example, consider boating. A consumer magazine on that subject will be aimed at the boat owner or enthusiast and could contain features on boats and the way they are handled. A trade magazine on the same subject is likely to be more interested in articles about the profits being made by the boating industry and pictures of shop displays of boating accessories.

Trade magazines do not necessarily have a separate section to themselves. If the subject is a common one, such as the example above in which there are both trade and consumer publications, they have been listed for your convenience under a common heading. Despite that, however, there *is* a section specifically for trade. This contains trade magazines that have no consumer counterparts, as well as magazines whose subject is actually trade itself and trading in general.

As you go through these listings, therefore, it is important for you to realise that there is a very real difference between the two sides of the subject, but it is a difference which is explained under each publication's requirements. So don't ignore trade magazines of whose existence you were not previously aware. Very often such a magazine will have just as big a market for your pictures and the fees will be just as good, if not better, than those offered by the consumer press.

It is often a good idea for the freelance to aim at some of the more obscure publications listed here, be they trade magazines or the smaller hobbyist magazines. Simply because they are a little obscure they may not have been noticed by other freelances and, as such, your sales potential may well be higher even if fees paid by some of these publications are relatively low.

When you are looking through the entries, don't stop at the section on illustrations. Read what the magazine needs in the way of text too. A publication that might appear to have a very small market for individual pictures often has a larger potential for illustrated articles, and all you need to do to make a sale is add a few words.

You will also find that many publications talk about needing mainly commissioned work. Don't be misled by this. The commissions are given to freelances and, although this means they won't consider your work on spec, they could well be interested in giving you a commission if you can prove you are worth it. That's where previous experience comes in. When trying for commissions, you should always have examples of previously published work to show an editor.

Many of the larger magazines employ a specific editor to deal with picture submissions and with photographers. They may go under various titles – picture editor, art editor, art director – but this is the person directly responsible for picture selection and for commissioning photographers for specific jobs. This, therefore, is the person you should approach when sending pictures or seeking photographic assignments. When sending written material though – illustrated or not – your approach is best made direct to the editor.

The magazine market is one of the largest available to the freelance. You might not receive as large a fee per picture as you would from, say, the calendar market, or for certain sales that might be made on your behalf by an agency, but what this field does offer is a *steady* income, especially once you have made a breakthrough with one or more titles.

There are so many magazines, covering so many different subjects, that freelances who have their wits about them would be hard put *not* to find one to which their own style and interests can be adapted. Make yourself known to a few chosen magazine editors, let them see that you can turn out good quality work on the right subject, at the right time, and there is no reason why this market shouldn't make you a good, regular income, either part time or full time.

New Listings, Changes & Deletions

The following is designed to alert readers to possible new markets as well as to important changes that have taken place since the last edition of the *Handbook*.

'New Listings' includes magazines that have been launched since the last edition appeared as well as established titles that appear in the *Handbook* for the first time. 'Title Changes' lists publications that have changed their names (previous titles in brackets). 'Deletions' lists publications that appeared in the previous edition but are omitted from this one. Publications under this heading have not necessarily ceased publication – they may have been deleted because they no longer offer a worthwhile market for the contributor.

To find the page number for any particular magazine, refer to the main index at the back of the book.

New Listings

How It Works
Practical Sportsbikes
Rotorhub

Title Changes

Visordown (Two Wheels Only)
Master Photography
 (Master Photo>Digital)
Waitrose Kitchen
 (Waitrose Food Illustrated)
Prima Baby & Pregnancy (Prima Baby)

Deletions

Building Services Journal
Chemistry & Industry
Flypast
Go Flying!
Hardware & Garden Review
Horse & Pony
House & Garden
International Rugby News
Italy
Scotland Outdoors
Scouting Magazine
Snowboard UK
Traditional Boats & Tall Ships

Subject Index

Only magazines are included in this index, but it should be noted that many of these subjects are also required by agencies, book publishers and card and calendar publishers.

Separate subject indexes for book publishers and picture agencies appear in the appropriate sections, on pages 153 and 177 respectively.

To find the page number for any magazine, refer to the main index at the back of the book.

Agriculture

BBC Countryfile
The Countryman
Crops
Dairy Farmer
Eurofruit Magazine
Farmers Guardian
Farmers Weekly
Home Farmer
Poultry World
Waitrose Kitchen

Aircraft

Aeroplane
Air International
Airforces Monthly
Airliner World
Aviation News
Defence Helicopter
Flight International
Flyer
How It Works
Jane's Defence Weekly
Pilot
Rotorhub
Today's Pilot

Arts/Crafts

Best of British
Classic Stitches
Furniture & Cabinetmaking
Good Woodworking
Knitting
The Lady
This England
Woodcarving
Woodturning
The Woodworker

Birds

BBC Wildlife
Bird Watching
Birdwatch
The Falconers & Raptor Conservation
    Magazine
Parrots
Pet Product Marketing
Racing Pigeon Pictorial

Boats/Nautical

Boat International
Canal Boat
Canals & Rivers
Classic Boat
Coast
International Boat Industry
Jet Skier & PW
Marine Engineers Review
Motor Boat and Yachting
Motor Boats Monthly
RYA Magazine
Rowing & Regatta
Sailing Today
Sportsboat & RIB Magazine
Towpath Talk
Water Craft
Waterways World
Yachting Monthly
Yachting World
Yachts and Yachting

Buildings

Architecture Today
BD
Build It
Country Homes and Interiors
The English Home
FX

House Beautiful
Housebuilder
Icon
Municipal Journal
Period Living
Planning
RIBA Journal
SelfBuild & Design
Stadium & Arena Management
World of Interiors

Business

Accountancy Age
CA Magazine
CNBC European Business
Computer Weekly
Director
EN
The Economist
Financial Management
Marketing
People Management

Celebrities

Bella
Best
Closer
Glamour
Grazia
Heat
Hello!
Look
Mizz
More
Now
OK!
Radio Times
Red
Reveal
Saga
The Stage
Sugar
TV Times
Woman

Children

Mother & Baby
Nursery World
Prima Baby & Pregnancy
Right Start
Scholastic Magazines

Domestic/Farm Animals

Dairy Farmer
Dogs Today
Farmers Guardian
Farmers Weekly
Home Farmer
Horse
Horse & Rider
K9 Magazine
Kennel and Cattery Management
The Lady
Pet Product Marketing
Your Cat
Your Dog

Fashion

Bella
Best
Company
Condé Nast Customer Publishing
Drapers
Elle
Esquire
Essentials
FHM
Front
GQ
Glamour
Good Housekeeping
Grazia
Harper's Bazaar
The Lady
Loaded
Look
Marie Claire
Mizz
More
Prima
Red
Refresh
She
Woman
Woman's Own
Woman's Weekly

Flowers/Plants

BBC Gardeners' World
Country Homes & Interiors
The English Garden
The Garden

Garden Answers
Garden News
Garden Trade News
Gardens Illustrated
Gardens Monthly
Good Homes
Good Housekeeping
Homes & Gardens
Horticulture Week
House Beautiful
The Lady
Woman&Home

Food/Drink

Bella
Best
British Baker
Caterer & Hotelkeeper
Country Homes & Interiors
Decanter
Essentials
Eurofruit Magazine
Food & Travel
France
French Magazine
Good Housekeeping
Home Farmer
Homes & Gardens
House Beautiful
Italia!
Lifescape
Olive
Prima
Publican
Red
Restaurant
Scottish Licensed Trade News
Waitrose Kitchen
Woman&Home

Glamour/Erotic

Club International
Escort
FHM
Front
Loaded
Mayfair
Men Only
Nuts
Zoo

Homes/Interiors

Best
Build It
Coast
Country Homes & Interiors
Elle Decoration
The English Home
Essentials
Glamour
Good Homes
Good Housekeeping
Homes & Gardens
House Beautiful
Ideal Home
Period Living
Prima
Real Homes
Red
SelfBuild & Design
25 Beautiful Homes
Woman&Home
World of Interiors
Your Home

Industry

Chemist & Druggist
Director
Education in Chemistry
The Engineer
Engineering
Financial Management
Industrial Diamond Review
People Management
Planning
Post Magazine
Professional Engineering
Urethanes Technology International
Utility Week
Works Management

Landscapes

Amateur Photographer
Best of British
Bird Watching
Camping
Cheshire Life
Coast
Cotswold Life
Country Life
Country Walking
The Countryman

Cumbria
Dalesman
Dorset
Dorset Life
The Great Outdoors
Hertfordshire Countryside
The Lady
Lancashire Life
Lincolnshire Life
Outdoor Photography
Photography Monthly
PhotoPlus
Practical Photography
The Scots Magazine
Somerset Life
Sussex Life
TGO – The Great Outdoors
This England/Evergreen
Trail
Walk
Waterways World
Yorkshire Life

Military

Air International
Airforces Monthly
Defence Helicopter
Jane's Defence Weekly

Motor Vehicles

American Car World
Auto Express
Autocar
The Automobile
Automotive Management
Boys Toys
Classic American
Classic Cars
Classic & Sports Car
Classic Plant & Machinery
Classics Monthly
Coach and Bus Week
Commercial Motor
Driving Magazine
Evo
4x4
Fleet News
Jaguar
Land Rover Monthly
Land Rover Owner International

Maxpower
Motor Trader
Motoring & Leisure
Motor Sport
911 & Porsche World
Octane
Performance Ford
Redline
Roadway
Top Gear Magazine
Total911
Tractor
Tractor & Machinery
Triumph World
Truck and Driver

Motorcycles

Back Street Heroes
Bike
Classic Bike
The Classic Motor Cycle
Dirt Bike Rider
Moto Magazine
Motor Cycle News
Practical Sportsbikes
Redline
Ride
Scootering
Superbike
Visordown

Pop/Rock

Blues and Soul
Heat
Kerrang!
Keyboard Player
Loaded
Metal Hammer
MixMag
Mojo
New Musical Express
Q
Rhythm
Total Guitar

Railways

Engineering in Miniature
Heritage Railway

International Railway Journal
Rail
Rail Express
Railnews
The Railway Magazine
Steam Railway
Today's Railways UK
Traction

Sport

All Out Cricket
Athletics Weekly
Badminton
Boat International
Boxing Monthly
Cycle Sport
Cycling Plus
Cycling Weekly
Darts World
Dirt Bike Rider
Esquire
F1 Racing
Fieldsports
Fighting Fit
FourFourTwo
GQ
Golf Monthly
Golf World
Horse & Hound
Loaded
Martial Arts Illustrated
Match
Men's Health
Motor Boats Monthly
Motor Cycle News
Motor Sport
Mountain Biking UK
Nuts
Redline
Rowing & Regatta
Rugby World
Running Fitness
Shooting Gazette
Shooting Times & Country Magazine
Ski & Board
The Skier & Snowboarder Magazine
Snooker Scene
Spin
Sports Boat & RIB Magazine
Sports Shooter
Stadium & Arena Management
Swimming Times

Today's Golfer
Visordown
Windsurf Magazine
The Wisden Cricketer
Yachts and Yachting
Zoo

Travel

A Place in the Sun
Australia & New Zealand
Business Life
Business Traveller
Coach and Bus Week
Condé Nast Customer Publishing
Condé Nast Traveller
Food & Travel
France
French Magazine
Geographical
Good Housekeeping
Italia!
The Lady
Living France
Motorhome Monthly
Motoring & Leisure
Olive
Real Travel
Saga Magazine
Spain
Sunday Times Travel Magazine
Travel & Leisure Magazine
The Traveller
Wanderlust
Woman&Home
Yours

Wildlife

Amateur Photographer
BBC Countryfile
BBC Wildlife
Bird Watching
Birdwatch
Coast
Country Life
Country Walking
The Countryman
Cumbria
Dalesman
Dorset
The Falconers & Raptor Conservation
    Magazine

The Field
Geographical
The Lady
Natural World
Outdoor Photography
Photography Monthly

PhotoPlus
Practical Photography
The Scottish Sporting Gazette
The Shooting Gazette
Shooting Times and Country Magazine
Sporting Shooter

Angling

ANGLER'S MAIL
IPC Media Ltd, Blue Fin Building, 110 Southwark Street, London SE1 0SU.
Tel: 020 3148 4159. E-mail: tim_knight@ipcmedia.com
Editor: Tim Knight.
Weekly publication with news and features for followers of coarse and sea fishing in the UK.
Illustrations: Topical news pictures of successful anglers with their catches. Captions should give full details concerning weight and circumstances of capture. Covers: pictures of anglers with exceptional specimen fish or catches.
Text: Features on coarse and sea fishing topics only. Up to 800 words.
Overall freelance potential: Minimal for non-angling freelances.
Editor's tips: Contributors really need knowledge and experience of the subject; pictures and text seen from non-anglers are rarely acceptable.
Fees: By agreement.

ANGLING TIMES
Bauer Media, Bushfield House, Orton Centre, Peterborough PE2 5UW.
Tel: 01733 395106. E-mail: rich.lee@bauermedia.co.uk
Editor: Richard Lee.
Weekly newspaper format publication covering mainly coarse angling. Includes news, features and general instruction.
Illustrations: General angling images, especially newsworthy catches, action and scenics. Covers: "stunning" action shots featuring anglers in the environment.
Text: Illustrated features on all aspects of the hobby. Up to 800 words.
Overall freelance potential: A good percentage used each week.
Fees: By agreement.

COARSE FISHERMAN
Metrocrest Ltd, 2 Harcourt Way, Meridian Business Park, Leicester LE19 1WP.
Tel: 0116 289 4567. E-mail: info@conceptdesignltd.co.uk
Editor: Stuart Dexter.
Monthly magazine covering all aspects of coarse fishing.
Illustrations: Pictures of anglers in action or riverside/lakeside scenes where coarse angling takes place. Covers: colour pictures showing anglers displaying particularly fine catches.
Text: Articles of 1,000–2,000 words, most usually first person accounts of angling experiences.
Overall freelance potential: Excellent scope for angling specialists.
Fees: Pictures from £10 upwards. £25 per 1,000 words for text.

FLY FISHING & FLY TYING
Rolling River Publications Ltd, The Locus Centre, The Square, Aberfeldy, Perthshire PH15 2DD.
Tel: 01887 829868. Fax: 01887 829856. E-mail: markb.ffft@btinternet.com
Editor: Mark Bowler.
Monthly for the fly fisherman and fly-tyer.
Illustrations: Shots of fly fishermen in action, scenics of locations, flies and fly-tying, and appropriate insect pictures.
Text: Illustrated articles on all aspects of fly fishing.
Overall freelance potential: Fairly good.

Are you working from the latest edition of The Freelance Photographer's Market Handbook? It's published on 1 October each year. Markets are constantly changing, so it pays to have the latest edition

Editor's tips: Make an effort to avoid bland backgrounds, especially at watersides.
Fees: Colour from £24–£58; covers £50. Text £50 per 1,000 words.

IMPROVE YOUR COARSE FISHING
Bauer Media, Media House, Lynchwood, Peterborough PE2 6EW.
Tel: 01733 468000. Fax: 01733 468300. E-mail: kevin.green@bauermedia.co.uk
Editor: Kevin Green.
Monthly, inspirational, "hints and tips" style magazine for coarse fishing enthusiasts.
Illustrations: Photographs depicting all aspects of coarse fishing.
Text: Ideas for illustrated features from experienced angling writers always considered. 2,500 words; submit a synopsis first.
Overall freelance potential: Limited; much of the editorial content is produced in-house.
Editor's tips: Always query the editor before submitting.
Fees: £50 per picture unless supplied with article; articles £100 – £200 inclusive of pictures.

SEA ANGLER
Bauer Media, Media House, Lynchwood, Peterborough PE2 6EA.
Tel: 01733 468000. E-mail: mel.russ@bauermedia.co.uk
Editor: Mel Russ.
Monthly magazine dealing with the sport of sea angling from both boat and beach.
Illustrations: Good sea fishing and shore fishing pictures, scenic coastline pictures from around the country, and proud anglers with good catches. Covers: Head shots of individual sea fish and anglers displaying an exceptional catch (must be a fresh catch).
Text: Instructional features, fishing expeditions, match articles, etc. 1,000 words.
Overall freelance potential: 50 per cent of published material comes from freelance sources.
Fees: By negotiation; good rates for the right kind of material.

TROUT & SALMON
Bauer Media, Media House, Lynchwood, Peterborough PE2 6EA.
Tel: 01733 465783. E-mail: andrew.flitcroft@bauermedia.co.uk
Editor: Andrew Flitcroft.
Monthly magazine for game fishermen.
Illustrations: Digital files preferred. Photographs of trout or salmon waters, preferably with an angler included in the picture. Close-up and action shots to illustrate particular techniques. Captioned news pictures showing anglers with outstanding catches. Covers: attractive pictures of game fishing waters, always with an angler present.
Text: Instructional illustrated articles on all aspects of game fishing.
Overall freelance potential: Excellent for those who can produce the right sort of material.
Fees: Pictures inside according to use. Cover shots, £80. Text according to length.

TROUT FISHERMAN
Bauer Media, Bushfield House, Orton Centre, Peterborough PE2 5UW.
Tel: 01733 395131. E-mail: russell.hill@bauermedia.co.uk
Editor: Russell Hill.
Monthly magazine for the trout fishing enthusiast.
Illustrations: Colour. Photographs depicting any aspect of angling for trout – outstanding catches, angling locations, techniques, flies and equipment.
Text: Illustrated articles on all aspects of trout fishing, around 1,500 words.
Overall freelance potential: Excellent scope for top quality material.
Editor's tips: Too much angling photography is dull and uninteresting; an original and lively approach would be welcome.
Fees: On a rising scale according to size of reproduction or length of text.

Animals & Wildlife

BBC WILDLIFE
Bristol Magazines Ltd, 14th Floor, Tower House, Fairfax Street, Bristol BS1 3BN.
Tel: 0117 927 9009. Fax: 0117 934 9008. E-mail: sophiestafford@bbcmagazinesbristol.com;
wandasowry@bbcmagazinesbristol.com
Editor: Sophie Stafford. **Picture Researcher:** Wanda Sowry.
Heavily-illustrated magazine for readers with a serious interest in wildlife and environmental
matters. 13 issues per year.
Illustrations: Digital files preferred. Top-quality wildlife and environmental photography of all
kinds, mostly to illustrate specific features. Lists of available stock imagery should be sent to picture
researcher; suggestions for special portfolios or illustrated features to editor. See
www.bbcwildlifemagazine.com for submission guidelines.
Text: Feature suggestions considered from contributors who have a genuine knowledge of their
subject.
Overall freelance potential: Only for the very best quality work.
Fees: Pictures from £50 (under quarter-page) to £150 (dps); covers £300.

BIRD WATCHING
Bauer Active Ltd, Media House, Lynchwood, Peterborough PE2 6EA.
Tel: 01733 468419. E-mail: sheena.harvey@bauermedia.co.uk
Editor: Sheena Harvey.
Monthly magazine devoted to bird watching and ornithology.
Illustrations: Top quality photographs of birds in the wild, both in the UK and overseas. Prefer to
use pictures that illustrate specific aspects of bird behaviour. Also, landscape shots of British bird-
watching sites and of people watching birds. Always query editor before submitting.
Text: Illustrated features on all aspects of birds and bird watching.
Overall freelance potential: Excellent scope for wildlife specialists but much is obtained from
regular contributors.
Fees: By negotiation.

BIRDWATCH
Solo Publishing Ltd, B403A The Chocolate Factory, 5 Clarendon Road, London N22 6XJ.
Tel: 020 8881 0550. E-mail: editorial@birdwatch.co.uk
Editor: Dominic Mitchell. **Picture Editor:** Steve Young.
Monthly for all birdwatchers. Includes a strong emphasis on the photographic side of the hobby.
Illustrations: Digital files only. Good photographs of British and European birds in their natural
habitat. Those with collections of such material should send lists of subjects available.
Text: Well-illustrated features on birdwatching topics, including practical articles on bird
photography. 1,000–1,200 words, but send a synopsis first.
Overall freelance potential: Average.
Fees: According to use.

DOGS TODAY
Pet Subjects Ltd, The Dog House, 4 Bonseys Lane, Chobham, Surrey GU24 8JJ.
Tel: 01276 858880. Fax: 01276 858860. E-mail: enquiries@dogstodaymagazine.co.uk
Editor: Beverley Cuddy.
Monthly magazine for the pet dog lover.
Illustrations: News pictures or shots showing dogs in action, in specific situations, and interacting
with people (especially children). Will also consider exciting or amusing photo sequences and
pictures of celebrities with their dogs. No simple dog portraits unless displaying a strong element of

humour or sentiment. Shots of crossbreeds always needed.

Text: General illustrated features about dogs. Should be positive and have a "human interest" feel.

Overall freelance potential: Excellent for the right material.

Fees: According to use.

THE FALCONERS & RAPTOR CONSERVATION MAGAZINE

PW Publishing Ltd, Arrowsmith Court, Station Approach, Broadstone, Dorset BH18 8PW.

Tel: 0845 803 1979. Fax: 01202 659950. E-mail: steve@pwpublishing.ltd.uk

Editor: Peter Eldrett. **Art Editor:** Stephen Hunt.

Quarterly magazine devoted to falconry and birds of prey.

Illustrations: Images usually only required to illustrate specific articles as below. Covers: Striking images of birds of prey.

Text: Articles on falconry and related topics. 1,000–5,000 words.

Overall freelance potential: Little scope for individual photographs, but complete illustrated articles always welcome.

Editor's tips: Free author's guide available on request.

Fees: By negotiation.

K9 MAGAZINE

K9 Media Solutions, 21 High Street, Warsop, Mansfield, Notts NG20 0AA.

Tel: 08700 114 115. E-mail: mail@k9magazine.com

Editor: Ryan O'Meara.

Quarterly magazine plus extensive website (www.k9magazine.com), described as the only lifestyle magazine for British dog lovers.

Illustrations: Colour. Digital files preferred. High quality dog images – breeds, puppies, dogs with people, dogs in action, etc. Submit low-res samples via e-mail in the first instance. Some commissions available to experienced animal photographers.

Text: Illustrated features on aspects of dog behaviour and dog ownership.

Overall freelance potential: Only top quality material considered.

Fees: By negotiation.

KENNEL AND CATTERY MANAGEMENT

Albatross Publications, PO Box 523, Horsham, West Sussex RH12 4WL.

Tel: 01293 871201. Fax: 01293 871301. E-mail: newsdesk123@aol.com

Editor: Carol Andrews.

Bi-monthly magazine for boarding kennel/cattery proprietors, dog/cat breeders, rescue homes, etc.

Illustrations: Pictures depicting relevant subjects, but only required as part of a complete illustrated feature.

Text: Illustrated articles on any topic relating to the above, including cat/dog care.

Overall freelance potential: Limited.

Fees: By negotiation.

NATURAL WORLD

The Wildlife Trusts, The Kiln, Waterside, Mather Road, Newark, Nottinghamshire NG24 1WT.

Tel: 01636 670000. Fax: 0870 0360101.

Editor: Rupert Paul.

The magazine of The Wildlife Trusts, concerned with all aspects of wildlife and countryside conservation in the UK. Published three times per year.

Illustrations: Interesting shots of British mammals, amphibians, insects, flowers and trees.

As a member of the Bureau of Freelance Photographers, you'll be kept up-to-date with markets through the BFP Market Newsletter, published monthly. For details of membership, turn to page 9

Subjects must be wild; no pets or zoo animals.
Text: Short photo-features on wildlife or conservation topics particularly connected with local Wildlife Trusts. Around 300 words.
Overall freelance potential: Limited.
Fees: £35 minimum.

YOUR CAT
BPG (Stamford) Ltd, Roebuck House, 33 Broad Street, Stamford, Lincs PE9 1RB.
Tel: 01780 766199. Fax: 01780 766416. E-mail: s.parslow@bournepublishinggroup.co.uk
Editor: Sue Parslow.
Monthly magazine for all cat lovers. Covers every type of cat including the household moggie and pedigree cats.
Illustrations: Mostly by commission to accompany features as below. Limited scope for interesting, unusual or humorous single pictures.
Text: Illustrated news items and features on the widest variety of topics relating to cats: famous cats, cats in the news, readers' cats, rare cats, cats that earn a living, etc. Also authoritative articles on practical matters: behaviour, grooming, training, etc.
Overall freelance potential: Limited.
Fees: By negotiation.

YOUR DOG
BPG (Stamford) Ltd, Roebuck House, 33 Broad Street, Stamford, Lincs PE9 1RB.
Tel: 01780 766199. Fax: 01780 766416. E-mail: s.wright@bournepublishinggroup.co.uk
Editor: Sarah Wright.
Monthly magazine for "the everyday dog owner", with the emphasis on care and training.
Illustrations: Top quality pictures showing dogs and their owners in a practical context, i.e. walking, training, grooming; dogs in the news; amusing pictures. For covers pictures must be of the highest technical quality.
Text: Illustrated news stories, practical features, and articles on any interesting canine subject, i.e. working dogs, dog charities, celebrities and their dogs, etc. Always contact editor before submitting.
Overall freelance potential: Fair.
Editor's tips: Make sure that pictures are recent and not just something dug up from the back of the filing cabinet.
Fees: According to size of reproduction and by negotiation.

Architecture & Building

ARCHITECTURE TODAY
Architecture Today plc, 161 Rosebery Avenue, London EC1R 4QX.
Tel: 020 7837 0143. Fax: 020 7837 0155. E-mail: chris.f@architecturetoday.co.uk
Editor: Chris Foges.
Independent monthly for the architectural profession. Covers the most important projects in the UK and Europe, from art galleries to social housing and from interiors to urban design.
Illustrations: Most photography is commissioned, but interesting pictures of current architectural projects are always of interest on spec.
Text: Illustrated articles of genuine interest to a professional readership; submit ideas only first. 800–2,000 words.
Overall freelance potential: Some scope for specialists.
Editor's tips: Potential contributors must contact the editors before submitting anything.
Fees: £100 per 1,000 words; photography by arrangement.

BD (BUILDING DESIGN)

CMP Information, Ludgate House, 245 Blackfriars Road, London SE1 9UY.
Tel: 020 7921 5000. Fax: 020 7921 8244. E-mail: abaillieu@cmpi.biz
Editor: Amanda Baillieu. News **Editor:** Will Hurst.
Weekly newspaper for architects and architectural technicians.
Illustrations: News pictures may be considered on spec but most photography commissioned to illustrate major stories and features. Photographers should have a proven record in architectural photography and a demonstrable understanding of what it should capture. Submit samples of work along with details of experience.
Text: News pieces and features on all aspects of building design, by those with real understanding of the subject matter. Always make contact before submitting.
Overall freelance potential: Good for those with the requisite expertise.
Fees: Pictures variable according to use etc. Text around £160 per 1,000 words.

BUILD IT

Ocean Media Group Ltd, 19th Floor, 1 Canada Square, Canary Wharf, London E14 5AP.
Tel: 020 7772 8300. Fax: 020 7772 8584. E-mail: duncan.hayes@oceanmedia.co.uk
Editor: Duncan Hayes.
Monthly devoted to the self-build and home improvement market – ranging from those building a one-off home or converting old buildings to major extension and renovation projects.
Illustrations: Commissions available to experienced photographers to cover architecture, building work and interiors. Some interest in relevant stock photographs of housing and interior decoration subjects.
Text: Authoritative features on building, landscaping and interior design, plus specialised articles on finance, legal issues, weatherproofing, etc.
Overall freelance potential: Excellent for the experienced contributor in the architecture and interiors field.
Fees: Good rates for photographers; text negotiable.

BUILDERS' MERCHANTS JOURNAL

Faversham House Group, Faversham House, 232A Addington Road, South Croydon CR2 8LE.
Tel: 020 8651 7100. Fax: 020 8651 7117. E-mail: colinpetty@fav-house.com
Editor: Mark Rowland.
Monthly business to business magazine for the builders merchants industry – wholesale distributors of building products, including heating, bathroom and kitchen fixtures.
Illustrations: Always interested in unusual photography of merchants' yards, computers, showrooms and vehicles. Ongoing requirement for shots of house building/refurbishment work. Possible scope for creative still life shots of items such as bricks, blocks, timber, etc. Commissions also available, depending on geographic location – write in with details of experience and rates.
Text: Limited scope for freelance articles on suitable subjects – send business card and samples of published work in the first instance.
Overall freelance potential: Limited.
Editor's tips: Most commissions here tend to be rather mundane, usually involving quite general shots of a merchant's yard. Need photographers who can provide a more creative approach. Write in the first instance – do not telephone.
Fees: Photographs by negotiation. Text around £125 per 1,000 words.

Are you working from the latest edition of The Freelance Photographer's Market Handbook? It's published on 1 October each year. Markets are constantly changing, so it pays to have the latest edition

FX

Wilmington Business Information Ltd, 91 Charterhouse Street, London EC1M 6HR.
Tel: 020 7336 5213. Fax: 020 7336 5201. E-mail: tdowling@fxmagazine.co.uk
Editor: Theresa Dowling. **Art Editor:** Wesley Mitchell.
Monthly interior design business magazine for the retail, hotel and commercial sectors. Aimed at architects, designers and their clients.
Illustrations: By commission only; experienced architectural and interiors photographers with fresh ideas always welcome.
Text: Articles on commercial design matters and related business issues, only from those with real expertise in these areas.
Overall freelance potential: Good for the experienced worker.
Editor's tips: The magazine is very receptive to original ideas. Articles should be hard-hitting and possibly contentious.
Fees: Photography around £200–£250 per day. £160 per 1,000 words.

H&V NEWS

EMAP Trenton, Greater London House, Hampstead Road, London NW1 7EJ.
Tel: 020 7728 4652. Fax: 020 7391 3435. E-mail: claudia.hathway@emap.com
Editor: Dennis Flower.
Weekly for those who purchase or specify heating, ventilating and air conditioning equipment.
Illustrations: Pictures of installations and equipment in active use, preferably with a human interest element.
Text: News stories, installation stories regarding heating, ventilating and air conditioning equipment, stories on companies and people. 200–300 words. Longer features by negotiation.
Overall freelance potential: Good scope for newsworthy material.
Editor's tips: The more current the information supplied the better its chance of success.
Fees: £12 per 100 words; pictures by negotiation.

HOUSEBUILDER

Housebuilder Publications Ltd, Byron House, 7-9 St James's Street, London SW1A 1DW.
Tel: 020 7960 1630. Fax: 020 7960 1631. E-mail: ben.roskrow@house-builder.co.uk
Editor: Ben Roskrow.
Monthly journal of the House Builders Federation. Aimed at key decision makers, managers, technical staff, marketing executives, architects and local authorities.
Illustrations: Some scope for housebuilding coverage, but only by prior consultation with the editor.
Text: Features on marketing, land and planning, government liaison, finance, materials, supplies, etc. Always to be discussed before submission. 1,000 words.
Overall freelance potential: Around 50 per cent comes from freelances.
Editor's tips: Authoritative articles and news stories only. No PR "puffs".
Fees: £150 per 1,000 words; pictures by agreement.

ICON

Media Ten Ltd, National House, High Street, Epping, Essex CM16 4BD.
Tel: 01992 570030. Fax: 01992 570031. E-mail: justin@icon-magazine.co.uk
Editor: Chris Turner. **Art Editor:** Shazai Chaudry.
Monthly magazine covering architecture and design, aimed at both professionals and interested consumers.
Illustrations: Top quality architectural and design photography, mostly by commission. Submit ideas and samples in the first instance. Also runs a regular monthly showcase, "Icon Hang", for individual photographer's portfolios.
Text: Suggestions considered, but contributors must really know their subject.
Overall freelance potential: Fair.
Editor's tips: Potential contributors should really study the magazine first in order to "tune in" to

what it is trying to do.

LANDSCAPE
Wardour Publishing & Design, Walmar House, 296 Regent Street, London W1B 3AW.
Tel: 020 7016 2555. E-mail: jeff@wardour.co.uk
Editor: George Bull. **Art Director:** Steven Gregor.
Official magazine of The Landscape Institute. Aimed at professionals either producing or commissioning landscape architecture and designed to showcase the best work in the field.
Illustrations: Mostly by commission only; always happy to hear from photographers who can offer high-level skills in architectural work.
Text: Ideas for features will be considered.
Overall freelance potential: Good scope for experienced workers.
Editor's tips: Requirements are very specific, so in the first instance submit only a couple of samples as an indication of style.
Fees: By negotiation.

RIBA JOURNAL
Atom Publishing Ltd, 45/47 Clerkenwell Green, London EC1R 0EB.
Tel: 020 7490 5595. Fax: 020 7490 4957. E-mail: hugh@atompublishing.co.uk
Editor: Hugh Pearman. **Art Editor:** Mark Bergin.
Monthly magazine of the Royal Institute of British Architects. Covers general aspects of architectural practice as well as criticisms of particular buildings, profiles and interviews.
Illustrations: Pictures of buildings, old, new and refurbished. Covers: colour pictures connected with main feature inside. Best to send list of subjects initially.
Text: Illustrated features on architectural subjects and criticisms of particular buildings.
Overall freelance potential: Fair.
Fees: By arrangement.

SELFBUILD & DESIGN
WW Magazines Ltd, 151 Station Street, Burton-on-Trent DE14 1BG.
Tel/fax: 01584 841417. E-mail: ross.stokes@sbdonline.co.uk
Editor: Ross Stokes.
Monthly practical consumer magazine covering self-build housing, including conversions and major extensions.
Illustrations: Striking photographs of recently completed self-builds (interiors and exteriors), particularly those of an innovative design or in unusual or visually appealing locations. Coverage of new builds by celebrities also welcomed.
Text: Authoritative and well illustrated articles covering all aspects of building and renovation, including brief items of a quirky, amusing or informative nature. Telephone to discuss ideas before submission.
Overall freelance potential: Good.
Fees: By negotiation.

STADIUM & ARENA MANAGEMENT
Alad Ltd. Editorial: 4 North Street, Rothersthorpe, Northants NN7 3JB.
Tel: 01604 832149. E-mail: mark.webb@tesco.net
Editor: Mark Webb.
Bi-monthly, international news magazine covering all aspects of stadium and arena design, construction and management.
Illustrations: Photographs of new stadia or arenas internationally, but especially in Europe, preferably at the construction stage. Also newsworthy images involving stadia.
Text: News items always considered.
Overall freelance potential: Fair.
Fees: By negotiation.

Arts & Entertainment

HEAT
Bauer Media, Endeavour House, 189 Shaftesbury Avenue, London WC2H 8JG.
Tel: 020 7295 5000. Fax: 020 7817 8847. E-mail: john.robinson@heatmag.com
Editor: Sam Delaney. Picture Director: John Robinson.
Popular entertainment weekly with news, reviews and heavy celebrity content.
Illustrations: Interested in hearing from photographers covering live events throughout the UK. Assignments available to shoot performances and behind-the-scenes coverage. Some scope for paparazzi-type material.
Text: No scope.
Overall freelance potential: Good.
Fees: By negotiation.

RADIO TIMES
BBC Worldwide Publishing, Woodlands, 80 Wood Lane, London W12 0TT.
Tel: 020 8433 2000. Fax: 020 8433 3160. E-mail: roger.dickson@bbc.co.uk
Editor: Ben Preston. **Picture Editor:** Roger Dickson.
Weekly TV and radio listings magazine, containing news and features on mainly BBC productions and personalities.
Illustrations: Coverage of broadcasting events, BBC productions, and TV personalities, usually by commission.
Text: Commissioned features on TV personalities or programmes of current interest.
Overall freelance potential: Fair for commissioned work.
Fees: Various.

THE STAGE
The Stage Newspaper Ltd, 47 Bermondsey Street, London SE1 3XT.
Tel: 020 7403 1818. Fax: 020 7357 9287. E-mail: editor@thestage.co.uk
Editor: Brian Attwood.
Weekly newspaper for professionals working in the performing arts and the entertainment industry.
Illustrations: News pictures concerning people and events in the theatre and television worlds.
Text: Features on the theatre and light entertainment. 800 words.
Overall freelance potential: Limited.
Fees: Pictures by agreement, text £100 per 1,000 words.

TV TIMES
IPC Media Ltd, Blue Fin Building, 110 Southwark Street, London SE1 0SU.
Tel: 020 3148 5570. Fax: 020 3148 8115. E-mail: elaine_mccluskey@ipcmedia.com
Editor: Ian Abbott. **Art Director:** Steve Fawcett. **Picture Editor:** Elaine McCluskey.
Weekly television programme listings magazine, plus features on major programmes.
Illustrations: Usually commissioned or requested from specialist sources. Mainly quality colour portraits or groups specific to current programme content.
Text: Articles on personalities and programmes.
Overall freelance potential: Between 50 and 75 per cent each week is freelance, but mostly from recognised contributors.
Fees: Negotiable.

As a member of the Bureau of Freelance Photographers, you'll be kept up-to-date with markets through the BFP Market Newsletter, published monthly. For details of membership, turn to page 9

Aviation

AEROPLANE
IPC Media Ltd, Blue Fin Building, 110 Southwark Street, London SE1 0SU.
Tel: 020 3148 4100. E-mail: editoraero@ipcmedia.com
Editor: Michael Oakey.
Monthly aviation history magazine, specialising in the period 1909–1960. Occasional features on modern aviation.
Illustrations: Colour; B&W archive material. Photographs for use in their own right or for stock. Main interests – veteran or vintage aircraft, including those in museums; preserved airworthy aircraft; unusual pictures of modern aircraft. Action shots preferred in the case of colour material – air-to-air, ground-to-air, or air-to-ground. Covers: high quality air-to-air shots of vintage or veteran aircraft.
Text: Short news stories concerning preserved aircraft, new additions to museums and collections, etc. Not more than 300 words.
Overall freelance potential: Most contributions are from freelance sources, but specialised knowledge and skills are often necessary.
Editor's tips: The magazine is always in the market for sharp, good quality colour images of preserved aircraft in the air.
Fees: Colour photographs: full page £80; centre spread £100; covers £180. B&W from £10 upwards.

AIR INTERNATIONAL
Key Publishing Ltd, PO Box 100, Stamford, Lincolnshire PE9 1XQ.
Tel: 01780 755131. Fax: 01780 757261. E-mail: mark.ayton@keypublishing.com
Editor: Mark Ayton.
Monthly general aviation magazine covering both modern military aircraft and the civil aviation industry. Includes some historical topics. Aimed at both enthusiasts and industry professionals.
Illustrations: Topical single pictures or picture stories on aviation subjects worldwide, e.g. aircraft in active war zones, airliners in new livery, new aircraft at Heathrow, etc. Overseas material welcomed. Air show coverage rarely required.
Text: Illustrated features on topics as above, from writers with in-depth knowledge of the subject. Length variable.
Overall freelance potential: Very good for suitable material.
Editor's tips: Remember the magazine is read by professionals and is not just for enthusiasts.
Fees: B&W from £10; colour based on page rate of £75. Covers, up to £120 for full-bleed sole reproduction. Text £50 per 1,000 words.

AIRFORCES MONTHLY
Key Publishing Ltd, PO Box 100, Stamford, Lincolnshire PE9 1XQ.
Tel: 01780 755131. Fax: 01780 751323. E-mail: edafm@keypublishing.com
Editor: Alan Warnes.
Monthly magazine concerned with modern military aircraft.
Illustrations: Mostly colour. Interesting, up-to-date pictures of military aircraft from any country. Must be current; archive material rarely used.
Text: Knowledgeable articles concerning current military aviation. No historical matter.
Overall freelance potential: Good for contributors with the necessary knowledge and access.
Fees: £25 minimum for colour; £10 minimum for B&W; covers £120. Text by negotiation.

AIRLINER WORLD
Key Publishing Ltd, PO Box 100, Stamford, Lincs PE9 1XQ.
Tel: 01780 755131. Fax: 01780 757261. E-mail: tony.dixon@keypublishing.com
Editor: Tony Dixon.

Heavily-illustrated monthly for civil aviation enthusiasts.
Illustrations: Colour, some B&W. Always interested in topical photos covering the commercial airline scene, including business jets – new aircraft being rolled out, new liveries, new airlines, airport developments, etc. International coverage. Some archive material used; send stock lists.
Text: Will consider ideas for articles on any civil aviation theme, around 2,000 words. Contributors must have in-depth knowledge of their subject.
Overall freelance potential: Excellent.
Fees: Pictures from £20; text £50 per 1,000 words.

AIRPORT WORLD

Insight Media Ltd, Sovereign House, 26-30 London Road, Twickenham TW1 3RW.
Tel: 020 8831 7507. Fax: 020 8891 0123. E-mail: joe@airport-world.com
Editor: Joe Bates.
Bi-monthly trade journal published for the Airports Council International, circulated to airport operators worldwide.
Illustrations: Recent photographs taken in airports and airport terminals in any part of the world – must be high quality pictures with a creative approach. Before submitting photographers should first send details of airports they have on file.
Text: No scope.
Overall freelance potential: Fair.
Fees: By negotiation.

AIRPORTS INTERNATIONAL

Key Publishing Ltd, PO Box 100, Stamford, Lincs PE9 1XQ.
Tel: 01780 755131. Fax: 01780 757261. E-mail: tom.allett@keypublishing.com
Editor: Tom Allett.
Published nine times a year, dealing with all aspects of airport construction, management, operations, services and equipment worldwide.
Illustrations: Photographs related to airport operational affairs. Particularly interested in high quality images for cover use, and coverage of "exotic" overseas locations. Always contact the editor before submitting.
Text: Possible scope for overseas material, depending on region; Middle East, Asia-Pacific, South America and Africa of particular interest.
Overall freelance potential: Fair.
Fees: By negotiation.

AVIATION NEWS

Key Publishing, PO Box 100, Stamford, PE9 1XQ.
Tel: 01780 755131. E-mail:editor@aviation-news.co.uk
Editor: David Baker.
Monthly magazine covering aviation in general, both past and present. Aimed at both the industry and the enthusiast.
Illustrations: Colour; B&W archive material. Photographs of all types of aircraft, civil and military, old or new. Captioned news pictures of particular interest, but no space exploration or aircraft engineering.
Text: News items about current aviation matters. Historical contributions concerning older aircraft.
Overall freelance potential: About 45 per cent is contributed by freelances.
Fees: On a rising scale according to size of reproduction or length of text.

DEFENCE HELICOPTER/ROTORHUB

The Shephard Press Ltd, 268 Bath Road, Slough, Berkshire SL1 4DX.
Tel: 01753 727020 Fax: 01753 727002. E-mail: ts@shephard.co.uk
Editor: Tony Skinner.
Defence Helicopter is concerned with military and parapublic helicopter use. Rotorhub magazine

covers the civil, public service and corporate rotorcraft market.

Illustrations: Pictures of military, public service (police, coastguard, etc), civil and corporate helicopters anywhere in the world. Must be accurately captioned. Covers: high quality pictures of appropriate helicopters. Should preferably be exclusive and in upright format. No "sterile" pictures; must be action shots.

Text: News stories and features on helicopters in service use and helicopter technology. Up to 1,500 words.

Overall freelance potential: Moderate.

Fees: By negotiation.

FLIGHT INTERNATIONAL

Reed Business Information Ltd, Quadrant House, The Quadrant, Sutton, Surrey SM2 5AS.
Tel: 020 8652 3842. Fax: 020 8652 3840. E-mail: gareth.burgess@flightglobal.com
Editor: Murdo Morrison. Group **Art Editor:** Gareth Burgess.
Weekly aviation magazine with worldwide circulation, aimed at aerospace professionals in all sectors of the industry.

Illustrations: Weekly requirement for news pictures of aviation-related events. Feature illustrations on all aspects of aerospace, from airliners to satellites. Covers: clean, uncluttered pictures of aircraft – civil and military, light and business.

Text: News items always welcomed. Features by prior arrangement only; submit ideas in the first instance.

Overall freelance potential: Limited for those without contacts in the industry.

Editor's tips: News material should be submitted on spec. Pictures should always be as new as possible or have a news relevance.

Fees: B&W, £19.61; colour, £56.38 up to 30 sq.in., £65.93 to £106.93 30–60 sq. in.; £223.30 for cover. News reports, minimum £7.07 per 100 words; commissioned features by negotiation.

FLYER

Seager Publishing Ltd, 9 Riverside Court, Lower Bristol Road, Bath BA2 3DZ.
Tel: 01225 481440. Fax: 01225 481262. E-mail: ianw@flyermag.co.uk
Editor: Ian Waller.
Monthly magazine for private pilots.

Illustrations: Attractive and striking photographs of light aircraft of the type commonly used by the private pilot, mainly required for DPS feature "Opening Shot". Details of material available should be sent first, rather than speculative submissions.

Text: News items and illustrated articles from those with good knowledge of the subject, with the aim of entertaining and amusing as much as conveying facts. Anecdotal personal experiences always of interest. 1,500–3,000 words for major features.

Overall freelance potential: Limited – mainly provided by established contributors.

Editor's tips: All contributors should have a genuine understanding of the flying scene.

Fees: By negotiation.

PILOT

Archant Specialist, 3 The Courtyard, Denmark Street, Wokingham, Berkshire RG40 2AZ.
Tel: 0118 989 7246. Fax: 01799 544201. E-mail: nick.bloom@pilotweb.co.uk
Editor: Nick Bloom.
Monthly publication for the general aviation (i.e. business and private flying) pilot.

Illustrations: Pictures on topics associated with this field of flying.

Text: Features, preferably illustrated, on general aviation. 2,000–4,000 words.

Overall freelance potential: Excellent. Virtually all of the editorial matter in the magazine is contributed by freelances.

Editor's tips: Read a copy of the magazine before submitting and study style, content, subject and coverage.
Fees: £150–£800 for features. Pictures inside £30; covers £250.

TODAY'S PILOT
Key Publishing Ltd, PO Box 100, Stamford, Lincs PE9 1XQ.
Tel: 01780 755131. Fax: 01780 757261. E-mail: dave.unwin@keypublishing.com
Editor: David Unwin.
Monthly aimed at both private and commercial pilots, those learning to fly, and general aviation enthusiasts.
Illustrations: Will consider any news-based or unusual photographs likely to be of interest to the readership.
Text: Always interested in well-illustrated, authoritative articles on any aspect of private or commercial flying, ranging from travelogues to technical pieces. Submit suggestions only in the first instance
Overall freelance potential: Good scope for illustrated articles.
Fees: By negotiation.

Boating & Watersport

BOARDS
Yachting Press Ltd, 1 West Smithfield, London, EC1A 9JU
Tel: 020 7332 9700.. E-mail: editorial@boards.co.uk
Editor: Dave White.
Monthly magazine devoted to boardsailing and windsurfing.
Illustrations: Good clear action shots of boardsailing or windsurfing; pictures of attractive girls in a boardsailing context; any other visually striking material relating to the sport. Covers: good colour action shots always needed.
Text: Articles and features on all aspects of the sport.
Overall freelance potential: Very good for high quality material.
Editor's tips: Action shots must be clean, clear and crisp.
Fees: By negotiation.

BOAT INTERNATIONAL
Boat International Media, First Floor, 41-47 Hartfield Road, Wimbledon, London SW19 3RQ,
Tel: 020 8545 9330. Fax: 020 8545 9333. E-mail: amandam@boatinternationalmedia.com
Editor: Amanda McCracken.
Monthly glossy magazine focusing on the top, luxury level of sailing and power vessels.
Illustrations: Will consider images of world class yacht racing and luxury cruising.
Text: Mostly staff produced or commissioned from top writers in the field.
Overall freelance potential: Excellent for the best in boating photography and marine subjects.
Editor's tips: Only the very best quality is of interest.
Fees: By negotiation.

BOATING BUSINESS
Mercator Media Ltd, The Old Mill, Lower Quay, Fareham, Hants PO16 0RA.
Tel: 01329 825335. Fax: 01329 825220. E-mail: pnash@boatingbusiness.com
Editor: Peter Nash.
Monthly magazine for the leisure marine trade.
Illustrations: News pictures relating to the marine trade, especially company and overseas news.

Some scope for commissioned work.
Text: Features on marine trade topics; always consult the editor first.
Overall freelance potential: Limited.
Fees: Photographs from £20; text £100 per 1,000 words.

CANAL BOAT

Archant Specialist, 3 The Courtyard, Denmark Street, Wokingham, Berkshire RG40 2AZ.
Tel: 0118 989 7215. E-mail: nick.wall@archant.co.uk
Editor: Nick Wall.
Monthly specialist title covering inland boating especially on canals, looking at boats, boat ownership and cruising.
Illustrations: Photographs depicting colourful boats, attractive waterways, scenery and seasonal elements, but mainly published as part of an illustrated article.
Text: Good opportunities for illustrated features on canal boats and boating personalities.
Overall freelance potential: Good opportunities for good freelance photojournalists.
Editor's tips: Good ideas will be enthusiatically received, but study the magazine before making contact.
Fees: According to use of material.

CANALS & RIVERS

A E Morgan Publications Ltd. Editorial: PO Box 618, Norwich NR7 0QT.
Tel: 01603 708930. E-mail: chris@themag.fsnet.co.uk
Editor: Chris Cattrall.
Monthly publication aimed at inland waterway enthusiasts and canal holidaymakers.
Illustrations: Photographs of all inland waterway subjects. Covers: colour pictures of attractive waterways subjects, preferably with an original approach.
Text: Illustrated articles on canals, rivers, boats and allied subjects.
Overall freelance potential: Good, especially for material with an original approach.
Fees: By negotiation.

CLASSIC BOAT

IPC Country & Leisure Group, Leon House, 233 High Street, Croydon CR9 1HZ.
Tel: 020 8726 8000. Fax: 020 8774 0943. E-mail: cb@ipcmedia.com
Editor: Dan Houston. **Art Editor:** Peter Smith.
Monthly magazine for the enthusiast interested in traditional or traditional-style boats from any part of the world. Emphasis on sailing boats, but also covers traditional power boats, steam vessels and modern reproductions of classic styles.
Illustrations: Digital files and transparencies accepted. Pictures to accompany features and articles. Single general interest pictures with 100 word captions giving full subject details. Particular interest in individual boat photo essays. Covers: spectacular sailing images, but exceptional boat building shots may be used. Upright format with space for logo and coverlines.
Text: Well-illustrated articles covering particular types of boat and individual craft, combining well-researched historical background with hard practical advice about restoration and maintenance. Some scope for humorous pieces and cruising articles involving classic boats. Always send a detailed synopsis in the first instance.
Overall freelance potential: Good for those with specialist knowledge or access.
Editor's tips: Well-documented and photographed practical articles do best.
Fees: £90-£100 per page pro rata; covers £200.

Are you working from the latest edition of The Freelance Photographer's Market Handbook? It's published on 1 October each year. Markets are constantly changing, so it pays to have the latest edition

INTERNATIONAL BOAT INDUSTRY
IPC Country & Leisure Media Ltd, Leon House, 233 High Street, Croydon CR9 1HZ.
Tel: 020 8726 8134. Fax: 020 8726 8196. E-mail: ed_slack@ipcmedia.com
Editor: Ed Slack.
Business publication dealing with the marine leisure industry worldwide. Eight issues a year.
Illustrations: Pictures of boat building and moulding, chandlery shops, showrooms, new boats and equipment. Also marinas.
Text: News items about the boat industry are always of interest.
Overall freelance potential: Good for those in touch with the boat trade.
Editor's tips: This is strictly a trade magazine – general pictures of cruising or racing are not required.
Fees: Linear scale – £100 per page down.

JET SKIER & PW
CSL Publishing Ltd, Alliance House, 49 Sydney Street, Cambridge CB2 3HX.
Tel: 01223 460490. Fax: 01223 315960. E-mail: spicer@jetskier.co.uk
Editor: Sue Baggaley.
Monthly magazine devoted to small, powered water craft and related sports activity. Features jet skis, wetbikes and other personal watercraft.
Illustrations: Spectacular action shots and pictures of unusual individual craft and uses. Events coverage usually by commission.
Text: Some scope for illustrated articles from those with good knowledge of the subject. Submit ideas only in the first instance.
Overall freelance potential: Good.
Fees: By negotiation.

MOTOR BOAT & YACHTING
IPC Media Ltd, Blue Fin Building, 110 Southwark Street, London SE1 0SU.
Tel: 020 3148 4651. Fax: 020 3148 8128. E-mail: mby@ipcmedia.com
Editor: Hugo Andreae. **Deputy Editor:** Stewart Campbell. **Art Editor:** Caroline Creighton-Metcalf.
Monthly magazine for owners and users of motor cruisers.
Illustrations: Mostly required as part of feature packages as below. May consider pictures of motor cruisers at sea, harbour scenes, workboats, people enjoying life on motor boats, but check with editor before submitting.
Text: Features on interesting, unusual or historic motor boats; first-person motor boat cruising accounts; technical motor boating topics. 1,500–2,500 words.
Overall freelance potential: Around 40 per cent of features and 20 per cent of pictures are freelance contributed.
Fees: Good; on a rising scale according to size of reproduction or length of article.

MOTOR BOATS MONTHLY
IPC Inspire, Blue Fin Building, 110 Southwark Street, London SE1 0SU.
Tel: 020 3148 4664. Fax: 020 3148 8128. E-mail: mbm@ipc.co.uk
Editor: Carl Richardson. **News Editor:** Sally Coffey.
Monthly magazine for all motorboating enthusiasts, but mainly aimed at owners of boats of up to 60 feet. Covers all aspects, from top level powerboat racing to inland waterway cruising.
Illustrations: Digital files preferred. News pictures, motor boat action, and shots of cruising locations, both in UK and overseas.
Text: Illustrated articles on any motorboat-related topic, UK and worldwide.
Overall freelance potential: Fairly good.
Fees: On a rising scale according to size of reproduction or length of text.

PRACTICAL BOAT OWNER
IPC Magazines Ltd, Westover House, West Quay Road, Poole, Dorset BH15 1JG.
Tel: 01202 440820. Fax: 01202 440860. E-mail: pbo@ipcmedia.com
Editor: Sarah Norbury. **Art Editor:** Kevin Slater.
Monthly magazine for yachtsmen, sail and power.
Illustrations: Up to date pictures of boats, harbours and anchorages. Covers: Action shots of cruising boats up to about 40ft (preferably sail). Must have strong colours.
Text: Features and associated illustrations of real use to the people who own boats. Subjects can cover any aspect of boating, from buying a boat through to navigation, seamanship, care and maintenance.
Overall freelance potential: About 25 per cent bought from contributors.
Fees: On a rising scale according to size of reproduction or length of feature.

RYA MAGAZINE
Royal Yachting Association, RYA House, Ensign Way, Hamble, Southampton SO31 4YA.
Tel: 023 8060 4100. E-mail: deborah.cornick@rya.org.uk
Editor: Deborah Cornick.
Quarterly publication for personal members of the RYA, affiliated clubs and class associations.
Illustrations: Digital files preferred. Pictures of boats, yachting events and personalities, used either in their own right or as illustrations for reports and articles. Covers: seasonal/topical shots of yachting subjects.
Text: Reports and articles on yachting.
Overall freelance potential: Moderate.
Fees: By arrangement.

ROWING & REGATTA
British Rowing Ltd, 6 Lower Mall, London W6 9DJ.
Tel: 020 8237 6700. Fax: 020 8237 6749. E-mail: wendy.kewley@britishrowing-rowing.org
Covers rowing and sculling – competitive, recreational and technical. Nine editions annually.
Illustrations: Any coverage of the subject considered, especially action pictures of rowing and rowing in scenic settings.
Text: Short, illustrated articles and longer features on all aspects of rowing. Technical topics such as coaching, training and boat-building.
Overall freelance potential: Good.
Fees: By arrangement with editor.

SAILING TODAY
Edisea, Swanwick Marina, Lower Swanwick, Southampton SO31 1ZL.
Tel: 01489 585209. Fax: 01489 565054. E-mail: stewart.wheeler@sailingtoday.co.uk
Editor: Duncan Kent. **Art Editor:** Stewart Wheeler.
Practical monthly for active sail cruising enthusiasts.
Illustrations: Dynamic action shots of cruising yachts from 30-55ft, from home waters to blue waters. Sunny Mediterranean shots, sailing or at anchor, always required for library. Contact sheets/thumbnails accepted for library.
Text: Well-illustrated features on boat improvements and cruising.
Overall freelance potential: Good.
Fees: By negotiation.

SPORTSBOAT & RIB MAGAZINE
CSL Publishing Ltd, Alliance House, 49 Sydney Street, Cambridge CB2 3HX.
Tel: 01223 460490. Fax: 01223 315960. E-mail: editor@sportsboat.co.uk
Editor: Alex Smith.
Monthly publication covering sports boats from 14–50 feet.
Illustrations: Top quality action shots of small sports boats. Also stylish pictures that show boats

as glamorous and exciting. Commissions may be available to illustrate major features. Covers: colour action shots with plenty of impact.
Text: Illustrated articles on all aspects of sports boats and waterskiing will always be considered. 500–3,000 words.
Overall freelance potential: Excellent.
Fees: By negotiation.

WATER CRAFT
Pete Greenfield Publishing, Bridge Shop, Gweek, Helston, Cornwall TR12 6UD.
Tel: 01326 221424. Fax: 01326 221728. E-mail: ed@watercraft-magazine.com
Editor: Pete Greenfield.
Bi-monthly magazine devoted to traditional small boats and boat building.
Illustrations: Photographs mainly required as part of complete feature packages, but interesting or unusual singles and sequences considered if accompanied by detailed caption information.
Text: Well-illustrated features on suitable subjects
Overall freelance potential: Limited at present; much is produced by regular contributors.
Fees: Around £60 per published page inclusive of pictures.

WATERWAYS WORLD
Waterways World Ltd, 151 Station Street, Burton-on-Trent DE14 1BG.
Tel: 01283 742950. Fax: 01283 742957. E-mail: editorial@waterwaysworld.com
Editor: Richard Fairhurst.
Monthly magazine that covers all aspects of canal and river navigations (not lakes) in Britain and abroad. Aimed at inland waterway enthusiasts and holiday boaters.
Illustrations: No scope for stand-alone pictures except for cover use. Covers: colourful canal or river scenes with boating activity prominently in the foreground.
Text: Well-illustrated features on inland waterways, 500–2,000 words. Send for or see website for contributors' guide.
Overall freelance potential: Around 20 per cent freelance contributed.
Fees: Covers £75.

WINDSURF MAGAZINE
Arcwind Ltd, The Blue Barns, Tew Lane, Wootton, Woodstock, Oxon OX20 1HA.
Tel: 01993 811181. Fax: 01993 811481. E-mail: mark@windsurf.co.uk
Publishing Editor: Mark Kasprowicz.
Published ten times a year. Aimed at the enthusiast and covering all aspects of windsurfing.
Illustrations: Sequences and singles of windsurfing action. Top quality shots always considered.
Text: Illustrated articles on any aspect of windsurfing.
Overall freelance potential: Excellent.
Fees: £5–£15 for B&W; up to £35 for full-page colour; £60 for centre-spread; £60 for covers.

YACHTING MONTHLY
IPC Media Ltd, Blue Fin Building, 110 Southwark Street, London SE1 0SU.
Tel: 020 3148 4872. Fax: 020 3148 8128. E-mail: yachting_monthly@ipcmedia.com
Editor: Paul Gelder. **News Editor:** Dick Durham. **Art Editor:** Simon Fevyer.
Monthly magazine for cruising yachtsmen.
Illustrations: News pictures considered for immediate use; location pictures for stock; pictures illustrating seamanship, navigation and technical subjects to illustrate features. Top quality images also considered for regular "Opening Shot" double-page spread and for covers (sailing boats, 25–45ft, under sail, at anchor or in harbour). No motorboats or dinghies.
Text: Articles relevant to cruising yachtsmen, and short accounts of cruising experiences. 1,000–2,250 words. Submit synopsis to the editor in the first instance.
Overall freelance potential: Around 40 per cent comes from outside contributors, but most are

experienced specialists.
Fees: Dependent upon size of reproduction or length of feature. Normally around £50–£110 for colour; £200 for covers. Text from £75 per 1,000 words.

YACHTING WORLD
IPC Media Ltd, Blue Fin Building, 110 Southwark Street, London SE1 0SU.
Tel: 020 3148 4835. Fax: 020 3148 8128. E-mail: david_glenn@ipcmedia.com
Editor: David Glenn. **Picture Editor:** Vanda Woolsey.
Monthly magazine for informed yachtsmen.
Illustrations: Digital files only. Pictures of general yachting techniques or types of boat; pictures of events and occasions; location shots and mood pictures. Major feature photography commissioned from known specialists. Covers: top quality pictures of yachts in 35ft+ range – action pictures on board, at sea.
Text: Informative or narrative yachting articles; technical yachting features; short humorous articles; and news. 1,000–1,500 words and 2,000–2,500 words. Send for writers' guidelines.
Overall freelance potential: Around 30 per cent comes from freelances.
Editor's tips: Contributors must know the subject and know the market. The most successful photographers we use are the ones who work the hardest.
Fees: Inside pictures according to size, from £16. Text up to £160 per 1,000 words.

YACHTS & YACHTING
PO Box 445, Southampton SO31 0BD.
Tel: 07855 849273. E-mail: gael@yachtsandyachting.com
Editor: Gael Pawson.
Fortnightly publication covering all aspects of racing, including dinghies and offshore racers.
Illustrations: Pictures of racing dinghies, yachts and general sailing scenes. Covers: Action shots of relevant subjects.
Text: Features on all aspects of the race sailing scene. 1,000–2,000 words.
Overall freelance potential: Quite good.
Fees: Negotiable.

Business

ACCOUNTANCY AGE
Incisive Media, 32–34 Broadwick Street, London W1A 2HG.
Tel: 020 7316 9000. Fax: 020 7316 9250. E-mail: accountancy_age@vnu.co.uk
Editor: Gavin Hinks.
Weekly publication for qualified accountants.
Illustrations: All commissioned, but new photographers are always welcome.
Text: News and features coverage for accountants. Synopsis preferred in first instance. 1,200 words.
Overall freelance potential: Fairly good for commissioned photography. About 25 per cent of the features come from freelances.
Editor's tips: To gain acceptance, articles must contribute something which cannot be provided by the in-house staff.
Fees: By agreement.

CA MAGAZINE
Connect Communications Ltd, Studio 2001, Mile End, Paisley PA1 1JS.
Tel: 0141 560 3145. Fax: 0141 561 0400. E-mail: rob@connectcommunications.co.uk
Editor: Rob Outram. **Art Editor:** Renny Hutchison .
Scottish financial and management magazine incorporating monthly journal of The Institute of Chartered Accountants of Scotland.

Illustrations: Will consider creative and innovative images which can be related to the subject and which attract readers' attention.
Text: Articles on accounting and auditing, company law, finance, taxation, management topics, company/personal profiles, the financial and management scene in the UK and overseas, investment, computer science, etc. Length: 1,200–3,000 words.
Overall freelance potential: Fair for business specialists.
Fees: By arrangement.

CNBC EUROPEAN BUSINESS
Future Inc Ltd, 141-143 Shoreditch High Street, London E1 6JE.
Tel: 020 7613 8777. Fax: 020 7613 8776. E-mail: lisa.jacobs@ink-publishing.com
Editor: Boyd Farrow. **Picture Editor:** Lisa Jacobs
London-based business monthly offering an entirely European perspective on business in Europe. Allied with CNBC Europe, the only pan-European television network devoted to financial and business news.
Illustrations: European-based business images, but mainly people-oriented, focusing on the individuals behind businesses rather than the companies themselves. Some stock material used but prefer not to use standard "grey suit" business imagery. Photographers available for shoots overseas should contact picture editor in the first instance.
Text: Will consider relevant articles from those who know about business and can write in a lively style. Articles are kept fairly short and have to be written so that they are easy to comprehend for non-native English speakers. Contact the editor with details of experience in the first instance.
Overall freelance potential: Good, especially for freelances based on or regularly visiting the Continent.
Editor's tips: Try to get away from "grey suits" and show business people in a more original and stimulating way.
Fees: By negotiation.

DIRECTOR
Director Publications Ltd, 116 Pall Mall, London SW1Y 5ED.
Tel: 020 7766 8950. Fax: 020 7766 8840. E-mail: director-ed@iod.co.uk
Group **Editor:** Richard Cree. **Art Director:** John Poile.
Monthly journal for members of the Institute of Directors.
Illustrations: B&W and colour. Top quality portraits of company chairmen or major business personalities. Covers: portraits as above or top quality business/industry subjects. More creative, avant-garde illustrations also used.
Text: Interviews; management advice; company profiles; business controversies; EC affairs.
Overall freelance potential: Good.
Fees: By negotiation.

EN
Entrepreneur Business Publishing, Portland Buildings, 127-129 Portland Street, Manchester M1 4PZ.
Tel: 0161 236 2782. Fax: 0161 236 2783. E-mail: martin.regan@excelpublishing.co.uk
Editor: Martin Regan.
Glossy business monthly for entrepreneurs, with separate editions for the North West and Yorkshire regions, aimed at owner-managed companies with turnover between £0.5m–£40m.
Illustrations: Captioned news pictures about developments in private businesses as above. General business/industrial photography by commission, mainly portraiture but some general

---

As a member of the Bureau of Freelance Photographers, you'll be kept up-to-date with markets through the BFP Market Newsletter, published monthly. For details of membership, turn to page 9

business/industrial work.

Text: Topical articles of interest to business people in the region – hard-edged, readable, jargon-free. Newsy items only.

Overall freelance potential: Quite good for the freelance with a professional and creative approach.

Editor's tips: Prefer a creative, even off-the-wall, style. Happy to consider newcomers as long as they are thoroughly professional and reliable.

Fees: By negotiation.

FINANCIAL MANAGEMENT

Caspian Publishing Ltd, 198 King's Road, London SW3 5XX.

Tel: 020 7368 7177. Fax: 020 7368 7201. E-mail: rp1@caspianpublishing.co.uk

Editor: Ruth Prickett.

Monthly publication for financial managers. Published for the Chartered Institute of Management Accountants.

Illustrations: B&W and colour. Regular profile photography to accompany business-related articles.

Text: Occasional freelance market for articles on management/accountancy subjects.

Overall freelance potential: Good.

Fees: By agreement.

MEED (MIDDLE EAST BUSINESS INTELLIGENCE)

EMAP, Greater London House, Hampstead Road, London NW1 7EJ.

Tel: +971 4390 0045. E-mail: colin.foreman@meed-dubai.com

Editorial Director: Richard Thompson. **News Editor:** Colin Foreman.

Weekly business journal covering the affairs of Middle Eastern countries. Now edited from Dubai.

Illustrations: Pictures of current major construction projects in the Middle East and stock shots of important personalities (politicians, leading businessmen) in the region. Recent general views of particular locations occasionally used. Covers: colour pictures of contemporary Middle East subjects, preferably with an obvious business flavour. Also, high-quality colour abstracts.

Text: Specialist articles on relevant business matters.

Overall freelance potential: Limited.

Fees: On a rising scale according to size of reproduction or length of text.

MARKETING

Haymarket Business Publications Ltd, 174 Hammersmith Road, London W6 7JP.

Tel: 020 8267 4048. Fax: 020 8267 4504. E-mail: lucy.barrett@haymarket.com

Editor: Gareth Jones. **News Editor:** Alex Brownfell.

Weekly publication for marketing management, both client and agency.

Illustrations: Requires only experienced business photographers for commissioned coverage of subjects relating to marketing.

Text: News and features with a marketing angle and objective case histories.

Overall freelance potential: Limited; for business specialists only.

Editor's tips: Photographers must be able to work accurately to a brief.

Fees: Negotiable.

NORTH EAST TIMES

North East Times Ltd, 5-11 Causey Street, Gosforth, Newcastle-upon-Tyne NE3 4DJ.

Tel: 0191 284 9994. Fax: 0191 284 9915. E-mail: info@accentmagazines.co.uk

---

Are you working from the latest edition of The Freelance Photographer's Market Handbook? It's published on 1 October each year. Markets are constantly changing, so it pays to have the latest edition

---

Editor: Richard Holmes.

Monthly up-market business magazine.

Illustrations: Digital files preferred. Any general interest pictures connected with the North East of England.

Text: Features on business, fashion, property, motoring, wining and dining, sport, etc, all with North East connections. Around 750 words with two pictures.

Overall freelance potential: Fully committed to freelances.

Fees: By agreement.

PEOPLE MANAGEMENT

Personnel Publications Ltd, 17 Britton Street, London EC1M 5TP.

Tel: 020 7880 6200. Fax: 020 7336 7635. E-mail: sam.kesteven@redactive.co.uk

Editor: Rob Maclachlan. **Picture Editor:** Sam Kesteven.

Fortnightly magazine of the Chartered Institute of Personnel and Development. Covers all aspects of staff management and training.

Illustrations: Photographs of people at work in business and industry, particularly any depicting staff education and training. Detailed lists of subjects available welcomed. Some commissions may be available to experienced workers.

Text: Ideas for articles always welcome; submit a short written proposal first.

Overall freelance potential: Quite good – a lot of stock pictures are used. Contributions here might also be used in Supply Management, a similar title produced by the same team for the Chartered Institute of Purchasing and Supply.

Fees: By negotiation.

POST MAGAZINE

Incisive Media, 32–34 Broadwick Street, London W1A 2HG.

Tel: 020 7316 9321. Fax: 020 7484 9992. E-mail: jonathan.swift@incisivemedia.com

Editor: Jonathan Swift. **Group Art Editor:** Nicky Brown.

Weekly publication covering insurance at home and abroad.

Illustrations: Digital files preferred. Pictures of traffic, houses, offices, building sites, damage (including fire and motoring accidents), shipwrecks or aviation losses, etc. Also political and industry personalities.

Text: News and features on insurance, including general insurance, reinsurance, financial services, investment, marketing, technology, offices and personnel areas.

Overall freelance potential: Most news and features are contributed by freelances.

Fees: By negotiation.

Camping & Caravanning

CAMPING

Warners Group Publications plc, The Maltings, West Street, Bourne, Lincs PE10 9PH.

Tel: 01778 392442. Fax: 01778 392422. E-mail: cliveg@warnersgroup.co.uk

Editor: Clive Garrett.

Monthly magazine covering all aspects of tent camping. Emphasises the range of activities that camping makes available.

Illustrations: Single pictures considered for cover use, strong images of campers obviously enjoying themselves on a family or lightweight camping holiday. Other pictures only used as an integral part of features as below.

Text: Picture-led features that show camping as "a means to an end" and illustrate the range of people and lifestyles that camping embraces. Always check with the editor before submitting.

Overall freelance potential: Excellent for covers.

Fees: £70 per published page, £100 for covers.

CAMPING & CARAVANNING

The Camping and Caravanning Club, Greenfields House, Westwood Way, Coventry CV4 8JH.
Tel: 02476 475274. Fax: 02476 475413. E-mail: magazine@thefriendlyclub.co.uk
Editor: Simon McGrath.
Monthly magazine concerning all aspects of tent camping, caravanning and motorhoming, exclusive to C&CC members.
Illustrations: Limited scope for good shots of camping and caravanning scenes, but usually only required in conjunction with feature articles.
Text: Illustrated features on camping and caravanning in Britain, around 1,200 words. Contact the editor with ideas only in the first instance.
Overall freelance potential: Fair.
Fees: By agreement.

CARAVAN

IPC Focus Network, Leon House, 233 High Street, Croydon CR9 1HZ.
Tel: 020 8726 8000. Fax: 020 8726 8299. E-mail: caravan@ipcmedia.com
Editor: Victoria Bentley.
Monthly magazine for all caravanners.
Illustrations: Occasional need for general illustrations of touring and caravan-related subjects to illustrate features. Send list of subjects and low-res samples in the first instance. Some opportunities for commissioned work, though in-house photographers handle much of this.
Text: Well-illustrated accounts of touring in specific areas, or more general caravanning-related items with a human interest angle. Call or write with ideas first.
Overall freelance potential: Fair, but most content is supplied by regulars.
Fees: By negotiation.

CARAVAN INDUSTRY

A.E.Morgan Publications Ltd, 8a High Street, Epsom, Surrey KT19 8AD.
Tel: 01372 741411. Fax: 01372 744493. E-mail: teamwork@ukonline.co.uk
Editor: David Ritchie.
Monthly publication for manufacturers, traders, suppliers and park operators in the caravan industry.
Illustrations: News pictures of interest to the industry – new caravan park developments, new models, new dealer depots, etc.
Text: Company profiles on park owners and their businesses, traders and manufacturers. 900–1,200 words.
Overall freelance potential: Up to 30 per cent of the content comes from freelance contributors.
Fees: By agreement.

MOTORHOME MONTHLY

Stone Leisure Ltd, Andrew House, 2a Granville Road, Sidcup, Kent DA14 4BN.
Tel: 020 8302 6150/6069 and 020 8300 2316. Fax: 020 8300 2315. E-mail: mhm@stoneleisure.com
Editor: Bob Griffiths.
Monthly magazine about motorhomes and their use. Covers travel, lifestyle, etc.
Illustrations: Good photographs related to above subjects will always be considered.
Text: Illustrated features on travel and motorhoming. 500–1,000 words. Also reports on shows or other relevant events.
Overall freelance potential: Good.
Editor's tips: Preference for copy that requires a minimum of subbing or rewriting.
Fees: Around £50 for illustrated articles.

PARK HOME & HOLIDAY CARAVAN

IPC Media, Leon House, 233 High Street, Croydon CR9 1HZ.
Tel: 020 8726 8252. Fax: 020 8726 8299. E-mail: alex_melvin@ipcmedia.com

Editor: Alex Melvin.
Monthly covering residential park homes and caravan holiday homes.
Illustrations: Always interested in good photographs of park homes, static holiday caravans (not touring caravans), residential and holiday parks.
Text: Illustrated features on the above.
Overall freelance potential: Fair.
Fees: According to use.

PRACTICAL CARAVAN
Haymarket Consumer Media, Teddington Studios, Broom Road, Teddington, Middlesex TW11 9BE.
Tel: 020 8267 5629. Fax: 020 8267 5725. E-mail: practical.caravan@haymarket.com
Editor: Nigel Donnelly. **Art Editor:** Simon Mortimer.
Monthly for caravanning holidaymakers.
Illustrations: Mostly commissioned to accompany specific features, but interesting or unusual caravanning images may be considered on spec.
Text: Feature ideas and first-person stories always considered.
Overall freelance potential: Only for those with experience.
Fees: Commissions start at £250 rising according to suitability and quality.

PRACTICAL MOTORHOME
Haymarket Publishing Ltd, Teddington Studios, Broom Road, Teddington, Middlesex TW11 9BE.
Tel: 020 8267 5629. Fax: 020 8267 5725. E-mail: practical.motorhome@haymarket.com
Editor: Rob Ganley. **Art Editor:** Elizabeth Paterson.
Monthly for all motorhome holidaymakers and enthusiasts.
Illustrations: Mostly commissioned to accompany specific features, but interesting motorhome images may be considered on spec.
Text: Feature ideas and first-person stories always considered.
Overall freelance potential: Only for those with experience.
Fees: Commissions £250–£350 per day; other material negotiable.

Children & Teenage

MIZZ
Panini UK Ltd, Brockbourne House, 77 Mount Ephraim, Tunbridge Wells TN4 8BS.
Tel: 01892 500100. Fax: 01892 545666. E-mail: mizz@panini.co.uk
Editor: Karen O'Brien. **Picture Researcher:** Kirsty Grant.
Fortnightly magazine aimed at girls in the 10–14 age group.
Illustrations: Youth celebrity pictures always of interest (young TV stars, boy/girl bands, etc). Most other photography by commission for specific features, but some scope for stock images that could illustrate "real life" situations encountered by teenage girls. Some scope for single captioned pictures of a humorous nature.
Text: Lively illustrated features on almost any topic that could be of interest to the the target age group. Text should be informative as well as entertaining. A detailed synopsis should always be submitted in the first instance.
Overall freelance potential: Good for the experienced contributor.
Fees: By negotiation.

SUGAR
Hachette Filipacchi (UK) Ltd, 64 North Row, London W1K 7LL.
Tel: 020 7150 7000. Fax: 020 7150 7001. E-mail: deborah.hughes@hf-uk.com
Editor: Annabel Brog. **Art Director:** Deborah Hughes.
Monthly for teenage girls.
Illustrations: Fashion, beauty, still-life and portraiture, all commissioned for specific features.

Some scope for celebrity stock.
Text: No scope.
Overall freelance potential: Only for experienced specialists.
Fees: Basic rate £350 per day.

County & Country

BBC COUNTRYFILE
BBC Magazines Bristol, 9th Floor, Tower House, Fairfax Street, Bristol BS1 3BN.
Tel: 0117 314 8849 (editor); 0117 314 8372 (pictures). E-mail: picturedesk@bbcmagazines.com; editor@bbccountryfile.com
Monthly magazine celebrating the British countryside. Linked to the popular BBC TV programme.
Editor: Fergus Collins. **Picture Editor:** Tor McIntosh.
Illustrations: Photographers based in rural areas often required for specific assignments. Also occasional need for photographers specialising in outdoor activities. Submit a few sample images in the first instance. No scope to submit general countryside or landscape pictures on spec.
Text: Mostly produced by regular specialists, but ideas always considered.
Overall freelance potential: Good possibilities for those with suitable skills.
Fees: By negotiation.

CHESHIRE LIFE
Archant Life, 3 Tustin Court, Port Way, Preston PR2 2YQ
Tel: 01772 722022. Fax: 01772 760905. E-mail: louise.taylor@cheshirelife.co.uk
Editor: Louise Taylor.
Monthly up-market county magazine specialising in regional features.
Illustrations: Prints and digital files accepted. Pictures of the Cheshire region, mainly to accompany features on topics such as property, antiques, wildlife, society, arts and crafts, sport. Picture postcard scenes of Cheshire also of interest – landscapes, towns, villages, heritage, etc.
Text: Articles and features on regional topics. Always consult the editor in the first instance.
Overall freelance potential: Good.
Fees: By negotiation.

COTSWOLD LIFE
Archant Life, Archant House, 3 Oriel Road, Cheltenham GL50 1BB.
Tel: 01242 216050. Fax: 01242 255116. E-mail: mike.lowe@archant.co.uk
Editor: Mike Lowe.
Monthly showcasing "the best of the Cotswolds".
Illustrations: Pictures of local scenes and events, preferably with some life in them. Covers: Medium format colour of lively local scenes, with clear space at top for title logo.
Text: Illustrated articles of varying lengths, on local people, places, events, etc.
Overall freelance potential: Most material comes from regular freelance contributors but new contributors always considered.
Fees: Cover shots £50. Articles and other illustrations negotiable.

COUNTRY LIFE
IPC Media Ltd, Blue Fin Building, 110 Southwark Street, London SE1 0SU.
Tel: 020 3148 4421. Fax: 020 3148 8129. E-mail: dominic_walters@ipcmedia.com
Editor: Mark Hedges. **Picture Editor:** Dominic Walters.
Weekly magazine for a general readership.

Illustrations: Pictures of British countryside, wildlife, interiors, country pursuits. Covers: Top quality pictures of landscapes, rural and urban.
Text: No scope.
Overall freelance potential: Limited; around 80 per cent of the magazine comes from regular suppliers.
Fees: Good; on a rising scale according to size of reproduction. Covers, £300–350.

COUNTRY WALKING
Bauer Active Ltd, Media House, Lynchwood, Peterborough PE2 6EA.
Tel: 01733 468208. E-mail: jonathan.manning@bauermedia.co.uk
Editor: Jonathan Manning.
Monthly magazine for all walkers who enjoy great days out in the countryside.
Illustrations: Pictures depicting walkers in attractive locations, who must be wearing proper outdoor gear. Also top quality landscapes of suitable parts of the country, historic locations, landscapes with elements of walking interest (eg. stile, path), nature and wildlife. Covers: seasonal pictures of very attractive landscape settings.
Text: Well-illustrated articles and features on any walking or countryside topics. Strong emphasis on inspiration and entertainment and capturing the essence of why people walk.
Overall freelance potential: Limited, as much is produced by regulars or obtained from picture libraries.
Editor's tips: The emphasis is always on getting enjoyment from walking and the countryside.
Fees: By negotiation.

THE COUNTRYMAN
Country Publications Ltd, The Water Mill, Broughton Hall, Skipton, North Yorkshire BD23 3AG.
Tel: 01756 701381. Fax: 01756 701326. E-mail: editorial@thecountryman.co.uk
Editor: Paul Jackson.
Monthly covering all matters of countryside interest other than blood sports.
Illustrations: Sequences of pictures about particular places, crafts, customs, farming practices, kinds of wildlife, etc. Must be accompanied by ample caption material. Only limited scope for single stock pictures, but always seeking high-quality wildlife/countryside images for covers.
Text: Well-illustrated articles of 800–1,200 words, on such subjects as mentioned above. Must be accurate, and usually based on the writer's own experience.
Overall freelance potential: Excellent; almost all photographs, and most articles, are from freelance contributors.
Fees: £30 upwards for photographs inside; £150 for cover. Text according to length and merit.

CUMBRIA
Country Publications Ltd, The Water Mill, Broughton Hall, Skipton, North Yorkshire BD23 3AG.
Tel: 01756 701381. Fax: 01756 701326. E-mail: editorial@dalesman.co.uk
Editor: Kevin Hopkinson.
Monthly countryside magazine for Cumbria and the surrounding area.
Illustrations: Attractive shots of local landscapes, rural characters, wildlife, country pursuits and heritage.
Text: Illustrated articles on any aspect of Lakeland country life. 800–1,200 words.
Overall freelance potential: Excellent.
Fees: Half-page £20; full-page £30; covers £100.

Are you working from the latest edition of The Freelance Photographer's Market Handbook? It's published on 1 October each year. Markets are constantly changing, so it pays to have the latest edition

---

DALESMAN

Country Publications Ltd, The Water Mill, Broughton Hall, Skipton, North Yorkshire BD23 3AG.
Tel: 01756 701381. Fax: 01756 701326. E-mail: editorial@dalesman.co.uk
Editor: Paul Jackson. **Picture Editor:** Eleanor Morton.
Monthly countryside magazine for Yorkshire.
Illustrations: Attractive shots of local landscapes, local characters, wildlife and heritage.
Text: Illustrated articles on any aspect of Yorkshire life. 800–1,200 words.
Overall freelance potential: Excellent.
Fees: Half-page £20; full-page £30; covers £100.

DORSET

Archant Life, Archant House, Babbage Road, Totnes, Devon TQ9 5JA.
Tel: 01803 860920. E-mail: helen.stiles@archant.co.uk
Editor: Helen Stiles.
Monthly for people who like to explore the Dorset region.
Illustrations: Good stock photographs of the region: people, places, landscapes, natural history, culture and heritage.
Text: Local news and illustrated articles on Dorset subjects as above, around 1,000 words.
Overall freelance potential: Good.
Fees: Pictures from £25–£45; text £75 per 1,000 words.

DORSET LIFE

Dorset County Magazines Ltd, 7 The Leanne, Sandford Lane, Wareham, Dorset BH20 4DY.
Tel: 01929 551264. Fax: 01929 552099. E-mail:office@dorsetlife.co.uk
Editor: John Newth.
Monthly magazine for the Dorset area.
Illustrations: Interesting and original photographs of the region, but usually required as part of an article, not in isolation. Covers: Attractive local scenes, suitable for upright reproduction. Must be original.
Text: Well-illustrated articles on any topic relating to Dorset, around 1,000 words.
Overall freelance potential: Most contributions come from regular freelance contributors but new contributors always considered.
Fees: According to size of reproduction and length of text.

THE FIELD

IPC Media Ltd, Blue Fin Building, 110 Southwark Street, London SE1 0SU.
Tel: 020 3148 4777. Fax: 020 3148 8179. E-mail: rebecca_hawtrey@ipcmedia.com
Editor: Jonathan Young. **Art Editor:** Rebecca Hawtrey.
Monthly publication concerned with all rural and country sports interests.
Illustrations: Digital files required. Good pictures illustrating relevant topics as below. Most used for article illustration but good single pictures always considered for cover use. Commissions available to specialists.
Text: Illustrated features on country and country sporting subjects, especially shooting, fly-fishing, working dogs (gundogs, terriers). Length according to article, in the range 1,000–2,000 words.
Overall freelance potential: Around 80 per cent comes from outside contributors, many of whom are specialists, but opportunities are good for the right material.
Fees: According to merit.

As a member of the Bureau of Freelance Photographers, you'll be kept up-to-date with markets through the BFP Market Newsletter, published monthly. For details of membership, turn to page 9

HERTFORDSHIRE COUNTRYSIDE
Beaumonde Publications, PO Box 5, Hitchin, Herts SG5 1GJ.
Tel: 01462 422014. Fax: 01462 422015. E-mail: martin_small@btconnect.com
Editor: Sandra Small.
Monthly county magazine for the named area.
Illustrations: B&W and colour. People, places, and events in the county. Covers: colourful local countryside views.
Text: Topical articles, of a cultural nature, on any aspect of the county.
Overall freelance potential: Limited because much is supplied by regular freelance contributors.
Fees: By negotiation.

LANCASHIRE LIFE
Archant Life, 3 Tustin Court, Port Way, Preston PR2 2YQ.
Tel: 01772 722022. Fax: 01772 736496. E-mail: roger.borrell@lancashirelife.co.uk
Editor: Roger Borrell.
Monthly up-market county magazine specialising in regional features, covering Lancashire and the Lake District.
Illustrations: Pictures of the Lancashire and the South Lakes region, mainly to accompany features. Pictures of nationally known personalities with a Lancashire connection. Covers: top quality regional scenes.
Text: Articles and features on regional topics. Always consult the editor in the first instance.
Overall freelance potential: Around 20 per cent is from freelance sources.
Editor's tips: Unlikely to be interested unless there is a definite Lancashire or Lake District angle.
Fees: By negotiation.

LINCOLNSHIRE LIFE
County Life Ltd, County House, 9 Checkpoint Court, Sadler Road, Lincoln LN6 3PW.
Tel: 01522 527127. Fax: 01522 842000. E-mail: editorial@lincolnshirelife.co.uk
Editor: Josie Thurston.
Monthly magazine, dealing with county life past and present from the Humber to the Wash.
Illustrations: Pictures of people and places within the county of Lincolnshire Covers: portrait format colour pictures of local landscapes, architecture, people, street scenes, etc. Submissions for annual calendar also accepted.
Text: Features on people and places within the appropriate area. No more than 1,600 words. Contact editor first to discuss.
Overall freelance potential: Fifty per cent of the magazine comes from freelance sources.
Fees: £50 for covers, other material by agreement.

THE SCOTS MAGAZINE
D. C. Thomson and Co. Ltd, 80 Kingsway East, Dundee DD4 8SL.
Tel: 01382 575178. E-mail: mail@scotsmagazine.com
Editor: Lorraine Wilson.
Monthly magazine for Scots at home and abroad, concerned with Scottish subjects.
Illustrations: Scottish scenes, but avoid the obvious. Non-Highland subjects particularly welcome. Scenics with one or more figures preferred to "empty pictures". Ongoing requirement for good vertical scenes for possible front cover use.
Text: Features on all aspects of Scottish life past and present. 500–1,500 words. E-mail outlining idea in the first instance.
Overall freelance potential: Around 80 per cent of the magazine comes from freelances.
Fees: Variable.

SCOTTISH FIELD
Craigcrook Castle, Craigcrook Road, Edinburgh EH4 3PE.
Tel: 0131 312 4550. Fax: 0131 312 4551. E-mail: editor@scottishfield.co.uk
Editor: Richard Bath.
Monthly magazine reflecting the quality of life in Scotland today for Scots at home and abroad.
Illustrations: Varied subjects of Scottish interest; must be accompanied by appropriate text.
Text: Illustrated features with a Scottish dimension. 850–1,200 words. Submit only ideas initially, rather than completed articles.
Overall freelance potential: There are only limited openings for new contributors.
Editor's tips: Market study is essential.
Fees: Negotiable.

SOMERSET LIFE
Archant Life, Archant House, Babbage Road, Totnes, Devon TQ9 5JA.
Tel: 01803 860914. Fax: 01803 860926. E-mail:
rachel.lovell@archant.co.uk/natalie.vizard@archant.co.uk
Editors: Rachel Lovell/Natalie Vizard.
Monthly magazine for Somerset and Bristol area.
Illustrations: Interesting and original photographs of the area, usually only required as part of a words and pictures package. Covers: always on the lookout for portrait-format shots that will carry the title and coverlines, preferably seasonal pictures of recognisable Somerset scenes.
Text: Well-illustrated articles on any topic relating to Somerset, around 1,000 words.
Overall freelance potential: Keen to find new contributors with photographic skills who can also write well.
Fees: By arrangement.

SUSSEX LIFE
Sussex Life Ltd, Baskerville Place, 28 Teville Road, Worthing, West Sussex BN11 1UG.
Tel: 01903 604208. Fax: 01903 820193. E-mail: jonathan.keeble@sussexlife.co.uk
Editor: Simon Irwin.
Monthly county magazine.
Illustrations: Stock photographs always welcomed, but complete illustrated articles are preferred. Covers: medium format transparencies of Sussex scenes, usually depicting landscapes, but houses, activities, interiors and personalities from Sussex also welcome.
Text: Well illustrated features on any topic relevant to the county. 1,000–2,000 words.
Overall freelance potential: Quite good.
Fees: 1,000-word article plus pics, £150.

TGO – THE GREAT OUTDOORS
Newsquest Magazines, 200 Renfield Street, Glasgow G2 3QB.
Tel: 0141 302 7700. Fax: 0141 302 7799. E-mail: emily.rodway@tgomagazine.co.uk
Editor: Emily Rodway.
Monthly magazine for walkers in the UK. Covers hill and mountain walking, and related topics.
Illustrations: Digital files preferred. Material required for stock – mostly landscapes featuring walkers; no towns or churches. Plus pictures to illustrate features. Covers: colour pictures in upright format considered independently of internal content. Photographs of walkers, backpackers and fell walkers in landscape settings. Must be contemporary, well-equipped people in photos; action shots preferred.
Text: Features on the subjects mentioned above. 2,000 words.
Overall freelance potential: Most of the magazine comes from freelance sources.
Editor's tips: Too many freelances send material which is outside the scope of the magazine – not interested in low level rambling. Send e-mail for guidelines.
Fees: Articles, £150–£450 depending on length and number of illustrations; covers, around £200.

THIS ENGLAND/EVERGREEN
This England Publishing Ltd, PO Box 52, Cheltenham, Gloucestershire GL50 1YQ.
Tel: 01242 537900. Fax: 01242 537901. E-mail: editor@thisengland.co.uk
Editor: Stephen Garnett. **Deputy Editor:** Angeline Wilcox.
Quarterly magazines about England and the United Kingdom respectively, mainly its people, places, customs and traditions and with strong emphasis on nostalgia.
Illustrations: Town, country and village scenes, curiosities, craftsmen at work, nostalgia, patriotism. Prefer people in the picture, but dislike modernity etc. Pictures for stock or use in their own right.
Text: Illustrated articles on all things traditionally British. 1,000–1,500 words.
Overall freelance potential: Around 50 per cent comes from freelance sources.
Editor's tips: Send SAE or e-mail for contributor guidelines.
Fees: By negotiation.

TRAIL
Bauer Active Ltd, Media House, Lynchwood, Peterborough PE2 6EA.
Tel: 01733 468363. E-mail: trail@bauermedia.co.uk
Editor: Matt Swaine.
Monthly magazine aimed at the more adventurous walker, plus rock climbers and mountain bikers.
Illustrations: Well-composed pictures of walkers, backpackers, climbers and mountain bikers in attractive and dramatic landscapes, UK or overseas, high viewpoints preferred. Walkers seen close up should be wearing proper outdoor gear. Covers: "stunning" colour shots as above.
Text: Illustrated articles on any aspect of hill walking, backpacking and overseas trekking, including diet, fitness, etc. Only accepted from contributors who clearly understand what the magazine is about and what the readers need. Always discuss ideas with the editor in the first instance.
Overall freelance potential: Very good for high quality material.
Editor's tips: It is essential that people in pictures be wearing proper walking/climbing clothes and shoes – no jeans and trainers.
Fees: From £25–£150 (DPS). Text £140 per 1,000 words.

WALK
The Ramblers, 2nd Floor, Camelford House, 87-90 Albert Embankment, London SE1 7TW.
Tel: 020 7339 8500. Fax: 020 7339 8501. E-mail: denise.noble@ramblers.org.uk
Editor: Dominic Bates. **Picture Editor:** Denise Noble.
Quarterly journal for members of the Ramblers.
Illustrations: Scenic views of the British countryside, preferably with walkers in shot. Also pictures of difficulties encountered when walking in the countryside, eg damaged bridges, locked gates, obstructed footpaths, etc. Walking images from abroad also required.
Text: Little scope for text as most articles are commissioned from regulars.
Overall freelance potential: Limited other than by commission.
Fees: By agreement.

YORKSHIRE LIFE
Archant Life, PO Box 163, Ripon HG4 9AG.
Tel: 01423 546216. E-mail: esther.leach@yorkshirelife.co.uk
Editor: Esther Leach.
Monthly up-market county magazine for Yorkshire.
Illustrations: Pictures of the Yorkshire region, mainly to accompany features. Pictures of nationally known personalities with a Yorkshire connection, and local society events, but most by commission. Covers: top quality regional scenes.
Text: Articles and features on regional topics, from those with a truly professional approach. Always consult the editor in the first instance.
Fees: By negotiation.

Cycling & Motorcycling

BACK STREET HEROES
Ocean Media Group, One Canada Square, Canary Wharf, London E14 5AP.
Tel: 020 7772 8300. Fax: 020 7772 8585. E-mail: bsh-magazine@yahoo.com
Editor: Stu Garland.
Monthly magazine for custom bike enthusiasts.
Illustrations: Pictures of individual customised or one-off machines, and coverage of custom bike meetings and events. The style of photography must be tailored to fit the style of the magazine.
Text: Limited freelance market.
Overall freelance potential: Good for those who can capture the flavour and style of the custom bike scene.
Editor's tips: This is something of a lifestyle magazine, and it is essential that the stylistic approach be absolutely right.
Fees: By negotiation.

BIKE
Bauer Automotive Ltd, Media House, Lynchwood, Peterborough PE2 6EA.
Tel: 01733 468000. Fax: 01733 468290. E-mail: tim@bikemagazine.co.uk
Editor: Tim Thompson. **Editorial Assistant:** Sally Barker.
Monthly motorcycling magazine aimed at all enthusiasts.
Illustrations: Interesting or unusual topical pictures always required for news section. Sporting pictures for file. Top quality action pictures, "moody" statics and shots that are strong on creative effects. Reportage/documentary shots of events/people.
Text: Interesting or unusual news items. Scope for features on touring, personalities, icons etc; 1,000–3,000 words.
Overall freelance potential: Good for those with experience.
Editor's tips: Always looking for new photographers and styles.
Fees: By agreement.

CLASSIC BIKE
Bauer Automotive Ltd, Media House, Lynchwood, Peterborough PE2 6EA.
Tel: 01733 468081. Fax: 01733 468290. E-mail: hugo.wilson@bauerautomotive.co.uk
Editor: Hugo Wilson. **Editorial Assistant:** Sally Barker.
Monthly magazine dealing with thoroughbred and classic motorcycles from 1896 to 1990.
Illustrations: Pictures of rallies, races, restored motorcycles.
Text: Technical features, histories of particular motorcycles, restoration stories, profiles of famous riders, designers etc. 500–2,000 words.
Overall freelance potential: Most photography is freelance.
Editor's tips: Contact the editor before submitting.
Fees: By agreement and on merit.

CLASSIC BIKE
Bauer Automotive Ltd, Media House, Lynchwood, Peterborough PE2 6EA.
Tel: 01733 468081. Fax: 01733 468290. E-mail: hugo.wilson@bauerautomotive.co.uk
Editor: Hugo Wilson. **Editorial Assistant**: Sally Barker.
Monthly magazine dealing with thoroughbred and classic motorcycles from 1896 to 1990.
Illustrations: Pictures of rallies, races, restored motorcycles.
Text: Technical features, histories of particular motorcycles, restoration stories, profiles of famous riders, designers etc. 500–2,000 words.
Overall freelance potential: Most photography is freelance.
Editor's tips: Contact the editor before submitting.
Fees: By agreement and on merit.

THE CLASSIC MOTORCYCLE

Mortons Media Group Ltd, PO Box 99, Horncastle, Lincs LN9 6LZ.
Tel: 01507 529405. Fax: 01507 529495. E-mail: jrobinson@mortons.co.uk
Editor: James Robinson.
Monthly magazine covering veteran, vintage and post-war motor cycles and motorcycling.
Illustrations: Mostly colour. Pictures that cover interesting restoration projects, unusual machines, personalities with a background story, etc. Covers: colour pictures, usually a well-restored and technically interesting motor cycle, always related to editorial.
Text: Features on subjects detailed above. 1,500–2,500 words.
Overall freelance potential: Around 50 per cent of the magazine comes from freelances, but much of it is commissioned.
Fees: Good; on a rising scale according to size of reproduction or length of article.

CYCLE SPORT

IPC Focus Network, Leon House, 233 High Street, Croydon CR9 1HZ.
Tel: 020 8726 8000. Fax: 020 8774 0952. E-mail: robert_garbutt@ipcmedia.com
Editor: Robert Garbutt.
Monthly devoted to professional cycle sport, offering a British perspective on this essentially Continental sport.
Illustrations: High quality, topical photographs relating to professional cycle racing.
Text: Illustrated features on the professional scene, but always query the editor before submitting. 1,500–4,000 words.
Editor's tips: Most interested in "the news behind the news".
Fees: Pictures according to nature and use. Text £100–£200 per 1,000 words.

CYCLING PLUS

Future Publishing Ltd, Beauford Court, 30 Monmouth Street, Bath BA1 2BW.
Tel: 01225 442244. Fax: 01225 732310. E-mail: warren.rossiter@futurenet.co.uk
Editor: Rob Spedding. **Art/Picture Editor:** Warren Rossiter.
Monthly magazine aimed at recreational cyclists, concentrating on touring and leisure/fitness riding. Some racing coverage.
Illustrations: Photographs that capture the excitement and dynamics of cycle sport. Speculative submissions welcomed; commissions also available.
Text: Little freelance scope; most is produced by a team of regular writers.
Overall freelance potential: Good for photographers.
Fees: By negotiation.

CYCLING WEEKLY

IPC Media Ltd, Leon House, 233 High Street, Croydon CR9 1HZ.
Tel: 020 8726 8000. Fax: 020 8774 0952. E-mail: cycling@ipcmedia.com
Editor: Robert Garbutt.
News-based weekly magazine covering all aspects of cycling; aimed at the informed cyclist.
Illustrations: Digital files preferred. Good photographs of cycle racing, plus any topical photographs of interest to cyclists. Covers: striking colour photographs of cycle racing; must be current.
Text: Well-illustrated articles on racing and technical matters. Around 1,500 words.
Overall freelance potential: Fairly good.
Fees: According to use.

DIRT BIKE RIDER

L&M Newspapers. Editorial: 12 Victoria Street, Morecambe, Lancs LA4 4AG.
Tel: 01524 834077. Fax: 01524 425469. E-mail: sean.lawless@dirtbikerider.co.uk
Editor: Sean Lawless.
Monthly covering all forms of off-road motorcycle sport, aimed at competitors and those who aspire

to compete.
Illustrations: Current pictures of off-road events, bikes and riders.
Text: Illustrated features on all aspects of off-road motorcycling and racing. Contact editor with suggestions in the first instance.
Overall freelance potential: Good.
Fees: Negotiable.

MOTO MAGAZINE
Factory Media Ltd, 1 West Smithfield, London EC1A 9JU.
Tel: 020 7332 9700. E-mail: adam@motomagazine.co.uk
Editor: Ben Johnson.
Bi-monthly magazine covering motocross from an international perspective.
Illustrations: Will consider any topical and relevant images on spec. Has two regular photographers covering main events but commissions may be available.
Text: Possible scope for features on leading riders - contact editor with suggestions.
Overall freelance potential: Quite good for specialists.
Fees: By negotiation.

MOTOR CYCLE NEWS
Bauer Automotive Ltd, Media House, Lynchwood, Peterborough PE2 6EA.
Tel: 01733 468006. Fax: 01733 468028. E-mail: marc.potter@motorcyclenews.com
Editor: Marc Potter.
Weekly tabloid for all road-riding and recreational motorcyclists. Also covers motorcycle sport.
Illustrations: Rarely use on-spec material, but frequently require freelances for assignments. Seek competent photographers with keen news sense, able to work closely to a given brief yet able to incorporate their own visual ideas. Successful applicants are added to a nationwide contact list and may be approached to cover stories at any time.
Text: Illustrated news stories on all aspects of motorcycling always considered. Lively tabloid style required.
Overall freelance potential: Good.
Editor's tips: Assignments are often at short notice and to tight deadlines – photographers who can work quickly and flexibly stand the best chance of success. Commission fees include copyright assignment to MCN, though permission for re-use by the photographer is rarely denied.
Fees: Single pictures from £50; day rate £200 plus expenses.

MOUNTAIN BIKING UK
Future Publishing Ltd, Beauford Court, 30 Monmouth Street, Bath BA1 2BW.
Tel: 01225 442244. Fax: 01225 822790. E-mail: danny.walter@futurenet.co.uk
Editor: Danny Walter.
Monthly magazine devoted to the sport of mountain biking.
Illustrations: Spectacular or unusual shots of mountain biking, action pictures that convey a sense of both movement and height. General coverage of events and individual riders may be of interest.
Text: Well-illustrated articles that show good knowledge of the sport.
Overall freelance potential: Good scope for individual and original photography.
Fees: By negotiation.

PRACTICAL SPORTSBIKES
Bauer Automotive Ltd, Media House, Lynchwood, Peterborough PE2 6EA.
Tel: 01733 468043. E-mail: jim.moore@bauermedia.co.uk
Editor: Jim Moore.
Quarterly magazine focused on sports motorcycles from the mid-70s to mid-90s era.
Illustrations: Only required as part of illustrated article packages as below.
Text: Well-illustrated feature stories about individual bikes and restoration projects, but contributors must have detailed knowledge of machines from the relevant era.

Overall freelance potential: Limited, only for the specialist.
Editor's Tips: Ideas or suggestions should be submitted to the editor along with examples of work that show the contributor genuinely knows the subject.
Fees: By negotiation.

RIDE
Bauer Automotive, Media House, Lynchwood, Peterborough PE2 6EA.
Tel: 01733 468081. Fax: 01733 468092. E-mail: colin.overland@bauermedia.co.uk
Editor: Colin Overland.
Monthly magazine for the motorcycling enthusiast.
Illustrations: Always interested in expanding network of photographers, for reader shots, news pictures etc. Commissions available to produce coverage for road tests and general features, but only for those with prior experience of motor sport or similar action photography.
Text: Little scope.
Overall freelance potential: Limited.
Fees: Around £250 per day.

SCOOTERING
PO Box 99, Horncastle, Lincs LN9 6LZ.
Tel/fax: 01507 524004. E-mail: editorial@scootering.com
Editor: Andy Gillard.
Monthly magazine for motor scooter enthusiasts.
Illustrations: Pictures of motor scooters of the Lambretta/Vespa type – shows, meetings, "runs", racing, special paint jobs, "chopped" scooters, etc. Covers: usually staff-produced, but a good freelance shot might be used.
Text: Original ideas considered. Contributors should be aware of the particular lifestyle and terminology attached to the scooter scene.
Overall freelance potential: Potential scope for those who know the current scooter scene and its followers, but most is produced by staff or regular contributors.
Editor's tips: Be aware that the readers have a very good knowledge of this specialised subject.
Fees: By negotiation.

SUPERBIKE
IPC Media, Leon House, 233 High Street, Croydon CR9 1HZ.
Tel: 020 8726 8445. Fax: 020 8726 8499. E-mail: kenny_pryde@ipcmedia.com
Editor: Kenny Pryde. **Art Editor:** Huw Williams.
Monthly for sports motorcycle enthusiasts. Specialising in new model tests and old model reviews, motorcycle Grand Prix, World Superbike and UK racing scene.
Illustrations: Pictures of unusual motorcycles, road-racing, drag-racing and other sports pictures of unusual interest or impact; crash sequences; motorcycle people.
Text: Features of general or specific motorcycle interest. Editorial style is humorous, irreverent. 1,500–3,000 words.
Overall freelance potential: Around 30 per cent of the magazine is contributed from outside sources.
Fees: Dependent on size and position in magazine.

Are you working from the latest edition of The Freelance Photographer's Market Handbook? It's published on 1 October each year. Markets are constantly changing, so it pays to have the latest edition

VISORDOWN
Magicalia Media, 15-18 White Lion Street, London N1 9PG.
Tel: 020 7843 8800. E-mail: ben.cope@magicalia.com
Editor: Ben Cope.
Wide-ranging monthly for all motorcycling enthusiasts. Covers road bikes, racing, touring and scooters.
Illustrations: Any strong and interesting images connected with any aspect of motorcycling and the biking lifestyle – unusual bikes or biking situations, good race action, celebrities with bikes, etc. Most major feature photography is handled by a regular team but commissions may be available to those with experience.
Text: Limited scope, but original ideas considered.
Overall freelance potential: Good for the specialist.
Editor's tips: Images from the sidelines of the motorcycling scene may be of more interest than action or straight shots of bikes.
Fees: Negotiable, depending on what is offered.

Electronics & Computing

PRACTICAL WIRELESS
PW Publishing Ltd, Arrowsmith Court, Station Approach, Broadstone, Dorset BH18 8PW.
Tel: 0845 803 1979. Fax: 01202 659950. E-mail: steve@pwpublishing.ltd.uk
Editor: Rob Mannion. **Art Editor:** Stephen Hunt.
Monthly magazine covering all aspects of radio of interest to the radio amateur and enthusiast.
Illustrations: B&W and colour. Usually only required to illustrate specific articles or covers.
Text: Articles on amateur radio or short wave listening, or on aspects of professional radio systems of interest to the enthusiast. 1,000–5,000 words.
Overall freelance potential: Little scope for individual photographs, but complete, illustrated articles always welcome.
Fees: By negotiation.

PRO SOUND NEWS
CMP Information, 7th Floor, Ludgate House, 245 Blackfriars Road, London SE1 9UR.
Tel: 020 7921 8319. Fax: 020 7921 8302. E-mail: david.robinson@cmpinformation.com
Editor: Dave Robinson.
Monthly news magazine for professionals working in the European sound production industry. Covers recording, live sound, post-production, mastering and broadcasting.
Illustrations: News pictures on all aspects of the industry, from equipment manufacture to live sound shows and concert performances to recording studios.
Text: Illustrated news items and features (800–1,000 words) on any aspect of the industry, but always check with the editor before submitting.
Overall freelance potential: Good for those with contacts in the audio and music business.
Fees: £140 per 1,000 words for text; photographs from £25.

RADIO USER
PW Publishing Ltd, Arrowsmith Court, Station Approach, Broadstone, Dorset BH18 8PW.
Tel: 0845 803 1979. Fax: 01202 659950. E-mail: roger@pwpublishing.ltd.uk
Editor: Roger Hall. **Art Editor:** Stephen Hunt.
Monthly magazine for anyone interested in the world of radio communications.
Illustrations: Pictures connected with the world of radio and communications including ships, aircraft and vehicles, but usually only required to illustrate specific articles.
Text: Features on radio systems or on other aspects of radio of interest to the enthusiast. News and reviews of equipment, clubs, etc. 1,000–2,000 words.

Overall freelance potential: Between 50 and 75 per cent comes from freelances.
Editor's tips: The magazine is always on the lookout for features on new and novel uses for radio communications. Visual articles on all aspects of communications welcome.
Fees: £40 per published page.

WHAT SATELLITE & DIGITAL TV
Future Publishing Ltd, 2 Balcombe Street, London NW1 6NW.
Tel: 020 7042 4000. Fax: 020 7042 4471. E-mail: alex.lane@futurenet.co.uk
Editor: Alex Lane.
Monthly magazine for satellite TV system buyers and users. Contains tests on receivers and dishes, general features, programme listings, reviews and the latest satellite news.
Illustrations: Photographs of satellite systems in situ, family/people shots with equipment in use.
Text: Technical topics, plus programme reviews and personality pieces. 500–1,200 words.
Overall freelance potential: Around 50 per cent from such sources.
Fees: By agreement.

Equestrian

EQUESTRIAN TRADE NEWS
Equestrian Management Consultants Ltd, Stockeld Park, Wetherby, West Yorkshire LS22 4AW.
Tel: 01937 582111. Fax: 01937 582778. E-mail: editor@equestriantradenews.com
Editor: Liz Benwell.
Monthly publication for business people and trade in the equestrian world.
Illustrations: Pictures covering saddlery, feedstuffs, new riding schools and business in the industry. Also news pictures of people connected with the industry – people retiring, getting married, etc.
Text: Features on specialist subjects and general articles on retailing, marketing and business. 1,000 words.
Overall freelance potential: Around 50 per cent comes from freelances.
Editor's tips: Only stories with a business angle will be considered. No scope for general horsey or racing material.
Fees: Text, £25 per 1,000 words; pictures by arrangement.

HORSE
IPC Media Ltd, Blue Fin Building, 110 Southwark Street, London SE1 0SU.
Tel: 020 3148 5000. E-mail: joanna_brown@ipcmedia.com
Editor: Jo Brown. **Picture Editor:** Eve Jones.
Monthly aimed at the serious leisure rider.
Illustrations: All photography by commission only to illustrate specific features. Experienced workers should send an introductory letter with examples of previously published work.
Text: No scope.
Overall freelance potential: Limited and only for the experienced equestrian specialist.
Fees: By negotiation.

HORSE & HOUND
IPC Media, Blue Fin Building, 110 Southwark Street, London SE1 0SU.
Tel: 020 3148 4554. E-mail: hhpictures@ipcmedia.com
Editor: Lucy Higginson. **Picture Editor:** Jayne Toyne.

Weekly news magazine covering all equestrian sports.

Illustrations: News and feature pictures considered on spec for immediate use or for stock, covering racing, point-to-pointing, showjumping, eventing, polo, hunting, driving and showing. Commissions available to experienced equestrian/countryside photographers; make appointment with the picture editor to show portfolio.

Text: Possible opportunities for those with knowledge and experience of the above disciplines.

Overall freelance potential: Good for those who can show skill in this field; enquiries from photographers are encouraged.

Fees: Single pictures according to size of reproduction. Commission rates £200 per day (all rights); £135 per day (first use).

HORSE & RIDER

D. J. Murphy (Publishers) Ltd, Headley House, Headley Road, Grayshott, Surrey GU26 6TU. Tel: 01428 601020. Fax: 01428 601030. E-mail: djm@djmurphy.co.uk

Editor: Nicky Moffatt.

Monthly magazine aimed at adult horse-riders.

Illustrations: Off-beat personality shots and pictures for photo stories illustrating equestrian subjects, eg plaiting up, clipping, etc. May also consider general yard pictures, riding pictures, people and horses, but only by prior arrangement.

Text: Illustrated instructional features on stable management, grooming, etc, from contributors with real knowledge of the subject. Submit ideas only in the first instance.

Overall freelance potential: Only for freelances who have a real understanding of the market.

Editor's tips: Material must be technically accurate – riders must be shown wearing the correct clothes, especially hats; horses must be fit and correctly tacked.

Fees: Pictures £25–£60. Text £65 per 1,000 words.

Farming

CROPS

Reed Farmers Publishing Group, Quadrant House, The Quadrant, Sutton, Surrey SM2 5AS. Tel: 020 8652 4081. Fax: 020 8652 8928. E-mail: richard.allinson@rbi.co.uk

Editor: Richard Allinson.

Monthly magazine catering exclusively for the arable farmer.

Illustrations: News pictures depicting anything of topical, unusual or technical interest concerning crop farming and production. Captions must be precise and detailed.

Text: Limited scope for short topical articles written by specialists.

Overall freelance potential: Good for farming specialists.

Fees: By negotiation.

DAIRY FARMER

CMP Information Ltd, Riverbank House, Angel Lane, Tonbridge, Kent TN9 1SE. Tel: 01732 377273. Fax: 01732 377543. E-mail: phollinshead@cmpibiz.com

Editor: Peter Hollinshead.

Monthly journal for dairy farmers.

Are you working from the latest edition of The Freelance Photographer's Market Handbook? It's published on 1 October each year. Markets are constantly changing, so it pays to have the latest edition

Illustrations: Captioned pictures, technical or possibly historical. Also humourous or unusual pictures concerning the dairy industry. Some assignments to visit farms available.
Text: In-depth, technical features to help dairy farmers run their businesses more profitably.
Overall freelance potential: Limited, but open to suggestions.
Fees: By arrangement.

FARMERS GUARDIAN

CMP Information Ltd, Unit 4, Fulwood Park, Caxton Road, Fulwood, Preston PR2 9NZ.
Tel: 01772 799445. Fax: 01772 654987. E-mail: teveson@cmpi.biz
Editor: Emma Penny. **Picture Editor:** Theresa Eveson.
Weekly news publication for all farmers, with the emphasis on commerce.
Illustrations: Current farming, rural and equestrian news pictures accompanied by story or extended captions.
Text: News items always of interest. Possible scope for articles on current agricultural and rural issues.
Overall freelance potential: Fair.
Fees: According to use.

FARMERS WEEKLY

Reed Business Information, Quadrant House, The Quadrant, Sutton, Surrey SM2 5AS.
Tel: 020 8652 4080. Fax: 020 8652 4005. E-mail: farmers.weekly@rbi.co.uk
Editor: Jane King. Group **Picture Editor:** Jodie Deakin.
Weekly publication covering all matters of interest to farmers.
Illustrations: News pictures relating to the world of farming and picture stories on technical aspects of agriculture. Also opportunities for assignments.
Text: Tight, well-written copy on farming matters and anything that will help farmers run their business more efficiently.
Overall freelance potential: Good.
Fees: News material by negotiation. Photo assignment work around £170 per day.
Editor's tips: News pages are started on Monday and close for press on Wednesday afternoon, so news material should be submitted during that period. Copy and pics can be received by e-mail.

HOME FARMER

The Good Life Press Ltd, The Old Pigsties, Clifton Fields, Lytham Road, Preston PR4 0XG.
Tel: 01772 633444. E-mail: editor@homefarmer.co.uk
Editors: Diana Sutton, Paul Peacock.
Monthly magazine aimed at anyone interested in small-scale farming and home-based food production, as well as environmental issues.
Illustrations: Will consider interesting images in their own right, but prefer to see them as part of a complete illustrated feature as below.
Text: Always interested in articles that can help readers realise their lifestyle dreams on subjects such as self-sufficiency, recycling, vegetable growing, urban poultry or pig keeping, beekeeping, caring for animals on a small acreage, etc. Initial contact by e-mail is preferred.
Overall freelance potential: Excellent for the right type of material.
Editor's Tips: Prefer to publish material on accessible and practical options that don't assume that people have a lot of land at their disposal.
Fees: By negotiation, depending upon what is on offer.

POULTRY WORLD

Reed Business Information, Quadrant House, The Quadrant, Sutton, Surrey SM2 5AS.
Tel: 020 8652 3500. Fax: 020 8652 4042. E-mail: poultry.world@rbi.co.uk
Editor: Philip Clarke.
Monthly publication aimed at the UK, EU and worldwide commercial poultry industries. Covers egg production as well as chickens, turkeys, ducks and geese. Includes Pure Breeds section.

Illustrations: News pictures and good general stock relating to the poultry industry, both in UK and overseas.
Text: News stories and ideas for features always considered; breeding, processing, packing, marketing, etc.
Overall freelance potential: Limited.
Fees: By negotiation.

Food & Drink

DECANTER
IPC Inspire, Blue Fin Building, 110 Southwark Street, London SE1 0SU.
Tel: 020 3148 5000. Fax: 020 3148 8524. E-mail: decanterpictures@decanter.com
Editor: Guy Woodward.
Monthly magazine for the serious wine enthusiast, featuring producer and regional profiles, tastings, and related food and travel features.
Illustrations: Stock images of wine-producing regions occasionally needed to illustrate features, including attractive travel images of the region, not necessarily specifically wine-related. Send details of coverage available in the first instance.
Text: Illustrated articles on topics as above; submit synopsis first.
Overall freelance potential: Limited.
Fees: By negotiation.

ITALIA UK
Italia UK Limited, 3 Brooklands Place, Brooklands Road, Sale, Manchester M33 3SD.
Tel: 0161 976 1212. Fax: 0161 976 2888. E-mail: gr@italiauk.net
Editor: Glenn Routledge.
Anglo-Italian publication distributed through catering and food retail outlets.
Illustrations: Images of Italian food, drink, restaurants. Send details of subjects available in the first instance.
Text: May consider quality restaurant reviews (with pictures) from main UK cities, and general feature suggestions.
Overall freelance potential: Limited.
Editor's tips: Bear in mind readership is pro-Italian and already has a reasonable knowledge of Italy.
Fees: By negotiation.

LIFESCAPE
Madafu Publishing Ltd, 353 Shenley Road, Borehamwood, Herts WD6 1TN.
Tel: 01707 859805. E-mail: rajasana@lifescapemag.com
Editor: Rajasana Otiende.
Magazine designed as a complete resource for vegetarians, covering not just food but also holidays, fair trade fashion/beauty and the use of organic products generally.
Illustrations: Agency pictures often used but the editor would prefer to use freelance stock or even commission images. In-house photographer produces most beauty coverage but possible opportunities for fashion work.
Text: Approaches from writers with expert knowledge of health subjects always welcomed.

As a member of the Bureau of Freelance Photographers, you'll be kept up-to-date with markets through the BFP Market Newsletter, published monthly. For details of membership, turn to page 9

Overall freelance potential: Fair.
Editor's tips: Would rather pay for something unique than rely on agencies, though it does have to be within budget.
Fees: By negotiation.

OLIVE
BBC Worldwide Publishing, Woodlands, 80 Wood Lane, London W12 0TT.
Tel: 020 8433 1769. Fax: 020 8433 3499. E-mail: elizabeth.galbraith@bbc.co.uk
Editor: Christine Hayes. **Creative Director:** Elizabeth Galbraith.
Monthly food and travel magazine for a young, upmarket readership.
Illustrations: Digital files preferred. Almost all by commission to illustrate major features. Experienced workers should make an an appointment to show portfolio to the creative director. Those with relevant stock collections should send lists.
Text: Will consider ideas from experienced contributors, especially for travel-related material, but no on spec submissions.
Overall freelance potential: Opportunities for specialists only.
Fees: By negotiation.

PUBLICAN
United Business Media, Ludgate House, 245 Blackfriars Road, London SE1 9UY.
Tel: 020 7955 3711. E-mail: cnodder@cmpinformation.com
Editor: Caroline Nodder.
Weekly independent newspaper for publicans and pub companies throughout the UK.
Illustrations: Topical pictures concerning pubs and publicans, brewery and pub company management, and the drinks trade generally. Must be newsworthy or have some point of unusual interest, and preferably include people. Call before submitting.
Text: News items and picture stories about publicans – humorous, unusual, or controversial. Stories that have implications for the whole pub trade, or that illustrate a problem; original ways of increasing trade. News items up to 250 words; features around 500–800 words, but discuss proposal before submitting.
Overall freelance potential: Good for original material, especially from outside London and the South East.
Editor's tips: Forget charity bottle smashes, pub openings, and pictures of people pulling or holding pints – hundreds of these are received already.
Fees: On a rising scale according to size of reproduction or length of text.

RESTAURANT
William Reed Business Media, Broadfield Park, Crawley, West Sussex RH11 9RT.
Tel: 01293 610214. E-mail: will.drew@william-reed.co.uk
Editor: Will Drew. **Art Director:** Gary Simons.
Monthly magazine for the restaurant trade, with coverage ranging from top London restaurants to high street operations. Also designed to appeal to serious food lovers and restaurant-goers.
Illustrations: Mostly by commission to shoot food, interiors, portraiture, reportage, still life and travel. Some scope for those with in-depth stock collections on suitable subjects. On-spec opportunities for coverage of restaurant openings, events and informal shots of trade personalities.
Text: Will consider ideas on any relevant subject.
Overall freelance potential: Good for experienced freelances.
Fees: By negotiation.

SCOTTISH LICENSED TRADE NEWS
Peebles Media Group, Berguis House, 20 Clifton Street, Glasgow G3 7LA.
Tel: 0141 567 6000. Fax: 0141 331 1395. E-mail: scott.wright@peeblesmedia.com
Editor: Scott Wright.
Fortnightly publication for Scottish publicans, off-licensees, hoteliers, caterers, restaurateurs,

drinks executives, drinks companies.
Illustrations: News pictures connected with the above subjects.
Text: News and features of specific interest to the Scottish trade.
Overall freelance potential: Limited.
Fees: By agreement.

WAITROSE KITCHEN
John Brown Publishing, 136-142 Bramley Road, London W10 6SR.
Tel: 020 7565 3000. Fax: 020 7565 3076. E-mail: food@johnbrowngroup.co.uk
Editor: William Sitwell. **Art Director:** Ben Brannen. **Art Editor:** Tabitha Hawkins.
Picture-led monthly concentrating on the "culture of food" as well as recipes and cookery.
Illustrations: Colour transparencies only. Very high quality food photography, plus coverage of food producers, gourmet travel, restaurants and chefs. Much commissioned from established specialists; those with suitable skills should initally submit some examples of previous work. Limited use of top quality specialist stock; send lists to picture editor. Commissions for interior/food shots for restaurant reviews around the UK are frequently sought.
Text: Scope for well-experienced food and drink writers.
Overall freelance potential: Excellent, but only for the experienced worker in the field.
Fees: By negotiation.

Gardening

BBC GARDENERS' WORLD MAGAZINE
BBC Worldwide, Media Centre, 201 Wood Lane, London W12 7TQ.
Tel: 020 8433 3959. Fax: 020 8433 3986. E-mail: guy.bennington@bbc.com
Editor: Adam Pasco. **Art Editor:** Guy Bennington.
Monthly magazine for gardeners at all levels of expertise.
Illustrations: No speculative submissions. Photographers with specialist gardening collections should send lists of material available with all plants properly named. Commissions may be available to photograph individual gardens; the editor will always be pleased to hear from photographers who can bring potential subjects to his attention. Also photographers prepared to set up small studios with lights on location: good studio, portrait and reportage photography also commissioned.
Text: All text is commissioned.
Overall freelance potential: Mainly for specialists.
Editor's tips: Always looking for interesting "real" gardens for possible coverage. Small gardens, patios and container gardening of particular interest.
Fees: By negotiation.

THE ENGLISH GARDEN
Archant Specialist, Archant House, Oriel Road, Cheltenham GL50 1BB.
Tel: 01242 211080. E-mail: theenglishgarden@archant.co.uk
Editor: Tamsin Westhorpe.
Picture-led monthly featuring the most attractive gardens in Britain, from cottage gardens to stately homes.
Illustrations: Pictures mainly required as part of complete feature packages as below and usually commissioned. Possible scope for library shots illustrating specific types of garden, plant or tree – send lists of subjects available in the first instance.
Text: High-quality, exclusive features on individual gardens accompanied by a good selection of pictures (15-20 published within each feature). Discuss with the editor first.
Overall freelance potential: A lot of photography is used but much is produced by regular contributors.

Editor's tips: Most interested in beautiful, idyllic gardens that readers can either visit or just fantasise about.
Fees: By negotiation and according to use.

THE GARDEN
RHS Publications, 4th Floor, Churchgate, New Road, Peterborough PE1 1TT.
Tel: 0845 260 0909. Fax: 01733 341633. E-mail: thegarden@rhs.org.uk
Editor: Ian Hodgson.
Monthly Journal of the Royal Horticultural Society. Publishes articles on plants and specialist aspects and techniques of horticulture.
Illustrations: Top quality photographs of identified plants, general horticultural subjects and specific gardens.
Text: Some freelance market; submit suggestions first.
Overall freelance potential: Some potential opportunities.
Fees: £40–£165 according to size of reproduction.

GARDEN ANSWERS
Bauer Media, Media House, Lynchwood, Peterborough PE2 6EA.
Tel: 01733 468000. E-mail: geoffstebbings@bauermedia.co.uk
Editor: Geoff Stebbings.
Monthly magazine for the enthusiastic gardener.
Illustrations: Little scope for speculative submissions, but always interested in receiving lists of subjects available from photographers. Do not send transparencies unless requested.
Text: Experienced gardening writers may be able to obtain commissions.
Overall freelance potential: Limited to the experienced gardening contributor.
Editor's tips: Practical gardening pictures are required, rather than simple shots of plants. Must be accompanied by detailed and accurate captions.
Fees: By arrangement.

GARDEN NEWS
Bauer Active Ltd, Media House, Lynchwood, Peterborough PE2 6EA.
Tel: 01733 468000. E-mail: clare.foggett@bauermedia.co.uk
Editor: Clare Foggett.
Weekly consumer newspaper for gardeners.
Illustrations: Digital files or medium format transparencies. Pictures of general horticultural subjects. Practical photographs to illustrate gardening techniques, top quality colour portraits of trees, shrubs, flowers and vegetables, and coverage of quality small/medium sized gardens.
Text: Short practical features of interest to gardeners. 600–800 words.
Overall freelance potential: Fair.
Fees: By agreement.

GARDEN TRADE NEWS
The Garden Communication and Media Company, The Old School, 4 Crowland Road, Eye, Peterborough PE6 7TN.
Tel: 01733 775700. Fax: 01733 775838. E-mail: editorial@gardentradenews.co.uk
Editor: Mike Wyatt.
Monthly business publication containing news, features and advice for retailers, wholesalers, manufacturers and distributors of horticultural products.
Illustrations: Pictures to illustrate news items or features.
Text: Illustrated news stories or articles concerning garden centres, nurseries and garden shops. Maximum 600 words.
Overall freelance potential: Limited.
Fees: £12.50 per 100 words; pictures from £17.50–£50 according to size of reproduction.

GARDENS ILLUSTRATED

Bristol Magazines Ltd, 14th Floor, Tower House, Fairfax Street, Bristol BS1 3BN.
Tel: 0117 314 8770. Fax: 0117 934 9008. E-mail: davidgrenham@originpublishing.co.uk
Editor: Juliet Roberts. **Art Director:** David Grenham.
Heavily-illustrated monthly with a practical and inspirational approach.
Illustrations: Usually commissioned, but high quality submissions may be considered on spec.
Photography should have a narrative and journalistic slant rather than just pretty pictures of
gardens. The gardens should be depicted in relation to the landscape, houses and the people who
own or work them. Coverage from outside UK welcome.
Text: Scope for experienced gardening writers – submit samples of previously published work first.
Overall freelance potential: Very good for the right material.
Editor's tips: Quality is key. Material previously published in the UK is not of interest.
Fees: By negotiation.

GARDENS MONTHLY

MyHobbyStore Ltd, Berwick House, 8-10 Knoll Rise, Orpington, Kent BR6 0EL.
Tel: 08444 122262. Fax: 01689 899266. E-mail: liz.dobbs@myhobbystore.com
Editor: Liz Dobbs.
Monthly aimed at gardeners of all levels, with an emphasis on easy to achieve success.
Illustrations: Stock images of gardening and garden subjects sometimes needed; send detailed list
of subjects available in the first instance.
Text: No scope.
Overall freelance potential: Limited.
Fees: From £15, to £100 for full page or cover.

HORTICULTURE WEEK

Haymarket Media Ltd, 174 Hammersmith Road, London W6 4JP.
Tel: 020 8267 4977. Fax: 020 8267 4987. E-mail: hortweek@haymarket.com
Editor: Kate Lowe. **Art Editor:** David Grant.
Weekly news magazine for commercial growers of plants and those employed in landscape work,
garden centres, public parks and gardens.
Illustrations: Captioned news and feature pictures relating to commercial horticulture,
landscaping, public parks, garden centres. Stock botanical images often needed – send details of
material available. Some commissions available.
Text: Short news items about happenings affecting the trade. Longer articles may be considered –
discuss ideas with the editor. 500–1,500 words.
Overall freelance potential: Limited.
Fees: By arrangement.

PROFESSIONAL LANDSCAPER & GROUNDSMAN

Albatross Publications, PO Box 523, Horsham, West Sussex RH12 4WL.
Tel: 01293 871201. Fax: 01293 871301. E-mail: newsdesk123@aol.com
Editor: Carol Andrews.
Quarterly magazine for landscapers, contractors, foresters, environmental designers, groundsmen
and local authorities. Covers both hard and soft landscape creation.
Illustrations: Pictures depicting subjects as below, usually only accepted as part of a complete
illustrated feature.
Text: Well-illustrated articles or case histories dealing with technical or practical landscaping
matters, horticulture, and general environmental and conservation issues. 1,200–1,500 words.
Overall freelance potential: Limited.
Fees: By negotiation.

General Interest

BEST OF BRITISH
Church Lane Publishing Ltd, 6 Market Gate, Market Deeping, Lincs PE6 8DL.
Tel/fax: 01778 342814. E-mail: linne@bestofbritishmag.co.uk
Editor: Linne Matthews.
Monthly magazine covering all aspects of British heritage and nostalgia, but with a strong emphasis on 1940s/1950s/1960s.
Illustrations: Mainly colour plus B&W for archive pictures from earlier eras. Top quality coverage of all British heritage subjects, from landscapes and museums to craftspeople and collectors; send details of material available in the first instance.
Text: Illustrated articles offering a positive view of aspects of Britain, past and present. Also profiles of people with unusual passions, humorous pieces about the British people and interviews with celebrities about aspects of Britain they love. Submit ideas or an outline first.
Overall freelance potential: Excellent.
Editor's tips: Pictures with good captions are always more interesting than those without. Material should always reflect a positive view of Britain. Nostalgic pictures always welcome, with a particular interest in the 1940s. See website at www.bestofbritishmag.co.uk.
Fees: By negotiation with editor.

BIZARRE
Dennis Publishing Ltd, 30 Cleveland Street, London W1T 4JD.
Tel: 020 7907 6000. Fax: 020 7907 6020. E-mail: bizarre.pictures@dennis.co.uk
Editor: David McComb. **Picture Editor:** Tom Broadbent.
Monthly magazine specialising in alternative (fetish and subversive) lifestyles. Heavily illustrated, including special 14-page photo section.
Illustrations: Will consider pictures depicting anything that broadly falls within the above parameters, with a heavy emphasis on shocking reportage photography. "Weird, disturbing and downright bizarre photos from around the world, the more unique the better." Prefer material that has not been previously published.
Text: Little freelance scope unless the contributor is a genuine expert in a specific subject.
Overall freelance potential: Very good.
Editor's tips: Always call first with details of what you have to offer. Please no "ghost" photos.
Fees: By negotiation and dependent on what is being offered.

COAST
The National Magazine Company Ltd, 72 Broadwick Street, London W1F 9EP.
Tel: 020 7439 5000. Fax: 7439 6880. E-mail: suzy.koo@natmags.co.uk
Editor: Clare Gogerty. **Art Director:** Joe McIntyre. **Picture Editor:** Suzy Koo.
Monthly glossy that celebrates the best of British coastal and seaside living.
Illustrations: High-quality seaside imagery, including coastal landscapes, seascapes, marine wildlife, etc, either for use in their own right with captions or to illustrate features. Mainly interested in hearing from photographers who can offer good coverage of specific coastal locations or subjects. Initial approach should be by e-mail with a small selection of low-res images. Also some opportunities for commissions, mainly for homes and interiors work – contact art editor in the first instance.
Text: Illustrated articles and features on suitable subjects always considered.
Overall freelance potential: Excellent for quality material.
Editor's tips: Keep in mind that requirements vary from month to month according to what features and locations are being included in each issue.
Fees: By negotiation.

CONDÉ NAST CUSTOMER PUBLISHING

6-8 Bond Street, London W1S 0AD.

Tel: 020 7152 3954. E-mail: michael.harrison@condenast.co.uk

Creative Director: Michael Harrison. **Group Picture Editor:** Victoria Lukens.

Contract publishing division of Condé Nast. Produces upmarket titles for corporate clients such as major store and hotel groups.

Illustrations: Opportunities for experienced photographers to obtain commissions in the fields of fashion, portraiture, travel, lifestyle and still life. Contact creative director by e-mail with details of previous experience and examples of work.

Text: N/A.

Overall freelance potential: Scope for photographers producing the highest quality work.

Fees: By negotiation.

READER'S DIGEST

Vivat Direct Ltd (T/A Reader's Digest) 11 Westferry Circus, Canary Wharf, London E14 4HE.

Tel: 020 7715 8029. Fax: 020 7715 8716. E-mail: theeditor@readersdigest.co.uk

Editor-in-Chief: Gill Hudson. **Picture Researcher:** Roberta Mitchell.

British edition of the monthly magazine for a general interest readership.

Illustrations: Pictures to illustrate specific general interest features. Some commission possibilities for experienced specialist workers.

Text: High quality features on all topics.

Overall freelance potential: Limited opportunities for new freelance contributors.

Fees: By agreement.

SAGA MAGAZINE

Saga Publishing Ltd, The Saga Pavilion, Enbrook Park, Sandgate, Folkestone CT20 3SE.

Tel: 01303 771523. Fax: 01303 776699.

Editor: Katy Bravery. **Art Director:** Paul Hayes-Watkins.

Monthly, subscription-only, general interest magazine aimed at readers over 50.

Illustrations: Photography is mainly by commission only, but some top quality photo features occasionally accepted.

Text: Will consider wide range of articles – human interest, "real life" stories, intriguing overseas interest (not travel), celebrity interviews, some natural history – all relevant to 50+ readership.

Overall freelance potential: Limited, but some possiblities for carefully-targeted ideas exclusive to UK.

Fees: Good, but by negotiation.

THE TRAVEL & LEISURE MAGAZINE

Travel & Leisure Magazines Limited, 103 Cranbrook Road, Ilford, Essex IG1 4PU.

Tel: 020 8477 1529. E-mail: peter@ellegard.co.uk

Editor: Peter Ellegard.

Family-oriented quarterly, covering not just travel but also motoring, health, interiors, gardens, food and drink.

Illustrations: Always interested in seeing potential front cover shots. These are always seasonal in nature and most frequently feature happy families in a seasonal setting.

Text: Some scope for illustrated articles, mainly on the travel side and for the magazine's regular sections – intending contributors should ask for a copy of the magazine so that they can see the usual format of the sections. Rarely take speculative pieces but often ask freelances to write on specific locations or topics.

Overall freelance potential: Limited.

Fees: By negotiation.

WORLD ILLUSTRATED
HotShoe International Ltd, 29-31 Saffron Hill, London EC1N 8SW.
Tel: 020 7421 6009. E-mail: ctaylor@photoshot.com
Editor: Melissa DeWitt.
Showcase magazine for established and up-and-coming photographic talent.
Illustrations: As above, photographic work across a wide range of styles and genres.
Text: No scope.
Overall freelance potential: Good for really top-quality material.
Editor's tips: Sets of images need to tell a story and have contemporary relevance.
Fees: By negotiation.

YOURS
Bauer Consumer Media, Media House, Lynchwood, Peterborough PE2 6EA.
Tel: 01733 468000. E-mail: yours@bauerconsumer.co.uk
Editor: Valery McConnell. **Picture Editor:** Davina Dunn.
Fortnightly publication aimed at 50-plus women.
Illustrations: Good stock shots of mature people engaged in a variety of activities, or depicted in varying moods (happy, worried, thoughtful, etc), always needed for general illustration purposes. The latter should be model-released. Send list of subjects and a few samples first. Experienced photographers required for commissions around the country, able to take strong, sympathetic shots to accompany news items and real life stories.
Text: Positive stories about older people's achievements and general features likely to be of particular interest to an older readership. 600–1,000 words.
Overall freelance potential: Very good.
Fees: By negotiation.

Health & Medical

GP
Haymarket Medical Ltd, 174 Hammersmith Road, London W6 7JP.
Tel: 020 8267 4849. Fax: 020 8267 4859. E-mail: pauline.lock@haymarket.com
Editor: Emma Bower. **Group Art Editor:** Pauline Lock.
Weekly newspaper for family doctors.
Illustrations: Pictures of general practitioners involved in news stories, and clinical/scientific pictures for features. Commissions frequently available to shoot portraits of GPs or practice nurses.
Text: News stories, up to 400 words, preferably by prior arrangement. Features considered, by prior arrangement with the features editor.
Overall freelance potential: The paper uses a lot of pictures from freelances.
Fees: By negotiation, but around £200-£300 per 1,000 words, and £100 for half-day photographic session.

H&E NATURIST
New Freedom Publications Ltd, Burlington Court, Carlisle Street, Goole, East Yorkshire DN14 5EG.
Tel: 01405 760298. Fax: 01405 763815. E-mail: editor@henaturist.net
Editor: Sam Hawcroft.
Monthly naturist/nudist magazine.
Illustrations: Attractive photos of naturists in landscapes, on beaches, in countryside. Couples and singles, male and female, any age from 18 upwards. Also travel and scenic shots used.
Text: Illustrated articles up to 1,200 words about naturist lives and resorts, and off the beaten track naturism.
Overall freelance potential: Excellent.
Editor's tips: Contributors' guidelines are available on request.
Fees: Cover £150; £20 per quarter page inside.

HEALTH & FITNESS
Dennis Publishing, 30 Cleveland Street, London W1T 4JD.
Tel: 020 7907 6000. E-mail: victoria_hill@dennis.co.uk
Editor: Mary Comber. **Deputy Art Editor:** Victoria Hill.
Glossy monthly covering all aspects of fitness, health and nutrition, aimed at women.
Illustrations: Photographs for use in illustrating articles and features on topics as above. Covers: outstanding and striking shots featuring an obviously fit and healthy young female model.
Text: Articles and features on suitable topics, with an appeal to women. Always query the editor before submitting.
Overall freelance potential: Good.
Fees: By negotiation.

PULSE
UBM Medica, Ludgate House, 245 Blackfriars Road, London SE1 9UY.
Tel: 020 7921 8102. Fax: 020 7921 8248. E-mail: mcollard@cmpmedica.com
Editor: Jo Haynes. Group **Picture Editor:** Marie Louise Collard.
Weekly newspaper for family doctors covering all aspects of general practice medicine.
Illustrations: Topical pictures with captions, involving GPs or illustrating relevant news stories. Commissions available for high quality portraiture, especially outside the London area. Pictures are also commissioned for the Pulse Picture Library, a specialist collection of life and medicine in general practice.
Text: News and topical features about general practice and GPs.
Overall freelance potential: Good, especially for portrait specialists.
Editor's tips: Most interested in photographers who can produce original and creative portrait work.
Fees: Negotiable. £100 per half day for commissions.

Hobbies & Craft

CLASSIC STITCHES
D C Thomson & Company Ltd, 80 Kingsway East, Dundee DD4 8SL.
Tel: 01382 575120. Fax: 01382 452491. E-mail: editorial@classicstitches.com
Editor: Bea Neilson.
Bi-monthly embroidery magazine which looks at the work of designers and their lifestyles. Includes project-based features.
Illustrations: Photography generally required only to accompany features, though feature ideas are often generated by photographs. Commissions available to experienced workers to shoot still life material.
Text: Illustrated embroidery-related articles and specific projects, up to 1,500 words. Look at previous issues for style.
Overall freelance potential: Good; 70% of content is freelance.
Editor's tips: Make sure any submissions are relevant. For photographs, lighting and focus are paramount.
Fees: By negotiation.

CLOCKS
Splat Publishing Ltd, 141B Lower Granton Road, Edinburgh EH5 1EX.
Tel: 0131 331 3200. Fax: 0131 331 3213. E-mail: editor@clocksmagazine.com
Editor: John Hunter.
Monthly magazine for clock enthusiasts generally, those interested in building, repairing, restoring and collecting clocks and watches.
Illustrations: Pictures of anything concerned with clocks, e.g. public clocks, clocks in private

collections or museums, clock movements and parts, people involved in clock making, repairing or restoration. Detailed captions essential.

Text: Features on clockmakers, repairers or restorers; museums and collections; clock companies. 1,000–2,000 words.

Overall freelance potential: Around 90 per cent of the magazine is contributed by freelances.

Editor's tips: Pictures unaccompanied by textual descriptions of the clocks, or articles about them, are rarely used.

Fees: By arrangement.

ENGINEERING IN MINIATURE

TEE Publishing Ltd, The Fosse, Fosse Way, Radford Semele, Leamington Spa, CV31 1XN.
Tel: 01926 614101. Fax: 01926 614293. E-mail: info@teepublishing.com

Managing Editor: Chris Deith.

Monthly magazine concerned with model engineering and working steam models.

Illustrations: B&W and colour. Photographs only used in conjunction with specific news items or articles. No stock photos required. Covers: colour of model steam locomotives, engines or other model engineering subjects. A4 portrait format.

Text: Well-illustrated articles and features on all aspects of model engineering and serious modelling, and on full size railways and steam road vehicles. Must be of a serious and technical nature.

Overall freelance potential: Some 80 per cent of contributions come from freelances.

Editor's tips: Ideally engines depicted should be true steam-operated, not electric steam outline. There is no coverage of model railways below "0" gauge, or of plastic models. Telephone contact is preferred in the first instance.

Fees: Negotiable.

FURNITURE & CABINETMAKING

GMC Publications Ltd, 86 High Street, Lewes, East Sussex BN7 1XN.
Tel: 01273 402843. Fax: 01273 402849. E-mail: derekj@thegmcgroup.com

Editor: Derek Jones.

Monthly magazine for the serious furniture maker.

Illustrations: Mostly by commission to illustrate step-by-step projects and features on individual craftsmen – write with details of experience and samples of work. Good stock shots of fine furniture often required to illustrate specific styles. Topical single pictures may be considered if accompanied by detailed supporting text.

Text: Ideas for illustrated features always welcome. Submit a synopsis and one sample picture in the first instance.

Overall freelance potential: Good for experienced workers.

Fees: £25 per single picture inside; illustrated articles £50–£70 per page.

GIBBONS STAMP MONTHLY

Stanley Gibbons Publications, 7 Parkside, Christchurch Road, Ringwood, Hampshire BH24 3SH.
Tel: 01425 472363. Fax: 01425 470247. E-mail: hjefferies@stanleygibbons.co.uk

Editor: Hugh Jefferies.

Monthly magazine for stamp collectors.

Illustrations: Pictures inside only as illustrations for articles. Covers: pictures of interesting or unusual stamps relating to editorial features.

Text: Features on stamp collecting. 500–3,000 words.

Overall freelance potential: Most of the editorial comes from freelance contributors.

Fees: From £50 per 1,000 words.

GOOD WOODWORKING

MyHobbyStore Ltd, Berwick House, 8-10 Knoll Rise, Orpington, Kent BR6 0EL.
Tel: 0844 412 2262. E-mail: dave.roberts@magicalia.com

Editor: Darren Louciades.
Four weekly magazine for the serious amateur woodworker.
Illustrations: By commission only. Assignments available to cover specific projects.
Text: Ideas and suggestions welcome, but writers must have good technical knowledge of the subject. Commissions available to interview individual woodworkers.
Overall freelance potential: Good for those with experience of the subject.
Fees: Photography by negotiation. Text around £150 per 1,000 words.

KNITTING

Guild of Master Craftsman Publications Ltd, 86 High Street, Lewes, East Sussex BN8 4TH.
Tel: 01273 402824. Fax: 01273 487692. E-mail emmak@thegmcgroup.com
Editor: Emma Kennedy.
Monthly magazine for hand knitting enthusiasts.
Illustrations: Seek interesting, unusual and colourful images of people knitting from around the world. Must be accompanied by detailed captions, up to 500 words. Images of celebrities knitting welcomed.
Text: Will consider features on knitting events, stitch 'n' bitch groups, new wool shops, and how-to articles about knitting and crochet. Up to 1500 words with about 10 pictures. Ideas always welcomed.
Overall freelance potential: Good.
Fees: By negotiation.

MODEL ENGINEER

MyHobbyStore Ltd, Berwick House, 8-10 Knoll Rise, Orpington, Kent BR6 0EL.
Tel: 01689 899200. Fax: 01689 876438. E-mail: david.clark@myhobbystore.com
Editor: David Clark.
Fortnightly magazine aimed at the serious model engineering enthusiast.
Illustrations: No stock shots required; all pictures must be part of an article. Covers: photographs depicting models of steam locomotives and traction engines; metalworking equipment and home workshop scenes; some full size vintage vehicles.
Text: Well-illustrated articles from specialists.
Overall freelance potential: Considerable for the specialist.
Fees: Negotiable.

PARROTS

Imax Visual Ltd, The Old Cart House, Applesham Farm, Coombes, West Sussex BN15 0RP.
Tel: 01273 464777. Fax: 01273 463999. E-mail: editorial@imaxweb.co.uk
Editor: John Catchpole.
Monthly magazine for the parrot enthusiast.
Illustrations: High quality photographs of specific types of parrots and parakeets. Must be well-posed and well lit, showing clear details of plumage. Full and accurate caption information (preferably including scientific names) also essential. Amusing pictures involving parrots considered if accompanied by a good story.
Text: Articles aimed at the parrot enthusiast.
Editor's tips: Do not submit unidentified generic pictures of the "parrot on a branch" variety, or shots taken from long distances in zoos or bird parks.
Fees: Dependent on quality.

Are you working from the latest edition of The Freelance Photographer's Market Handbook? It's published on 1 October each year. Markets are constantly changing, so it pays to have the latest edition

---

PRACTICAL FISHKEEPING
Bauer Active Ltd, Media House, Lynchwood, Peterborough PE2 6EA.
Tel: 01733 468000. E-mail: matt.clarke@bauermedia.co.uk
Editor-in-Chief: Matt Clarke.
Monthly magazine for all tropical freshwater, marine, pond and coldwater fishkeepers, aimed at every level from hobbyist to expert.
Illustrations: Pictures of all species of tropical, marine and coldwater fish, plants, tanks, ponds and water gardens. Fish diseases, pond and tank maintenance, and pictures of things that have "gone wrong" are especially welcome. Prefer to hold material on file for possible future use.
Text: Emphasis on instructional articles on the subject. 1,000–2,000 words.
Overall freelance potential: Most is supplied by contributors with a specific knowledge of the hobby, but freelance material is considered on its merit at all times.
Editor's tips: Telephone first to give a brief on the intended copy and/or photographs available. Caption all fish clearly and get names right.
Fees: Negotiable.

TREASURE HUNTING
Greenlight Publishing, The Publishing House, 119 Newland Street, Witham, Essex CM8 1NF.
Tel: 01376 521900. Fax: 01376 521901. E-mail: greg@acguk.com
Editor: Greg Payne.
Monthly magazine for metal detecting and local history enthusiasts.
Illustrations: Colour prints or digital files. Usually only as illustrations for features detailed below, but captioned news pictures may be of interest. Covers: colour pictures of people using metal detectors in a countryside or seaside setting.
Text: Illustrated stories and features on individual finds, club treasure hunts, lost property recovery, local history, etc. However, fees nominal.
Overall freelance potential: Approximately 50 per cent of the magazine comes from freelances.
Editor's tips: Advisable to telephone the magazine before attempting a cover.
Fees: Covers, £50; features £20 per 1,000 words.

WOODCARVING
Guild of Master Craftsman Publications Ltd, 86 High Street, Lewes, East Sussex BN7 1XN.
Tel: 01273 477374. Fax: 01273 487692. E-mail: micheller@thegmcgroup.com
Editor: Michelle Robertson.
Magazine published six times per year and aimed at both amateur and professional woodcarvers.
Illustrations: Mostly to illustrate specific articles, but some scope for news pictures and shots of interesting pieces of work accompanied by detailed captions. Covers: striking colour shots of exceptional woodcarvings or woodcarvers in action, relating to article inside.
Text: Illustrated articles on all aspects of serious woodcarving, including profiles of individual craftsmen.
Overall freelance potential: Good for the right material.
Fees: Negotiable for one-off reproductions inside. £70 per published page for articles, including photos.

WOODTURNING
Guild of Master Craftsman Publications Ltd, 86 High Street, Lewes, East Sussex BN7 1XN.
Tel: 01273 477374. Fax: 01273 486300. E-mail: markb@thegmcgroup.com
Editor: Mark Baker.
Monthly magazine aimed at both amateur and professional woodturners.
Illustrations: Mostly to illustrate specific articles, but some scope for unusual or interesting single pictures with full captions. Covers: striking colour shots of turned items, relating to article inside.

Text: Illustrated articles on all aspects of woodturning, including profiles of individual craftsmen.
Overall freelance potential: Good for the right material.
Fees: £25 for one-off reproductions inside. £50 per published page for articles, including photos.

THE WOODWORKER

MyHobbyStore Ltd, Berwick House, 8-10 Knoll Rise, Orpington, Kent BR6 0EL.
Tel: 0844 412 2262. E-mail: mike.lawrence@myhobbystore.com
Editor: Mike Lawrence.
Monthly magazine for all craftspeople in wood. Readership includes schools and woodworking businesses, as well as individual hobbyists.
Illustrations: Pictures relating to wood and wood crafts, mostly as illustrations for features. Covers: pictures of fine furniture.
Text: Illustrated features on all facets of woodworking crafts, including profiles of individual woodworkers, how-to articles and material on period furniture and woodworking through the ages.
Overall freelance potential: Excellent; most content bought from outside contributors.
Editor's tips: Clear, concise authoritative writing in readable, modern style essential.
Fees: By negotiation.

Home Interest

COUNTRY HOMES & INTERIORS

Southbank Publishing Group, Blue Fin Building, 110 Southwark Street, London SE1 0SU.
Tel: 020 3148 7642. E-mail: petra_manley-leach@ipcmedia.com
Editor: Rhoda Parry. **Art Director:** Petra Manley-Leach.
Monthly magazine concerning up-market country homes, interiors and gardens.
Illustrations: Top quality coverage of architecture, interiors, gardens and landscapes. Mostly by commission, but speculative submissions of picture features on specific country houses or gardens, or other country-based topics, may be considered if of the highest quality. Covers: always related to a major feature inside.
Text: Top level coverage of country home and lifestyle subjects, only by commission.
Overall freelance potential: Excellent for photographers who can provide the right sort of material.
Fees: Negotiable from a minimum of £100.

ELLE DECORATION

Hachette Filipacchi (UK) Ltd, 64 North Row, London W1K 7LL.
Tel: 020 7150 7000. Fax: 020 7150 7001. E-mail: elledecopictures@hf-uk.com
Editor: Michelle Ogundehin. **Picture Editor:** Flora Bathurst.
Monthly interior decoration magazine aimed at a trend-setting readership.
Illustrations: By commission only, but always interested in hearing from photographers experienced in this field.
Text: Ideas for features always of interest.
Overall freelance potential: Plenty of scope for the experienced freelance.
Editor's tips: Particular projects must always be discussed in detail beforehand to ensure that the magazine's specific styling requirements are observed.
Fees: Photography according to commission.

THE ENGLISH HOME

Archant Specialist, Archant House, 3 Oriel Road, Cheltenham GL50 1BB.
Tel: 01242 211080. E-mail: englishhome@archant.co.uk
Editor: Kerryn Harper-Cuss.

Bi-monthly home interest title emphasising classic, elegant and country English style.
Illustrations: Mainly by commission. Opportunities for experienced architectural and interiors photographers to obtain assignments. Suggestions, with sample pictures, of suitable homes or beautiful regional localities to feature always welcome.
Text: Illustrated features on elegantly classic English homes, decoration, UK travel and events. Submit ideas in the first instance.
Overall freelance potential: Good.
Fees: By negotiation.

GOOD HOMES

Kelsey Publishing Group, Cudham Tithe Barn, Berry's Hill, Cudham, Kent TN16 3AG.
Tel: 01959 541444. Fax: 01959 541400. E-mail: x.x@kelsey.co.uk
Editor: Emma Dublin. **Art Director:** Natalie Williams.
Glossy monthly aimed at people who love their homes and love to decorate. Maintains some links with BBC TV programmes on home topics.
Illustrations: Top quality photography of interiors, gardens, home products, etc, all by commission. Photographers who have previously worked on top quality homes publications should write with details of their experience.
Text: No scope.
Overall freelance potential: Limited to those experienced in producing the highest standard of work.
Editor's tips: Not interested in hearing from photographers who have not done editorial interiors work before, no matter how skilled in other fields.
Fees: Standard day rate £450.

HOMES & GARDENS

IPC Media Ltd, Blue Fin Building, 110 Southwark Street, London SE1 0SU.
Tel: 020 3148 5000. E-mail: caroline_harrington@ipcmedia.com
Editor: Deborah Barker. **Art Director:** Caroline Harrington.
Monthly glossy magazine devoted to quality interior design and related matters.
Illustrations: High quality commissioned coverage of interior decoration, design, architecture, gardens, furnishings, food and travel. Emphasis on homes decorated in a tasteful style, up-market and attractive rather than wacky. Ideas for coverage always welcome.
Text: Heavily-illustrated features as above.
Overall freelance potential: Good for really top quality work.
Editor's tips: Out of London material particularly welcome.
Fees: By negotiation.

HOUSE BEAUTIFUL

National Magazine Company Ltd, 72 Broadwick Street, London W1F 9EP.
Tel: 020 7439 5642. Fax: 020 7437 6886. E-mail: chris.thurston@natmags.co.uk
Editor: Julia Goodwin. **Art Director:** Chris Thurston. **Picture Researcher:** Pascale Rowan.
Monthly magazine with the emphasis on practical home decorating ideas.
Illustrations: Usually by commission. Photographs of houses, interior decoration, furnishings, cookery and gardens. Complete picture features depicting houses and interiors of interest.
Text: Features on subjects as above, invariably commissioned, but possible scope for speculative features on suitable subjects.
Overall freelance potential: Quite good for experienced contributors in the home interest and interiors field.
Fees: By negotiation.

IDEAL HOME

IPC Media Ltd, Blue Fin Building, 110 Southwark Street, London SE1 0SU.
Tel: 020 3148 5000. E-mail: warren_filmer@ipcmedia.com

Editor: Isobel McKenzie-Price.
Monthly devoted to interiors and decorating.
Illustrations: Major feature photography always by commission; make appointment to show portfolio. Some scope for good general home style and decorating images for stock and general illustration.
Text: No scope.
Overall freelance potential: Very good for experienced workers.
Editor's tips: Research past issues to see what subjects have already been covered and to anticipate the types of issues likely to be covered in the future.
Fees: By negotiation.

PERIOD LIVING

Centaur Special Interest Media, St Giles House, 50 Poland Street, London W1V 4AX.
Tel: 020 7970 4433. Fax: 020 7970 4438. E-mail: period.living@centaur.co.uk
Editor: Sarah Whelan. **Art Editor:** Puishun Li.
Monthly magazine covering traditional homes and gardens, antiques and renovation.
Illustrations: Commissions available to experienced architectural and interiors photographers, who should make appointment to show portfolios in the first instance.
Text: No scope.
Overall freelance potential: Good.
Fees: By negotiation.

REAL HOMES

Ascent Publishing Ltd, 2 Sugarbrook Court, Aston, Birmingham B60 3EX.
Tel: 01527 834454. E-mail: firstname.lastname@centaur.co.uk
Editor: Caron Bronson. Deputy **Editor:** Helena Fulford.
Monthly aiming to help homeowners make the most of the home they have.
Illustrations: By commission only, but always interested in hearing from photographers experienced in this field. For those seeking house shoots, contact homes editor; for other images contact deputy editor.
Text: Ideas for features always considered, mainly practical, accessible solution-focused ideas.
Overall freelance potential: Good scope for the experienced freelance.
Editor's tips: Feature ideas must always be discussed in detail beforehand to ensure that the magazine's specific styling requirements are observed.
Fees: By negotiation.

25 BEAUTIFUL HOMES

IPC Media Ltd, Blue Fin Building, 110 Southwark Street, London SE1 0SU.
Tel: 020 3148 7290. E-mail: penny_botting@ipcmedia.com
Editor: Deborah Barker. **Commissioning Editor:** Penny Botting.
Interior design magazine featuring 25 individual homes per issue.
Illustrations: High-res digital files or medium format transparencies. Top quality interiors photography illustrating specific homes. Always looking for homes to feature: initially send a selection of recce snaps showing each room, plus an exterior shot, with brief details about the home and its owners; a commission to produce a full feature may follow.
Text: Features as above.
Overall freelance potential: Very good for the experienced interiors photographer.
Fees: Fee for complete feature package of words and pictures normally around £1,000.

THE WORLD OF INTERIORS

The Condé Nast Publications Ltd, Vogue House, Hanover Square, London W1S 1JU:
Tel: 020 7152 3831. Fax: 020 7493 4013. E-mail: mark.lazenby@condenast.co.uk
Editor-in-Chief: Rupert Thomas. **Art Director:** Mark Lazenby.
Monthly magazine showing the best interior decoration of all periods and in all countries.

Illustrations: Mainly colour, occasional B&W. Subjects as above. Extra high standard of work required.
Text: Complete coverage of interesting houses; occasionally public buildings, churches, shops, etc. 1,000–2,000 words.
Overall freelance potential: Much of the work in the magazine comes from freelances.
Fees: Negotiable.

YOUR HOME
Hubert Burda Media UK, The Tower, Phoenix Square, Colchester, Essex CO4 9HU.
Tel: 01206 851117. Fax: 01206 849078. E-mail: yourhome@burdamagazines.co.uk
Editor: Anna-Lisa De'ath.
Monthly home interest magazine concerned with real homes, makeovers, decorating, home improvements, DIY and creative projects.
Illustrations: Only as part of complete packages as detailed below.
Text: Scope for experienced interiors writers and photographers who can supply words/picture packages on a First Rights basis, for budget room makeovers and affordable real reader homes.
Overall freelance potential: Limited and only for the experienced contributor.
Fees: By negotiation.

Industry

CLASSIC PLANT & MACHINERY
Kelsey Publishing Group, Cudham Tithe Barn, Berry's Hill, Cudham, Kent TN16 3AG.
Tel: 01959 541444. Fax: 01959 541400. E-mail: cpm.ed@kelsey.co.uk
Editor: George Bowstead.
Monthly magazine covering vintage construction and mining plant and ancillary equipment.
Illustrations: Pictures of collectable, classic and vintage machinery, including dumptrucks, excavators, forklifts, road making and mining machinery. Must be accompanied by detailed and accurate captions. Contact editor before preparing a submission.
Text: Suggestions from those with suitable knowledge of these subjects always welcomed.
Overall freelance potential: Good.
Fees: By arrangement.

ENERGY IN BUILDINGS & INDUSTRY
Pinede Publishing Ltd, PO Box 825, Guildford, Surrey GU4 8WQ.
Tel/fax: 01483 452854. E-mail: mark.thrower@btinternet.com
Editor: Mark Thrower.
Monthly magazine concerned with the use and conservation of energy in large buildings and the industrial environment.
Illustrations: Pictures of relevant and interesting installations.
Text: Some scope for writer/photographers who have good knowledge of the energy business.
Overall freelance potential: Limited unless contributors have connections within the field.
Fees: £30–£40 per picture; £140 per 1,000 words for text.

ENGINEERING
Gillard Welch Ltd, 6a New Street, Warwick CV34 4RX.
Tel: 01926 408244. Fax: 01926 408206. E-mail: steve@engineeringnet.co.uk

As a member of the Bureau of Freelance Photographers, you'll be kept up-to-date with markets through the BFP Market Newsletter, published monthly. For details of membership, turn to page 9

Managing Editor: Steve Welch.

Monthly magazine dealing with all areas of manufacturing engineering from a design viewpoint.

Illustrations: Photographs depicting all aspects of design in industrial engineering, from aerospace and computers to energy management and waste disposal. Much from manufacturers but some by commission. Covers: Abstract and "artistic" photography.

Text: Short illustrated news items up to major design features. 250–2,000 words.

Overall freelance potential: Good for commissioned work.

Fees: £100 per published page for text. Covers £300–£400. Other commissioned photography around £120 per day.

INDUSTRIAL DIAMOND REVIEW

Odeon House, 146 College Road, Harrow, Middlesex HA1 1BH.

Tel: 020 8863 2767. E-mail: martin.jennings@idr-online.com

Editor: Martin Jennings.

Quarterly publication designed to promote a wider and more efficient use of diamond tools, i.e. grinding wheels, drill bits, saw blades, etc. in all branches of engineering.

Illustrations: Will consider pictures of any type of diamond tool in action.

Text: Case histories on the use of diamond tools in engineering, mining, etc. Up to 2,000 words for finished feature.

Overall freelance potential: Excellent but highly specialised.

Editor's tips: Technical case histories are welcome, but check acceptance with editor before submitting material. Potential contributors are requested to consult the editor before pursuing any possible editorial leads.

Fees: Excellent; by arrangement.

INDUSTRIAL FIRE JOURNAL

Hemming Information Services, No 8, The Old Yarn Mills, Westbury, Sherborne, Dorset DT9 3RG.

Tel: 01935 816030. Fax: 01935 817200. E-mail: am.knegt@hisdorset.com

Editor: Ann-Marie Knegt.

Quarterly magazine concerning firefighting in the industrial sector.

Illustrations: Pictures of anything concerning or involving firefighting services in an industrial context, including firefighting personnel in action. Covers: powerful colour images of the same.

Text: No scope for non-specialists.

Overall freelance potential: Fair.

Editor's tips: Seek editor's agreement before submitting. No photos of ordinary car fires or firefighters/engines at domestic home/high street fires. Look for racy, exciting and explicit shots to interest and educate a readership of fire professionals who've "seen it all before".

Fees: Negotiable, but generally good. Up to £200 for a really good cover picture.

MANUFACTURING CHEMIST

HPCI Ltd, Paulton House, 8 Shepherdess Walk, London N1 7LB.

Tel: 020 7549 2566. Fax: 020 7549 8622. E-mail: hilarya@hpcimedia.com

Editor: Hilary Ayshford.

Monthly journal for the pharmaceutical industry. Read by senior management involved in research, development, manufacturing and marketing of pharmaceuticals.

Illustrations: Pictures of any aspect of the pharmaceutical industry.

Text: Features on any aspect of the pharmaceutical industry as detailed above. 1,000–2,000 words.

Overall freelance potential: Approximately 30 per cent is contributed by freelances.

Fees: Text, £170 per 1,000 words for features, £15 per 100 words for news stories; pictures by agreement.

MARINE ENGINEERS REVIEW

Institute of Marine Engineering, Science & Technology, 80 Coleman Street, London EC2R 5BJ.

Tel: 020 7382 2600. Fax: 020 7382 2670. E-mail: mer@imarest.org

Editor: John Barnes.
Monthly publications for marine engineers.
Illustrations: Interesting topical photographs of ships and marine machinery.
Text: Articles on shipping and marine engineering, including naval and offshore topics.
Overall freelance potential: Good, but enquire before submitting.
Fees: By negotiation.

NEW CIVIL ENGINEER

EMAP Construct, Greater London House, Hampstead Road, London NW1 7EJ.
Tel: 020 7728 4541. Fax: 020 7728 4666. E-mail: anthony.oliver@emap.com
Editor: Anthony Oliver.
Weekly news magazine for professional civil engineers.
Illustrations: Up-to-date pictures depicting any civil engineering project. Must be well captioned and newsworthy.
Text: By commission only.
Overall freelance potential: Limited.
Fees: On a rising scale according to size of reproduction or length of text.

NEW DESIGN

Gillard Welch Ltd, 6a New Street, Warwick CV34 4RX.
Tel: 01926 408244. Fax: 01926 408206. E-mail: info@newdesignmagazine.co.uk
Managing Editor: Steve Welch.
Monthly for professional designers and manufacturers, covering developments in industrial and product design.
Illustrations: Photographs depicting new or current product, industrial and interior design, including architecture, theatre, textile, medical and transport design. Pictures should either have a news angle or be particularly strong images in their own right that might be used for covers.
Text: Illustrated news stories or features on any aspect of contemporary commercial design.
Overall freelance potential: Good.
Fees: Dependent on use, up to £300–£400 for covers.

PROFESSIONAL ENGINEERING

Caspian Publishing, 198 Kings Road, London, SW3 5XP.
Tel: 020 7973 1299. Fax: 020 7973 0462. E-mail: pe@pepublishing.com
Editor: Lee Hibbert.
Fortnightly publication for members of the Institution of Mechanical Engineers and decision-makers in industry.
Illustrations: Digital files preferred. Pictures of relevant people, locations, factories, processes and specific industries.
Text: Features with a general engineering bias at a fairly high management level, eg management techniques, new processes, materials applications, etc. 1,500 words maximum.
Overall freelance potential: Limited, and usually commissioned specifically.
Fees: Not less than around £200 per 1,000 words; pictures by agreement.

URETHANES TECHNOLOGIES INTERNATIONAL

Crain Communications Ltd, 3rd Floor, 21 St Thomas Street, London SE1 9RY.
Tel/fax: 020 7457 1400. E-mail: lwhite@crain.co.uk
Editor: Liz White.
Bi-monthly publication for the polyurethane producing, processing, and using industries.
Illustrations: Pictures of production, equipment, and application of polyurethane materials. Also news pictures and shots of trade personalities. Covers: top quality and graphically striking medium format colour of polyurethane-related subjects.
Text: Features on new applications of polyurethanes; new products; new equipment and processing. Business, marketing, personnel and technical news items. Up to 2,000 words.

Overall freelance potential: Good scope for those with access to the industries involved.
Fees: By arrangement.

UTILITY WEEK
Faversham House Group, 232A, Addington Road, South Croydon, Surrey, CR2 8LE
Tel: 020 8651 7103. Fax: 020 8651 7100. E-mail: steve.hobson@rbi.co.uk
Editor: Janet Wood.
Weekly business magazine for the three major supply utilities: electricity, gas and water.
Illustrations: News pictures concerning the major utilities. Possible scope for good stock coverage of industry subjects. Commissions often available to experienced portrait and business/industry workers.
Text: Contributors with expert knowledge always welcomed. Submit details of experience in the first instance.
Overall freelance potential: Very good for industrial specialists.
Fees: By negotiation.

WORKS MANAGEMENT
Findlay Publications Ltd, Hawley Mill, Hawley Road, Dartford, Kent DA2 7TJ.
Tel: 01322 221144. Fax: 01322 221188. E-mail: khurst@findlay.co.uk
Editor: Ken Hurst. **Art Editor:** Neil Young.
Monthly publication for managers and engineers who directly control or perform the works management function in selected manufacturing concerns.
Illustrations: Occasional need for regional coverage of managers and workers in realistic work situations in factories. Mostly pictures are used only to illustrate features.
Text: Illustrated features of interest to management, eg productivity, automation in factories, industrial relations, employment law, finance, energy, maintenance, handling and storage, safety and welfare. Around 1,500 words.
Overall freelance potential: Up to 30 per cent is contributed by freelances.
Fees: By agreement.

Local Government & Services

CHILDREN & YOUNG PEOPLE NOW
Haymarket Publishing Ltd, 174 Hammersmith Road, London W6 7JP.
Tel: 020 8267 4707. Fax: 020 8267 4728. E-mail: cypnow.editorial@haymarket.com
Editor: Ravi Chandiramani. **Art Editor:** David McCullough.
Weekly publication for youth workers, social workers, careers officers, teachers, counsellors and others working in the the children's service and youth affairs sectors.
Illustrations: Mainly commissioned shoots to cover youth work and youth workers around the country. Contact art editor with details and samples in the first instance.
Text: Small proportion of copy is from freelance contributors.
Overall freelance potential: Occasional news pictures and one or two features using freelance photos per issue.
Fees: According to use.

FIRE RISK MANAGEMENT
Fire Protection Association, London Road, Moreton in Marsh, Gloucestershire GL56 0RH.
Tel: 01608 812518. Fax: 01608 812501. E-mail: rgilbey@thefpa.co.uk

Editor: Rupert Gilbey.
Monthly technical publication on fire safety. Aimed at fire brigades, fire equipment manufacturers, architects, insurance companies, and those with responsibility for fire safety in public sector bodies, commerce and industry.
Illustrations: Pictures of large and small fires to illustrate reports. Also pictures showing different types of building design and occupancy (offices, commercial premises, warehouses, etc), and of emergency services at work.
Text: Technical articles and news items on fire prevention and protection. Features 1,000–2,000 words.
Overall freelance potential: Good pictures of fires and unusual fire safety experiences are always welcome.
Fees: Pictures, negotiable from £15. Text, negotiable from £110 per 1,000 words.

JANE'S POLICE REVIEW
IHS Jane's, 2nd Floor, 133 Houndsditch, London EC3A 7BX.
Tel: 020 3159 3579. Fax: 020 3159 3276. E-mail: chris.herbert@ihsjanes.com
Editor: Chris Herbert. **Art Editor:** David Playford.
Weekly news magazine for the police service.
Illustrations: All aspects of the police service. Particular interest in up-to-date news pictures covering the previous seven days (e-mail policereviewnews@janes.com). Some commissioned work available, with a need for more photographers to carry out regional work. Contact art editor first to show portfolio.
Text: Limited scope because of specialist subject matter, but will consider any subject of contemporary interest to police officers, 1,000–1,500 words.
Overall freelance potential: Good.
Editor's tips: The magazine is published on Friday with a Tuesday morning deadline for news pictures. Photographs for features should be good photojournalism and reportage; not interested in "publicity-style" photos.
Fees: Negotiable, minimum £50.

LEGAL ACTION
The Legal Action Group, 242 Pentonville Road, London N1 9UN.
Tel: 020 7833 2931. Fax: 020 7837 6094. E-mail: vwilliams@lag.org.uk
Editor: Valerie Williams.
Monthly publication for lawyers, advice workers, law students and academics.
Illustrations: Pictures of lawyers and judges, especially other than the standard head and shoulders shot. Plus stock pictures to illustrate features covering a wide range of subjects (e.g. housing, police, immigration, advice services).
Text: Features on legal services and professional issues, including the courts. High technical detail required. Also information for news and feature material that can be written in-house.
Overall freelance potential: Always interested in hearing from photographers holding suitable material.
Fees: By negotiation.

MUNICIPAL JOURNAL
Hemming Group Ltd, 32 Vauxhall Bridge Road, London SW1V 2SS.
Tel: 020 7973 6400. Fax: 020 7233 5051.
Editor: Michael Burton.
Weekly publication for senior local government officers, councillors, Whitehall departments and academic and other institutions.
Illustrations: B&W and colour. News pictures; relevant personalities, vehicles, buildings, etc;

general stock shots of local government subjects and situations to illustrate features.
Text: Features on local government issues. 750–1,000 words.
Overall freelance potential: Very good.
Fees: Good; on a rising scale according to the size of reproduction or length of feature.

PLANNING
Haymarket Business Publications Ltd, 174 Hammersmith Road, London W6 7JP
Tel: 020 8267 4469. Fax: 020 8267 4013. E-mail: planning@haymarket.com
Editor: Huw Morris.
Weekly news magazine for all involved with town and country planning and related issues. Official journal of the Royal Town Planning Institute.
Illustrations: News pictures always of interest, on specific planning issues. Also good generic shots of subjects planning touches on, e.g. conservation, transport, rivers, waste disposal, housing, energy, industry, retailing, etc. Some commissions available to illustrate major features.
Text: Illustrated news stories and longer features from contributors with good knowledge of planning issues, up to 1,500 words. Must be relevant to planners.
Overall freelance potential: Good for genuinely relevant topical material.
Editor's tips: Photos can be of general or specific interest.
Fees: Photography according to use or assignment; text £100 per 1,000 words.

SCHOLASTIC MAGAZINES
Scholastic Ltd, Villiers House, Clarendon Avenue, Leamington Spa CV32 5PR.
Tel: 01926 887799. Fax: 01926 883331.
Design Manager: Sarah Garbett.
Range of monthly publications for teachers in primary and nursery education.
Illustrations: Digital files preferred. News pictures and good, unposed pictures of school children from 3-12 years, in classrooms and other school situations. Cover pictures as above often commissioned. Pictures are retained within a large in-house library.
Text: No scope.
Fees: By agreement.

THE TEACHER
National Union of Teachers, Hamilton House, Mabledon Place, London WC1H 9BD.
Tel: 020 7380 4708. Fax: 020 7387 8458. E-mail: teacher@nut.org.uk
Editor: Ellie Campbell-Barr.
Official magazine of the National Union of Teachers.
Illustrations: News pictures concerning any educational topic, especially those taken in schools and colleges. Coverage of union activities, personalities, demonstrations, etc.
Text: Short articles and news items on educational matters.
Overall freelance potential: Limited; interested in good pictures though.
Editor's tips: Consult the editor before submitting.
Fees: According to use.

Male Interest

ATTITUDE
Third Floor, 207 Old Street, London EC1V 9NR.
Tel: 020 7608 6300. E-mail: matthew.todd@attitudemag.co.uk
Editor: Matthew Todd. Deputy **Editor:** Daniel Fulvio.
Monthly style magazine aimed primarily, but not exclusively, at gay men.
Illustrations: Mostly by commission to illustrate specific features. Some opportunities for experienced fashion and style workers (contact fashion editor). Also some scope for travel, reportage and popular culture material.
Text: Ideas for features – human interest, travel, celebrities – always considered; submit an outline first. Should appeal to a gay readership even if written from a "straight" perspective.
Overall freelance potential: Fair.
Fees: £100 per page for photography; text £150 per 1,000 words.

BOYS TOYS
Freestyle Publications Ltd, Alexander House, Ling Road, Poole, Dorset BH12 4NZ.
Tel: 01202 735090. Fax: 01202 733969. E-mail: tperkins@freestyle-group.com
Editor: Tom Perkins.
Monthly for young men, covering all lifestyle topics but with an emphasis on desirable products and technology.
Illustrations: Mostly commissioned in the fields of sport, fashion, motoring, technology and portraiture. Portfolios can be viewed in London. On spec material also considered if it fits the magazine's style.
Text: Ideas always considered.
Overall freelance potential: Excellent.
Fees: By negotiation.

CLUB INTERNATIONAL
Paul Raymond Publications, 3rd Floor, 207 Old Street, London EC1V 9NR.
Tel: 020 7608 6300. E-mail: mattb@paulraymond.com
Editor: Matt Berry.
Popular glamour monthly for men.
Illustrations: Requires top quality glamour sets of very attractive girls (aged 18 – 25).
Text: Articles on sexual or humorous topics, or factual/investigative pieces. 1,000–2,000 words.
Overall freelance potential: Most of the published glamour material comes from freelances, but they are normally experienced glamour photographers.
Editor's tips: Study the magazine to appreciate style. As well as being very attractive, girls featured must look contemporary and fashionable.
Fees: £600 for glamour sets. Text up to £200 per 1,000 words.

ESCORT
Paul Raymond Publications, 3rd Floor, 207 Old Street, London EC1V 9NR.
Tel: 020 7608 6300. E-mail: escort@paulraymond.com
Editor: James Hundleby.
Monthly glamour magazine; less sophisticated than the other Paul Raymond publications, Men Only and Club International.
Illustrations: Transparency or digital. Looks for glamour sets of "normal, healthy, girl-next-door" types. Each issue contains about 10 glamour sets running to 2–5 pages each.
Text: Purely "readers' contributions".
Overall freelance potential: Good.
Fees: £400+ for glamour sets, or from £25 per picture.

ESQUIRE

The National Magazine Company Ltd, 72 Broadwick Street, London W1F 9EP.
Tel: 020 7439 5000. Fax: 020 7439 5675. E-mail: henny.manley@natmags.co.uk
Editor: Jeremy Langmead. **Art Director:** David McKendrick. **Picture Editor:** Henny Manley.
Up-market general interest monthly for intelligent and affluent men in the 25–44 age group.
Illustrations: Top-quality material only, invariably by commission. Mostly portraiture, fashion and photojournalism.
Text: Scope for "name" writers only.
Overall freelance potential: Good for photographers, but restricted to those experienced at the highest level of magazine work.
Fees: By negotiation.

FHM

Bauer Media, Endeavour House, 189 Shaftesbury Avenue, London WC2H 8JG.
Tel: 020 7295 8534. E-mail: simon.everitt@bauerconsumer.co.uk
Editor: Colin Kennedy. **Photo Director:** Simon Everitt. **Picture Editor:** Samantha Webster.
Monthly lifestyle and fashion magazine for young men.
Illustrations: Mainly colour. Main feature and fashion photography always by commission. Stock images relating to subjects of major interest (sports, travel, adventure, cars, sex) often required – send details of coverage available.
Text: Will consider interesting short items of interest to a young male readership, and feature ideas from experienced workers.
Overall freelance potential: Good for the experienced contributor.
Fees: By negotiation.

FRONT

The Kane Corporation Ltd, 2nd Floor, 2–4 Noel Street, London W1F 8GB.
Tel: 020 3141 9840. E-mail: adam.gordon@frontarmy.co.uk
Editor: Joe Barnes. **Picture Editor:** Adam Gordon.
Alternative lifestyle monthly for 18-24 year old men.
Illustrations: Mostly commissioned. Opportunities for portrait photographers who can capture the energy of the magazine in a portrait, alternative scene music photographers for live and posed shots, and glamour photographers with a fashion background and plenty of new ideas.
Text: Little scope.
Overall freelance potential: Good.
Editor's tips: Always looking for new, keen photographers.
Fees: By negotiation.

GQ

Condé Nast Publications Ltd, Vogue House, Hanover Square, London W1S 1JU.
Tel: 020 7499 9080. Fax: 020 7629 2093. E-mail: james.mullinger@condenast.co.uk
Editor: Dylan Jones. Photo **Editor:** James Mullinger.
Up-market general interest magazine for men in the 20–45 age group.
Illustrations: Mainly colour. Top-quality illustrations for articles on a range of topics, invariably by commission.
Text: Top level investigative, personality, fashion and style features, plus articles on other subjects likely to be of interest to successful and affluent men.

Are you working from the latest edition of The Freelance Photographer's Market Handbook? It's published on 1 October each year. Markets are constantly changing, so it pays to have the latest edition

---

Overall freelance potential: Only for the contributor experienced at the top level of magazine work.
Editor's tips: See from the magazine itself what sort of style and quality is required.
Fees: By negotiation.

LOADED
IPC Media Ltd, Blue Fin Building, 110 Southwark Street, London SE1 0SU.
Tel: 020 3148 6818. E-mail: joel_gilgallon@ipcmedia.com
Editor: Martin Daubney. **Picture Editor:** Joel Gilgallon.
General interest monthly for men in their 20s. Covers music, sport, humour, fashion and popular culture in a down-to-earth and irreverent manner.
Illustrations: Mostly by commission to accompany features, but speculative submissions always considered.
Text: Fashion features, reportage (clubs, drugs, crime, etc), interviews, humour and "anything off the wall".
Overall freelance potential: Always open to fresh and original photography and ideas.
Fees: By negotiation.

MAYFAIR
Paul Raymond Publications, 3rd Floor, 207 Old Street, London EC1V 9NR.
Tel: 020 7608 6300. E-mail: mayfair@paulraymond.com
Editor: Matt Berry. **Art Editor:** Matt Hampson.
Glamour-based monthly for men.
Illustrations: Only top quality material will be considered. Glamour sets taken in up-market surroundings and real-life locations, such as a luxury furnished flat. Outdoor material needs strong sunlight.
Text: No scope.
Overall freelance potential: Only for high-quality material; much is produced by regular contributors.
Editor's tips: For glamour thought should be given to the erotic use of clothing and suggestion of sex appeal or sexual situation, together with striking but simple colour co-ordination. Always call before submitting.
Fees: £250–£1,000 for glamour sets, or dependent on use. Covers: from £50.

MEN ONLY
Paul Raymond Publications, 3rd Floor, 207 Old Street, London EC1V 9NR.
Tel: 020 7608 6300. E-mail: mattb@paulraymond.com
Editor: Matt Berry.
Sophisticated erotic monthly for men.
Illustrations: Imaginative glamour sets featuring "the most beautiful women". Models must be young, fresh, athletic and natural. Sets welcomed from new photographers as well as established contributors. Also picture-led supporting features.
Text: Laid-back humour, sport, male interests etc.
Overall freelance potential: Excellent.
Editor's tips: Attention to detail in clothes and make-up, a wide variety of poses, and imaginative locations will always set you apart. New ideas and faces always welcome.
Fees: £350-£750 for glamour sets. Other pictures by negotiation.

MEN'S HEALTH
NatMag Rodale Ltd, 72 Broadwick Street, London W1F 9EP.
Tel: 020 7339 4400. Fax: 020 7339 4444. E-mail: ash.gibson@natmag-rodale.co.uk
Editor: Morgan Rees. **Art Director:** Ash Gibson.

Magazine published 10 times per year and covering sports, fitness, grooming and other aspects of male lifestyle.
Illustrations: Mainly colour. Mostly by commission, though possible scope for good generic stock shots of fitness etc. subjects.
Text: Articles on male lifestyle subjects, especially health and fitness. Write with ideas and details of experience in the first instance.
Overall freelance potential: Only for the experienced contributor.
Fees: By negotiation.

NUTS

IPC Inspire, Blue Fin Building, 110 Southwark Street, London SE1 0SU.
Tel: 020 3148 6937. Fax: 020 3148 8107. E-mail: nutspictures@ipcmedia.com
Editor: Dominic Smith. **Picture Editor:** John Gooch.
Weekly general interest magazine for young men.
Illustrations: Always interested in "amazing, spectacular and extreme" images – single pictures or series of pictures often used over double-page spreads, usually 4–5 per issue. Must have obvious appeal to the target market, anything from spectacular sports shots through sensational photojournalism to unusual animal pics. Also relevant news pictures (sport, celebrities) which have not been seen elsewhere. Limited opportunities for commissioned work, but will consider approaches from experienced photographers working in suitable areas.
Text: Little scope.
Overall freelance potential: Excellent.
Fees: Dependent on the individual image and how it is used, as well as on level of exclusivity.

REFRESH

reFRESH Magazines Ltd, 3rd Floor, 207 Old Street, London EC1V 9NR.
Tel: 020 7608 6509. E-mail: editorial@refreshmag.co.uk
Editor: David Tickner.
Monthly magazine for affluent gay men.
Illustrations: Mostly by commission, but opportunities often available. Main scope is for fashion shoots, both studio and location. Some portraiture, interiors and travel. E-mail samples with a CV in the first instance.
Text: Ideas for features always considered.
Overall freelance potential: Good – always looking to broaden the range of photographers used.
Fees: By negotiation.

ZOO

Bauer Media, Endeavour House, 189 Shaftesbury Avenue, London WC2H 8JG.
Tel: 020 7437 9011. E-mail: zoopictures@zootoday.com
Editor: Tom Etherington. Features **Editor:** Richard Innes. Associate Editor (Pictures): Matt Velazquez. **Picture Editor:** Gemma Parker.
Weekly general interest magazine for young men.
Illustrations: Always need topical, unusual and visually striking images for the magazine's news section – several double-page spreads per issue displaying spectacular or unusual images of all kinds. Also unusual or exclusive sports images. Commissions in relevant areas may be available.
Text: Will consider ideas for topical features and real life stories. Material should have a laddish/humorous approach but be backed with genuine knowledge of the subject. Submit suggestions to features editor in the first instance.
Fees: Negotiable, dependent on the nature of images and their exclusivity.

As a member of the Bureau of Freelance Photographers, you'll be kept up-to-date with markets through the BFP Market Newsletter, published monthly. For details of membership, turn to page 9

Motoring

AMERICAN CAR WORLD
Shut Up and Drive Publishing Ltd, 321 Broadstone Mill, Stockport, Cheshire SK5 7DL..
Tel: 0161 443 4122. E-mail: andy.craig@shutupanddrivepublishing.com
Editor: Andy Craig.
Monthly magazine covering custom cars and hot rods based on pre-1975 vehicles, British or
American; and American cars, standard and modified, up to present day.
Illustrations: Newsy and well-captioned single pictures depicting happenings on the UK custom
and American car scene. Other pictures usually as part of a story/picture package on subjects
detailed below. Prefers British-sourced material.
Text: Well-illustrated features on completed cars, step-by-step illustrated material on how to do it,
track tests of modified cars and coverage of shows and events. Always phone or write first to discuss
ideas.
Overall freelance potential: Good for the right sort of material.
Editor's tips: Not interested in front-wheel drive or post-1980 vehicles.
Fees: £50 for news items; text £125 per 1,000 words.

AUTO EXPRESS
Dennis Publishing, 30 Cleveland Street, London W1T 4JD.
Tel: 020 7907 6000. Picture library: 020 7907 6132. Fax: 020 7917 5556. E-mail:
editorial@autoexpress.co.uk
Editor-in-Chief: David Johns. **News/Features Editor:** Julie Sinclair. **Picture Editor:** Dawn
Tennant.
Popular weekly magazine, aimed at the average motorist rather than the car enthusiast.
Illustrations: Hard news pictures and topical motoring subjects with impact may be considered on
spec, but most is by commission.
Text: Features on any motoring topic, to appeal to a general readership. May be practical but should
not be too technical. 1,000–2,000 words. Always submit a synopsis in the first instance.
Overall freelance potential: Limited for the non-specialist.
Editor's tips: Although a popular non-technical title, accuracy is essential.
Fees: Photographs according to size of reproduction. Text usually £200 per 1,000 words.

AUTOCAR
Haymarket Publishing Ltd, Teddington Studios, Broom Road, Teddington, Middlesex TW11 9BE.
Tel: 020 8267 5630. Fax: 020 8267 5759. E-mail: peter.charles@haymarket.com
Editor: Chas Hallett. **Art Editor:** Peter Charles.
High quality general interest motoring weekly. Includes road tests, new car descriptions,
international motor sport, motor shows, etc.
Illustrations: Mostly by commission for top quality general car coverage, test reports, performance
cars, industry picture stories and portraits – submit CV/portfolio to the Art Editor. Always
interested in scoop pictures of pre-production models under test or any other exclusive motor
industry photo items.
Text: Illustrated features on motoring subjects, by prior arrangement with the editor. 1,000–2,000
words.
Overall freelance potential: Good for those with experience.
Editor's tips: Technical accuracy and full information on the cars featured is essential. Familiarise
yourself with the magazine first; too much material received is unsuitable.
Fees: Features by negotiation.

THE AUTOMOBILE
Enthusiast Publishing Ltd. Editorial: PO Box 153, Cranleigh, Surrey, GU6 8ZL
Tel: 01483 268818 Fax: 01483 268993. E-mail: jonathanrishton@hotmail.com

Editor: Jonathan Rishton.

Monthly publication featuring veteran, vintage, and pre-1960s motor vehicles.

Illustrations: Not much scope for single pictures unless of particular interest. Main requirement is for well-illustrated articles concerning any pre-1960s motor vehicle; not only cars but also commercial vehicles. Also limited room for coverage of race meetings, exhibitions or other events at which old motor vehicles are present. All images must be accompanied by detailed captions.

Text: Informative illustrated articles as above. Of particular interest are good restoration features, with both "before" and "after" pictures showing what can be achieved.

Overall freelance potential: Although limited there is scope for illustrated features – consult the editor before starting on feature.

Editor's tips: Do not submit material concerning post-1960s vehicles.

Fees: By negotiation.

CAR & ACCESSORY TRADER

Haymarket Publishing Ltd, Teddington Studios, Broom Road, Teddington, Middlesex TW11 9BE.
Tel: 020 8267 5992. Fax: 020 8267 5993. E-mail: cat.eds@haymarket.com

Editor: Emma Butcher.

Monthly magazine for traders involved in the selling of car parts and accessories.

Illustrations: Captioned news pictures concerning new products, openings of new premises, handover of sales awards, etc. Much is commissioned. Covers: excellent relevant photographs considered.

Text: Varied subjects of interest to the trade, by commission only.

Overall freelance potential: About 50 per cent of contributions are from freelance sources.

Fees: £100 per £1,000 words. Photographs negotiable.

CLASSIC AMERICAN

Mortons Media Group Ltd, Media Centre, Morton Way, Horncastle, Lincs LN9 6JR.
Tel: 01507 529503. E-mail: bklemenszon@mortons.co.uk

Editor: Ben Klemenzson.

Monthly magazine concerning American cars mainly of the '50s, '60s and '70s.

Illustrations: Striking or unusual pictures of classic US vehicles. However, much of the photography is commissioned from regulars or staff-produced.

Text: Illustrated articles on specific cars or bikes and their owners, plus features on other aspects of American-style youth culture such as clothing, music, sport, etc. 1,000–2,000 words. Always check with the editor before submitting.

Overall freelance potential: Car coverage welcome, but best scope is for lifestyle features.

Fees: Pictures by negotiation. £150 per 1,000 words for text.

CLASSIC CARS

Bauer Automotive Ltd, Media House, Lynchwood, Peterborough PE2 6EA.
Tel: 01733 468000. Fax: 01733 468888. E-mail:
classic.cars@bauermedia.co.uk/tony.turner@bauermedia.co.uk

Editor: Phil Bell. Deputy **Editor:** Mike Goodbun. **Picture Researcher:** Tony Turner.

Glossy, heavily-illustrated monthly covering classic cars of all eras.

Illustrations: Will consider on-spec reportage-style coverage of classic car gatherings around the country. Major feature photography mostly handled by a team of regulars. E-mail picture researcher in the first instance.

Text: Limited scope, but suggestions considered.

Are you working from the latest edition of The Freelance Photographer's Market Handbook? It's published on 1 October each year. Markets are constantly changing, so it pays to have the latest edition

---

Overall freelance potential: Very good for the right sort of material.
Editor's tips: Detailed captions and a contact number for each car's owner are essential.
Fees: On a rising scale according to size of reproduction, up to £150 for a full-bleed page.

CLASSIC & SPORTS CAR
Haymarket Publishing Ltd, Teddington Studios, Broom Road, Teddington, Middlesex TW11 9BE.
Tel: 020 8267 5399. Fax: 020 8267 5318. E-mail: james.elliott@haymarket.com
Editor: James Elliott.
Monthly magazine covering mainly post-1945 classic cars, generally of a sporting nature. Strong coverage of the owners' scene.
Illustrations: Colour; B&W archive material. Mainly interested in coverage of club or historic car gatherings, unless staff photographer is present. Feature photography always commissioned.
Text: Articles of interest to the classic car enthusiast and collector, up to 2,500 words.
Overall freelance potential: Small, as much material is staff produced.
Editor's tips: Always get in touch before submitting.
Fees: According to merit.

CLASSICS MONTHLY
Future Publishing Ltd, Beauford Court, 30 Monmouth Street, Bath BA1 2BW.
Tel: 01225 442244. E-mail: classicsmonthly@futurenet.co.uk
Editor: Gary Stretton.
Practical monthly for classic car owners.
Illustrations: Captioned pictures of newsworthy cars and events, including relevant motorsport coverage, always considered on spec. Also scope for commissions to do photo shoots of featured cars; send samples of previous work in the first instance.
Text: Well-illustrated features about restoring classic cars; reports from events.
Overall freelance potential: Good.
Editor's tips: Look at mag carefully before submitting work, particularly the editorial profile and style. Always interested in hearing about cars which might make a good feature subject. Send a sample shot with some details about the car and a commission to shoot may be offered.
Fees: Pictures, typically £100 per feature; £120 per 1,000 words; commissioned photography, £200 per day.

DRIVING MAGAZINE
Safety House, Beddington Farm Road, Croydon CR0 4XZ.
Tel: 020 8665 5151. Fax: 020 8665 5565. E-mail: dia@driving.org
Editor: Stephen Picton.
Bi-monthly road safety publication for advanced drivers, road safety educationists and driving instructors.
Illustrations: Pictures of home or overseas motorists/driving school vehicles in unusual surroundings or circumstances. Humorous incidents, traffic accidents of an unusual nature, unusual road signs, humorous signs or those in extraordinary positions.
Text: Features on road safety, driver training occasionally accepted. 500–2,000 words.
Overall freelance potential: Modest.
Fees: Photographs from £15–£20, variable according to subject and quality.

EVO
Evo Publications Ltd, 5 Tower Court, Irchester Road, Wollaston, Wellingborough NN29 7PJ.
Tel: 020 7907 6310. E-mail: eds@evo.co.uk
Editorial Director: Harry Metcalfe. **Art Director:** Paul Lang.

Glossy monthly covering the high-performance end of the car market.
Illustrations: Digital files preferred. All by commission. Will consider approaches from freelances who can produce good action photography of cars on the move.
Text: No scope.
Overall freelance potential: Good for the experienced car photographer.
Fees: By negotiation.

FLEET NEWS

Bauer Automotive Ltd, Media House, Lynchwood, Peterborough Business Park, Peterborough PE2 6EA.
Tel: 01733 468000. Fax: 01733 468296. E-mail: fleetnews@bauermedia.co.uk
Editor: Stephen Briers. News **Editor:** Daniel Attwood.
Weekly newspaper aimed at those responsible for running company car and light commercial vehicle fleets.
Illustrations: Captioned news pictures concerning company car operations, handover of car fleets to companies, appointments in the trade, etc.
Text: News, articles on business car management and related subjects.
Overall freelance potential: Excellent.
Editor's tips: Always write or e-mail first.
Fees: Negotiable.

4X4

Kelsey Publishing Group, Cudham Tithe Barn, Berry's Hill, Cudham, Kent TN16 3AG.
Tel: 01959 541444. Fax: 01959 541400. E-mail: 4x4.ed@kelsey.co.uk
Editor: Hils Everett.
Monthly magazine devoted to four-wheel-drive vehicles.
Illustrations: Pictures of new vehicles, travel and other "off road" events. Must be captioned with full details of driver, event and location.
Text: Illustrated articles concerning four-wheel-drive vehicles and off-road activities. 1,000–2,000 words.
Overall freelance potential: Limited, but there is room for new contributors.
Fees: By negotiation.

JAGUAR

Haymarket Publishing Ltd, Teddington Studios, Broom Road, Teddington, Middlesex TW11 9BE.
Tel: 020 8267 5331. Fax: 020 8267 5872. E-mail: jaguar-magazine@haymarket.com
Editor: Richard Robinson.
Glossy general interest quarterly for owners of Jaguar cars.
Illustrations: High quality commissioned photography of Jaguar cars, travel and general lifestyle subjects. Opportunities only for experienced workers with medium format equipment.
Text: Strongly-illustrated articles on travel and lifestyle subjects. All work is by commission, no unsolicited work is accepted.
Overall freelance potential: Good for experienced workers, though limited by the publishing frequency.
Fees: Photography by negotiation. Articles around £400; pictures, £600.

LAND ROVER MONTHLY

Dennis Publishing Ltd, 5 Tower Court, Irchester Road, Wollaston, Wellingborough NN29 7PJ.
Tel: 020 7907 6878. E-mail: editorial@lrm.co.uk
Editor: Richard Howell-Thomas.
Monthly magazine for Land Rover enthusiasts.
Illustrations: Little scope for individual photographs unless accompanied by extended captions or background text.
Text: Well-illustrated articles on all matters relating to Land Rover, Range Rover, Discovery and

Freelander vehicles; travel/adventure stories, features on interesting individual vehicles and off-roading personalities, competition and club event reports. Limited scope for vehicle test reports.
Overall freelance potential: Excellent for those who can add words to their pictures, and have good knowledge of Land Rover products.
Fees: By negotiation.

LAND ROVER OWNER INTERNATIONAL
Bauer Automotive Ltd, Media House, Lynchwood, Peterborough PE2 6EA.
Tel: 01733 468000. Fax: 01733 468238. E-mail: info@lro.com
Editor-in-Chief: John Pearson.
Magazine for Land Rover owners and enthusiasts. 13 issues a year.
Illustrations: Interesting or unusual pictures of Land Rovers, Range Rovers, Freelanders, Defenders and Discoverys. Celebrities pictured with such vehicles.
Text: Illustrated articles on overland expeditions using Land Rovers. Length 1,000 words, plus around six pictures.
Overall freelance potential: Good.
Fees: Text, £100 per 1,000 words; pictures by negotiation.

MAX POWER
Bauer Automotive Ltd, Media House, Lynchwood, Peterborough PE2 6EA.
Tel: 01733 468000. Fax: 01733 468001. E-mail: mark.guest@bauermedia.co.uk
Editor: Mark Guest.
Monthly for young men heavily involved with fast cars and modifying them.
Illustrations: Pictures of smart and well-modified cars; also "sheds" (particularly badly modified cars). Also picture stories of likely interest to the target readership, including coverage of car gatherings.
Text: Ideas for features of interest to "lads" in their twenties always considered.
Overall freelance potential: Good for those in touch with this scene.
Editor's tips: Freelances need to be able to recognise the particular type of "cool" car that is featured here, and be aware of the general mood of the magazine.
Fees: Picture stories around £200–£300; single pictures according to use.

MOTOR SPORT
38 Chelsea Wharf, 15 Lots Road, London SW10 0QJ.
Tel: 020 7349 8484. Fax: 020 7349 8494. E-mail: editorial@motorsportmagazine.co.uk
Editor: Damien Smith. Deputy **Editor:** Gordon Cruickshank. **Picture Editor:** Ian Marshall.
Monthly devoted to motor sport and sports cars, both old and new.
Illustrations: Colour; B&W archive material. Will always consider coverage of classic or vintage sports car meetings and racing. Archive collections always of interest.
Text: No scope.
Overall freelance potential: Fair.
Fees: From around £35 upwards.

MOTOR TRADER
Metropolis Business Publishing, 6th Floor, Davis House, Robert Street, Croydon CRO 1QQ.
Tel: 020 8253 8711. Fax: 020 8253 8727. E-mail: curtis.hutchinson@metropolis.co.uk
Editor: Curtis Hutchinson.
Weekly trade newspaper and website read by dealers & manufacturers in the car and component industries, garage owners, body shop workers.
Illustrations: News pictures on anything connected with the motor trade.
Text: News and features relevant to the motor trade and industry. 300–1,000 words.
Overall freelance potential: Good for those in touch with the trade.
Fees: Negotiable.

MOTORING & LEISURE

CSMA Club, Britannia House, 21 Station Street, Brighton BN1 4DE.
Tel: 01273 744744. Fax: 01273 744761. E-mail: jeremy.whittle@csmaclub.co.uk
Editor: Jeremy Whittle.
Monthly journal of the Civil Service Motoring Association, covering motoring, travel and leisure activities.
Illustrations: General car-related subjects and Continental travel.
Text: Illustrated articles on motoring, travel, camping and caravanning. 750–1,000 words.
Overall freelance potential: Fair.
Fees: By arrangement.

911 & PORSCHE WORLD

CH Publications Ltd, Nimax House, 20 Ullswater Crescent, Ullswater Business Park, Coulsdon, Surrey CR5 2HR.
Tel: 020 8655 6400. Fax: 020 8763 1001. E-mail: chp@chpltd.com
Editor: Steve Bennett.
Magazine published nine times a year and devoted to Porsche or Porsche-derived cars.
Illustrations: All commissioned, with opportunities for those who have original ideas and can produce top quality car photography.
Text: Ideas for articles always of interest; write with details in the first instance.
Overall freelance potential: Very good for specialist coverage.
Fees: Photography by arrangement; around £100 per 1,000 words.

OCTANE

Dennis Publishing Ltd, Tower Court, Irchester Road, Wollaston, Northants NN29 7PJ.
Tel: 020 7907 6585. E-mail: rob@octane-magazine.co.uk
Editor: Robert Coucher. **Art Editor:** Robert Gould.
Monthly covering both contemporary high-performance cars and prestige classics from all eras.
Illustrations: Colour and historic B&W. Mostly by commission with good opportunities for experienced car photographers. Possible on-spec scope for picture stories covering specific events such as meets, rallies, races, etc. Relevant archive material also of interest.
Text: Suggestions always considered.
Overall freelance potential: Good.
Fees: By negotiation.

PERFORMANCE FORD

Unity Media Communications Ltd, Becket House, Vestry Road, Sevenoaks, Kent TN14 5EJ.
Tel: 01732 748000. Fax: 01732 748001. E-mail: performanceford@unity-media.com
Editor: Luke Wood. **Features Editor:** Alex Robbins.
Monthly magazine devoted to Ford and Ford-based vehicles, with the emphasis on high-performance road use.
Illustrations: Pictures commissioned to illustrate features, or topical single pictures of particular quality, i.e. prototypes, one-offs, etc.
Text: Illustrated articles on maintenance and modification of Ford-based cars. Personality profiles with a direct relevance to Ford products.
Overall freelance potential: Fair.
Editor's tips: Always raise ideas with the editor before submitting material.
Fees: Pictures according to size of reproduction or day rate by arrangement; text £120 per 1,000 words.

REDLINE

Future Publishing Ltd, Beauford Court, 30 Monmouth Street, Bath BA1 2BW.
Tel: 01225 442244. Fax: 01225 822793. E-mail: tim.durant@futurenet.co.uk
Editor: Davy Lewis. **Art Editor:** Tim Durant.

Motoring monthly for young men who want to get the best out of their modified cars.
Illustrations: Exciting and dramatic pictures of modified cars, sporting and speed events, unusual vehicles and fast lifestyles. Commissions available for car shoots, also some glamour; make appointment with the art editor.
Text: Will always consider suggestions for illustrated articles on suitable subjects, such as touring trips, unusual events, weird car-based experiences, etc.
Overall freelance potential: Moderate.
Editor's tips: Although photographers should know how to light and shoot cars, non-specialists are welcome if they can produce something exciting and different.
Fees: Single pictures £25–£250; page rate £50–£125; day rate £150–£300.

TOP GEAR MAGAZINE
BBC Magazines, 2nd Floor A, Energy Centre, Media Village, 201 Wood Lane, London W12 0TT.
Tel: 020 8433 2313. Fax: 020 8576 3754. E-mail: queries.tgmag@bbc.co.uk
Editor: Charlie Turner.
General interest motoring magazine designed to complement the BBC TV programme of the same name.
Illustrations: All by commission and much from known specialists, but photographers with a fresh approach and a good portfolio are welcomed. Send samples and details of previous experience in the first instance, or call for appointment. Stock images of pre-1990 cars often needed to illustrate articles.
Text: Motoring-related features considered, preferably out of the ordinary.
Overall freelance potential: Good opportunities for talented car photographers.
Fees: By negotiation.

TOTAL 911
9 Publishing, PO Box 6815, Matlock, Derbyshire DE4 4WZ.
Tel: 0845 450 6964. E-mail: phil@9publishing.co.uk
Editor: Philip Raby.
Monthly for Porsche 911 car enthusiasts, covering both classic and modern models.
Illustrations: All by commission only. Interested in hearing from professional car photographers who can offer something different. Write first enclosing samples of work.
Text: Ideas from professional motoring writers always welcome – apply in writing only.
Overall freelance potential: Good.
Editor's tips: Study the magazine before getting in touch.
Fees: Negotiable, but from around £150 for photo assignments, £100 per 1,000 words for text.

TRIUMPH WORLD
Kelsey Publishing Group, PO Box 13, Westerham, Kent TN16 3WT.
Tel: 01895 623612. E-mail: tw.ed@kelsey.co.uk
Editor: Simon Goldsworthy.
Monthly magazine for Triumph car (not motorcycle) enthusiasts.
Illustrations: Photographs of newsworthy or unusual Triumph cars, especially the "classics" such as Heralds, TRs, Spitfires and Stags. Some opportunities for experienced photographers to produce commissioned work for major features.
Text: Illustrated articles likely to appeal to the dedicated enthusiast. Phone first to discuss ideas.
Overall freelance potential: Good.
Fees: By negotiation.

As a member of the Bureau of Freelance Photographers, you'll be kept up-to-date with markets through the BFP Market Newsletter, published monthly. For details of membership, turn to page 9

Music

BLUES & SOUL
Blues & Soul Ltd, 153 Praed Street, London W2 1RL.
Tel: 020 3174 8020. E-mail: editorial@bluesandsoul.com
Editor: Lee Tyler.
Online publication with quarterly print edition, covering soul, R&B, funk, fusion, jazz, house, garage, dance – all forms of black music.
Illustrations: Will always consider original and exclusive pictures of relevant performers in the above fields.
Text: Small amount of scope for exclusive articles or interviews.
Overall freelance potential: Limited.
Editor's tips: Think of the readership, and the format, in order to produce something really striking and eye-catching.
Fees: By negotiation.

CLASSICAL MUSIC
Rhinegold Publishing Ltd, 241 Shaftesbury Avenue, London WC2H 8TF.
Tel: 020 7333 1742. Fax: 020 7333 1769. E-mail: classical.music@rhinegold.co.uk
Editor: Keith Clarke.
Fortnightly news and feature magazine for classical music professionals and the interested general public.
Illustrations: Digital files preferred. Very limited scope as most pictures are supplied by promoters, etc, but always happy to look at portfolios, subject to appointment. Occasional urgent need for a musician or group in the news – most easily met if freelances can supply lists of photographs they hold.
Text: Short news items and news stories about events in the music/arts world, including politics and performance, up to 800 words. Longer background features about musicians, usually relating to a forthcoming event, up to 2,000 words. All work is commissioned.
Overall freelance potential: Limited for photographers, but most text is from commissioned freelance sources.
Fees: Pictures by negotiation; text from £125 per 1,000 words.

FROOTS
Southern Rag Ltd, PO Box 337, London N4 1TW.
Tel: 020 8340 9651. Fax: 020 8348 5626. E-mail: froots@frootsmag.com
Editor: Ian Anderson.
Monthly publication concerned with folk and world roots music.
Illustrations: Pictures to be used in conjunction with interviews, reviews of records or reports on events. Mostly commissioned.
Text: Interviews and reviews concerned with folk and world music.
Overall freelance potential: Limited for the contributor unknown in this field. The magazine favours its regular contributors.
Fees: By agreement.

KERRANG!
Bauer Media, Endeavour House, 189 Shaftesbury Avenue, London WC2H 8JG.
Tel: 020 7295 5000. E-mail: kerrang@bauerconsumer.co.uk
Editor: Nichola Brown. News **Editor:** Simon Young.
Weekly magazine covering a wide range of hard rock.
Illustrations: Pictures of relevant bands. On-stage performance shots preferred, with the emphasis on action. Some posed shots and portraits of top performers also used.
Text: Little freelance market.

Overall freelance potential: Very good. The magazine is heavily illustrated.
Fees: According to size of reproduction.

KEYBOARD PLAYER
Bookrose Ltd, 100 Birkbeck Road, Enfield, Middlesex EN2 0ED.
Tel: 020 8245 5840. E-mail: steve@keyboardplayer.com
Editor: Steve Miller.
Monthly magazine for players of all types of keyboard instrument. Covers pianos, organs, keyboards and synthesisers; and all forms of music, from pop to classical.
Illustrations: Photographs of keyboard instruments and their players, preferably accompanied by a newsy caption. Covers: striking colour pictures of keyboard instruments.
Text: Articles of around 1,000 words on any topic of interest to keyboard players.
Overall freelance potential: Fairly limited, but scope is there for the right type of material.
Editor's tips: Run-of-the-mill pictures of players seated at their instruments will not be met with much enthusiasm – a strikingly different approach is required.
Fees: By negotiation.

METAL HAMMER
Future Publishing Ltd, 2 Balcombe Street, London NW1 6NW.
Tel: 020 7042 4000. Fax: 020 7042 4471. E-mail: amilas@futurenet.co.uk
Editor: Alexander Milas. **Art Editor:** James Isaacs.
Monthly for heavy metal and hard rock fans.
Illustrations: Good action and group portrait photographs of hard rock or heavy metal performers – send lists of subjects available. Commissions available to experienced rock photographers.
Text: Illustrated articles, interviews and reviews. Submit suggestions only in the first instance.
Overall freelance potential: Excellent for those in touch with this scene.
Fees: By negotiation.

MIXMAG
Development Hell, 90-92 Pentonville Road, London N1 9HS.
Tel: 020 7078 8400. Fax: 020 7833 9900. E-mail: mixmag@mixmag.net
Editor: Nick de Cosemo.
Monthly covering the dance music and clubbing scene.
Illustrations: Photographs of clubs and clubbers throughout the country; portraits of musicians; photo features. Fresh young photographers always welcome.
Text: Reports from clubs nationwide; young writers welcome.
Overall freelance potential: Very good.
Editor's tips: Contributors don't have to have experience, just a good sense of what the dance scene is about.
Fees: By negotiation.

MOJO
Bauer Media, Mappin House, 4 Winsley Street, London W1W 8HF.
Tel: 020 7295 5000. E-mail: matt.turner@bauerconsumer.co.uk
Editor-in-Chief: Phil Alexander. **Picture Editor:** Matt Turner.
Monthly rock music magazine aimed at fans of all ages.
Illustrations: Colour and archive B&W. Photographs of leading rock artists, both contemporary and from earlier eras. Archive material from the '50s, '60s and '70s always of interest. Good opportunities for commissioned work.
Text: In-depth profiles of individual artists and bands, but scope mainly for established writers.
Overall freelance potential: Good.
Editor's tips: Previously unpublished or unseen photographs, or those that have not been used for some years, are of particular interest.
Fees: According to use.

NEW MUSICAL EXPRESS
IPC Media Ltd, Blue Fin Building, 110 Southwark Street, London SE1 0SU.
Tel: 020 3148 6864. Fax: 020 3148 8107. E-mail: nmepics@ipcmedia.com
Editor: Krissi Murison. **Art Director:** Joe Frost. **Picture Director:** Marian Paterson.
Weekly magazine covering all aspects of popular music and allied youth culture.
Illustrations: All aspects of contemporary popular music, but see below.
Text: Scope for exclusive news stories or interviews with rock musicians, film stars, or other
personalities of interest to a young and aware readership. Always write or phone with suggestions
first.
Overall freelance potential: Good, but very dependent on subject matter.
Editor's tips: NME only covers those parts of the music scene considered worthwhile by the
editorial team – study recent issues.
Fees: On a rising scale according to size of reproduction.

Q
Bauer Media, Mappin House, 4 Winsley Street, London W1W 8HF.
Tel: 020 7295 5000. Fax: 020 7182 8547. E-mail: russ.o'connell@qthemusic.com
Editor: Paul Rees. **Picture Director:** Russ O'Connell.
Monthly rock music magazine aimed at the 18–35 age group.
Illustrations: Most pictures staff-produced or commissioned from a pool of regular contributors, but
suitable stock pictures of relevant personalities will always be considered.
Text: Top quality profiles, interviews and feature articles of interest to a rock-oriented readership,
invariably by commission.
Overall freelance potential: 50 per cent is commissions; good for library/stock shots.
Fees: Set rates.

RHYTHM
Future Publishing Ltd, Beauford Court, 30 Monmouth Street, Bath BA1 2BW.
Tel: 01225 442244. Fax: 01225 732285. E-mail: chris.barnes@futurenet.co.uk
Editor: Chris Barnes.
Monthly magazine for drummers and percussionists in the rock and pop music field.
Illustrations: Mostly colour. Interesting photographs relating to contemporary percussion
instruments and their players, including the use of electronic and computer-aided equipment.
Text: Illustrated profiles, interviews and features about leading contemporary drummers and
percussionists. Articles on technique and programming from knowledgeable contributors.
Overall freelance potential: Limited.
Fees: £110 per 1,000 words for text; photographs according to use.

TOTAL GUITAR
Future Publishing Ltd, Beauford Court, 30 Monmouth Street, Bath BA1 2BW.
Tel: 01225 442244. Fax: 01225 462986. E-mail: totalguitar@futurenet.co.uk
Editor: Stephen Lawson. **Art Editor:** John Blackshaw.
Monthly magazine for guitar players at all levels, concentrating on practical advice.
Illustrations: Mostly commissioned to accompany features and reviews. Stock shots of well-known
players and individual instruments always of interest; send lists first.
Text: Profiles and interviews with leading guitarists, and practical articles. Submit ideas only in the
first instance.
Overall freelance potential: Limited.
Fees: By negotiation.

---

*Are you working from the latest edition of The Freelance Photographer's
Market Handbook? It's published on 1 October each year. Markets are
constantly changing, so it pays to have the latest edition*

Parenting

MOTHER & BABY
Bauer Consumer Media, Endeavour House, 189 Shaftesbury Avenue, London WC2H 8JG.
Tel: 020 7295 5560. E-mail: mother&baby@bauermedia.co.uk
Editor: Miranda Levy. **Art Editor:** Ruth Hulbert.
Monthly aimed at pregnant women and mothers of young children.
Illustrations: May consider high quality photographs of mothers with babies, or babies (under one year) on their own, but the magazine is closely linked with the Mother & Baby Picture Library so has ready access to stock images. Experienced child photographers may be able to obtain commissions for editorial features and real life stories.
Text: Articles on all subjects related to pregnancy, birth, baby care and the early years.
Overall freelance potential: Limited.
Editor's tips: Looking for top quality pictures with a fresh eye on parenting.
Fees: From £30 upwards for stock shots, negotiable for commissions.

NURSERY WORLD
Haymarket Publishing Ltd, 22 Bute Gardens, London W6 7HN.
Tel: 020 8267 8410. E-mail: calvin.mckenzie@haymarket.com
Editor: Liz Roberts. **Picture Editor:** Calvin McKenzie.
Weekly publication on child care. Aimed at professional baby and child care workers such as teachers, nursery nurses and nannies.
Illustrations: Pictures of babies and young children (up to five years old) involved in various activities in childcare settings. Covers: Location shots of children, always linked to a feature inside.
Text: Features on child care, education, health, and any aspect of bringing up children, e.g. physical, intellectual, emotional etc. Ideas for nurseries and playgroups.
Overall freelance potential: Many features come from freelance contributors.
Fees: By arrangement.

PREGNANCY & BIRTH
Bauer Media, Endeavour House, 189 Shaftesbury Avenue, London WC2H 8JG.
Tel: 020 7295 5563. E-mail: jo.elston@bauermedia.co.uk
Editor: Ellie Hughes. **Art Editor:** Jo Elston.
Monthly covering pregnancy from conception to birth.
Illustrations: Mostly by commission. Opportunities for experienced photographers to produce cover shots, pregnancy fashion, interior shoots of nurseries, and "real life" material; contact art editor in the first instance. Always interested in hearing of good specialist stock collections.
Text: No scope.
Overall freelance potential: Good for experienced workers.
Editor's tips: Photographers need to be capable of working with real people rather than models.
Fees: By negotiation.

PRIMA BABY & PREGNANCY
National Magazine Company, 72 Broadwick Street, London W1F 9EP.
Tel: 020 7439 5000. Fax: 020 7312 3744. E-mail: lisa.mcsorley@natmags.co.uk
Editor: Elaine Griffiths. **Art Director:** Lisa McSorley.
Glossy monthly covering pregnancy, babies and toddlers up to three years.
Illustrations: Top quality pictures of babies and toddlers, with/without parents, in situations, engaged in activities, etc. Also pictures relating to aspects of childcare, health, fashion and home life. Must be warm, natural lifestyle images rather than posed "stock" shots. Write with details in the first instance. Some commissions available, mainly for reportage and studio photographers; call first to discuss possibilities.
Text: Limited freelance scope.

Overall freelance potential: Very good for quality material.
Fees: Variable; day rate around £400.

RIGHT START
Ten Alps Publishing, 9 Savoy Street, London WC2E 7HR.
Tel: 020 7878 2338. Fax: 020 7379 6261. E-mail: lynette.lowthian@tenalpspublishing.com
Editor: Lynette Lowthian.
Bi-monthly magazine for parents of pre-school and primary school age children, covering health, behaviour, education and family life.
Illustrations: Mostly by commission but some scope for good stock coverage of children in educational and learning situations; send only lists or details of coverage available in the first instance.
Text: Opportunities for education and child care specialists. Approach with details of ideas and previous experience.
Overall freelance potential: Limited.
Fees: By negotiation.

Photography & Video

AV
Haymarket Specialist, 174 Hammersmith Road, London W6 7NH.
Tel: 020 8267 8005. E-mail: bhavna.mistry@haymarket.com
Editor: Bhavna Mistry. Assistant **Editor:** Paul Milligan.
Monthly magazine for managers in industry and commerce, public services, government etc who use audiovisual communication techniques, eg slides, film, video, overhead projection and filmstrips, plus the new technologies of computer graphics and telecommunication.
Illustrations: Pictures of programmes being shown to audiences, preferably supported by case history details; relevant news; new products or location shooting pictures. All must be backed with solid information. Covers: colour pictures of same, but check before submitting.
Text: Case histories of either shows, conferences or studies of a particular company's use of AV techniques. Good location/conference stories always welcome. 1,000–2,500 words.
Overall freelance potential: Up to 25 per cent comes from freelances.
Fees: Text, £180-£200 per 1,000 words; pictures by agreement.

AMATEUR PHOTOGRAPHER
IPC Inspire, Blue Fin Building, 110 Southwark Street, London SE1 0SU.
Tel: 020 3148 4138. Fax: 020 3148 8130. E-mail: amateurphotographer@ipcmedia.com
Editor: Damien Demolder.
Weekly magazine for all photographers, from beginners to experienced enthusiasts.
Illustrations: B&W and colour. Pictures to illustrate specific photo techniques and general photo features. General portfolios in B&W and colour. Send no more than 10 pictures, prints unmounted, slides in a plastic slide wallet. Digital files on CD should be saved as JPEG or TIFF and accompanied by contact sheet.
Text: No scope.
Overall freelance potential: Good.
Fees: £50 per published page, pictures and text, except "Reader Spotlight".

Are you working from the latest edition of The Freelance Photographer's Market Handbook? It's published on 1 October each year. Markets are constantly changing, so it pays to have the latest edition

---

BLACK & WHITE PHOTOGRAPHY
GMC Publications Ltd, 86 High Street, Lewes, East Sussex BN7 1XN.
Tel: 01273 477374. Fax: 01273 402849. E-mail: lizr@thegmcgroup.com
Editor: Elizabeth Roberts.
Published 13 times a year, the magazine is devoted to showcasing the best in black and white photography.
Illustrations: B&W only. Features and portfolios showcasing the work of individual photographers, usually a cohesive body of work on a specific subject or theme. Regular "Reader Gallery" feature devotes up to two pages per reader/contributor. Photojournalistic work of particular interest, especially long-term projects produced over an extended period. Also step by step features showing all stages from a straight print to the final print. Digital techniques also covered. Little scope for single images. Also runs annual Black & White Photographer of the Year competition.
Text: Illustrated articles on printing techniques, film/paper combinations, equipment choices, etc. Submit sample prints and synopsis in the first instance.
Overall freelance potential: Excellent for the dedicated B&W worker.
Fees: According to subject and use.

THE BRITISH JOURNAL OF PHOTOGRAPHY
Incisive Media, 32–34 Broadwick Street, London W1A 2HG.
Tel: 020 7316 9658. Fax: 020 7316 9003. E-mail: bjp.features@bjphoto.co.uk
Editor: Simon Bainbridge. **Deputy Editor:** Diane Smyth.
Monthly magazine for professional and semi-professional photographers, students, advanced amateurs and all those engaged in professional photography.
Illustrations: B&W and colour. Portfolios along with some biographical notes about the photographer concerned. Contact deputy editor in the first instance.
Text: Interested in anything related to professional photography, particularly the more unusual and technical aspects.
Overall freelance potential: Good for bringing freelances to the attention of potential clients.
Editor's tips: Contributors do need to offer something special. Remember the magazine is aimed at those engaged in professional and semi-professional photography – technical features must therefore be of the highest calibre.
Fees: Portfolios not normally paid for; exposure in the magazine frequently leads to commissions elsewhere. Negotiable for text.

CAMCORDER BUYER HD READY MAGAZINE
Bright Publishing Ltd, Bright House, 82 High Street, Sawston, Cambridge CB2 4HJ.
Tel: 01223 499450. Fax: 01223 839953. E-mail: editorial@bright-publishing.com
Editor: Adam Scorey.
Bi-monthly buyers' guide aimed at the camcorder beginner. Concentrates primarily on high definition models but includes standard definition models too.
Illustrations: Always interested in hearing from new photographers.
Text: Looking for feature ideas, camcorder and gear reviewers, technical bods and general writers.
Overall freelance potential: Excellent.
Fees: By negotiation.

DIGITAL CAMERA
Future Publishing Ltd, Beauford Court, 30 Monmouth Street, Bath BA1 2BW.
Tel: 01225 442244. Fax: 01225 732295. E-mail: editor.dcm@futurenet.co.uk
Editor: Geoff Harris.
Monthly for the mid-market of digital camera users, those mainly using digital SLRs in the £600–£1400 price range.
Illustrations: Good single images required to illustrate seasonal subjects and topical events, and as examples of creative digital manipulations/compositions. Should be accompanied by detailed captions.

Text: Well-illustrated "how to" articles on digital photography and image editing. Contributors need to have some prior experience of producing such material.

Overall freelance potential: Good.

Editor's tips: Contributors should supply as much background detail about their images as they can.

Fees: Single images by negotiation and according to use; features £80 per published page.

DIGITAL PHOTO

Bauer Active Ltd, Media House, Lynchwood, Peterborough PE2 6EA.

Tel: 01733 468000. E-mail: jon.adams@bauermedia.co.uk

Editor: Jon Adams.

Monthly aimed at photographers keen to use their computer to enhance their pictures.

Illustrations: B&W and colour. Need for high-quality – technically and pictorially – original images that inspire readers to produce similar work. Ideally submissions should be accompanied by step-by-step screengrabs and words illustrating the thought processes and the stages involved in producing the work. Creative work always needed for the portfolio pages; require ten outstanding digitally manipulated images.

Text: Good potential for quality, step-by-step tutorials, but the final image must be outstanding and relevant. Contact editor in the first instance.

Overall freelance potential: Excellent for step-by-step tutorials.

Editor's tips: Look at and read the magazine first, then e-mail ideas and low-resolution JPEGs to illustrate. If submitting on CD always enclose high-quality inkjet prints too.

Fees: Negotiable, but typically £60 per page or £120 per 1,000 words.

DIGITAL PHOTOGRAPHER

Imagine Publishing Ltd, Richmond House, 33 Richmond Hill, Bournemouth BH2 6EZ.

Tel: 01202 586218. Fax: 01202 299955. E-mail: rosie.tanner@imagine-publishing.co.uk

Editor: Rosie Tanner.

Digital photography magazine for the more advanced user, aimed at serious enthusiasts and professionals.

Illustrations: Pictures mainly required to illustrate features on contemporary digital photography. Opportunities best for photographers using digital for specialist subjects (landscape, wildlife, portraiture, etc) or those experienced in Photoshop techniques.

Text: Practical illustrated articles and features on topics as above.

Overall freelance potential: Good for those with well-developed skills in digital work.

Fees: Negotiable, depending on what is on offer.

DIGITAL SLR PHOTOGRAPHY

Dennis Publishing, 6 Swan Court, Cygnet Park, Hampton, Peterborough PE7 8GX.

Tel: 01733 567401. Fax: 01733 352650. E-mail: jo_lezano@dennis.co.uk

Editor: Daniel Lezano. Editorial Co-ordinater: Jo Lezano.

Monthly for all photographers who use digital SLRs.

Illustrations: Regular requirement for high-quality images produced on digital SLRs. Most interested in seeing portfolios of between 20-100 images. For all submissions, supply TIFFs or maximum-quality JPEGs on CD/DVD, with thumbnail printouts (maximum 20 images per A4 sheet).

Text: Mostly produced by regulars, but ideas always considered.

Overall freelance potential: Excellent.

Editor's tips: See website at www.digitalslrphoto.com for a flavour of the content of the magazine along with details of picture requirements and submission guidelines.

Fees: On a standard scale according to use.

DIGITAL SLR USER

Bright Publishing Ltd, Bright House, 82 High Street, Sawston, Cambridge CB2 4HJ.

Tel: 01223 499450. Fax: 01223 839953. E-mail: editorial@bright-publishing.com
Editor-in-Chief: Terry Hope. **Deputy Editor:** Adam Scorey.
Monthly magazine for owners of digital SLR cameras, aimed at beginners and semi-proficient users. Emphasis on photographic technique, digital workflow and all things digital.
Illustrations: Normally images and articles as a package, but always interested in hearing from new photographers.
Text: Ideas, suggestions or draft articles on all aspects of digital SLR photography – technique, software reviews, location guides etc – are always welcome. Check with the editor before submitting.
Overall freelance potential: Excellent.
Fees: By negotiation.

EOS MAGAZINE
Robert Scott Publishing Ltd, The Old Barn, Ball Lane, Tackley, Kidlington, Oxon OX5 3AG.
Tel: 01869 331741. Fax: 01869 331641. E-mail: editorial@eos-magazine.com
Editor: Angela August.
Quarterly magazine for users of Canon EOS cameras.
Illustrations: Digital files only. Top quality photographs of any subject taken with Canon EOS cameras. Should demonstrate some aspect of photographic technique or the use of equipment. Comparison shots always of interest.
Text: Contributions are welcomed, but always phone or e-mail first to discuss.
Overall freelance potential: Very good.
Editor's tips: For photo requirements e-mail request with "Notes for Contributors" in subject box.
Fees: Minimum fee for pictures is £15, but most are paid at between £20 and £60 depending on usage. Cover and dps, £100-£250. Text £90–£150 per 1,000 words (higher rates are for technique material which is comprehensive and well researched).

HOTSHOE INTERNATIONAL
Hotshoe International Ltd, 29-31 Saffron Hill, London EC1N 8SW.
Tel: 020 7421 6009. Fax: 020 7421 6006. E-mail: melissa.dewitt@photoshot.com
Editor: Melissa De Witt.
Bi-monthly contemporary photography magazine covering all genres.
Illustrations: High-quality photography and portfolios of all kinds, including fine art, documentary, reportage, photojournalism and creative photography.
Text: Only in support of material as above.
Overall freelance potential: Very good for high-quality, original material.
Editor's tips: Contributions need to be of real interest to other working photographers.
Fees: By negotiation.

MARKET NEWSLETTER
Bureau of Freelance Photographers, Focus House, 497 Green Lanes, London N13 4BP.
Tel: 020 8882 3315. E-mail: eds@thebfp.com
Editor: John Tracy.
Monthly journal of the BFP, mainly devoted to detailing markets for photography. For members only.
Illustrations: Photographs required for "Pictures that Sell" feature – photographs taken by BFP members that have proven commercial success, having earned high fees and/or having sold to a wide range of markets.
Text: Photographer profiles in which a successful photographer outlines his or her freelance

As a member of the Bureau of Freelance Photographers, you'll be kept up-to-date with markets through the BFP Market Newsletter, published monthly. For details of membership, turn to page 9

activities, or general features on aspects of selling photography, backed up with examples of successful pictures and hints and tips to encourage others. Around 1,000 words.
Overall freelance potential: Limited.
Fees: £40 for "Pictures that Sell", £150 for photographer profile.

MASTER PHOTOGRAPHY

Icon Publications Ltd, Maxwell Lane, Kelso, Roxburghshire TD5 7BB.
Tel: 01573 226032. Fax: 01573 26000. E-mail: iconmags@btconnect.com
Editor: David Kilpatrick.
Magazine for the UK's commercial and studio photographers, with the emphasis on photographing people for profit. Official journal of the Master Photographers Association (MPA). Ten issues per year.
Illustrations: Images only required to accompany and illustrate specific articles mainly relating to commercial studio or events photography.
Text: Illustrated articles and features on topics as above, mainly profiles/interviews with successful practitioners. Some technical articles.
Overall freelance potential: Limited; most material is contributed on a voluntarary basis by MPA members.
Fees: Interviews and technical material, £60-£90 per published page.

OUTDOOR PHOTOGRAPHY

GMC Publications, 86 High Street, Lewes, East Sussex BN7 1XN.
Tel: 01273 477374. Fax: 01273 478606. E-mail: stevew@thegmcgroup.com
Editor: Steve Watkins.
Monthly devoted to the photography of all types of outdoor subject matter.
Illustrations: Mainly colour, digital or transparencies. Top-quality photographs of British landscapes, countryside, wildlife, gardens and architecture. Scope for good single images in the portfolio gallery section, but prefer packages of both words and pictures.
Text: Well-illustrated articles on all aspects of outdoor photography, accompanied by full background details on location or subject.
Overall freelance potential: Excellent; the magazine relies on freelances contributors.
Editor's tips: The magazine is seasonally-led, so subject matter needs to be relevant to the month of publication. Don't send on-spec pictures by e-mail.
Fees: By negotiation.

PENTAX USER

The Turbine, Shireoaks Business Park, Coach Close, Shireoaks S81 8AP.
Tel: 01909 512147. Fax: 01909 512147. E-mail: info@pentaxuser.co.uk
Editor: Peter Bargh.
Exclusive magazine for members of the Pentax User club. Features techniques reviews and how-to articles on all areas of photography with an emphasis on Pentax camera equipment.
Illustrations: B&W and colour. Images mainly required for cover – any image that is taken on a Pentax, with space available to allow logo to appear top right and tasters bottom left. Other images usually only as part of a complete package of words and pictures.
Text: Well-illustrated articles on all aspects of photography with an emphasis on Pentax camera equipment. How-to articles on using modes of compacts and SLRs particularly sought after, along with techniques on using flash, lenses, filters etc. Please submit suggestions in writing in first instance. The editor will then phone or reply to discuss commission.
Overall freelance potential: Most of the magazine is based on articles from club members or freelances.
Fees: £50 per published page.

PHOTO PRO MAGAZINE
Bright Publishing Ltd, Bright House, 82 High Street, Sawston, Cambridge CB2 4HJ.
Tel: 01223 499450. Fax: 01223 839953. E-mail: editorial@bright-publishing.com
Editor: Terry Hope. **Deputy Editor:** Charlotte Griffiths, **Web, News & Features Editor:**
Charlotte Griffiths.
Monthly magazine dedicated to aspiring professional photographers and established pros. Strong
emphasis on business, technique and the life of a modern professional.
Illustrations: Normally images and articles submitted as a package, but always interested in
brilliant one-offs or portfolios of images.
Text: Ideas, suggestions or draft articles on all aspects of professional photography – equipment,
workflow, technique – are always welcome. Check with the editor before submitting.
Overall freelance potential: Excellent.
Fees: By negotiation.

PHOTOGRAPHY MONTHLY
Archant Specialist, Archant House, Oriel Road, Cheltenham GL50 1BB.
Tel: 01242 211080. E-mail: pm@photographymonthly.co.uk
Editor: Grant Scott.
Magazine for the beginner and enthusiast, with the emphasis on helping readers improve their
images using the latest imaging techniques and equipment.
Illustrations: High quality photography of all types, especially images that illustrate specific points
of camera and computing technique. All subjects welcome but in particular landscapes, nature and
people. Step-by-step digital tutorials are also of interest.
Text: Much is produced by regular writers but the magazine is always on the lookout for new
contributors and ideas.
Overall freelance potential: Excellent.
Editor's tips: Best scope is for well-conceived ideas that tie in with the existing style of the title.
Fees: According to use.

PHOTOPLUS
Future Publishing Limited, 30 Monmouth Street, Bath BA1 2BW.
Tel: 01225 442244. E-mail: chris.george@futurenet.com
Editor: Chris George.
Photography magazine aimed at users of Canon digital SLRs. 13 issues a year.
Illustrations: Always happy to consider good images taken with Canon DSLR cameras. Subjects
should be those of general appeal to the keen photo enthusiast, such as landscapes, nature,
portraiture, etc. Send a few low-res samples via e-mail, weblink or on CD/DVD in the first instance.
Text: Mostly staff-produced.
Overall freelance potential: Good for strong enthusiast-type material.
Fees: According to use, but typically around £60 half page, £120 full page, £200 dps or cover.

PRACTICAL PHOTOGRAPHY
Bauer Media, Media House, Lynchwood, Peterborough PE2 6EA.
Tel: 01733 468000. E-mail: practical.photography@bauermedia.co.uk
Editor-in-Chief: Andrew James. **Deputy Editor:** Ben Hawkins.
Monthly magazine aimed at all photographers, with news, interviews and equipment tests, with
emphasis on digital SLRs and imaging techniques.
Illustrations: Colour and B&W. Photographs of any subject considered for general illustration and

---

*Are you working from the latest edition of The Freelance Photographer's
Market Handbook? It's published on 1 October each year. Markets are
constantly changing, so it pays to have the latest edition*

for the magazine's files. Images should have strong impact and be original, also illustrating some aspect of photographic technique – use of filters, shooting at the right time of day, camera viewpoint, etc. Colour and B&W portfolios regularly featured.

Text: Some potential, but contact editor in the first instance. Will use writers who can offer something the staff writers can't.

Overall freelance potential: Excellent for pictures and digital techniques; fewer opportunities for words but ideas still welcome.

Editor's tips: Read the magazine and study the pictures; if you can produce comparable work, send it in.

Fees: Negotiable but typically £80 per page and £120–£140 per 1,000 words.

PROFESSIONAL PHOTOGRAPHER
Archant Specialist, Archant House, Oriel Road, Cheltenham GL50 1BB.
Tel: 01242 211080. E-mail: grant.scott@archant.co.uk
Editor: Grant Scott.
Monthly magazine for professional photographers.
Illustrations: B&W and colour. Images only used as part of features as below.
Text: Check with the editor before submitting ideas.
Overall freelance potential: Only for the right material appropriately written.
Editor's tips: The magazine appeals to readers who find other magazines too superficial. It is therefore more important than ever that potential contributors study recent issues.
Fees: By negotiation.

WHAT DIGITAL CAMERA
IPC Inspire, Blue Fin Building, 110 Southwark Street, London SE1 0SU.
Tel: 020 3148 4796. Fax: 020 3148 8123. E-mail: wdc@ipcmedia.com
Editor: Nigel Atherton.
Monthly consumer magazine for digital photography enthusiasts.
Illustrations: Will consider original, creative, digital images and portfolios, either digitally originated or manipulations from conventional film.
Text: Illustrated features about the techniques and applications of digital cameras. Contact editor with suggestions first.
Overall freelance potential: Good.
Fees: Pictures by negotiation and according to use. Text £100 per 1,000 words.

Politics & Current Affairs

THE BIG ISSUE
1-5 Wandsworth Road, London SW8 2LN.
Tel: 020 7526 3200. Fax: 020 7526 3241. E-mail: sam.price@bigissue.com
Editor: Charles Howgego. **Art Director:** Sam Price.
Current affairs weekly sold in support of the homeless.
Illustrations: B&W and colour. Broad range of mainly news-based images covering politics, social issues and the arts. For hard news pictures contact the news desk; for general feature photography contact the art director.
Text: Suitable reportage-type features always considered. usually around 1,200 with with 2-3 illustrations.
Overall freelance potential: Very good for the right sort of material.
Fees: By negotiation.

THE ECOLOGIST
Unit 102D, Lana House Studios, 116-118 Commercial Street, London E1 6NF.
Tel: 020 7422 8100. E-mail: editorial@theecologist.org
Editor: Mark Anslow.
Online magazine covering all ecological and environmental topics.
Illustrations: News pictures and images to illustrate features on current environmental or ethical concerns.
Text: News items and articles on relevant topical issues. Contributors must have good, in-depth knowledge of their subject.
Overall freelance potential: Fair.
Fees: According to use.

THE ECONOMIST
The Economist Newspaper Ltd, 25 St James's Street, London SW1A 1HG.
Tel: 020 7830 7000. Fax: 020 7830 7130. E-mail: celinadunlop@economist.com
Editor: John Micklethwait. **Picture Editor:** Celina Dunlop.
Weekly publication covering world political, business and scientific affairs.
Illustrations: Pictures of politicians, businessmen, social conditions (housing, health service, etc), major industries (coal, steel, oil, motor, agriculture, etc). Always prepared to keep digital images for stock.
Text: All staff-produced.
Overall freelance potential: Only for serious and experienced photojournalists. Commissions not available.
Editor's tips: Telephone picture editor in the first instance.
Fees: On a rising scale according to size of reproduction inside.

JANE'S DEFENCE WEEKLY
IHS Jane's, Sentinel House, 163 Brighton Road, Coulsdon, Surrey CR5 2YH.
Tel: 020 8700 3700. Fax: 020 8763 1007. E-mail: jdw@janes.com
Editor: Peter Felstead.
News magazine concentrating on developments in all military fields.
Illustrations: News pictures of defence subjects worldwide – exercises, deployments, equipment, etc. Contact the editor initially.
Text: News items and informed articles on the military, industrial and political aspects of global defence.
Overall freelance potential: Limited for those without contacts in the forces or defence industry, but work submitted here may also be published in the various annuals produced by the Jane's Information Group.
Fees: Photographs £40 inside; covers negotiable; text from £200 per 1,000 words.

THE JEWISH CHRONICLE
Jewish Chronicle Newspapers Ltd, 25 Furnival Street, London EC4A 1JT.
Tel: 020 7415 1500 Fax: 020 7405 9040. E-mail: editorial@thejc.com
Editor: Stephen Pollard.
Weekly newspaper publishing news and features concerning, and of interest to, the British Jewish community.
Illustrations: Any topical pictures related to the purpose stated above. Also material for the paper's wide range of supplements that deal with subjects such as holidays, fashion, interior decoration, regional development, etc.
Text: Features on topics detailed above. 600–2,500 words.
Overall freelance potential: At least 30 per cent of the content comes from freelance sources.
Fees: By negotiation.

LIBERAL DEMOCRAT NEWS
Liberal Democrats, 4 Cowley Street, London SW1P 3NB.
Tel: 020 7227 1361. Fax: 020 7222 7904. E-mail: ldn@libdems.org.uk
Editor: Deirdre Razzall.
Weekly tabloid newspaper of the Liberal Democrats.
Illustrations: Prints or digital files accepted. Pictures of Liberal Democrat activities around the country and general political news pictures.
Text: News and features: politics, current affairs.
Overall freelance potential: Limited.
Fees: By negotiation.

THE MIDDLE EAST
IC Publications Ltd, 7 Coldbath Square, London EC1R 4LQ.
Tel: 020 7713 7711. Fax: 020 7713 7970. E-mail: p.lancaster@africasia.com
Editor: Pat Lancaster.
Monthly publication directed at senior management, governmental personnel and universities. Covers Middle Eastern current affairs of a political, cultural and economic nature.
Illustrations: B&W and colour. Pictures of all topical Middle Eastern subjects, personalities and scenes.
Text: Features on Middle Eastern subjects or world subjects that relate to the area. 1,000–3,000 words.
Overall freelance potential: Most of the pictures come from freelances.
Fees: B&W pictures £15–£35; covers by agreement. Text, from £80 per 1,000 words.

NEW INTERNATIONALIST
55 Rectory Road, Oxford OX4 1BW.
Tel: 01865 811400. Fax: 01865 793152. E-mail: ni_ed@newint.org
Co-Editors: (UK) Vanessa Baird, Dinyar Godrej, Jess Worth
Monthly magazine covering global issues from a mainly Southern (Africa, Asia, Latin American) perspective.
Illustrations: Pictures to illustrate news stories and topical features on subjects such as social justice, human rights, environmental issues, poverty, sustainable development, etc.
Text: Illustrated stories and features on relevant topics as above.
Overall freelance potential: Good.
Editor's tips: Each editor edits individually themed issues and is responsible for his/her own picture research.
Fees: Pictures, from a minimum of £40 to £250 for front cover.

PCS VIEW
The Public & Commercial Services Union, 160 Falcon Road, Clapham, London SW11 2LN.
Tel: 020 7924 2727 Fax: 020 7801 2822. E-mail: editor@pcs.org.uk
Editor: Sharon Breen.
Monthly publication for members of the PCS Union, the biggest civil service union. Also has large private sector membership.
Illustrations: News pictures of trade union activity, especially involving members of PCS. Other topical pictures of current affairs that may impinge on Union members may also be of interest.
Text: No scope.
Overall freelance potential: Good, 75 per cent of pictures come from outside contributors.
Fees: Good; on a rising scale according to size of reproduction.

Railways

HERITAGE RAILWAY
Mortons Media Group Ltd, Media Centre, Morton Way, Horncastle, Lincs LN9 6JR.
Tel: 01507 529300. Fax: 01507 529301. E-mail: rjones@mortons.co.uk
Editor: Robin Jones.
Monthly magazine devoted to railway preservation – steam, diesel and electric.
Illustrations: Mainly colour. Captioned news pictures depicting restoration projects, restored locomotives on their first runs, special events etc, especially from less well-known lines and museums. Mainly UK-based but will also consider overseas coverage of locomotives with a British connection, especially really "stunning and attractive" pictures.
Text: Well-illustrated features on preservation and restoration topics; write with suggestions first.
Overall freelance potential: Very good.
Fees: By negotiation.

INTERNATIONAL RAILWAY JOURNAL
Simmons-Boardman Publishing Corporation, 46 Killigrew Street, Falmouth, Cornwall TR11 3PP.
Tel: 01326 313945. Fax: 01326 211576. E-mail: irj@railjournal.co.uk
Editor: David Briginshaw. **Associate Editor:** Keith Barrow.
Monthly publication for the principal officers of the railways of the world (including metro and light rail systems), ministers and commissioners of transport, railway equipment manufacturers and suppliers.
Illustrations: Pictures of new line construction projects, electrification projects, track or signalling improvements, new locomotives, passenger coaches and freight wagons. Interesting pictures of railway operations from far-flung corners of the world. No steam or nostalgia material. Covers: colour shots tied in with the theme of a particular issue.
Text: Features on any sizeable contracts for railway equipment; plans for railway developments, eg new line construction, track or signalling improvements; almost anything which involves a railway spending money or making improvements and techniques. No padding or speculation.
Overall freelance potential: Quite good for the right business-oriented material.
Fees: Rising scale according to size of pictures; text, £120 per 1,000 words.

RAIL
Bauer Media Ltd, Media House, Lynchwood, Peterborough PE2 6EA.
Tel: 01733 468000. Fax: 01733 468586. E-mail: rail@bauermedia.co.uk
Managing Editor: Nigel Harris.
Fortnightly magazine dealing with modern railways.
Illustrations: Mostly colour, some B&W. Single photographs and up-to-date news pictures on any interesting railway topic in Britain, particularly accidents and incidents of all kinds. Covers: Colour shots with strong impact.
Text: Illustrated articles of up to 1,500 words on any railway topic. Check recent issues for style.
Overall freelance potential: Excellent.
Editor's tips: Topicality is everything for news coverage. For other pictures try to get away from straightforward shots of trains; be imaginative. Always looking for something different.
Fees: Pictures range from £25–£70; illustrated articles around £90–£150. Will pay more for high-impact special pics that give the magazine a commercial advantage.

RAIL EXPRESS
Mortons Media Group Ltd, Media Centre, Morton Way, Horncastle, Lincs LN9 6JR.
Tel: 01507 529529. E-mail: gbayer@mortons.co.uk
Editor: Gareth Bayer.
Monthly magazine for modern railway enthusiasts.
Illustrations: Any good or unusual photographs of the contemporary railway scene, but really need

to be of current and newsworthy interest (new locomotives, new colour schemes, etc). Some scope for historic diesel/electric coverage.
Text: Suggestions for articles welcome, from anyone with good background knowledge of the subject, especially traction. Consult with the editor first.
Overall freelance potential: The magazine features lots of photography and always needs more.
Editor's tips: Topicality is the key, and images should always be taken in sunshine.
Fees: From basic rate of £20 per picture.

RAILNEWS

Railnews Ltd, Business & Technology Centre, Bessemer Drive, Stevenage, Herts, SG1 2D.
Tel: 01438 310011. Fax: 0844 443 2700. E-mail: newsdesk@railnews.co.uk
Managing Editor: Sim Harris.
Monthly newspaper for people in the rail industry, covering the modern railway scene in the UK.
Illustrations: Digital files preferred, B&W and colour prints accepted. Railway news pictures, unusual pictures of events, operations, activities, with good captions.
Text: No scope.
Overall freelance potential: Good.
Editor's tips: Approach before submitting.
Fees: By negotiation.

THE RAILWAY MAGAZINE

IPC Media Ltd, Blue Fin Building, 110 Southwark Street, London SE1 0SU.
Tel: 020 3148 4683. Fax: 020 3148 8521. E-mail: railway@ipcmedia.com
Editor: Nick Pigott.
Monthly for all rail enthusiasts, covering both main line and heritage railways, modern and historic.
Illustrations: News pictures concerning the current rail network, as well as images from recent heritage events, galas or rail tours. Also pictures of new liveries, new trains on test, accidents/derailments, and rare or unusual workings. Previously unpublished material from the 1940s onwards always of interest for historical features. Top quality non-news pictures may be used for spreads and/or occasional calendars. For digital, e-mail thumbnails (10 images max) in first instance; CDs (50 images max) must have thumbnail sheet. For film submissions, captions should be supplied on individual slide mounts or prints, not on separate caption sheet.
Text: Well-researched illustrated articles on any British railway topic, current or historic; discuss ideas with the editor first.
Overall freelance potential: Excellent.
Editor's tips: News pictures must be recent – no more than six weeks old.
Fees: From £15 minimum for news pictures, to £50+ for larger reproductions.

STEAM RAILWAY

Bauer Active Ltd, Media House, Lynchwood, Peterborough PE2 6EA.
Tel: 01733 468000. E-mail: steam.railway@bauermedia.co.uk
Editor: Danny Hopkins.
Four-weekly magazine for the steam railway enthusiast. Closely concerned with railway preservation.
Illustrations: Mostly colour; archive B&W. Accurately captioned photographs depicting steam trains and railways past and present, preserved railway lines, and railway museums (topical subjects especially welcomed).
Text: Illustrated articles on relevant subjects.
Overall freelance potential: Most of the photographic content is contributed by freelances.
Editor's tips: Material should be lively, topical and newsworthy, although some nostalgic or historic material is accepted. Always query the editorial team before submitting.
Fees: By arrangement.

TODAY'S RAILWAYS UK
Platform 5 Publishing, 3 Wyvern House, Sark Road, Sheffield S2 4HG.
Tel: 0114 255 2625. Fax: 0114 255 2471. E-mail: editorial@platform5.com
Editor: Paul Abell.
Monthly covering the contemporary British railway scene, aimed at both rail professionals and enthusiasts.
Illustrations: News pictures relating to current or planned UK rail operations, accompanied by detailed captions or stories. Stock material may be of interest – send detailed lists in the first instance.
Text: Feature suggestions always considered, but only from writers who have in-depth knowledge of their subject.
Overall freelance potential: Limited, as much is obtained from industry sources.
Editor's tips: Always contact editor before submitting as many stories may already be covered.
Fees: Pictures from £12.50; text £50 per page.

TRACTION
Warners Group Publications plc, The Maltings, West Street, Bourne, Lincs PE10 9PH.
Tel: 01778 392455. Fax: 01778 425437. E-mail: richardw@warnersgroup.co.uk
Editor: Richard Wilson.
Monthly magazine dedicated to classic diesel and electric locomotives.
Illustrations: Mostly colour; B&W archive material. Photographs of classic diesels and electrics operating on British railways from the 1940s to the present day. Particular interest in archive shots from the earlier eras up to the early 1980s.
Text: Limited scope at present.
Overall freelance potential: Good.
Fees: From £15–£50 according to size of reproduction.

Religion

THE CATHOLIC HERALD
Herald House, 15 Lamb's Passage, Bunhill Row, London EC1Y 8TQ.
Tel: 020 7448 3602. Fax: 020 7256 9728. E-mail: editorial@catholicherald.co.uk
Editor: Luke Coppen.
Weekly newspaper reflecting on Catholicism/Christianity and its place in the wider world, plus church news.
Illustrations: Principal need for news photographs of events involving churches, clerics or prominent Catholics.
Text: Articles of up to 1,200 words on the social, economic and political significance of the church domestically and internationally, plus spiritual and reflective writings.
Overall freelance potential: Better for features than other material.
Fees: By arrangement but not high.

THE CATHOLIC TIMES
Gabriel Communications Ltd, Fourth Floor, Landmark House, Station Road, Cheadle Hulme SK8 7JH.
Tel: 0161 488 1753. Fax: 0161 237 6690. E-mail: kevin.flaherty@totalcatholic.com
Editor: Kevin Flaherty.
Weekly newspaper covering Catholic affairs.
Illustrations: Topical news pictures of Catholic interest. Also off-beat devotional shots.
Text: News stories and short features. 900 words maximum.
Overall freelance potential: Very good.
Fees: Text around £40 per 1,000 words; pictures by negotiation.

CHURCH OF ENGLAND NEWSPAPER

Religious Intelligence Ltd, 14 Great College Street, London SW1P 3RX.
Tel: 020 7878 1002. Fax: 020 7878 1031. E-mail: colin.blakely@churchnewspaper.com
Editor: Colin Blakely.
Weekly newspaper covering Anglican news and views.
Illustrations: Colour print and digital accepted. Will consider any news pictures that relate to the Church of England.
Text: News stories, plus features that relate Christian faith to politics, the arts and everyday life. Up to 1,000 words, but submit ideas only in the first instance.
Overall freelance potential: Good for those with Church connections.
Fees: £20 – £40 per published picture; text about £40 per 1,000 words.

CHURCH TIMES

G.J.Palmer & Sons Ltd, 13-17 Long Lane, London EC1A 9PN.
Tel: 020 7776 1064. E-mail: news@churchtimes.co.uk
Editor: Paul Handley.
Weekly newspaper covering Church of England affairs.
Illustrations: Up-to-the-minute news pictures of Anglican events and personalities. Detailed captions essential.
Text: Short articles on current religious topics; up to 1,000 words.
Overall freelance potential: Fair.
Editor's tips: It is preferred that people in pictures are engaged in activities rather than just looking at the camera.
Fees: Photographs according to use, average £70; text £100 per 1,000 words.

Science & Technology

BBC FOCUS

Bristol Magazines Ltd, 14th Floor, Tower House, Fairfax Street, Bristol BS1 3BN.
Tel: 0117 927 9009. Fax: 0117 934 9008. E-mail: jamescutmore@originpublishing.co.uk
Editor: Jheni Osman. **Art Editor:** Steve Sayers. **Picture Editor:** James Cutmore.
Popular science monthly relating to all BBC science content. Aimed at both adults and teenagers.
Illustrations: Will consider colour photo essays on popular science, technology, space exploration, medicine and the environment. Contact art editor in the first instance.
Text: Interesting features on subjects above always considered. Submit a synopsis first.
Overall freelance potential: Fair.
Editor's tips: Only top quality material is considered; study the magazine before submitting.
Fees: Negotiable; generally good.

EDUCATION IN CHEMISTRY

The Royal Society of Chemistry, Thomas Graham House, Science Park, Cambridge, CB4 0WF.
Tel: 01223 420066. E-mail: eic@rsc.org
Editor: Laura Howes.
Bi-monthly publication for teachers, lecturers in schools and universities, concerning all aspects of chemical education.
Illustrations: Pictures that deal with chemistry in the classroom, laboratories or the chemical industry.
Text: Features concerned with chemistry or the teaching of it. Under 2,500 words.
Overall freelance potential: Limited.
Fees: By agreement.

HOW IT WORKS
Imagine Publishing Ltd, Richmond House, 33 Richmond Hill, Bournemouth BH2 6EZ.
Tel: 01202 586200. E-mail: dave.harfield@imagine-publishing.co.uk
Editor-in-Chief: Dave Harfield.
Heavily-illustrated popular science and technology monthly for the general reader.
Illustrations: Images of any subject that broadly falls within the magazine's remit, including science, technology, transportation, space, history and the environment, but usually tied-in with specific articles or features.
Text: Illustrated articles on any up-to-date science and technology topic, with the emphasis on explaining "how it works" to the lay reader.
Overall freelance potential: Very good for the right kind of material.
Editor's Tips: Ensure all facts are fully checked and correct before submitting.
Fees: By negotiation, dependent on what is being offered.

NEW SCIENTIST
Reed Business Information, Lacon House, 84 Theobalds Road, London WC1X 8RR.
Tel: 020 7611 1200. Fax: 020 7611 1280. E-mail: adam.goff@rbi.co.uk
Editor: Roger Highfield. **Picture Editor:** Adam Goff.
Weekly magazine about science and technology for people with some scientific or technical education and also for the intelligent layman.
Illustrations: Pictures on any topic that can be loosely allied to science and technology. Particularly interested in news photographs related to scientific phenomena and events. Covers: usually connected with a feature inside.
Text: News and features on scientific/technical subjects that might appeal to a wide audience.
Overall freelance potential: A lot of freelance work used, but consult the magazine before submitting.
Fees: Photographs on a rising scale according to size of reproduction. Text £150 per 1,000 words.

T3
Future Publishing Ltd, 2 Balcombe Street, London NW1 6NW.
Tel: 020 7042 4000. Fax: 020 7042 4471. E-mail: stuart.james@futurenet.co.uk
Editor: Luke Peters. **Art Editor:** Stuart James.
Monthly technology and gadget magazine aimed primarily at young men.
Illustrations: Always interested in pictures of new technology and new designs for consumer durables, especially exclusive shots of latest developments, pre-production models, new releases etc. Also general stock of any technology-related subject.
Text: Mainly staff produced but exclusive news items on new products always of interest.
Overall freelance potential: Fair
Fees: By negotiation. Will pay top rates for exclusives.

Sport

AIR GUNNER
Archant Specialist, 3 The Courtyard, Denmark Street, Wokingham, Berkshire RG40 2AZ.
Tel: 0118 989 7203. Fax: 01189 772903. E-mail: matthew.clark@archant.co.uk
Editor: Matt Clark.
Monthly magazine for all airgun enthusiasts.
Illustrations: Illustrated news items, and stock shots of small field animals (rats, rabbits) and pest species of birds (pigeons, magpies, crows). Covers: Usually commissioned, but a speculative picture might be used.
Text: Articles on any aspect of airgun use, 700–1,000 words, and accompanied by a good selection of images.

Overall freelance potential: Good for file photos and well illustrated articles.
Fees: In the region of £60 per published page.

ALL OUT CRICKET

Unit 3.23, Canterbury Court, Kennington Park Business Centre, 1-3 Brixton Road, London SE11 5SS.
Tel: 020 7820 4190. E-mail: aff@alloutcricket.co.uk
Editor: Andy Afford.
Official magazine of the Professional Cricketer's Association. Published 10 times a year.
Illustrations: Assignments available to shoot individual cricketers or teams for profiles – submit details of experience and areas covered by e-mail in the first instance. No scope for stock images, which are supplied via agency contract.
Text: Suggestions for profiles and features always considered.
Overall freelance potential: Fair.
Fees: By negotiation.

ATHLETICS WEEKLY

Athletics Weekly Ltd, PO Box 614, Farnham, Surrey GU9 1GR.
Tel: 01733 808550. Fax: 01733 808530.
E-mail: jason.henderson@athletics-weekly.com
Editor: Jason Henderson.
Weekly news magazine for the competitive and aspiring athlete. Focuses on events and results.
Illustrations: Coverage of athletics events at grass roots level, such as area championships, rather than top events (the latter are supplied by agency photographers). Always interested in anything out of the ordinary, such as well-known athletes off the track or in unusual situations.
Text: No scope.
Overall freelance potential: Fair.
Editor's tips: Freelances aware of what is happening locally can often obtain coverage missed by the nationals and agencies – top athletes "dropping in" to take part in local events etc.
Fees: According to size of reproduction, from £10 – £30. Published pictures frequently gain extra sales via reader requests.

BADMINTON

iSPORTgroup, No.4 The Spinney, Chester Road, Poynton, Cheshire SK12 1HB.
Tel: 07973 544719. E-mail: rachel.pullan@isportgroup.com
Editor: Rachel Pullan.
The only magazine in the UK devoted to badminton. Published quarterly.
Illustrations: Will consider good action coverage, sports fashion, health material.
Text: Little scope for writing on the sport itself, but may consider articles on sports fashion, health, fitness and diet. 750–1,000 words.
Overall freelance potential: Limited.
Fees: By agreement.

BOXING MONTHLY

Topwave Ltd, 40 Morpeth Road, London E9 7LD.
Tel: 020 8986 4141. Fax: 020 8986 4145. E-mail: mail@boxing-monthly.co.uk
Editor: Glyn Leach.
Heavily illustrated publication for boxing enthusiasts, covering both professional and amateur boxing.
Illustrations: B&W and colour. Coverage of boxing at all levels, including the amateur scene.
Text: Knowledgeable articles, features, interviews, etc. on any aspect of the boxing scene. Always contact the editor in the first instance.
Fees: By negotiation.

CLIMBER
Warners Group Publications plc, The Maltings, West Street, Bourne, Lincs PE10 9PH.
Tel: 01778 392425. Fax: 01778 394748. E-mail: andym@warnersgroup.co.uk
Editor: Andy McCue.
Monthly magazine dealing with world-wide climbing from Lakeland fells to Everest. Highly literate readership. Contributors range from "unknowns" to top climbers like Chris Bonington.
Illustrations: First ascents and newsworthy events but, in the main, used only with text. Covers: action shots of climbers or dramatic mountain pictures.
Text: Features on rock climbing, Alpinism, high altitude climbing, mountain skiing (not downhill racing). 1,500–2,000 words.
Overall freelance potential: Good; 90 per cent of articles and 100 per cent of pictures come from freelances, but many are regulars.
Editor's tips: This is a specialist field and is full of good writer/photographers. There is potential for the freelance to break in, but the magazine is heavily commissioned and usually well stocked with material.
Fees: Variable.

DARTS WORLD
World Magazines Ltd, 25 Orleston View, Ham Street, Ashford, Kent TN26 2LB.
Tel: 01233 733558. E-mail: mb.graphics@virgin.net
Editor: Michael Beeken.
Monthly magazine for darts players and organisers.
Illustrations: Pictures on any darts theme, action shots and portraits of leading players. Good material also required for the annual Darts Player.
Text: Features on all darts subjects.
Overall freelance potential: Most of the copy and pictures comes from freelances.
Editor's tips: The darts-playing environment is often dim and smoky, which can make it difficult to produce bright, interesting pictures. Photographers who can come up with colourful shots that catch the eye are welcomed.
Fees: Good, on a rising scale according to size of reproduction or length of feature.

DIVE
Dive International, 1 Victoria Villas, Richmond, Surrey TW9 2GW.
Tel: 020 8332 8401. Fax: 020 8332 9307. E-mail: simon@dive.uk.com
Editor: Simon Rogerson. **Art Editor:** Angela Finnegan.
Monthly magazine for divers and underwater enthusiasts.
Illustrations: Top-quality underwater photography, usually published within photojournalistic features. Most interested in material that tells a story and involves people, with images showing divers in action.
Text: Features as above.
Overall freelance potential: Excellent for underwater specialists.
Editor's tips: Good quality material from British waters stands a good chance of being published, as this is harder to find than that from clearer waters abroad.
Fees: £150 per published page.

F1 RACING
Haymarket Publishing Ltd, Teddington Studios, Broom Road, Teddington TW11 9BE.
Tel: 020 8267 5163. Fax: 020 8267 5022. E-mail: ross.stonefeld@haymarket.com
Editor: Hans Seeberg. **Picture Editor:** Ross Stonefeld.
Glossy monthly devoted to Formula One motor racing.
Illustrations: All coverage of Formula One, past and present; professionals with collections of

relevant material should send lists. Commissions available to experienced portrait and reportage photographers who can deliver high quality whatever the circumstances – contact picture editor by email .

Text: Will always consider ideas for any F1 related material, which should always be discussed with the editor before submission.

Overall freelance potential: Fair.

Editor's tips: Write or e-mail first, don't phone.

Fees: Set rates, from £60 minimum to £230 full page, £320 dps, £400 cover.

FIELDSPORTS

BPG (Stamford) Ltd, Roebuck House, 33 Broad Street, Stamford, Lincs PE9 1RB.
Tel: 01780 766199. Fax: 01780 754774. E-mail: m.barnes@bournepublishinggroup.co.uk
Editor: Mike Barnes.

Heavily-illustrated quarterly for the serious game shooter who also enjoys a spot of fishing in the summer months.

Illustrations: High-quality images depicting all aspects of game shooting and fishing, for general illustration purposes. Commissioned photography generally handled by regulars.

Text: Will consider illustrated articles from contributors who really know their subject and can write in depth with real enthusiasm.

Overall freelance potential: Fair.

Editor's tips: Readers are not casual sportsmen but people who spend heavily on the sport and have a real passion for it.

Fees: By negotiation.

FIGHTING FIT

Newsquest Specialist Media Ltd, 30 Cannon Street, London EC4M 6YJ.
Tel: 020 7618 3072. E-mail: tris.dixon@fightingfitmagazine.co.uk
Editor: Tris Dixon.

Monthly magazine covering boxing, martial arts, judo, taekwondo, karate and Thai boxing, focusing on health, nutrition and training techniques.

Illustrations: The magazine obtains most pictures from specialist agencies, but will always consider original material from freelance photographers.

Text: Will consider illustrated profiles and interviews with leading fighters. Also expert articles on strength, power, nutrition, fitness and psychology. Also gyms, product reviews and articles on trends in the industry. Submit suggestions via e-mail in the first instance.

Overall freelance potential: Good for those with the right connections or expertise.

Editor's tips:

Fees: Dependent on subject matter and the specialist expertise of the contributor.

FOURFOURTWO

Haymarket Publishing, Teddington Studios, Broom Road, Teddington, Middlesex TW11 9BE.
Tel: 020 8267 5339. Fax: 020 8267 5354. E-mail: jeff.beasley@haymarket.com
Editor: David Hall. **Picture Editor:** Jeff Beasley.

Monthly magazine aimed at the adult soccer fan.

Illustrations: Especially interested in exclusive or unusual shots of footballers and football people. Always interested to know of good stock collections, both current and historic. Commissions possible for photographers with at least some sports experience – submit samples of work via e-mail in the first instance.

Text: Some scope for specialists.

Overall freelance potential: Quite good but best for specialists.

Fees: According to size of reproduction. Text £100–£175 per 1,000 words.

GOLF MONTHLY
IPC Media Ltd, Blue Fin Building, 110 Southwark Street, London SE1 0SU.
Tel: 020 3148 5000. Fax: 020 3148 8130. E-mail: golfmonthly@ipcmedia.com
Editor: Michael Harris. **Art Editor:** Paul Duggan.
Monthly international consumer magazine for golfers.
Illustrations: Mainly for use as illustrations to articles. Small market for one-off pictures from golf tournaments of golf-related events.
Text: Illustrated features on instruction and other golf-related topics. Also in-depth profiles of leading world players. Around 2,000 words, but not critical.
Overall freelance potential: Most of the magazine is commissioned. Room for more material of the right type from freelances.
Editor's tips: This is an international magazine so material must have a wide appeal. No features of a parochial nature.
Fees: By agreement.

GOLF WORLD
Bauer Active Ltd, Media House, Lynchwood, Peterborough PE2 6EA.
Tel: 01733 468243. Fax: 01733 468001. E-mail: paul.ridley@bauermedia.co.uk
Editor: Chris Jones. **Art Director:** Paul Ridley.
Monthly publication for golfers, covering all aspects of the sport.
Illustrations: Unusual golfing pictures always of interest.
Text: Profiles of leading golfers and general or instructional features. 1,500–2,000 words.
Overall freelance potential: Around 20 per cent comes from freelance sources.
Fees: By agreement.

MARTIAL ARTS ILLUSTRATED
Martial Arts Ltd, Revenue Chambers, St Peter Street, Huddersfield, West Yorkshire HD1 1EL.
Tel: 01484 435011. Fax: 01484 422177. E-mail: martialartsltd@btconnect.com
Editor: Bob Sykes.
Monthly magazine covering all forms of Oriental fighting and self-defence techniques.
Illustrations: Will always consider single pictures or sets depicting well-known martial artists, club events, tournament action and aspects of technique.
Text: Well-illustrated articles on any relevant subject – profiles of leading figures and individual clubs, interviews, technique sequences and self-defence features.
Overall freelance potential: Excellent for those with access to the martial arts scene.
Editor's tips: Always write in the first instance with suggestions.
Fees: Should be negotiated before submission, as many contributions are supplied free of charge.

MATCH
Bauer Media, Media House, Lynchwood, Peterborough PE2 6EA.
Tel: 01733 468000. E-mail: james.bandy@bauermedia.co.uk
Editor: James Bandy.
Weekly publication for younger readers, looking at the whole spectrum of soccer. Aimed at the 8–16 age group.
Illustrations: Action shots all agency-supplied, but will consider unusual non-action images featuring top players. Usually bought only after consultation with the editor.
Text: Profiles and interviews concerning personalities in the soccer field. Length by arrangement.
Overall freelance potential: Limited – most is staff or agency produced.
Fees: By agreement.

Are you working from the latest edition of The Freelance Photographer's Market Handbook? It's published on 1 October each year. Markets are constantly changing, so it pays to have the latest edition

---

THE NON-LEAGUE PAPER

The Football Paper Ltd, Tuition House, St George's Road, Wimbledon, London SW19 4DS.
Tel: 020 8971 4333. Fax: 020 8971 4366. ISDN: 020 8605 2391.
E-mail: leaguenewsdesk@bhtmedia.com
Editor: David Emery. **News Editor:** John Lyons. **Picture Editor:** Sam Emery.
Weekly tabloid covering the non-League soccer scene, published every Sunday.
Illustrations: Digital files required. Always interested in hearing from capable football photographers able to produce regular coverage of their local teams, but must have the ability/facilities to send material direct via modem on the Saturday night. Submit details of experience and area covered in the first instance.
Text: No scope – all staff or agency produced.
Overall freelance potential: Much is produced by freelance regulars but replacements are often needed.
Fees: According to assignment and/or use.

RACING PIGEON PICTORIAL INTERNATIONAL

The Racing Pigeon Co Ltd, Unit G5, The Seedbed Centre, Wyncolls Road, Colchester, Essex CO4 9HT.
Tel: 01206 843456. E-mail: racing123@btconnect.co.uk
Editor: Lee Fribbins.
Monthly magazine for pigeon fanciers. Provides in-depth articles on methods, successful fanciers, scientific information, etc.
Illustrations: Pictures to illustrate features, plus some one-off pictures of pigeons, pigeon lofts, pigeon fanciers and related subjects.
Text: Features on subjects as above, from contributors with serious knowledge of the sport. 1,500 words.
Overall freelance potential: Around 10–15 per cent of the pictures come from freelance photographers. Articles are mostly by specialist writers.
Editor's tips: Short, colourful, exotic articles with good illustrations stand a reasonable chance.
Fees: £20 per published page minimum.

RUGBY WORLD

IPC Media Ltd, Blue Fin Building, 110 Southwark Street, London SE1 0SU.
Tel: 020 3148 4702. E-mail: kevin_eason@ipcmedia.com
Editor: Paul Morgan. **Art Editor:** Kevin Eason.
Britain's biggest selling monthly rugby magazine giving general coverage of Rugby Union.
Illustrations: Main scope is for regional/local coverage, since the top level matches are covered by regulars. Photographs of Cup matches, County championships, personalities, off-beat shots, etc. Covers: Good action shots of top players.
Text: Good articles with different angles are always of interest.
Overall freelance potential: Dependent on quality and appeal.
Fees: On a rising scale according to size of reproduction or length of text.

RUNNER'S WORLD

Natmag-Rodale, 6th Floor, 33 Broadwick Street, London W1F 0DQ.
Tel: 020 7339 4409. Fax: 020 7339 4420. E-mail: russell.fairbrother@natmag-rodale.co.uk
Editor: Andy Dixon. **Art Editor:** Russell Fairbrother.
Monthly publication for running enthusiasts.
Illustrations: Pictures relating to sports, recreational and fitness running. Consult art editor before submitting.
Text: Feature material considered, but only by prior consultation with the editor.
Overall freelance potential: Fair.
Fees: By agreement.

RUNNING FITNESS
Kelsey Publishing, 14 Priestgate, Peterborough PE1 1JA.
Tel: 01733 347559. Fax: 01733 891342. E-mail: rf.ed@kelseypb.co.uk
Editor: David Castle.
Monthly magazine for active running enthusiasts, those who run for health or recreation.
Illustrations: Coverage of competitions and running events at local or regional level, off-beat pictures, and general stock shots of runners. Both racing and training pictures are welcome. Some scope for general atmospheric pictures incorporating runners and athletic-looking subjects in picturesque and inspirational settings. Possible commission scope for "fashion" features. Covers: usually by commission – interested in hearing from photographers who can bring a creative approach to the subject.
Text: Illustrated articles of a practical nature, giving advice on training, diet, etc., and on unusual or exciting running events worldwide 1,000–1,500 words. Features of an inspirational nature also welcome – well-written and illustrated pieces on elite athletes, or other sportspeople who run as part of their training. Discuss ideas with the editor first.
Overall freelance potential: Good.
Fees: From a minimum of £20 up to £80 for a full page; text £70 per 1,000 words.

SGB UK
Datateam Publishing Ltd, London Road, Maidstone ME16 8LY.
Tel: 01622 699140. Fax: 01622 757646. E-mail: rknowles@datateam.co.uk
Editor: Rebecca Knowles.
Monthly magazine for the UK sports retail trade.
Illustrations: Topical pictures concerning the retail trade, usually to illustrate specific news stories, features and new products.
Text: Illustrated features and news stories on anything to do with the sports retail industry, including manufacturer and retailer profiles etc.
Overall freelance potential: Limited.
Fees: Text, £150 per 1,000 words; pictures by negotiation.

THE SCOTTISH SPORTING GAZETTE
BPG (Stamford) Ltd, Roebuck House, 33 Broad Street, Stamford, Lincs PE9 1RB.
Tel: 01780 766199. Fax: 01780 766416. E-mail: m.barnes@bournepublishinggroup.co.uk
Editor: Mike Barnes.
Annual publication to market Scottish shooting, fishing, stalking and allied services. Aimed at the upper income bracket in the UK, Europe and America.
Illustrations: Digital files preferred. High quality scenic photography, plus pictures of shooting, fishing, stalking, live game animals, whisky production, antique Scottish weapons, tartans, castles and hunting lodges. Covers: exceptional colour pictures of game animals or action sporting shots.
Text: Features on shooting, fishing and stalking in Scotland or articles on other topics that are particularly Scottish, as above. 600–2,000 words.
Overall freelance potential: Good.
Editor's tips: Pictures and text must be unusual, not the normal anecdotes associated with this field. Material should have a good Scottish flavour. It does not have to be essentially sporting, but should be allied in some way.
Fees: Open to negotiation.

THE SHOOTING GAZETTE
IPC Country & Leisure Media. Editorial: PO Box 225, Stamford, Lincolnshire PE9 2HS.
Tel: 01780 485350. Fax: 01780 754774. E-mail: will_hetherington@ipcmedia.com
Editor: Will Hetherington.

Britain's only monthly magazine covering exclusively game and rough shooting, wildlife, countryside.

Illustrations: Pictures for general illustration, including countryside scenes, hunting, shooting, fishing, farming, birds and animals – quarry and non-quarry species.

Text: Well-illustrated articles from those with specialist knowledge, and profiles or interviews. Up to 2,000 words.

Overall freelance potential: Good.

Fees: By negotiation.

SHOOTING TIMES AND COUNTRY MAGAZINE

IPC Media Ltd, Blue Fin Building, 110 Southwark Street, London SE1 0SU.
Tel: 020 3148 4741. Fax: 020 3148 8104. E-mail: steditorial@ipcmedia.com
Editor: Alastair Balmain .

Weekly magazine concentrating on all aspects of quarry shooting (game, pigeon, rough shooting, wildfowling and stalking). Also covers clay shooting, other fieldsports and general country topics.

Illustrations: Good photographs of shooting subjects plus gundogs, wildlife, rural crafts, country food. Some scope for good generic photographs of British counties, showing known landmarks. Covers: shots should be vertical in shape with room for title at the top.

Text: Illustrated features on all aspects of quarry shooting and general country topics as above. In the region of 900 words.

Overall freelance potential: Excellent; plenty of scope for new contributors.

Editor's tips: The magazine likes to keep pictures on file as it is not always possible to know in advance when a picture can be used. For features, remember that the readers are real country people.

Fees: Pictures £10–£60 according to size; covers £70–£90. Features £40 per 500 words.

SKI + BOARD

Ski Club of Great Britain Ltd, The White House, 57-63 Church Road, Wimbledon Village, London SW19 5SB.
Tel: 0845 4580780. Fax: 0845 4580781. E-mail: editor@skiclub.co.uk
Editor: Arnie Wilson.

Published four times a year. Official magazine of Ski Club of Great Britain, covering the sport at all levels.

Illustrations: Pictures for general illustration and for special gallery section, including holiday skiing, ski-touring, racing and equipment, good adventure/action shots, shots illustrating snowcraft and particular techniques. Also good, attractive pictures of specific ski resorts and ski slopes in season.

Text: Very interested in adventure skiing articles, especially with a good selection of images.

Overall freelance potential: Fair.

Fees: By arrangement.

THE SKIER & SNOWBOARDER MAGAZINE

Mountain Marketing Ltd, PO Box 386, Sevenoaks, Kent TN13 1AQ.
Tel: 0845 310 8303. E-mail: frank.baldwin@skierandsnowboarder.co.uk
Editor: Frank Baldwin.

Published five times a year: July, Sep/Oct, Nov/Dec, Jan/Feb, Mar/Apr. Covers all aspects of skiing and snowboarding.

Illustrations: Good action pictures and anything spectacular, odd or humorous that summons up the spirit of skiing. Also a special "Photo File" section in which photographers can submit up to three favourite shots backed by text which tells the reader about the set-ups/techniques used, linked with a short biog of the photographer.

Text: Original ideas for illustrated features always welcome. Possible scope for resort reports and news items.
Overall freelance potential: Very good.
Fees: By negotiation.

SNOOKER SCENE
Hayley Green Court, 130 Hagley Road, Hayley Green, Halesowen B63 1DY.
Tel: 0121 585 9188. Fax: 0121 585 7117. E-mail: clive.everton@talk21.com
Editor: Clive Everton.
Monthly publication for snooker players and enthusiasts.
Illustrations: Snooker action pictures and coverage related to tournaments, or material of historical interest.
Text: Features on snooker and billiards. 250–1,000 words.
Overall freelance potential: Small.
Fees: By arrangement.

SPIN
WW Magazines Ltd. Editorial: Sunnyhill House, 3/7 Sunnyhill Road, London SW16 2UG.
Tel: 020 8696 6200. E-mail: editors@spincricket.com
Editor: Duncan Steer.
Monthly cricket magazine focusing on the game at international level. Aims for a modern and youthful approach to the sport.
Illustrations: No scope for match coverage, but keen to see material documenting the lifestyle and culture that exists around the game, especially anything exotic or unusual that is rarely seen. Also interested in hearing from freelances who can supply top quality photo essays and stories on other aspects of the sport.
Text: Text with pictures is welcomed, but should be kept short and snappy in tabloid style.
Overall freelance potential: Good opportunities for unusual cricket coverage.
Fees: By negotiation.

SPORTING SHOOTER
Archant Specialist, Jubilee House, 2 Jubilee Place, London SW3 3TQ.
Tel: 020 7751 4917. E-mail: james@sportingshooter.co.uk
Editor: James Marchington.
Monthly aimed at sports shooters and gamekeepers.
Illustrations: Will consider good stock images depicting pigeon, clay and pheasant shooting, deer stalking, gun dogs, gamekeeping and relevant wildlife. Some commissions possible to photograph specific features.
Text: also very interested in illustrated articles on shooting topics
Overall freelance potential: Good.
Editor's tips: The magazine has a very specific style so always call to discuss ideas first.
Fees: By negotiation.

SWIMMING TIMES
Pavilion 3, SportPark, 3 Oakwood Drive, Loughborough, Leics LE11 3QF.
Tel: 01509 640230. Fax: 01509 640191. E-mail: swimmingtimes@swimming.org
Editor: Peter Hassall.
Official monthly magazine of the Amateur Swimming Association and Institute of Swimming.
Covers all aspects of swimming including diving, synchro-swimming, water polo, etc.
Illustrations: News pictures of swimmers at major events and any off-beat or particularly

interesting shots of swimming-related activity.
Text: Human interest stories about individual swimmers.
Overall freelance potential: Limited.
Fees: Negotiable.

TODAY'S GOLFER

Bauer Media, Media House, Lynchwood, Peterborough PE2 6EA.
Tel: 01733 468000. Fax: 01733 468843. E-mail: andy.calton@bauermedia.co.uk
Editor-in-Chief: Andy Calton.
Monthly for golfing enthusiasts.
Illustrations: Stock shots of leading players and courses, and anything off-beat, considered on spec.
Text: Instructional material; player profiles; equipment features; course tests.
Overall freelance potential: Limited.
Fees: By negotiation.

THE WISDEN CRICKETER

Wisden Cricketer Publishing Ltd, 2nd Floor, 123 Buckingham Palace Road, London SW1W 9SL.
Tel: 020 7705 4911. E-mail: twc@wisdencricketer.com
Editor: John Stern. **Art Director:** Nigel Davies.
Monthly publication aimed at all cricket lovers. Concentrates on the game at first-class and especially international level.
Illustrations: Exceptional photographs of the above always considered.
Text: Scope for exclusive news stories and features. But check first before submitting. 400–2,500 words.
Overall freelance potential: Fair.
Fees: On a rising scale according to size of pictures or length and significance of article.

Trade

AM

Bauer Automotive Ltd, Media House, Lynchwood, Peterborough PE2 6EA.
Tel: 01733 468261. Fax: 01733 468350. E-mail: jeremy.bennett@bauermedia.co.uk
Editor: Jeremy Bennett.
Fortnightly publication for the motor industry, mainly franchised dealers.
Illustrations: News photographs covering the motor trade generally. Some scope for commissions to photograph industry figures and premises.
Text: News items and news features of interest to industry executives.
Overall freelance potential: Good for those with contacts in the trade and local freelances.
Fees: By negotiation.

THE BOOKSELLER

The Bookseller Media Ltd, 5th Floor, Endeavour House, 189 Shaftesbury Avenue, London WC2H 8TJ.
Tel: 020 7420 6006. Fax: 020 7420 6103. E-mail: neill.denny@bookseller.co.uk
Editor-in-Chief: Neill Denny.
Weekly trade magazine for booksellers, publishers, librarians and anyone involved in the book industry. Covers trade trends and events, authors, etc.
Illustrations: Pictures of bookshops and book-related activities outside London. Busy book fairs, busy book shops, etc. Portraits of authors and book trade figures.

Text: Serious, humorous, analytical, descriptive articles connected with the book trade, plus author interviews.
Overall freelance potential: Only for those freelances who have good access to the book trade.
Fees: Variable; depends on material.

BRITISH BAKER

William Reed Publishing, Broadfield Park, Crawley, West Sussex RH11 9RT.
Tel: 01293 846595. Fax: 01293 846538. E-mail: sylvia.macdonald@william-reed.co.uk
Editor: Sylvia Macdonald.
Fortnightly business-to-business news magazine covering the entire baking industry.
Illustrations: Interesting photographs relating to working bakeries, especially news items such as shop openings, promotions, charity events, etc. Also good stock shots of bakery products.
Text: Short news stories (300 words) or features (500–1,000 words) on any baking industry topic.
Overall freelance potential: Fair, for those who can supply relevant material.
Fees: £125 per 1,000 words for text; photographs by negotiation.

CABINET MAKER

Manning Publishing Ltd, The Irwin Centre, Scotland Road, Dry Drayton, Cambridge CB23 8AR.
Tel: 01954 212906. Fax: 01954 212105. E-mail: info@cabinet-maker.co.uk
Features **Editor:** James Dickson. News **Editor:** Katie Matthews.
Weekly publication for all those in the furniture and furnishing trade and industry.
Illustrations: Freelances commissioned to cover news assignments in the trade. Some scope for pictures to illustrate features.
Text: Features about companies making furniture for sale to retailers and interior designers.
Overall freelance potential: Around 10 per cent contributed, including news coverage.
Editor's tips: Approach the editor for a brief before submitting.
Fees: By agreement.

CATERER & HOTELKEEPER

Reed Business Information Ltd, Quadrant House, The Quadrant, Sutton, Surrey SM2 5AS.
Tel: 020 8652 4210. Fax: 020 8652 8973. E-mail: mark.lewis@rbi.co.uk
Editor: Mark Lewis. **Art Editor:** Chris Russell. Picture Librarian: Sue Hockins.
Weekly magazine for the hotel and catering trade.
Illustrations: News pictures relevant to hotel and catering establishments – openings, extensions, refurbishments, people, etc. Special interest in regional material. Commissions possible to cover establishments, equipment and food.
Text: Specialist articles of interest to the trade, by commission only.
Overall freelance potential: Mainly limited to those with connections within the trade.
Editor's tips: Also welcomes tip-offs concerning the industry, for which a fee of £15–£25 is paid.
Fees: On a rising scale according to size of reproduction or length of text.

CHEMIST AND DRUGGIST

CMP Information Ltd, Riverbank House, Angel Lane, Tonbridge TN9 1SE.
Tel: 01732 377487. Fax: 01732 367065. E-mail: chemdrug@cmpinformation.com
Editor: Gary Paragpuri.
Weekly news publication for retail pharmacists; the pharmaceutical, toiletries and cosmetics industries; pharmaceutical wholesalers, etc.
Illustrations: B&W and colour. Digital files preferred. News pictures concerning individual retailers and retailing related events, plus industry events relating to pharmaceutical companies.
Text: Local news stories relating to community pharmacy.
Overall freelance potential: Limited.
Fees: On a rising scale, according to contribution.

CONTAINERISATION INTERNATIONAL
Informa UK Ltd, 69-77 Paul Street, London EC2A 4LQ.
Tel: 020 7017 4820. Fax: 020 7017 4976. E-mail: john.fossey@informa.com
Editor: John Fossey. **Art Editor:** Ralph Murray.
Monthly business-oriented magazine on issues facing the international container transport industry.
Illustrations: Unusual pictures of container shipping activities, especially in exotic locations overseas, or interesting/amusing uses for containers.
Text: Well-researched and exclusive articles, preferably on some aspect of the container transport business not covered by staff writers. Around 2,000 words.
Overall freelance potential: Limited.
Fees: By agreement.

CONVENIENCE STORE
William Reed Ltd, Broadfield Park, Crawley, West Sussex RH11 9RT.
Tel: 01293 613400. Fax: 01293 610330. E-mail: david.rees@william-reed.co.uk
Editor: David Rees.
Fortnightly magazine for independent neighbourhood retailers and convenience stores, and their wholesale suppliers.
Illustrations: Photographs usually to illustrate specific features; little scope for pictures on their own.
Text: Illustrated features or stories concerning late-night, local, food-based stores. Should ideally feature a retailer who is doing something a bit different, or who has been highly successful in some way.
Overall freelance potential: Modest.
Fees: By negotiation.

DRAPERS
EMAP Ltd, Greater London House, Hampstead Road, London NW1 7EJ.
Tel: 020 7728 5000. E-mail: jessica.price-brown@emap.com
Editor: Jessica Price-Brown. **Art Editor:** Alison Fisher.
Weekly news publication for clothing and textile retailers.
Illustrations: News pictures of interest to the clothing and fashion trade. Some scope for portraits and fashion shoots by commission.
Text: Features, fashion and news items of relevance to retailers in the fashion and textile fields.
Overall freelance potential: Limited for news; fair for commissioned work.
Editor's tips: Do not send unsolicited material – call the art editor first.
Fees: Good; on a rising scale according to size of illustration or length of feature.

EUROFRUIT MAGAZINE
Market Intelligence Ltd, 4th Floor, Market Towers, One Nine Elms Lane, London SW8 5NQ.
Tel: 020 7501 3700. Fax: 020 7498 6472. E-mail: michael@fruitnet.com
Editor: Mike Knowles.
Monthly magazine of the European fresh fruit and vegetable trade. Aimed at producers, exporters, importers, merchants and buyers.
Illustrations: Subjects such as harvesting fruit, loading on to ships or lorries, quality checks on fruit, packing etc. Photographs accepted mostly for the magazine's own picture library.
Text: Topical features on fruit and vegetables, e.g. Chilean apples in Europe, French Iceberg lettuce, Egypt's expanding export range, Norway as an alternative market, etc. 1,250–2,000 words.
Overall freelance potential: Quite good. Some regular contributors, but scope for the freelance writer who can also supply pictures.
Editor's tips: It is best to work in close contact with the editorial department to get names of people who would be of interest to the publication.
Fees: Negotiable.

FISHING NEWS/FISHING NEWS INTERNATIONAL

IntraFish Media, 6th Floor, Eldon House, 2 Eldon Street, London EC2M 7LS.
Tel: 020 7650 1030. Fax: 020 7650 1050. E-mail: cormac.burke@intrafish.com
Editor: Cormac Burke.
Fishing News is a weekly newspaper for the commercial fishing industry in Britain and Ireland.
Fishing News International is the leading monthly newspaper for the global commercial fishing industry.
Illustrations: Captioned news pictures covering any subject relating to the UK/Irish and international commercial fishing industries.
Text: Illustrated news stories always considered.
Overall freelance potential: Very good; a lot of photographs are used.
Fees: Standard £25 per picture.

THE FLORIST & WHOLESALE BUYER

Wordhouse Publishing Group Ltd, 68 First Avenue, Mortlake, London SW14 8SR.
Tel: 020 8939 6470. Fax: 020 8878 9983. E-mail: info@thewordhouse.co.uk
Editor: Austin Clark.
Publication for retail florists, published 10 times a year.
Illustrations: News pictures about the trade and other interesting pictures of floristry in the retail context, i.e. special displays, promotions, etc.
Text: Features on anything relating to floristry and retailing, shop profiles, practical aspects, advertising and promotion, etc.
Overall freelance potential: Limited.
Fees: Text, £150 per 1,000 words published; pictures by agreement.

FOOD TRADER FOR BUTCHERS

National Federation of Meat & Food Traders, 1 Belgrove, Tunbridge Wells, Kent TN1 1YW.
Tel: 01892 541412. Fax: 01892 535462. E-mail: info@nfmft.co.uk
Editor: Jayne Cottrell.
Official magazine of the National Federation of Meat & Food Traders. Published 10 times a year.
Illustrations: Topical pictures related to news and issues in the meat and related food industry.
Text: Topical features on the food industry, primarily the meat trade. Up to 2,000 words.
Overall freelance potential: Fair for those in close contact with the trade.
Editor's tips: Only exclusive material will be considered.
Fees: By negotiation.

FORECOURT TRADER

William Reed Publishing Ltd, Broadfield Park, Crawley, West Sussex RH11 9RT.
Tel: 01293 610219. Fax: 01293 610330. E-mail: merril.boulton@william-reed.co.uk
Editor: Merril Bolton.
Monthly magazine for petrol station operators.
Illustrations: News pictures relating to petrol stations and the petrol sales business generally.
Text: News and features relating to all areas of petrol retailing.
Overall freelance potential: Fair.
Fees: Text, £120 per 1,000 words; pictures according to use.

FORESTRY JOURNAL

PO Box 7570, Dumfries DG2 8YD.
Tel/fax: 01387 702272. E-mail: editor@forestryjournal.co.uk
Editor: Mark Andrews.
Monthly magazine covering all aspects of forestry and timber production – arboriculture, estate management, harvesting, haulage, and recreational use of forests and woodland.
Illustrations: Plenty of photographs used, but usually only as accompaniment to features on topics as above/below.

Text: Always seeking freelances to produce well-illustrated local stories on forestry topics, and for profiles of individual contractors etc. Write or e-mail the editor with suggestions and/or details of areas covered.
Overall freelance potential: Good for complete illustrated features.
Fees: £150 per published page.

INDEPENDENT RETAIL NEWS

Metropolis Business Publishing, 6th Floor Davis House, 2 Robert Street, Croydon, CR0 1QQ.
Tel: 020 8253 8704. Fax: 01322 616375. E-mail: david.shrimpton@metropolis.co.uk
Editor: David Shrimpton.
Fortnightly publication for independent, convenience, licensed and CTN retailers. Assists them in being more profitable and aware of new products and campaigns.
Illustrations: Captioned news pictures and picture stories of interest to independent grocery and convenience store traders. Stock images to illustrate people buying goods in independent/corner stores, retail crime, under-age sales, bootlegging, national lottery sales, etc.
Text: Articles and stories relevant to small retailers.
Overall freelance potential: Fair.
Editor's tips: A sample copy of the magazine is available to potential contributors. Always phone first with ideas.
Fees: Photographs according to how sourced, but up to £150 for features and £50-£100 for news stories. For commissioned features £170 per 1,000 words and negotiable for news stories.

MEAT TRADES JOURNAL

William Reed Ltd, Broadfield Park, Crawley, West Sussex RH11 9RT.
Tel: 01293 846567. Fax: 01293 610330. E-mail: ed.bedington@william-reed.co.uk
Editor: Ed Bedington.
Fortnightly journal for the whole meat and poultry trade.
Illustrations: Pictures relating to any current meat trade issue, including legislation, food scares, court cases, etc.
Text: Stories on current issues as above. Illustrated features on current food issues, research, technology, and profiles of individual businesses.
Overall freelance potential: Good for those in a position to cover this industry.
Editor's tips: It is much preferred if material offered is exclusive.
Fees: Negotiable, according to use.

PET PRODUCT MARKETING

Bauer Active Ltd, Media House, Lynchwood, Peterborough PE2 6EA.
Tel: 01733 468000. E-mail: sandra.pearce@bauermedia.co.uk
Editor in Chief: Matt Clarke.
Monthly publication for the pet trade, supplying information about new products, pet market news and business advice.
Illustrations: Will consider high-quality portfolios of common pets, companion animals and exotic pet species, including portrait or action shots.
Text: Will consider features written by those with experience in the pet trade.
Fees: Negotiable.

WORLD FISHING

Mercator Media Limited, The Old Mill, Lower Quay, Fareham, Hampshire PO16 0RA.
Tel: 01329 825335. Fax: 01329 825330. E-mail: cwills@worldfishing.net
Editor: Carly Wills.
Monthly journal for the commercial fishing industry. Covers fisheries and related industries from an

international perspective.
Illustrations: Mainly to accompany specific articles, but some scope for scene-setting shots of commercial fishing activity in specific locations worldwide.
Text: Illustrated articles on any commercial fishing topic. Should always contain some international interest. Maximum 1,500 words.
Overall freelance potential: Good for those with connections in the industry.
Fees: By negotiation.

Transport

COACH AND BUS WEEK
Rouncy Media Ltd, 3 The Office Village, Cygnet Park, Peterborough PE7 8GX.
Tel: 01733 293240. Fax: 0845 2802927. E-mail: andrew.sutcliffe@rouncymedia.co.uk
Editorial Director: Andrew Sutcliffe. News Reporter: Gareth Evans. Editor, 'Out & About': Bernard Horton. Editor, 'Minibus': Martin Cole.
Weekly news magazine covering coach and bus operations. Aimed at licensed coach, bus and tour operators. Includes monthly supplements 'Out & About', containing tourism information for drivers and tour organisers, and 'Minibus' for minbus operators.
Illustrations: Pictures as illustrations to features mentioned below; coach and bus related news items. Places of interest to coach parties.
Text: Features on coach and bus operators, hotels, ferry operations, resorts and venues, anything that would be of interest to a coach party or an operator. Articles on subjects that an operator might find useful in their day-to-day business. Up to 1,000 words.
Overall freelance potential: Always interested in seeing work from freelances.
Fees: By negotiation.

COMMERCIAL MOTOR
Reed Business Information Ltd, Quadrant House, The Quadrant, Sutton, Surrey SM2 5AS.
Tel: 020 8652 3500. Fax: 020 8652 8969. E-mail: justin.stanton@rbi.co.uk
Editor: Justin Stanton.
Weekly publication devoted to the road haulage industry. Aimed at vehicle enthusiasts as well as industry readers.
Illustrations: Mostly commissioned; arrange to show portfolio to the art editor first. Possible interest in professional stock photographs of commercial vehicles and aspects of road haulage – send lists of subjects available.
Text: Technical articles on road haulage topics, from expert contributors only.
Overall freelance potential: Only for experienced contributors.
Fees: Day rate around £250–£300 plus expenses. Other material by negotiation.

OLD GLORY
Mortons Media Group Ltd, PO Box 43, Horncastle, Lincs LN9 6JR.
Tel: 01507 529306. Fax: 01507 529301. E-mail: ctyson@mortons.co.uk
Editor: Colin Tyson.
Monthly devoted to industrial/commercial transport and machinery heritage and vintage restoration including traction engines, tractors, etc.
Illustrations: Pictures of all forms of traction engines, tractors, buses, commercial vehicles, fairground machinery and maritime subjects such as old steamboats. News pictures of individual machines, restoration projects, etc. Detailed captions necessary including where and when picture taken. Covers: colourful pictures of traction engines in attractive settings.
Text: Illustrated articles on subjects as above.
Overall freelance potential: A lot of scope for good colour material.
Fees: Pictures £20–£75 dependent on size used.

ROADWAY

Roadway House, 35 Monument Hill, Weybridge, Surrey KT13 8RN.
Tel: 01932 838922. E-mail: roadway@rha.uk.net
Editor: Caroline Bullock.
Monthly news magazine for the road haulage industry. Official magazine of the Road Haulage Association.
Illustrations: Pictures of trucks on motorways, at depots etc. Should be newsworthy or of unusual interest.
Text: Articles on any aspect of the road haulage industry. Length by prior agreement with the editor.
Overall freelance potential: Limited.
Fees: By arrangement.

TOWPATH TALK

Mortons Media Group Ltd, Media Centre, Morton Way, Horncastle, Lincs LN9 6JR.
Tel: 01507 523456. E-mail: jrichardson@mortons.co.uk
Editor: Janet Richardson.
Specialist monthly newspaper covering all aspects of Britain's waterways.
Illustrations: News pictures and picture stories relevant to all forms of waterways and towpath use, including boating, cycling, horse riding, angling or walking.
Text: Will consider news stories and features on anything concerning the UK's waterways, such as the environment, canal restoration and heritage. Also specialist articles on technical matters such as engine maintenance and boat care.
Overall freelance potential: Good.
Fees: According to use.

TRACTOR

Mortons Media Group Ltd, Media Centre, Morton Way, Horncastle, Lincs LN9 6JR.
Tel: 01507 529304. Fax: 01507 529495. E-mail: thoyland@mortons.co.uk
Editor: Tony Hoyland.
Monthly magazine celebrating the farm tractor and its development.
Illustrations: Mainly colour; archive B&W. Images of interesting classic or vintage tractors, restoration projects, tractor rallies and events. Detailed captions about individual machines and their history always essential. Also archive pictures depicting farm life and machinery from WW1 to the 1960s.
Text: Well-illustrated articles on relevant subjects always considered.
Overall freelance potential: Very good.
Fees: By negotiation.

TRACTOR & MACHINERY

Kelsey Publishing Group, Cudham Tithe Barn, Berry's Hill, Cudham, Kent TN16 3AG.
Tel: 01959 541444. Fax: 01959 541400. E-mail: martin.oldaker@kelsey.co.uk
Editor: Martin Oldaker.
Monthly magazine for tractor enthusiasts, covering classic, vintage and contemporary machines from all parts of the world.
Illustrations: Pictures of tractors in the news, classic and vintage gatherings, unusual and interesting tractors, and related machinery. Captions must include details of type, model and year of tractor and name of driver. Contact editor before preparing a submission.
Text: Those who can add words to their images are welcomed.
Overall freelance potential: Good.
Fees: By arrangement.

TRUCK & DRIVER
Reed Business Information, Quadrant House, The Quadrant, Sutton, Surrey SM2 5AS.
Tel: 020 8652 3500. Fax: 020 8652 8988. E-mail: will.shiers@rbi.co.uk
Editor: Will Shiers.
Monthly magazine for truck drivers.
Illustrations: Interesting individual trucks, unusual situations involving drivers and their vehicles, news items and some studio work.
Text: Commissioned features on anything of interest to truck drivers. Looks for freelances with ideas.
Overall freelance potential: Very good.
Fees: By negotiation.

Travel

AUSTRALIA & NEW ZEALAND
Evolve Digital Publishing Ltd, Unit 3, The Old Estate Yard, North Stoke Lane, Upton Cheyney, Bristol BS30 6ND.
Tel: 0117 932 3586. E-mail: leanne.voisey@edpltd.co.uk
Editor: Leanne Voisey.
Monthly magazine aimed at both holidaymakers and migrants.
Illustrations: Very limited scope for photography on its own as much is sourced from the travel and migration trade. Pictures only required as part of complete feature packages as below, or possibly for covers which usually feature action shots of people on beaches.
Text: Well-illustrated features of around 1,200 – 2,000 words. Real-life stories of those who have emigrated to Australia or NZ, plus coverage of specific locations, cities, activities, food and culture. Should have wide rather than niche appeal. Submit ideas only in the first instance, along with examples of previous work.
Overall freelance potential: Good for experienced travel freelances who can provide the complete package.
Editor's tips: Looking for material that strikes a good balance between inspiration and information.
Fees: Up to £200 for cover images. Features £180 per 1,000 words inclusive of pictures.

BUSINESS TRAVELLER
Panacea Publishing International Ltd, 2nd Floor, Cardinal House, Albemarle Street, London W1S 4TE.
Tel: 020 7647 6330. Fax: 020 7647 6331. E-mail: editorial@businesstraveller.com
Editor: Tom Otley. **Art Editor:** Annie Harris.
Monthly consumer publication aimed at the frequently travelling international and domestic business executive.
Illustrations: Pictures to illustrate destination features on a wide variety of cities around the world – request features list of upcoming destinations.
Text: Illustrated features on business travel, but only by prior consultation with the editor.
Overall freelance potential: Around 65 per cent of the magazine is contributed by freelances.
Editor's tips: Submit low-res digital or dupes in the first instance.
Fees: Pictures from £50 up to £180 for a full page; covers £250. Text, £200 per 1,000 words.

CONDE NAST TRAVELLER
The Condé Nast Publications Ltd, Vogue House, Hanover Square, London W1S 1JU.
Tel: 020 7499 9080. Fax: 020 7493 3758. E-mail: cntraveller@condenast.co.uk

Editor: Sarah Miller. **Director of Photography:** Caroline Metcalfe.
Heavily-illustrated glossy monthly for the discerning, independent traveller.
Illustrations: Colour and occasional B&W. Top quality photo-feature material covering all aspects of travel, from luxury hotels and food, restaurant interiors to adventure travel, ecological issues, and reportage, etc. Very stylish and striking B&W photography also sought. Always interested in hearing from experienced photographers who are planning specific trips.
Text: Mostly commissioned from top name writers.
Overall freelance potential: Very good for material of the highest quality.
Editor's tips: The magazine seeks to use material with an original approach. Particularly interested in hearing from photographers who can produce excellent work but who are not necessarily travel specialists.
Fees: Variable depending on what is offered, but top rates paid for suitable material.

FOOD AND TRAVEL
Green Pea Publishing, Suite 51, The Business Centre, Ingate Place, Queenstown Road, London SW8 3NS.
Tel: 020 7501 0511. E-mail: edits@foodandtravel.com
Editor: TBA. **Creative Director:** Angela Dukes.
Up-market monthly for affluent people interested in food, wine and travel.
Illustrations: High quality food and travel photography, invariably produced on commission. Specialist photographers are advised to contact the creative director with details of experience and ideas. No scope for travel stock material since most is commissioned.
Text: Ideas for articles always considered, but invariably produced on commission by specialist writers.
Overall freelance potential: Good for specialists; better for travel than for food.
Fees: By negotiation.

FRANCE
Archant House, Oriel Road, Cheltenham, Gloucestershire GL50 1BB.
Tel: 01242 216050. Fax: 01242 216094. E-mail: editorial@francemag.com
Editor: Carolyn Boyd. **Art Editor:** Adam Vines.
Monthly magazine for Francophiles, with the emphasis on the real France.
Illustrations: Picture stories, and top quality individual pictures to illustrate articles, on French regions, annual events, cuisine, travel, arts and history. Covers: pictures that capture the essence of France. Photographs also required for annual calendar – selected early in each new year.
Text: Lively and colourful illustrated features on the life, culture and history of France. Normally around 1,200 words, but up to 2,000 words considered. Factual accuracy essential.
Overall freelance potential: Good for top quality material but much supplied by regular writers.
Editor's tips: E-mail with outlines/summary before submitting material. Features list fills 6-12 months in advance.
Fees: Photographs from £25 up to £100 for cover or DPS. £100 per 1,000 words.

FRENCH MAGAZINE
Horizon New Media,12 George Street, Bath BA1 2EH.
Tel: 01225 329381. E-mail: justin@horizonnewmedia.com
Editor: Justin Postlethwaite.
Monthly magazine for regular travellers to France and those with, or seeking, property there.
Illustrations: Digital files preferred. Typical French images for general illustration purposes –

Are you working from the latest edition of The Freelance Photographer's Market Handbook? It's published on 1 October each year. Markets are constantly changing, so it pays to have the latest edition

---

historic sites, vineyards, food/restaurants, activities, and homes and interiors etc. Submit lists of subjects available in the first instance. Commissions may be available to photographers with medium format or high-end digital equipment.

Text: Well-illustrated articles always welcomed, especially on gastronomy, buying property and regional features. Around 1,500 words plus 8-10 illustrations.

Overall freelance potential: Excellent.

Fees: Single pictures according to use; features from £150 per 1,000 words; packages negotiable.

GEOGRAPHICAL

Circle Publishing, One Victoria Villas, Richmond, Surrey TW9 2GW.

Tel: 020 8332 2713. Fax: 020 8332 9307. E-mail: magazine@geographical.co.uk

Editor: Geordie Torr. **Art Director:** Liz Fensome.

Monthly magazine of the Royal Geographical Society. Covers a wide spread of topics including travel, culture, environment, wildlife, conservation, history and exploration.

Illustrations: Mainly looking for photo-stories on geographical topics – human, political, ecological, economic and physical. Relevant news pictures always considered.

Text: Well-illustrated articles on any geographical subject, written in an informative but accessible way. Feature proposals should be sent to proposals@geographical.co.uk in the form of a 150-200 word synopsis.

Overall freelance potential: Excellent for the right type of material.

Fees: Negotiable, but in the region of £100 per published page. Single pictures according to use.

ITALIA!

Anthem Publishing Limited, Suite 6, Picadilly House, London Road, Bath BA1 3PL.

Tel: 01225 489984. Fax: 01225 489980. E-mail: debra.hughes@anthem-publishing.com

Editor: Amanda Robinson. **Art Editor:** Debra Hughes.

Highly-pictorial monthly covering regional travel and property in Italy. Also has sister-title Taste Italia focusing on Italian food and drink.

Illustrations: Happy to hear from photographers, particularly those based in or regularly visiting Italy, and those with large collections of existing images. Pictures used mainly scenic/landscape and people/local colour images.

Text: little scope as the magazine generates most topics in-house and commissions from known writers.

Overall freelance potential: Fair.

Fees: By negotiation.

LIVING FRANCE

Archant Life, Archant House, Oriel Road, Cheltenham GL50 1BB.

Tel: 01242 216050. Fax: 01242 216074. E-mail: editorial@livingfrance.com

Editor: Eleanor O'Kane.

Monthly magazine for those thinking of buying property in or moving to France, or hoping to work there.

Illustrations: Images reflecting working and living in France – property, French lifestyle, working life in France, retirement in France, children's education. Submit subject lists to deputy editor in the first instance. Covers: Images showing an aspirational and obviously French house, with space for coverlines.

Text: Suggestions for articles always considered. Main scope for destination pieces, interviews/profiles with expats in France, practical articles on buying property, living and working in France. E-mail synopsis in the first instance.

Overall freelance potential: Fair.

Fees: Individual pictures according to use; illustrated articles £300 for 1,000–1,500 words.

A PLACE IN THE SUN

APITS Ltd, 2nd Floor, Rear West Office, 16 Winchester Walk, London, SE1 9AQ

Tel: 020 3207 2920. E-mail: simong@apits.com
Editor: Richard Way. **Art Editor:** Simon Grover.
Glossy monthly for prospective buyers of overseas property. Official magazine of the C4 TV series of the same name.
Illustrations: Mostly by commission, though some stock images are used. Will consider sets of images based around people moving or living abroad, or suggestions for subjects, which could lead to a full-scale commission. Other general commissions also possible – submit details of experience and a few samples in the first instance.
Text: Illustrated feature stories as above.
Overall freelance potential: Good for the more experienced worker.
Fees: By negotiation.

REAL TRAVEL
Create Publishing, Castlemead, Lower Castle Street, Bristol, BS1 3AG.
Tel: 0117 917 5099. E-mail: hannah@realtravelmag.com
Editor: Hfu Reisenhofer. **Art Editor:** Dave Partridge.
Magazine for "active travellers" rather than holidaymakers.
Illustrations: Pictures of real people experiencing the world on career breaks or gap years or just for adventure, charity work, sporting activity, etc. Also stock pictures of less "touristy" destinations; submit details of coverage available in the first instance.
Text: Will always consider illustrated features focusing on "exciting yet attainable" destinations. From the more experienced contributor, expert advice and travel tips, on practical topics such as health, staying safe, etc.
Overall freelance potential: Good for the right sort of material as described.
Editor's tips: Contributions must have been clearly produced by active travellers from their own personal experience.
Fees: By negotiation.

SPAIN
The Media Company Publications Ltd, 21 Royal Circus, Edinburgh EH3 6TL.
Tel: 0131 226 7766. Fax: 0131 226 4567. E-mail: sue.hitchen@googlemail.com
Editor: Sue Hitchen.
Monthly magazine for lovers of Spain, especially those owning or aiming to buy property in the country or with an interest in the culture and history of Spain.
Illustrations: Commissions may be available to photographers resident in or visiting Spain. Stock images mostly sourced from agencies though photographers with in-depth collections may find it worthwhile to submit lists of subjects available.
Text: Ideas for illustrated features welcomed, on topics such as property, food and drink, travel and leisure activities. Submit outline first.
Overall freelance potential: Fair.
Fees: Negotiable and dependent on what is on offer.

THE SUNDAY TIMES TRAVEL MAGAZINE
Times Newspapers Ltd, 1 Pennington Street, London E98 1ST.
Tel: 020 7782 5000. E-mail: firstname.surname@sundaytimes.co.uk
Editor: Ed Grenby. **Picture Editor:** Polly Teller.
Monthly glossy aimed at up-market travellers. Published on behalf of The Sunday Times.
Illustrations: Will always consider high-quality travel material on spec, including especially striking single images for use in double-page spreads. Lists of stock material always of interest. Only limited scope for commissions.
Text: Will always consider suggestions for original illustrated travel features.
Overall freelance potential: Good for top-quality work.
Fees: Negotiable and according to use.

TRAVELLER
& Publishing for WEXAS International Ltd, 45-49 Brompton Road, London SW3 1DE.
Tel: 020 7581 6156. E-mail: traveller@and-publishing.co.uk
Editor: Amy Sohanpaul.
Quarterly publication containing narrative features on unusual and adventurous travel, usually in the developing countries of the world. Aimed at the independent traveller who prefers to travel off the beaten track.
Illustrations: High quality documentary travel pictures, usually from developing countries, rarely Europe or North America. Usually required as an integral part of illustrated articles as below, but there is also a six-page photo-essay (action/reportage). No tourist brochure-type shots.
Text: Well-illustrated travel articles from contributors with in-depth knowledge of the area/subject covered. Around 900 words, plus about 10 pictures. Unusual subject matter preferred, including coverage of world hot spots.
Overall freelance potential: Good, but limited by the magazine's frequency.
Editor's tips: Excellent photographic work is essential.
Fees: Photographs, From £50, full-page £80, £150 for cover. Text, £200 per 1,000 words.

WANDERLUST
Wanderlust Publications Ltd, PO Box 1832, Windsor, Berks SL4 1EB.
Tel: 01753 620426. Fax: 01753 620474. E-mail: info@wanderlust.co.uk
Editor: Dan Linstead. **Art Director:** Graham Berridge.
Magazine for the "independent-minded" traveller, published eight times a year.
Illustrations: Colour transparency or digital files (should be available at 60MB, no upsizing). Majority required for use in conjunction with features. Send a summary stock list in the first instance with a small selection of sample work. Covers: Always looking for bold, bright and uncluttered images that shout "travel", preferably with strong colours such as blue/yellow or red/orange.
Text: Well-illustrated features on independent and special interest travel at any level and in any part of the world. Contributors must have in-depth knowledge of their subject area and be prepared to cover both good and bad aspects. Short pieces up to 750 words; longer articles from 1,800–2,500 words.
Overall freelance potential: Excellent for complete packages of words and pictures.
Editor's tips: Don't send unsolicited originals; photocopies or prints will do as samples. Detailed "Notes for Contributors" and "Guidelines for Photographers" can be viewed on website: www.wanderlust.co.uk.
Fees: Photographs by negotiation and according to use; text £200 per 1,000 words.

Women's Interest

BELLA
H. Bauer Publishing Ltd, Academic House, 24-28 Oval Road, London NW1 7DT.
Tel: 020 7241 8000. Fax: 020 7241 8056. E-mail: lizzie.rowe@bauerconsumer.co.uk
Editor: Julia Davis. **Picture Editor:** Lizzie Rowe.
Weekly magazine for women, covering human interest stories, fashion, cookery and celebrities.
Illustrations: Pictures of celebrities and royalty, off-beat pictures and curiosities considered on spec. Fashion and food, mostly commissioned.
Text: Some scope for exclusive human interest features and celebrity interviews. Always check with the editor first.
Fees: By negotiation.

BEST
National Magazine Company, 72 Broadwick Street, London W1F 9EP.
Tel: 020 7439 5000. Fax: 020 7437 6886. E-mail: alison.thurston@natmags.co.uk
Editor: Jackie Hatton. **Picture Editor:** Alison Thurston.
Weekly magazine for women, covering affordable fashion, health matters, cookery, home
improvements, features etc.
Illustrations: Scope for off-beat, general human interest and curiosity shots, and informal celebrity
material. Commissioned coverage of fashion, food, features, etc.
Text: Articles with a practical slant, aimed at working women.
Overall freelance potential: Quite good.
Fees: Commissioned photography by negotiation; other material according to use.

CLOSER
Bauer Consumer Media, Endeavour House, 189 Shaftesbury Avenue, London WC2H 8JG.
Tel: 020 7859 8685. Fax: 020 7859 8685. E-mail: emma.peel@bauerconsumer.co.uk
Editor: Lisa Burrow. **Picture Editor:** Emma Peel.
Weekly women's magazine with the emphasis on celebrities and true-life stories.
Illustrations: Mainly by commission. Opportunities for experienced photographers to shoot a range
of celebrity material, from paparazzi street photography to studio work. Exclusive paparazzi
material also considered on spec, but much is sourced from agencies. Photographers in all parts of
the UK also needed to shoot portraits to illustrate true-life stories – submit details of experience and
area of the country covered.
Text: True-life stories about ordinary people always wanted – submit brief details in the first
instance.
Overall freelance potential: Good for those with some experience in these areas.
Fees: Photography by negotiation or according to job. True-life stories, up to £500.

COMPANY
National Magazine Company Ltd, 72 Broadwick Street, London W1F 9EP.
Tel: 020 7439 5000. Fax: 020 7312 3051. E-mail: abi.dillon@natmags.co.uk
Editor: Victoria White. **Picture Editor:** Abi Dillon.
Monthly magazine aimed at up-market young women in their twenties.
Illustrations: Photographs to illustrate features on fashion, beauty, relationships, careers, travel
and personalities, invariably by commission.
Text: Articles on the above topics, of varying lengths. Also, more topical and "newsy" features.
Overall freelance potential: Fair scope for experienced contributors.
Fees: By negotiation.

COSMOPOLITAN
National Magazine Company Ltd, 72 Broadwick Street, London W1V 2BP.
Tel: 020 7439 5000. Fax: 020 7439 5016. E-mail: joan.tinney@natmags.co.uk
Editor: Louise Court. **Creative Director:** Stuart Selner. **Picture Editor:** Joan Tinney.
Monthly magazine for women in the 18–34 age group.
Illustrations: Photographs to illustrate features on fashion, style and beauty, by commission only.
Some top quality stock situation pictures may be used to illustrate more general features on
emotional, sexual or social issues.
Text: Articles of interest to sophisticated young women. Always query the editor first
Overall freelance potential: Only for the experienced contributor to the women's press.
Fees: By negotiation.

ELLE
Hachette Filipacchi (UK) Ltd, 64 North Row, London W1K 7LL.
Tel: 020 7150 7348. Fax: 020 7150 7670. E-mail: hannah.ridleyl@hf-uk.com
Editor: Lorraine Candy. **Picture Editor:** Hannah Ridley.

Up-market monthly magazine with the emphasis on fashion.
Illustrations: Top quality images of fashion and style subjects, portraiture and still life, always by commission.
Text: Some scope for top quality feature articles, usually by commission and from established contributors.
Overall freelance potential: Good for contributors experienced at the top level of magazine journalism.
Fees: By negotiation.

ESSENTIALS

IPC Media Ltd, Blue Fin Building, 110 Southwark Street, London SE1 0SU.
Tel: 020 3148 5000. E-mail: tracey_pocock@ipcmedia.com
Editor: Julie Barton-Breck. **Creative Director:** Stuart Thomas. **Picture Editor:** Tracey Pocock.
Monthly mass-market magazine for women with the emphasis on practical matters.
Illustrations: Images of health, interior decoration, travel, food, etc. Some commissioned work available.
Text: Practical articles, health, features of interest to women. Synopsis essential in first instance.
Overall freelance potential: Good for experienced contributors to quality women's magazines.
Fees: By negotiation.

GLAMOUR

The Condé Naste Publications Ltd, 6-8 Old Bond Street, London W1S 4PH.
Tel: 020 7499 9080. Fax: 020 7491 2551. lucy.slade@condenast.co.uk
Editor: Jo Elvin. Features **Editor:** Corrie Jackson. Picture Director: Lucy Slade.
Mid-market general interest monthly for the 18-32 age group.
Illustrations: Mostly by commission to shoot features, portraiture, still life and interiors; make an appointment to show portfolio. Possible but limited scope for stock, including celebrity material.
Text: Always interested in celebrity interviews, investigative articles and features on relationships, careers, fashion, health and fitness. Send short synopsis in the first instance.
Overall freelance potential: Good for the experienced worker.
Fees: By negotiation.

GOOD HOUSEKEEPING

National Magazine Company Ltd, National Magazine House, 72 Broadwick Street, London W1V 2BP.
Tel: 020 7439 5000. Fax: 020 7439 5591. E-mail: contact@goodhousekeeping.co.uk
Editorial Director: Lindsay Nicholson. **Picture Editor:** Laura Meckiff.
General interest magazine for up-market women. Concentrates on home and family life.
Illustrations: Interiors, gardening, food, fashion, travel and reportage. Usually by commission to illustrate specific articles.
Text: Articles of interest to up-market women – interesting homes (with photos), gardening, personality profiles, emotional features, humorous articles, etc.
Overall freelance potential: Good scope for the highest quality material.
Fees: By negotiation.

GRAZIA

Bauer Media, Endeavour House, 189 Shaftesbury Avenue, London WC2H 8JG.
Tel: 020 7437 9011. Fax: 020 7520 6599. E-mail: deborah.brown@graziamagazine.co.uk
Editor: Jane Bruton. **Picture Director:** Deborah Brown.
Britain's first women's glossy to be published on a weekly basis, offering a mixture of celebrity coverage, real life stories, reportage, fashion and beauty.
Illustrations: Pictures of leading personalities at premieres, parties and generally out and about, plus paparazzi street shots. Pictures also required for news section containing hard news with the focus on women's issues and interests alongside celebrity stories. News pictures can be submitted on

spec to graziapics1@graziamagazine.co.uk. Opportunities for experienced workers in portraiture, beauty, still life and interiors; contact the picture director in the first instance with details of prior experience and coverage offered.

Text: Little freelance scope.

Overall freelance potential: Wide range of opportunities for experienced photographers.

Editor's tips: Celebrity coverage must be strictly A list, not C or D list. A short lead time means the magazine goes to press on Friday for sale the following Tuesday.

Fees: By negotiation.

HARPER'S BAZAAR

National Magazine Company Ltd, 72 Broadwick Street, London W1F 9EP.

Tel: 020 7439 5000. Fax: 020 7439 5506.

Editor: Lucy Yeomans. **Picture Director:** Chloe Limpkin. **Picture Editor:** Liz Pearn.

Monthly glossy magazine featuring fashion, design, travel, interiors, beauty and health.

Illustrations: Colour and high-quality B&W. Top quality photography to illustrate subjects as above, only by commission.

Text: General interest features of very high quality. 1,500–3,000 words. Only by commission.

Overall freelance potential: Good for those who can produce the right material.

Fees: Good; on a rising scale according to length of feature.

HELLO!

Hello Ltd, Wellington House, 69/71 Upper Ground, London SE1 9PQ.

Tel: 020 7667 8700. Fax: 020 7667 8711. E-mail: pictures@hellomagazine.com

Editor: Kay Goddard. **Picture Editor:** Freddie Sloan.

Weekly magazine for women covering people and current events.

Illustrations: Pictures and picture stories on personalities and celebrities of all kinds. People in the news and current news events. Off-beat pictures. Dramatic picture stories of bravery, courage or rescue.

Text: Interviews and/or reports to accompany photos.

Overall freelance potential: Excellent for quality material.

Editor's tips: The magazine has short lead times which it likes to exploit to the full – can include late stories in colour up to the Friday of the week before publication.

Fees: By negotiation.

THE LADY

The Lady, 39–40 Bedford Street, Strand, London WC2E 9ER.

Tel: 020 7379 4717. Fax: 020 7836 4620. E-mail: editors@lady.co.uk

Editor: Rachel Johnson. **Picture Editor:** Tamsan Barratt.

Weekly general interest magazine for women.

Illustrations: Photographs only required to accompany particular articles. Covers: Lifestyle images of women aged 35–50 years, travel or occasional famous faces.

Text: Illustrated articles on British and foreign travel, the countryside, human interest, wildlife, pets, cookery, gardening, fashion, beauty, British history and commemorative subjects. 700–850 words.

Overall freelance potential: Excellent for complete illustrated articles.

Fees: Pictures from £18, text £80 per 1,000 words.

LOOK

IPC Media Ltd, Blue Fin Building, 110 Southwark Street, London SE1 0SU.

Tel: 020 3148 5000. E-mail: jo_walker@ipcmedia.com

Editor: Ali Hall. **Picture Editor:** Desney Ryan.

Young women's weekly offering a mix of affordable fashion, celebrity style and gossip, and true life stories.

Illustrations: Mostly by commission. Those seeking fashion or portrait work should make an appointment to show their portfolio. Those experienced in "real-life" work should make initial contact by e-mail. Celebrity images or other material that may be relevant to the target readership will be be considered on spec.

Text: Little scope.

Overall freelance potential: Good opportunities for experienced workers in this field.

Fees: By negotiation.

LOVE IT!

Hubert Burda Media UK, Swan House, 37-39 High Holborn, London WC1V 6AA.

Tel: 0845 481 0661. E-mail: arlene.brown@burdamagazines.co.uk

Editor: Jo Checkley. **Picture Editor:** Arlene Brown. **Deputy Picture Editor:** Verina Durand.

Real life weekly aimed at younger women.

Illustrations: Freelances around the country needed to shoot reportage, portraits and some studio work. Sample portfolios or CDs should be sent by post or e-mail to the picture desk.

Text: Original and exclusive real life stories always required.

Overall freelance potential: Excellent for the experienced worker.

Fees: Dependent on the nature of the job, but full day rate is £350, more typically £250 For shorter shoots.

MARIE CLAIRE

European Magazines Ltd, Blue Fin Building, 110 Southwark Street, London SE1 0SU.

Tel: 020 3148 5000. E-mail: sian_parry@ipcmedia.com

Editor: Trish Halpin. **Picture Editor:** Sian Parry.

Fashion and general interest monthly for sophisticated women in the 25–35 age group.

Illustrations: Top quality fashion, beauty, portraits, reportage, interiors, still life, etc, usually by commission.

Text: In-depth articles, features and profiles aimed at an intelligent readership. Up to 4,000 words.

Overall freelance potential: Very good for experienced contributors in this field.

Fees: By negotiation.

MORE

Bauer Media, Endeavour House, 189 Shaftesbury Avenue, London WC2H 8JG.

Tel: 020 7208 3397. Fax: 020 7208 3595. E-mail: tijen.denizmen@moremagazine.co.uk

Editor: Chantelle Horton. Picture Director: Tijen Denizmen.

Weekly magazine for young women in the 18–24 age group.

Illustrations: Up-to-date news pictures featuring celebrities, formal and informal. Fashion, beauty, health and pictures to illustrate specific articles, always by commission.

Text: Articles and features, often with a practical slant, of general interest to young women. Submit ideas only in the first instance.

Overall freelance potential: Quite good for quality material.

Editor's tips: No unsolicited features – commissions only.

Fees: By negotiation.

NOW

IPC Media Ltd, Blue Fin Building, 110 Southwark Street, London SE1 0SU.

Tel: 020 3148 5000. E-mail: nowpictures@ipcmedia.com

Editor: TBA. **Picture Editor:** Francesca D'Avanzo.

Weekly entertainment for women with the focus on celebrities and "true-life" stories.

Illustrations: Digital files preferred. Topical coverage of current film and TV stars, both formal and informal shots. Some commissions available to illustrate fashion, true-life stories and general features.

Text: Ideas for stories and interviews always considered.

Overall freelance potential: Limited.

Fees: Variable according to the material or assignment; top rates paid for good exclusives.

OK!

Northern & Shell plc, Northern & Shell Building, Number 10 Lower Thames Street, London EC3R 6EN.

Tel: 0871 434 1010. Fax: 0871 520 7766. E-mail: sophie.mutter@express.co.uk

Editor: Lisa Byrne. Picture Director: Tarkan Algin. **Picture Editor:** Sophie Mutter. **Picture Researcher:** Anna Williams.

Weekly, picture-led magazine devoted to celebrity features and news pictures.

Illustrations: Shots of celebrities of all kinds considered on spec, especially exclusives or unpublished archive material. Commissions available to experienced photographers.

Text: Exclusive stories/interviews with celebrities always of interest.

Overall freelance potential: Excellent for the right type of material.

Fees: Negotiable; depends on nature of the material or assignment.

PICK ME UP

IPC Media Ltd, Blue Fin Building, 110 Southwark Street, London SE1 0SU.

Tel: 020 3148 6441. Fax: 020 3148 8112. E-mail: natalie_jones@ipcmedia.com

Editor: June Smith-Sheppard. **Picture Editor:** Natalie Jones.

True life weekly presenting stories more graphically and in more detail than its rivals. Includes a limited amount of health material, but no celebrities.

Illustrations: Happy to hear from capable photographers around the country who are able to shoot stories as they arise. Initial contact should be made in writing, giving details of area covered and of any previous experience in the field.

Text: Suggestions for stories always welcomed, not only UK-based but also from overseas.

Overall freelance potential: Good for experienced contributors in this field.

Editor's tips: More is asked of contributors than is usually the case with real life material. Photographers will be expected to cover more angles, such as going to where an event took place or covering other aspects of a story.

Fees: Variable depending on what the photographer is required to do and how much travel is involved.

PRIMA

National Magazine Company, 72 Broadwick Street, London W1F 9EP.

Tel: 020 7439 5000. Fax: 020 7312 4100. E-mail: jo.lockwood@natmags.co.uk

Editor: Maire Fahey. **Art Director:** Jacqueline Hampsey. **Picture Editor:** Jo Lockwood. **Picture Researcher:** Bianca Topham.

General interest women's monthly with a strong emphasis on practical subjects. Major topics covered include cookery, gardening, crafts, health, fashion and homecare.

Illustrations: Top quality work in the fields of food, fashion, still-life, interiors and portraiture, usually by commission. Some scope for good stock shots of family and domestic situations, food, pets, etc that could be used for general illustration purposes, but query needs before before submitting.

Text: Short, illustrated practical features with a "how-to-do-it" approach.

Overall freelance potential: The magazine relies heavily on freelances.

Fees: Commissioned photography in the region of £400 per day. Other fees according to use.

PSYCHOLOGIES

Hachette Filipacchi (UK) Ltd, 64 North Row, London W1K 7LL.

Tel: 020 7150 7000. Fax: 020 7150 7001. E-mail: liz.simon@hf-uk.com

Editor: Louise Chunn. **Features Editor:** Rebecca Alexander. **Photo Editor:** Liz Simon.

Up-market women's monthly with the focus on "positive living", including topics such as work,

---

Are you working from the latest edition of The Freelance Photographer's Market Handbook? It's published on 1 October each year. Markets are constantly changing, so it pays to have the latest edition

health, family and social issues, travel.

Illustrations: Digital files preferred. Interested in both high-quality stock and in commissioning for specific features. Most images used are lifestyle-based, but relaxed and natural. Also opportunities for top-quality portraiture and beauty images. Initial approach should be by e-mail or telephone.

Text: Possible scope for high-quality lifestyle features.

Overall freelance potential: Good for experienced photographers.

Editor's tips: Examine the magazine closely to get a feel for its style.

Fees: By negotiation.

REAL PEOPLE

ACP-NatMag, 33 Broadwick Street, London W1F 0DQ.

Tel: 020 7439 5000. Fax: 020 7339 4650. E-mail: sue.miles@natmags.co.uk

Editor: Samm Taylor. **Picture Editor:** Sue Miles.

Real life weekly for women.

Illustrations: Requires experienced freelances in all parts of the country who may be available to undertake reportage and portrait shoots to illustrate stories. Initial contact by e-mail is preferred, giving brief details of any previous experience.

Text: Real life stories always required.

Overall freelance potential: Excellent for the experienced worker.

Fees: Around £150–£200 per assignment, depending on the nature of the shoot and rights licensed. Up to £500 for real life stories.

RED

Hachette Filipacchi (UK) Ltd, 64 North Row, London W1K 7LL.

Tel: 020 7150 7000. Fax: 020 7150 7001. E-mail: beverley.croucher@hf-uk.com

Editor: Sam Baker. **Art Director:** Jonathan Whitelocke. **Picture Editor:** Beverley Croucher.

Sophisticated monthly aimed at women in their 30s.

Illustrations: High quality commissioned photography covering portraiture, fashion, interior design, food and celebrities. Telephone to make an appointment to drop off portfolio in the first instance. Little scope for stock material.

Text: Ideas always welcome from experienced writers.

Overall freelance potential: Good for the experienced worker.

Fees: By negotiation.

REVEAL

The National Magazine Company Ltd, 33 Broadwick Street, London W1F 0DQ.

Tel: 020 7339 4524. E-mail: dara.levan-harris@natmags.co.uk

Editor: Jane Ennis. **Picture Editor:** Dara Levan-Harris.

A "five magazines in one" weekly package, with a mix of celebrities, real-life stories, fashion, lifestyle and TV listings.

Pictures: Good scope for celebrity shots, especially paparazzi-style pictures. Happy to hear from freelances if they think they have something, but ideally should be an exclusive. Send an e-mail first rather than sending images. Many opportunities for commissions to shoot celebrity, real-life or lifestyle features.

Text: Good, illustrated real-life stories always being sought; e-mail features.reveal@natmags.co.uk with suggestions.

Overall freelance potential: Excellent for the right type of material.

Fees: Photography by negotiation; £500 upwards for real-life stories.

SHE
National Magazine Company, National Magazine House, 72 Broadwick Street, London W1V 2BP.
Tel: 020 7439 5000. Fax: 020 7439 5350. E-mail: editor@shemagazine.co.uk
Editor: Claire Irvin. **Art Director:** Chris Lupton. **Picture Editor:** Chloe Trayler-Smith.
General interest monthly for the 30-something woman.
Illustrations: Most material by commission for specific articles; anything else only considered by appointment.
Text: Top quality features of interest to intelligent women; suggestions welcomed but always query the editor first.
Overall freelance potential: Little unsolicited material used, but quite good for commissions.
Editor's tips: Please study the content and style before contacting magazine.
Fees: By arrangement.

THAT'S LIFE!
H.Bauer Publishing Ltd, 24-28 Oval Road, London NW1 7DT.
Tel: 020 7241 8000. Fax: 020 7241 8008. E-mail: jim.taylor@bauer.co.uk
Editor: Sophie Hearsey. **Picture Editor:** Matt Wevill.
Popular women's weekly concentrating on true-life stories and confessions.
Illustrations: Mostly commissioned shots of people to accompany stories; photographers who can produce good informal portrait work should write to the picture editor enclosing a couple of samples. Also limited opportunities in fashion, food and still life. Quirky and amusing "readers' pictures" always considered on spec – should be accompanied by a brief story or anecdote.
Text: Personal true-life stories always of interest – shocking, scandalous, embarrassing, tear-jerking, etc. Around 300 words. Contact the editor with suggestions first.
Overall freelance potential: Good.
Fees: Story shoots around £150; readers' pictures £25; other photography by negotiation. £200 for true stories.

WI LIFE
NFWI, 104 New Kings Road, Fulham, London SW6 4LY.
Tel: 020 7731 5777. Fax: 020 7736 4061. E-mail: h&ced@nfwi.org.uk
Editor: Neal Maidment.
Published eight times a year for Women's Institute members, includes WI news and features.
Illustrations: Pictures of WI events, members, craft and cookery projects.
Text: Mostly written in-house.
Overall freelance potential: Modest scope for picture sales.
Editor's tips: Always consult the editor before submitting.
Fees: By agreement.

WOMAN
IPC Media Ltd, Blue Fin Building, 110 Southwark Street, London SE1 0SU.
Tel: 020 3148 5000. E-mail: michelle_filmer@ipcmedia.com
Editor: Karen Livermore. **Picture Editor:** Michelle Filmer.
Weekly magazine devoted to all women's interests.
Illustrations: Most pictures commissioned to illustrate specific features. Some scope for human interest shots which are dramatic, off-beat or unusual.
Text: Interviews with leading personalities, human interest stories. Other features mostly staff-produced. Submit a synopsis in the first instance.
Overall freelance potential: Only for experienced contributors in the field.
Fees: Good; on a rising scale according to size of reproduction or length of articles.

WOMAN & HOME
IPC Media Ltd, Blue Fin Building, 110 Southwark Street, London SE1 0SU.
Tel: 020 3148 5000. Fax: 020 3148 8120. E-mail: sharon_mears@ipcmedia.com
Editor: Sue James. **Picture Editor:** Sharon Mears.
Monthly magazine for all women concerned with family and home.
Illustrations: All photography commissioned from experienced freelances, to illustrate subjects including cookery, fashion, beauty, interior design, DIY, gardening, travel, topical issues and personality articles.
Text: Articles on personalities, either well-known or who lead interesting lives. 1,500 words.
Overall freelance potential: Very good for the experienced worker. Including regular contributors, about 50 per cent of the magazine is produced by freelances.
Fees: By negotiation.

WOMAN'S OWN
IPC Media Ltd, Blue Fin Building, 110 Southwark Street, London SE1 0SU.
Tel: 020 3148 5000. Fax: 020 3148 8112. E-mail: fran_jepps@ipcmedia.com
Editor: Vicky Mayer. **Picture Editor:** Fran Jepps.
Weekly publishing articles and practical features of interest to women.
Illustrations: Mostly commissioned to illustrate features on fashion, interior design, crafts, etc.
Text: Mostly staff-produced. Send a brief outline of any proposed feature in the first instance to the features editor.
Overall freelance potential: Fair for commissioned work, but much is produced by regulars.
Fees: Good; on a rising scale according to size of reproduction or length of article.

WOMAN'S WEEKLY
IPC Media Ltd, Blue Fin Building, 110 Southwark Street, London SE1 0SU.
Tel: 020 3148 6628. E-mail: sue_de_jong@ipcmedia.com
Editor: Diane Kenwood. **Art Editor:** Fiona Watson. **Picture Editor:** Sue De Jong.
General interest family-oriented magazine for women in the 35+ age group.
Illustrations: Mostly by commission to illustrate features on fashion, beauty, cookery, decoration, etc.
Text: Practical features on general women's topics, plus human interest stories and celebrity pieces.
Overall freelance potential: Fairly good for the experienced contributor.
Fees: By negotiation.

NEWSPAPERS

In this section we list the national daily and Sunday newspapers, and their associated magazine supplements. While the supplements may publish a wide range of general interest subject matter, the parent papers are obviously only likely to be interested in hard news pictures and stories of genuine interest to a nationwide readership.

News pictures

Despite the heavy presence of staff and agency photographers at major events, it is still perfectly possible for an independent freelance to get the shot that makes the front page. And when it comes to the unexpected, the freelance is often the only one on the spot to capture the drama.

If you think you have obtained a "hot" news picture or story, the best plan is to telephone the papers most likely to be interested as soon as possible and let them know what you have to offer.

Note that newspapers prefer to work from digital files and will not want to handle transparencies. They will, however, accept colour print or negative if that is all that is available.

In the listings that follow, as well as the main switchboard number you will find direct line telephone numbers which take you directly through to the picture desk of the paper concerned.

There should be little cause to use fax numbers for newspapers these days, but if you do it is advisable to always check the correct number for the department you want. Newspaper offices have numerous fax machines; the numbers listed here are necessarily general editorial numbers and if used without checking might delay your message getting to the department you need.

Other material

There is some scope for other material apart from hard news in most of the papers. Some use the occasional oddity or human interest item as a "filler", while in the tabloids there is always a good market for celebrity pictures.

Finally, of course, there is a market for top quality glamour material of the "Page 3" variety in several of the tabloids.

The supplements operate much like any other general interest magazine. Most of their content is commissioned from well-established photographers and writers, though some will accept exceptional photojournalistic features or exclusives on spec.

Fees

Fees paid by newspapers can vary tremendously according to what is offered and how it is used. However, it can be taken for granted that rates paid by the national papers listed here are good.

Generally, picture fees are calculated on standard rates based on the size of the reproduction, with the minumum fee you might expect from a national newspaper being around £65.

However, for material that is exclusive or exceptional the sky is almost literally the limit. If you think you have something very special and are prepared to offer it as an exclusive, make sure you negotiate a fee, and perhaps get several offers, before committing the material to anyone.

National Daily Newspapers

DAILY EXPRESS
Express Newspapers, 10 Lower Thames Street, London EC3R 6EN.
Tel: 020 8612 7000. Picture desk: 020 8612 7171.
E-mail: expresspix@express.co.uk
Editor: Peter Hill. **Picture Editor:** Neil McCarthy.

DAILY MAIL
The Daily Mail Ltd, Northcliffe House, 2 Derry Street, London W8 5TT.
Tel: 020 7938 6000. Picture desk: 020 7938 6373. Fax: 020 7937 5560.
E-mail: pictures@dailymail.co.uk
Editor: Paul Dacre. **Picture Editor:** Paul Silva.

DAILY MIRROR
Mirror Group Newspapers Ltd, Canary Wharf Tower, 1 Canada Square, London E14 5AP.
Tel: 020 7293 3000. Picture desk: 020 7293 3851. Fax: 020 7293 3983.
E-mail: picturedesk@mirror.co.uk
Editor: Richard Wallace. **Picture Editor:** Ian Down.

DAILY RECORD
The Scottish Daily Record and Sunday Mail Ltd, One Central Quay, Glasgow G3 8DA.
Tel: 0141 309 3000. Picture desk: 0141 309 3245. ISDN: 0141 309 4879.
E-mail: a.baird@dailyrecord.co.uk
Editor: Bruce Waddell. **Picture Editor:** Alasdair Baird.

DAILY SPORT
Sport Newspapers Ltd, 19 Great Ancoats Street, Manchester M60 4BT.
Tel: 0161 236 4466. Picture desk: 0161 238 8169. Fax: 0161 236 4535.
E-mail: pictures@sportnewspapers.co.uk
Editor: Pam McVitie. **Picture Editor:** Paul Currie.

DAILY STAR
Express Newspapers, 10 Lower Thames Street, London EC3R 6EN.
Tel: 020 8612 7000. Picture desk: 020 8612 7382.
E-mail: rob.greener@dailystar.co.uk
Editor: Dawn Neesom. **Picture Editor:** Rob Greener.

THE DAILY TELEGRAPH
Telegraph Media Group, Victoria Plaza, 111 Buckingham Palace Road, London SW1W 0SR.
Tel: 020 7931 2000. Picture desk: 020 7931 2660.
E-mail: photo@telegraph.co.uk
Editor: Tony Gallagher. **Picture Editor:** Kim Scott-Clark.
TELEGRAPH MAGAZINE
Editor: Michele Lavery. **Picture Editor:** Cheryl Newman.

As a member of the Bureau of Freelance Photographers, you'll be kept up-to-date with markets through the BFP Market Newsletter, published monthly. For details of membership, turn to page 9

FINANCIAL TIMES
The Financial Times Ltd, Number One Southwark Bridge, London SE1 9HL.
Tel: 020 7873 3000. Picture desk: 020 7873 3151.
E-mail: jamie.han@ft.com
Editor: Lionel Barber. **Picture Editor:** Jamie Han.

THE GUARDIAN
Kings Place, 90 York Way, London N1 9GU.
Tel: 020 3353 2000. Picture desk: 020 3353 4070.
E-mail: pictures@guardian.co.uk
Editor: Alan Rusbridger. **Picture Editor:** Roger Tooth.
WEEKEND GUARDIAN
Editor: Merope Mills. **Picture Editor:** Kate Edwards.

THE HERALD
200 Renfield Street, Glasgow G2 3QB.
Tel: 0141 302 7000. Picture desk: 0141 302 6668. Fax: 0141 333 1147. ISDN: 0141 302 2101.
E-mail: pictures@theherald.co.uk
Editor: Jonathan Russell. **Picture Editor:** Brodie Duncan.

THE INDEPENDENT
Independent News & Media Plc, Northcliffe House, 2 Derry Street, London W8 5TT.
Tel: 020 7005 2000. Picture desk: 020 7005 2830. Fax: 020 7005 2086.
E-mail: picturedesk@independent.co.uk
Editor: Simon Kelner. **Picture Editor:** Lynn Cullen.
THE INDEPENDENT MAGAZINE
Picture Editor: Nick Hall.

THE SCOTSMAN
The Scotsman Publications Ltd, Barclay House, 108 Holyrood Road, Edinburgh EH8 8AS.
Tel: 0131 620 8620. Picture desk: 0131 620 8560.
E-mail: tspics@scotsman.com
Editor: John McLellan. **Picture Editor:** Andy O'Brien.

THE SUN
News International Newspapers Ltd, 1 Virginia Street, London E98 1SN.
Tel: 020 7782 4000. Picture desk: 020 7782 4199. Fax: 020 7782 4335.
E-mail: pictures@thesun.co.uk; john.edwards@thesun.co.uk
Editor: Dominic Mohan. **Picture Editor:** John Edwards.

THE TIMES
News International Newspapers Ltd, 1 Pennington Street, London E98 1TT.
Tel: 020 7782 5000. Picture desk: 020 7782 5877. Fax: 020 7782 5449.
E-mail: pictures@thetimes.co.uk
Editor James Harding. **Picture Editor:** Paul Sanders.
THE TIMES MAGAZINE
Editor: Louise France. **Picture Editor:** Graham Wood.

National Sunday Newspapers

THE INDEPENDENT ON SUNDAY
Independent News & Media Plc, Northcliffe House, 2 Derry Street, London W8 5TT.
Tel: 020 7005 2000. Picture desk: 020 7005 2837/2828. Fax: 020 7005 2086.
E-mail: picturedesk@independent.co.uk
Editor: John Mullin. **Picture Editor:** Sophie Batterbury.
THE SUNDAY REVIEW
Editor: Lisa Markwell. **Picture Editor:** Hannah Brenchley.

THE MAIL ON SUNDAY
Northcliffe House, 2 Derry Street, Kensington, London W8 5TS.
Tel: 020 7938 6000. Picture desk: 020 7938 7017. Fax: 020 7938 6609.
E-mail: pix@mailonsunday.co.uk
Editor: Peter Wright. **Picture Editor:** Liz Cocks.
YOU MAGAZINE
Editor: Sue Peart. **Picture Editor:** Eve George.
NIGHT & DAY
Editor: Gerard Greaves. **Picture Editor:** Sam Reilly.

NEWS OF THE WORLD
News International Newspapers Ltd, Virginia Street, London E1 9XR.
Tel: 020 7782 4000. Picture desk: 020 7782 4421. Fax: 020 7782 4463.
ISDN: 020 7680 1010/7702 9140. E-mail: nowpicture@newsint.co.uk
Editor: Colin Myler. **Picture Editor:** Paul Ashton.
FABULOUS
Editor: Sally Eyden. **Picture Director:** Kim Mayers.

THE OBSERVER
Kings Place, 90 York Way, London N1 9GU.
Tel: 020 3353 2000. Picture desk: 020 3353 4304. E-mail: picture.desk@observer.co.uk
Editor: John Mulholland. **Picture Editor:** Greg Whitmore.
THE OBSERVER MAGAZINE
Editor: Tim Lewis. **Picture Editors:** Kit Burnet and Matthew Glynn.
OBSERVER FOOD MONTHLY
Editor: Allan Jenkins. **Picture Editor:** Kit Burnet and Matthew Glynn.

THE PEOPLE
Mirror Group plc, 1 Canada Square, Canary Wharf, London E14 5AP.
Tel: 020 7293 3000. Picture desk: 020 7293 3901. Fax: 020 7293 3810.
ISDN: 020 7572 5801 (Easy Transfer); 020 7513 2427 (Foresight).
E-mail: pictures@people.co.uk
Editor: Lloyd Embley. **Picture Editor:** Mark Moylan.
TAKE IT EASY
Editor: Hannah Tavner. **Picture Editor:** TBC.

SCOTLAND ON SUNDAY
The Scotsman Publications Ltd, Barclay House, 108 Holyrood Road, Edinburgh EH8 8AS.
Tel: 0131 620 8438. Fax: 0131 620 8491. ISDN: 0131 556 5379/1230.
E-mail: sospics@scotsman.com
Editor: Ian Stewart. **Picture Editor:** Alan Macdonald.

SUNDAY EXPRESS
Express Newspapers, 10 Lower Thames Street, London EC3R 6EN.
Tel: 020 8612 7000. Picture desk: 020 8612 7172 / 7176.
E-mail: sundayexpresspix@express.co.uk
Editor: Martin Townsend. **Picture Editor:** Terry Evans.
SUNDAY EXPRESS MAGAZINE
Editor: Louise Robinson. **Picture Editor:** Jane Woods.

SUNDAY HERALD
200 Renfield Street, Glasgow G2 3QB.
Tel: 0141 302 7000. Picture desk: 0141 302 7876. Fax: 0141 302 7815. ISDN: 0141 302 2103.
E-mail: sunday.pictures@sundayherald.com
Editor: Richard Walker. **Picture Editor:** Elaine Livingstone.
SUNDAY HERALD MAGAZINE
Editor: Susan Flockhart. **Picture Editor:** Leanne Thompson.

THE SUNDAY MAIL
The Scottish Daily Record and Sunday Mail Ltd, 1 Central Quay, Glasgow G3 8DA.
Tel: 0141 309 7000. Picture desk: 0141 309 3434. Fax: 0141 309 3587.
ISDN: 0141 309 4884/4886. E-mail: a.hosie@sundaymail.co.uk
Editor: Bruce Waddell. **Picture Editor:** Andy Hosie.

SUNDAY MIRROR
Mirror Group plc, 1 Canada Square, Canary Wharf, London E14 5AP.
Tel: 020 7293 3000. Picture desk: 020 7293 3335/6. Fax: 020 7510 6991.
E-mail: pictures@sundaymirror.co.uk
Editor: Tina Weaver. **Picture Editor:** Ivor Game.
CELEBS ON SUNDAY
Editor: Mel Brodie. **Picture Editor:** Jo Aspill.

THE SUNDAY POST
D. C. Thomson & Co Ltd, Courier Place, Dundee DD1 9QJ.
Tel: 01382 223131. Fax: 01382 201064. ISDN: 01382 575935.
E-mail: mail@sundaypost.com
Editor: Domald Martin. **News Editor:** Tom McKay. **Picture Editor:** Alan Morrison.
POST PLUS MAGAZINE
Editor: Jan Gooderham.

SUNDAY SPORT
Sport Newspapers Ltd, 19 Great Ancoats Street, Manchester M60 4BT.
Tel: 0161 236 4466. Picture desk: 0161 238 8169. Fax: 0161 236 4535.
E-mail: paul.currie@sportnewspapers.co.uk
Editor: Nick Appleyard. **Picture Editor:** Paul Currie.

THE SUNDAY TELEGRAPH
Telegraph Media Group, Victoria Plaza, 111 Buckingham Palace Road, London SW1W 0SR.
Tel: 020 7931 2000. Picture desk: 020 7931 3542.
E-mail: stpics@telegraph.co.uk
Editor: Ian McGregor. **Picture Editor:** Mike Spillard.
STELLA
Editor: Anna Murphy.

THE SUNDAY TIMES
Times Newspapers Ltd, 1 Pennington Street, London E98 1ST.
Tel: 020 7782 5000. Picture desk: 020 7782 5666. Fax: 020 7782 5563.
E-mail: pictures@sunday-times.co.uk
Editor: John Witherow. **Picture Editor:** Ray Wells.
THE SUNDAY TIMES MAGAZINE
Editor: Sarah Baxter. **Picture Editor:** Monica Allende.

BOOKS

Books represent a substantial and ever-growing market for the photographer. In an increasingly visual age the market for heavily illustrated books continues to expand, with hundreds of new titles being published every year.

In this section we list major book publishers, and specifically those companies that make considerable use of photographic material.

As well as regular publishers, also included here are book packagers. These are companies that offer a complete editorial production service and specialise in producing books that can be sold as finished packages to publishers internationally. The majority of their products are of the heavily illustrated type, and thus these companies can often present a greater potential market for photographic material than do the mainstream publishers.

Making an approach

In this field the difficulty for the individual freelance is that there is no easy way of knowing who wants what and when.

Obviously book publishers only require pictures of specific subjects when they are currently working on a project requiring such material. Much of the time they will rely heavily on known sources such as picture libraries, but this does not mean that there is not good scope for the individual photographer who has a good collection of material on particular subjects, or who may be able to produce suitable work to order.

The solution for the photographer, therefore, is to place details of what he or she has to offer in front of all those companies that might conceivably require material of that type.

The initial approach is simply to send an introductory letter outlining the sort of material that you can supply. A detailed list of subjects can be attached where appropriate.

There is little point however, in sending any photographs at this stage, unless it be one or two samples to indicate a particular style. And one should not expect an immediate response requesting that work be submitted; most likely the publisher will simply keep your details on file for future reference.

Preceding the listings of book publishers is a subject index that should assist in identifying the most promising markets for those areas in which you have good coverage.

In the listings that follow, the major areas of activity for each publisher are detailed under "Subjects". Of course, the larger companies publish on the widest range of subjects and therefore their coverage may be stated as "general", but in most entries you will find a list of specific subject areas. These are by no means a complete list of all the subjects handled by each publisher, but indicate those areas where the company is most active and therefore most likely to be in need of photographic material.

In some entries a "Contact" name is given. However, in a lot of cases it is not possible to give a specific name as larger book publishers usually have large numbers of editorial personnel with constantly shifting responsibilities for individual projects. In addition, many companies frequently use the services of freelance picture researchers. A general approach should therefore simply be addressed to the editorial director.

Rights and fees

Whereas the rights sold in the magazine world are invariably for UK use only, book publishers – and especially packagers – make a good deal of their profit from selling their products to other publishers in overseas markets.

It is therefore quite likely that when work is chosen for use in a particular book the publisher may at some stage request, in addition to British publishing rights, rights for other areas such as "Commonwealth", "North American", "French language", etc. These differing rights will, of course, affect the fees that the photographer receives – the more areas the book sells into, the higher the fees.

Other major factors affecting fees are the size of reproduction on the page and the quantity of the print-run.

Thus there is no easy way to generalise about the sort of fees paid in this field. On the whole, however, fees in book publishing are quite good and comparable with good magazine rates. For packages destined for the international co-edition market they can be substantially higher.

A word about names and imprints

The use by large publishers of a multiplicity of names for different divisions can be quite confusing.

Many famous publishing names, though still in existence, now belong to huge publishing conglomerates. A few are still run as separate companies, but most have effectively become "imprints".

These imprints are used by large publishers for specific sections of their list. In the past many imprints were run as completely separate operations, but in an age of consolidation most have now been incorporated into their parent company.

Only especially relevant imprints are given full listings here, that is those that are run as separate operations and use photography to any extent. Most imprints are simply listed under their parent company.

Subject Index

Archaeology

Cambridge University Press
The History Press Ltd
Souvenir Press Ltd
Thames & Hudson Ltd

Architecture/Design

Anova Books
Antique Collectors Club Ltd
Cambridge University Press
Robert Hale Ltd
Laurence King Publishing Ltd
Phaidon Press Ltd
RotoVision
Thames & Hudson Ltd
Yale University Press

Arts/Crafts

Anness Publishing
Anova Books
Antique Collectors Club Ltd
Appletree Press
A & C Black (Publishers) Ltd
Breslich & Foss
Cambridge University Press
The Crowood Press
David & Charles Publishing Ltd
Laurence King Publishing Ltd
Ebury Publishing
Focus Publishing
W. Foulsham & Co Ltd
Guild of Master Craftsman Publications Ltd
Robert Hale Ltd
Frances Lincoln Ltd
Lutterworth Press
New Holland Publishers
Octopus Publishing Group Ltd
Orion Publishing Group Ltd
Pan Macmillan
Phaidon Press Ltd
Quarto Group
Reader's Digest Association Ltd
Souvenir Press Ltd
Thames & Hudson Ltd
Usborne Publishing
Virgin Books Ltd

Aviation

Ian Allan Publishing
Amber Books Ltd
The Crowood Press
Grub Street
Osprey Publishing Ltd

DIY

The Crowood Press
Focus Publishing
W. Foulsham & Co Ltd
Haynes Publishing
Orion Publishing Group Ltd
Reader's Digest Association Ltd

Fashion

Anova Books
Laurence King Publishing Ltd
Piatkus Books
Plexus Publishing Ltd
Thames & Hudson Ltd

Food/Drink

Anness Publishing
Anova Books
Kyle Cathie Ltd
Ebury Publishing
Focus Publishing
W. Foulsham & Co Ltd
Grub Street
Robert Hale Ltd
Hodder Headline Ltd
Frances Lincoln Ltd
New Holland Publishers
Octopus Publishing Group Ltd
Orion Publishing Group Ltd
Quarto Group
Reader's Digest Association Ltd
Ryland, Peters & Small
Sheldrake Press
Simon & Schuster
Souvenir Press Ltd

Gardening

Anness Publishing
Antique Collectors' Club Ltd
Breslich & Foss
Kyle Cathie Ltd
The Crowood Press
Focus Publishing
W. Foulsham & Co Ltd
Guild of Master Craftsman Publications Ltd
Hodder Headline Ltd
Frances Lincoln Ltd
New Holland Publishers
Octopus Publishing Group Ltd
Orion Publishing Group Ltd
Pan Macmillan
Quarto Group
Reader's Digest Association Ltd
Ryland, Peters & Small
Souvenir Press Ltd

Health/Medical

Anova Books
Breslich & Foss
Cambridge University Press
Carroll & Brown Publishers
Kyle Cathie Ltd
Constable & Robinson
Ebury Publishing
Focus Publishing
W. Foulsham & Co Ltd
Grub Street
Piatkus Books
Quarto Group
Simon & Schuster
Souvenir Press Ltd
Transworld Publishers

Interior Design

Ebury Publishing
Frances Lincoln Ltd
New Holland Publishers
Octopus Publishing Group Ltd
Orion Publishing Group Ltd
Ryland, Peters & Small
Thames & Hudson

Military

Ian Allan Publishing
Amber Books Ltd
Anova Books

Cassell Military
Constable & Robinson
The Crowood Press
Robert Hale Ltd
The History Press Ltd
Osprey Publishing
Transworld Publishers
Weidenfeld & Nicolson Ltd

Motoring

Ian Allan Publishing
The Crowood Press
Haynes Publishing

Music

Cambridge University Press
Ebury Publishing
Faber & Faber Ltd
Guinness Publishing Ltd
Robert Hale Ltd
Hodder Headline Ltd
Omnibus Press/Book Sales Ltd
Pan Macmillan
Plexus Publishing Ltd
Thames & Hudson
Virgin Books Ltd

Natural History

Appletree Press
A & C Black (Publishers) Ltd
Cambridge University Press
The Crowood Press
Robert Hale Ltd
Christopher Helm Publishers Ltd
Kingfisher Publications
New Holland Publishers
Orion Publishing Group Ltd
T & A D Poyser
Reader's Digest Association Ltd
Souvenir Press Ltd
Usborne Publishing

Photography

David & Charles Publishing Ltd
Derby Books Publishing Ltd
Phaidon Press Ltd
Photographer's Institute Press
RotoVision
Thames & Hudson Ltd

Politics/Current Affairs

Bloomsbury Publishing Ltd
Chatto & Windus
Constable & Robinson
Faber & Faber Ltd
Hutchinson
Pan Macmillan
Yale University Press

Railways

Ian Allan Publishing
The History Press Ltd
Railways – Milepost 92½

Science

Amber Books Ltd
Cambridge University Press
Lutterworth Press
Orion Publishing Group Ltd
Transworld Publishers

Sport

A & C Black (Publishers) Ltd
The Crowood Press
Derby Books Publishing Ltd
Ebury Publishing
Focus Publishing

W. Foulsham & Co Ltd
Guinness Publishing Ltd
Robert Hale Ltd
The History Press Ltd
Hodder Headline Ltd
Octopus Publishing Group Ltd
Orion Publishing Group Ltd
Transworld Publishers
Virgin Books Ltd

Travel

AA Publishing
Amber Books Ltd
Appletree Press
Bloomsbury Publishing Ltd
Cambridge University Press
Chatto & Windus
Constable & Robinson
The Crowood Press
Ebury Publishing
W. Foulsham & Co Ltd
Robert Hale Ltd
Hutchinson
New Holland Publishers
Octopus Publishing Group Ltd
Orion Publishing Group Ltd
Pan Macmillan
Quarto Group
Sheldrake Press
Thames & Hudson Ltd

Book Publishers

AA PUBLISHING
Automobile Association, Fanum House, Basingstoke, Hampshire RG21 2EA.
Tel: 01256 491588. Fax: 01256 492440. E-mail: travelimages@theaa.com
Contact: Ian Little, Head of Picture Library.
Subjects: Travel images for guide books, maps and atlases. Commissions only.

IAN ALLAN PUBLISHING
Riverdene Business Park, Molesey Road, Hersham, Surrey KT12 4RG.
Tel: 01932 266600. Fax: 01932 266601.
Web: www.ianallanpublishing.com
Subjects: Aviation, military, motoring, railways, road transport.

AMBER BOOKS LTD
Bradley's Close, 74-77 White Lion Street, London N1 9PF.
Tel: 020 7520 7600. Fax: 020 7520 7606. E-mail: terry@amberbooks.co.uk
Web: www.amberbooks.co.uk
Contact: Terry Forshaw, Picture Manager.
Subjects: General; aviation, fitness and survival, military, naval, popular science, transport.

ANNESS PUBLISHING LTD
Hermes House 88-89 Blackfriars Road, London SE1 8HA.
Tel: 020 7401 2077. Fax: 020 7633 9499. E-mail: info@anness.com
Web: www.lorenzbooks.com
Contact: Picture Library Manager.
Imprints: Aquamarine, Hermes House, Lorenz Books, Southwater.
Subjects: Crafts, cookery, gardening, health, reference.

ANOVA BOOKS
10 Southcombe Street, London W14 0RA.
Tel: 020 7605 1400. Fax: 020 7605 1401.
Web: www.anovabooks.com
Imprints: Batsford, Collins & Brown, Conway Maritime Press, Pavilion, Robson.
Subjects: General illustrated; architecture, arts & crafts, biography, cookery, fashion, health, military, transport.

ANTIQUE COLLECTORS CLUB LTD
Sandy Lane, Old Martlesham, Woodbridge, Suffolk IP12 4SD.
Tel: 01394 389950. Fax: 01394 389999.
Web: www.antique-acc.com
Contact: Diana Steel, Managing Director (by letter only).
Subjects: Antiques, architecture, art, gardening. (Digital not accepted).

Are you working from the latest edition of The Freelance Photographer's Market Handbook? It's published on 1 October each year. Markets are constantly changing, so it pays to have the latest edition

APPLETREE PRESS LTD
The Old Potato Station, 14 Howard Street South, Belfast BT7 1AP.
Tel: 028 90 243074. Fax: 028 90 246756. E-mail: editorial@appletree.ie
Web: www.appletree.ie
Subjects: Irish and Scottish interest; arts & crafts, cookery, nature, UK travel.

A & C BLACK (PUBLISHERS) LTD
38 Soho Square, London W1D 3HB.
Tel: 020 7758 0200. Fax: 020 7758 0222. E-mail: enquiries@acblack.co.uk
Web: www.acblack.com
Imprints: Adlard Coles Nautical, Christopher Helm, Methuen Drama, T&AD Poyser.
Subjects: Arts and crafts, children's educational, nautical, natural history, reference, sport, theatre.

BLOOMSBURY PUBLISHING PLC
36 Soho Square, London W1D 3QY.
Tel: 020 7494 2111. Fax: 020 7434 0151. E-mail: csm@bloomsbury.com
Web: www.bloomsbury.com
Subjects: General; biography, children's, current affairs, reference, travel.

BRESLICH & FOSS LTD
2a Union Court, 20-22 Union Road, London, SW4 6JP
Tel: 020 7819 3990. Fax: 020 7819 3998. E-mail: sales@breslichfoss.com
Web: www.breslichfoss.co.uk
Contact: Janet Ravenscroft.
Subjects: Arts, children's, crafts, gardening, health, lifestyle.

CAMBRIDGE UNIVERSITY PRESS
The Edinburgh Building, Shaftesbury Road, Cambridge CB2 8RU.
Tel: 01223 312393. Fax: 01223 315052. E-mail: information@cambridge.org
Web: www.cambridge.org
Subjects: Archaeology, architecture, art, astronomy, biology, drama, geography, history, medicine, music, natural history, religion, science, sociology, travel.

CARROLL & BROWN PUBLISHERS LTD
20 Lonsdale Road, London NW6 6RD.
Tel: 020 7372 0900. Fax: 020 7372 0460. E-mail: mail@carrollandbrown.co.uk
Web: www.carrollandbrown.co.uk
Contact: Chrissie Lloyd, Art Director.
Subjects: General illustrated reference, health, parenting.

KYLE CATHIE LTD
122 Arlington Road, London NW1 7HP.
Tel: 020 7692 7215. Fax: 020 7692 7260. E-mail: vicki.murrell@kyle-cathie.com
Web: www.kylecathie.com
Contact: Vicki Murrell, Editorial Assistant.
Subjects: Beauty, food and drink, gardening, health, reference.

CHATTO & WINDUS LTD
Random House, 20 Vauxhall Bridge Road, London SW1V 2SA.
Tel: 020 7840 8540. Fax: 020 7233 6117. E-mail: chattoeditorial@randomhouse.co.uk
Web: www.randomhouse.co.uk
Subjects: General; biography and memoirs, current affairs, history, travel.

THE CROWOOD PRESS LTD
The Stable Block, Crowood Lane, Ramsbury, Marlborough, Wiltshire SN8 2HR.
Tel: 01672 520320. Fax: 01672 520280. E-mail: enquiries@crowood.com
Web: www.crowoodpress.co.uk
Subjects: Angling, aviation, climbing, country interests, crafts, DIY, equestrian, gardening, motoring, military, natural history, sport, travel.

DAVID & CHARLES PUBLISHING LTD
Brunel House, Newton Abbot, Devon TQ12 4PU.
Tel: 01626 323200. Fax: 01626 323317.
Web: www.davidandcharles.co.uk
Contact: Prudence Rogers.
Subjects: Crafts, nostalgia, photography, railways.

DERBY BOOKS PUBLISHING CO LTD
3 The Parker Centre, Mansfield Road, Derby DE21 4SZ.
Tel: 01332 384235. Fax: 01332 292755. E-mail: steve.caron@dbpublishing.co.uk
Web: www.dbpublishing.co.uk
Contact: Steve Caron, Managing Director; Alex Morton, Publishing Manager.
Subjects: Archive photography, British heritage and local history, sport (especially football).

EBURY PUBLISHING
Random House, 20 Vauxhall Bridge Road, London SW1V 2SA.
Tel: 020 7840 8400. Fax: 020 7840 8406. E-mail: eburyeditorial@randomhouse.co.uk
Web: www.eburypublishing.co.uk
Imprints: BBC Books, Ebury Press, Rider, Time Out Guides,Vermilion.
Contact: Vicky Orchard, Editorial Assistant.
Subjects: Biography, cookery, crafts, current affairs, decorating and interiors, health and beauty, history, mind, bidy spirit, music, parenting, sport, travel guides.

FABER & FABER LTD
Bloomsbury House, 74-77 Great Russell Street, London WC1B 3DA.
Tel: 020 7927 3800. Fax: 020 7927 3801. E-mail: gadesign@faber.co.uk
Web: www.faber.co.uk
Contact: Design Department.
Subjects: Biography, film, music, politics, theatre, wine.

FOCUS PUBLISHING (SEVENOAKS) LTD
11A St Botolph's Road, Sevenoaks, Kent TN13 2EB.
Tel: 01732 742456. Fax: 01732 743381. E-mail: info@focus-publishing.co.uk
Web: www.focus-publishing.co.uk
Contact: Guy Crofton, Managing Director.
Subjects: General illustrated; crafts, DIY, food and drink, gardening, health, photography, sport, transport.

W. FOULSHAM & CO
The Oriel, Thames Valley Court, 183-187 Bath Road, Slough, Berkshire SL1 4AA.
Tel: 01753 526769. Fax: 01753 535003. E-mail: marketing@foulsham.com
Web: www.foulsham.com
Contact: Barry Belasco, Managing Director.
Subjects: Crafts, collecting, cookery, DIY, gardening, health, hobbies, sport, travel.

GRUB STREET PUBLISHING
4 Rainham Close, London SW11 6SS.
Tel: 020 7924 3966. Fax: 020 7738 1009. E-mail: post@grubstreet.co.uk
Web: www.grubstreet.co.uk
Subjects: Aviation history, cookery.

GUILD OF MASTER CRAFTSMAN PUBLICATIONS LTD
86 High Street, Lewes, East Sussex BN7 1XN.
Tel: 01273 477374. Fax: 01273 402849.
Web: www.thegmcgroup.com/www.pipress.co.uk
Imprints: Photographers' Institute Press
Contact: Anthony Bailey, Chief Photographer.
Subjects: Crafts; gardening, needlework, photography, woodworking.

GUINNESS WORLD RECORDS LTD
3rd Floor, 184 Drummond Street, London NW1 3HP.
Tel: 020 7891 4567. Fax: 020 7891 4501.
Web: www.guinnessworldrecords.com
Contact: Design Department.
Subjects: Guinness World Records book, TV and merchandising, sport and popular music.

HALDANE MASON
PO Box 34196, London NW10 3YB.
Tel: 020 8459 2131. Fax: 020 8728 1216. E-mail: info@haldanemason.com
Web: www.haldanemason.com
Contact: Ron Samuel, Art Director.
Subjects: Children's illustrated non-fiction.

ROBERT HALE LTD
Clerkenwell House, 45-47 Clerkenwell Green, London EC1R 0HT.
Tel: 020 7251 2661. Fax: 020 7490 4958.
Web: www.halebooks.com
Contact: Nikki Edwards, Non Fiction Editor
Subjects: General; architecture, cookery, crafts, equestrian, gemmology, horology, mind, body and spirit, military, music, natural history, sport, topography, travel.

HARPERCOLLINS PUBLISHERS
77-85 Fulham Palace Road, London W6 8JB.
Tel: 020 8741 7070. Fax: 020 8307 4440. E-mail: enquiries@harpercollins.co.uk
Web: www.harpercollins.co.uk
Imprints: Collins, Fourth Estate, HarperElement, HarperPress, HarperSport, HarperThorsons.
Subjects: General.

HARVILL SECKER
Random House, 20 Vauxhall Bridge Road, London SW1V 2SA.
Tel: 020 7840 8540. Fax: 020 7233 6117. E-mail: harvillseckereditorial@randomhouse.co.uk
Web: www.randomhouse.co.uk
Contact: Lily Richards.
Subjects: General non-fiction.

HAYNES PUBLISHING
Sparkford, Yeovil, Somerset BA22 7JJ.
Tel: 01963 440635. Fax: 01963 440023.
Web: www.haynes.co.uk
Imprints: G.T.Foulis, Patrick Stephens.
Contact: Christine Smith, Adminstration Manager.
Subjects: Transport, DIY.

CHRISTOPHER HELM PUBLISHERS/T&AD POYSER
(Imprints of A&C Black Publishers)
36 Soho Square, London W1D 3QY.
Tel: 020 7758 0200. Fax: 020 7758 0222. E-mail: nredman@acblack.com
Web: www.acblack.com
Contact: Nigel Redman, Commissioning Editor.
Subjects: Ornithology and natural history.

THE HISTORY PRESS LTD
The History Press Ltd, The Mill, Brimscombe Port, Stroud, Gloucestershire GL5 2QG.
Tel: 01453 883300. Fax: 01453 883233. E-mail: submissions@thehistorypress.co.uk
Web: www.thehistorypress.co.uk
Contact: Katie Beard, Head of Design & Origination.
Imprints: Pathfinder, Phillimore, Pitkin, Spellmount, Stadia, Sutton, Tempus.
Subjects: Archaeology, arts, biography, crime, general history, local interest, military, royalty, social history, sport, transport & industrial, walking guides.

HODDER EDUCATION GROUP
338 Euston Road, London NW1 3BH.
Tel: 020 7873 6000. Fax: 020 7873 6325.
Web: www.hodderheadline.co.uk
Contact: Helen Townson, Design Manager.
Subjects: Education including geography, health, history, science, travel.

HODDER HEADLINE LTD
338 Euston Road, London NW1 3BH.
Tel: 020 7873 6000. Fax: 020 7873 6024.
Web: www.hodderheadline.co.uk
Contact: Picture Manager, c/o division.
Imprints: Hachette Children's Books, Headline, Hodder Education, Hodder & Stoughton.
Subjects: General; academic, biography, children's, food and wine, history, music, sport.

HUTCHINSON
Random House, 20 Vauxhall Bridge Road, London SW1V 2SA.
Tel: 020 7840 8564. Fax: 020 7233 6127. E-mail: hutchinsoneditorial@randomhouse.co.uk
Web: www.randomhouse.co.uk
Contact: Sue Freestone.
Subjects: Biography, current affairs, history, travel.

LAURENCE KING PUBLISHING LTD
361–373 City Road, London EC1V 1LR.
Tel: 020 7841 6900. Fax: 020 7841 6969. Web: www.laurenceking.com
Contact: Julia Ruxton, Picture Manager.
Subjects: Arts and architecture, design, fashion. (Digital not accepted).

KINGFISHER PUBLICATIONS
The Macmillan Building, 20 New Wharf Raoad, London N1 9RR.
Tel: 020 7014 4166. E-mail: c.weston-baker@macmillan.co.uk
Web: www.kingfisherpub.com
Contact: Cee Weston-Baker.
Subjects: Children's non-fiction, natural history, reference.

FRANCES LINCOLN LTD
4 Torriano Mews, Torriano Avenue, London NW5 2RZ.
Tel: 020 7284 4009. Fax: 020 7485 0490. E-mail: fl@frances-lincoln.com
Web: www.franceslincoln.com
Contact: Sue Gladstone, Picture Department.
Subjects: General; architecture, art, gardening, travel.

LITTLE, BROWN BOOK GROUP
100 Victoria Embankment, London EC4Y 0DY.
United KingdomTel: 020 7911 8000. Fax: 020 7911 8100. E-mail: info@littlebrown.co.uk
Web: www.littlebrown.co.uk
Imprints: Little, Brown; Abacus; Piatkus; Sphere.
Subjects: General.

THE LUTTERWORTH PRESS
P O Box 60, Cambridge CB1 2NT.
Tel: 01223 350865. Fax: 01223 366951. E-mail: publishing@lutterworth.com
Web: www.lutterworth.com
Contact: Adrian Brink.
Subjects: Antiques, art and architecture, biography, crafts, natural history, reference, religion, science.

NEW HOLLAND PUBLISHERS (UK) LTD
Garfield House, 86-88 Edgware Road, London W2 2EA.
Tel: 020 7724 7773. Fax: 020 7258 1293. E-mail: enquires@nhpub.co.uk
Web: www.newhollandpublishers.com
Subjects: Biography, crafts, cookery, gardening, history, interior design, natural history, sports and outdoor pursuits, travel.

OCTOPUS PUBLISHING GROUP LTD
2-4 Heron Quays, London E14 4JP.
Tel: 020 7531 8400. Fax: 020 7531 8650. E-mail: info@octopus-publishing.co.uk
Web: www.octopus-publishing.co.uk
Imprints: Cassell Illustrated, Conran Octopus, Gaia Books, Godsfield Press, Hamlyn, Mitchell Beazley.
Subjects: Illustrated general reference and non-fiction.

OMNIBUS PRESS/MUSIC SALES LTD
14-15 Berners Street, London W1T 3LJ.
Tel: 020 7612 7400. Fax: 020 7612 7545.
Contact: Chris Charlesworth, Editor; Jacqui Black, Picture Researcher.
Subjects: Rock, pop and classical music.

ORION PUBLISHING GROUP LTD
Orion House, 5 Upper St Martin's Lane, London WC2H 9EA.
Tel: 020 7240 3444. Fax: 020 7240 4822.
Web: www.orionbooks.co.uk
Contact: Design Department.
Imprints: Orion; Gollancz; Weidenfeld & Nicolson; Cassell Military; Halban Publishers; Allen & Unwin.
Subjects: General; biography, cookery, design, gardening, history, interiors, natural history, popular science, sport, travel.

OSPREY PUBLISHING LTD
Midland House, West Way, Botley, Oxford OX2 0HP.
Tel: 01865 727022. Fax: 01865 727017. E-mail: editorial@ospreypublishing.com
Web: www.ospreypublishing.com
Contact: Kate Moore, Publisher.
Subjects: Illustrated military history and aviation.

OXFORD UNIVERSITY PRESS
Great Clarendon Street, Oxford OX2 6DP.
Tel: 01865 556767. Fax: 01865 556646.
Web: www.oup.co.uk
Imprints: Clarendon Press, Oxford Paperbacks.
Subjects: General; academic, educational, reference.

PAN MACMILLAN
20 New Wharf Road, London N1 9RR.
Tel: 020 7014 6000. Fax: 020 7014 6001. E-mail: nonfiction@macmillan.co.uk
Web: www.panmacmillan.com
Imprints: Boxtree, Macmillan, Pan, Picador, Sidgwick & Jackson.
Subjects: General; biography, crafts, current affairs, gardening, music, popular history, practical, travel.

PENGUIN GROUP (UK)
80 Strand, London WC2R 0RL.
Tel: 020 7010 3000. Fax: 020 7010 3294. E-mail: lesley.hodgson@uk.penguingroup.com
Web: www.penguin.co.uk
Imprints: Allen Lane, Hamish Hamilton, Michael Joseph, Penguin, Viking.
Contacts: Lesley Hodgson, Samantha Johnson (Picture Editors).
Subjects: General.

PHAIDON PRESS LTD
Regent's Wharf, All Saints Street, London N1 9PA.
Tel: 020 7843 1000. Fax: 020 7843 1010. E-mail: enquiries@phaidon.com
Web: www.phaidon.com
Subjects: Architecture, decorative and fine arts, design, photography.

PHOTOGRAPHERS' INSTITUTE PRESS
(Imprint of GMC Publications)
166 High Street, Lewes, East Sussex BN7 1XN.
Tel: 01273 477374. Fax: 01273 402849. E-mail: jonathonb@thegmcgroup.com
Web: www.pipress.co.uk
Contact: Jonathan Bailey, Associate Publisher.
Subjects: Photography.

PIATKUS BOOKS LTD
Little, Brown Book Group, 100 Victoria Embankment, London EC4Y 0DY.
Tel: 020 7911 8000. Fax: 020 7911 8100. E-mail: info@littlebrown.co.uk
Web: www.piatkus.co.uk
Contact: Managing Editor.
Subjects: Biography, health, leisure, lifestyle, mind body & spirit, popular culture, women's interests.

PLAYNE BOOKS LTD
Park Court Barn, Trefin, Haverfordwest, Pembrokeshire SA62 5AU.
Tel: 01348 837073. Fax: 01348 837063. E-mail: info@playne.books.co.uk
Web: www.playnebooks.co.uk
Contact: Gill Davies, Editorial Director.
Subjects: General illustrated books for adults and children.

PLEXUS PUBLISHING LTD
25 Mallinson Road, London SW11 1BW.
Tel: 020 7924 4662. Fax: 020 7924 5096. E-mail: info@plexusuk.demon.co.uk
Web: www.plexusbooks.com
Contact: Sandra Wake, Editorial Director.
Subjects: Biography, fashion, film, music, popular culture.

THE QUARTO GROUP
26 City Road, London EC1V 2TT.
Tel: 020 7700 9000. Fax: 020 7253 4437. E-mail: info@quarto.com
Web: www.quarto.com
Contact: Caroline Guest, Art Director.
Subjects: General; arts and crafts, cookery, gardening, health, home interest, new age, reference, travel.

RAILWAYS – MILEPOST 92½
Newton Harcourt, Leicestershire LE8 9FH.
Tel: 0116 259 2068. E-mail: studio@railphotolibrary.com
Contacts: Colin Garratt, Director; Colin Nash, Picture Library Manager.
Subjects: Railways worldwide – past and present.

RANDOM HOUSE UK LTD
Random House, 20 Vauxhall Bridge Road, London SW1V 2SA.
Tel: 020 7840 8400. Fax: 020 7233 8791.
Web: www.randomhouse.co.uk
Contact: Suzanne Dean, Creative Director.
Imprints: Bodley Head, Jonathan Cape, Century, Chatto & Windus, Harvill Secker, William Heinemann, Hutchinson, Pimlico, Yellow Jersey.
Subjects: Various; see individual imprints.

READER'S DIGEST ASSOCIATION
11 Westferry Circus, Canary Wharf, London E14 1HE.
Tel: 020 7715 8000. Fax: 020 7715 8181.
Web: www.readersdigest.co.uk
Subjects: General illustrated; cookery, crafts, DIY, encyclopaedias, folklore, gardening, guide books, history, natural history.

ROTOVISION
Sheridan House, 112-116 Western Road, Hove BN3 1DD.
Tel: 01273 727268. Fax: 01273 727269. E-mail: isheetam@rotovision.com
Web: www.rotovision.com
Contact: Isheeta Mustafi, Commissioning Editor.
Subjects: Design, photography.

ROUTLEDGE
2 Park Square, Milton Park, Abingdon, Oxon OX14 4RN.
Tel: 020 7017 6000. Fax: 020 7017 6699.
Web: www.routledge.com
Contact: Design Department.
Subjects: Built environment, education, humanities, nursing and health, social sciences.

RYLAND PETERS & SMALL LTD
20-21 Jockey's Fields, London WC1R 4BW.
Tel: 020 7025 2200. Fax: 020 7025 2201. E-mail: leslie.harrington@rps.co.uk
Web: www.rylandpeters.com
Contact: Leslie Harrington, Art Director.
Subjects: Body and soul, food and drink, gift, home and garden.

SHELDRAKE PRESS LTD
188 Cavendish Road, London SW12 0DA.
Tel: 020 8675 1767. Fax: 020 8675 7736. E-mail: jsr@sheldrakepress.demon.co.uk
Web: www.sheldrakepress.co.uk
Contact: Simon Rigge, Publisher.
Subjects: Cookery, history, travel.

SHIRE PUBLICATIONS
Midland House, West Way, Botley, Oxford OX2 0HP.
Tel: 01865 727022. Fax: 01865 727017. E-mail: editorial@shirebooks.co.uk
Web: www.shirebooks.co.uk
Contact: Nick Wright, Publisher.
Subjects: Art & antiques, archaeology,history and motoring.

SIMON & SCHUSTER
1st Floor, 222 Gray's Inn Road, London, WC1X 8HB.
Tel: 020 7316 1900. Fax: 020 7316 0332. E-mail: Editorial.enquiries@simonandschuster.co.uk
Web: www.simonandschuster.co.uk
Imprints: Simon & Schuster, Pocket Books.
Subjects: Biography, cookery, health, history, self-help, childrens books and lifestyle.

SOUVENIR PRESS LTD
43 Great Russell Street, London WC1B 3PD.
Tel: 020 7580 9307. Fax: 020 7580 5064. E-mail: souvenirpress@ukonline.co.uk
Subjects: General; archaelogy, art, animals, childcare, cookery, gardening, health, hobbies, plants, practical, sociology.

As a member of the Bureau of Freelance Photographers, you'll be kept up-to-date with markets through the BFP Market Newsletter, published monthly. For details of membership, turn to page 9

THAMES & HUDSON LTD
181a High Holborn, London WC1V 7QX.
Tel: 020 7845 5000. Fax: 020 7845 5050. E-mail: s.ruston@thameshudson.co.uk
Web: www.thamesandhudson.com
Contact: Sam Ruston, Head of Picture Research.
Subjects: Art, architecture, archaeology, anthropology, cinema, fashion, interior design, music, photography, practical guides, religion and mythology, theatre, travel.

TOUCAN BOOKS LTD
3rd Floor, 89 Charterhouse Street, London EC1M 6HR.
Tel: 020 7250 3388. Fax: 020 7250 3123. E-mail: info@toucanbooks.co.uk
Web: www.toucanbooks.co.uk
Contact: Christine Vincent, Picture Manager
Subjects: General illustrated.

TRANSWORLD PUBLISHERS
61-63 Uxbridge Road, London W5 5SA.
Tel: 020 8579 2652. Fax: 020 8579 5479. E-mail: info@transworld-publishers.co.uk
Web: www.transworld-publishers.co.uk
Imprints: Bantam, Doubleday, Expert.
Subjects: General non-fiction; biography, food & drink, health, military, music, popular science, social history, sport, travel.

USBORNE PUBLISHING
83-85 Saffron Hill, London EC1N 8RT.
Tel: 020 7430 2800. Fax: 020 7242 0974. E-mail: mail@usborne.co.uk
Web: www.usborne.com
Contacts: Steve Wright; Mary Cartwright.
Subjects: General children's; crafts, natural history, practical, reference.

VIRGIN BOOKS LTD
Random House, 20 Vauxhall Bridge Road, London SW1V 2SA.
Tel: 020 7840 8352. E-mail: lstevens@virgin-books.co.uk
Web: www.virgin-books.co.uk
Contacts: Lucy Stevens (design department), Louisa Joyner, Editorial Director.
Subjects: Biography, current affairs, health, lifestyle, music, sport.

WEIDENFELD & NICOLSON LTD
Orion House, 5 Upper St Martin's Lane, London WC2H 9EA.
Tel: 020 7240 3444. Fax: 020 7240 4822.
Web: www.orionbooks.co.uk
Imprints: Cassell Military, Weidenfeld.
Subjects: Biography, history, military.

YALE UNIVERSITY PRESS
47 Bedford Square, London WC1B 3DP.
Tel: 020 7079 4900. Fax: 020 7079 4901. E-mail: x.x@yaleup.co.uk
Web: www.yalebooks.co.uk
Contact: Picture Manager.
Subjects: Architecture, art, history, politics, sociology.

CARDS, CALENDARS, POSTERS & PRINTS

This section lists publishers of postcards, greetings cards, calendars, posters and prints, along with their requirements. There is some overlap here, with many of the companies listed producing a range of products that fall into more than one of these categories,

With the exception of traditional viewcard producers, who have always offered rather meagre rates for freelance material, fees in this area are generally good. However, only those who can produce precisely what is required as far as subject matter, quality and format are concerned, are likely to succeed.

Market requirements

While digital is generally accepted here, a number of companies continue to express a preference for transparencies – particularly large format such as 6x7cm or 6x9cm.

But whether it's digital or film, the need for material of the highest quality cannot be too strongly emphasised. The market is highly specialised with very specific requirements. If you aim to break into this field, you must be very sure of your photographic technique. You must be able to produce professional quality material that is pin sharp and perfectly exposed with excellent colour saturation.

You must also know and be able to supply *exactly* what the market requires. The listings will help you, but you should also carry out your own field study by examining the photographic products on general sale.

After a period in the doldrums the photographic greetings card has been making something of a comeback in recent years. Neverthless, the big mass-market card publishers still employ mostly art or graphics. Those that do use photography tend to be smaller, specialised companies, many of them publishing a full range of photographic products. These companies also use a lot of work from top photographers or picture libraries, which means that there is greater competition than ever to supply material for these products.

The calendar market is equally demanding, though fortunately there are still large numbers of calendars using photographs being produced every year. Many calendar producers obtain the material they need from picture agencies, but this is not to say that individual photographers cannot successfully break into this field. Once again, though, you must be sure of your photographic technique and be able to produce really top quality work.

Make a point of studying the cards, calendars or posters that you see on general sale or hanging up in places you visit. Don't rely solely on what *you* think would make a good card or calendar picture; familiarise yourself with the type of pictures actually being used by these publishers.

Finally, it is worth noting that whilst many firms will consider submissions at any time, some in the calendar or greetings card market only select material at certain times of the year or when they are renewing their range. So when contemplating an approach to one of these firms, always check first to see if they are accepting submissions at the time.

Rights and fees

Where provided by the company concerned, fee guidelines are quoted. Some companies prefer to negotiate fees individually, depending upon the type of material you offer. If you are new to this field, the best plan is to make your submission (preferably after making an initial enquiry, outlining the material you have available) and let the company concerned make you an offer. Generally speaking, you should not accept less than about £75 for Greetings Card or Calendar Rights.

Remember, you are not selling your copyright for this fee; you are free to submit the same photograph to any *non-competitive* market (for example, a magazine) at a later date. But you should not attempt to sell the picture to another greetings card publisher once you have sold Greetings Card Rights to a competing firm.

CHRIS ANDREWS PUBLICATIONS LTD
15 Curtis Yard, North Hinksey Lane, Oxford OX2 0LX.
Tel: 01865 723404. Fax: 01865 725294. E-mail: chris.andrews1@btclick.com
Web: www.cap-ox.co.uk
Contact: Chris Andrews (Proprietor).
Products: Calendars, postcards, guidebooks, diaries, address books.
Requirements: Atmospheric colour images of recognisable places (towns, villages) throughout central England, specifically the Cotswolds, Oxfordshire, Cherwell Valley, Thames and Chilterns. Expanding range now covers London, the Thames, Isle of Wight, Windsor/Eton, Portsmouth/Gosport, Bristol, Winchester, Gloucester and York. Winterscapes especially welcome. Photographs not required for immediate use may be accepted into the Oxford Picture Library which is run in parallel.
Formats: Digital files on CD/DVD.
Fees: By negotiation.

THOMAS BENACCI
Unit 12, Bessemer Park, 250 Milkwood Road, London SE24 0HG.
Tel: 020 7924 0635. Fax: 020 7924 0636. E-mail: thomasbenacciltd@btconnect.com
Web: www.thomasbenacci.co.uk
Contact: Massimo Carminati (Manager).
Products: Postcards.
Requirements: Always interested in new views of London for sale to the tourist market – landmarks, scenes and buildings that are easily recognisable or interesting to tourists. Images should be bright and lively.
Formats: All considered.
Fees: £50 for postcard rights.

GB EYE LTD
1 Russell Street, Kelham Island, Sheffield S3 8RW.
Tel: 0114 292 0088. E-mail: mike@gbeye.com
Web: www.gbeye.com
Contact: Mike Cunsolo (Creative Executive).
Products: Posters, prints, postcard packs, 3D lenticulars, badges, stickers, etc.
Requirements: Pin-up type images of youth-culture celebrities – contemporary pop stars, young film and TV actors/actresses, popular young sports stars. Colour or B&W, but must have immediate appeal to the youth market. Also open to new ideas for possible generic subjects – landscapes, animals, humour, etc.
Formats: 35mm transparencies considered but medium format preferred. Digital accepted, 32x45cm at 300dpi.
Fees: Negotiable.

HALLMARK CARDS PLC
Bingley Road, Heaton, Bradford BD9 6SD.
Tel: 01274 252000. Fax: 01274 252675.
Web: www.hallmark.co.uk
Contact: (Studio Manager).
Products: Greetings cards, postcards, giftwrap.
Requirements: Will consider any images suitable for these products.
Formats: All considered.
Fees: Dependent on work and use.

IMAGES & EDITIONS LTD/OTTER HOUSE LTD
Water Lane, Haven Banks, Exeter EX2 8BY.
Tel: 01392 427 333. E-mail: m.jennings@ottherhouse.co.uk

Web: www.images-editions.co.uk/www.otterhouse.co.uk
Contact: Michelle Jennings (Art Studio Manager).
Products: Greetings cards, calendars and stationery.
Requirements: Will consider British landscapes and wildlife, domestic pets (especially cats, dogs, horses), florals, transport, travel.
Formats: Digital files preferred, transparencies considered.
Fees: By negotiation for purchase or on royalty basis.

INDIGO ART LTD

Indigo House, Brunswick Place, Liverpool L20 8DT.
Tel: 0151 933 9779. Fax: 0151 922 1524. E-mail: info@indigoart.co.uk
Web: www.indigoart.co.uk
Contact: Dave Bertram (Proprietor).
Products: Large-scale display prints for use in interior design projects.
Requirements: Striking colour or B&W images with a modern/contemporary look. Wide variety of styles considered: abstracts, close-ups, experimentation with light, angles or digital manipulation. Work in series preferred. See the Indigo Collection on website for current range of styles. Submission guidelines are available for download.
Formats: Digital (20–50MB), transparencies, prints or high-res scans (50MB).
Fees: On a royalties basis, 10% of wholesale print price.

INFOCADO

Gooch's Court, Stamford, Lincs PE9 2RE.
Tel: 01780 481498Fax: 01780 766031. E-mail: submissions@infocado.co.uk
Web: www.infocado.co.uk
Contact: Brian Oliver (General Manager).
Products: Calendars.
Requirements: Anything depicting "the true character of Britain". British countryside; architecture and heritage; flowers and gardens; animals both domestic and wild, natural and humorous; transport.
Formats: Digital submissions only (50MB TIFF). See website for full submission guidelines.
Fees: Subject to negotiation.

JUDGES POSTCARDS LTD

176 Bexhill Road, St Leonard's on Sea, East Sussex TN38 8BN.
Tel: 01424 710377. Fax: 01424 438538. E-mail: michelle.renno@judges.co.uk
Web: www.judges.co.uk
Contact: Michelle Renno (Product Co-ordinator).
Products: Postcards, calendars, greetings cards.
Requirements: Images of England and Wales, local and regional, appealing to the tourist industry. Must be bright, sunny and vibrant. Landscapes, flowers, animals and any other imagery may be considered.
Formats: Film and digital. Small JPEG files may be sent for viewing purposes. Final digital submission must be to A3 at 300dpi, TIFFs in CMYK (convert RGB before submitting). Prefer unretouched original files.
Fees: Dependent on quality and quantity.

KARDORAMA LTD

PO Box 85, Potters Bar, Herts EN6 5AD.
Tel: 01707 271710.
Web: www.kardorama.co.uk
Contact: Brian Elwood (Managing Director).
Products: Postcards.
Requirements: Always seeking new views of London – major tourist sights or subjects that tourists

would consider typical such as red buses, phone boxes, policemen, taxis, etc. Should be good record shots but with "a hint of romance" and plenty of detail in the main subject. Also, humorous images, any subject or location providing the image needs no explanation, but must be sharp and well exposed under good lighting conditions.

Formats: Digital files preferred (with print copy); 35mm and medium format transparencies also considered.

Fees: Variable, depending on quality of work, subject matter and quantities

PHOTODIMENSION
600 Liverpool Road, Ainsdale, Southport PR8 3BQ.
Tel: 07840 918131. E-mail: ian@photodimension.co.uk
Web: www.photodimension.co.uk
Contact: Ian Homewood (Proprietor).
Products: Limited edition fine art and canvas prints, sold via website.
Requirements: Top quality images suitable for large format decoration and wall display in hotels, bars, businesses or homes. Any subject considered but mainly landscapes, florals, abstracts, architecture, portraiture, wildlife/captive animals, sports/action, documentary and photographic art. Must be eligible for limited edition sales.
Formats: Digital files, JPEGs sized to A3 at 300dpi.
Fees: 75 per cent of net sale profit (after printing, shipping and transaction costs) to the photographer.

PINEAPPLE PARK LTD
Unit 9, Henlow Trading Estate, Henlow, Bedfordshire, SG16 6DS.
Tel: 01462 814817. Fax: 01462 819443. E-mail: sarah@pineapplepark.co.uk
Web: www.pineapplepark.co.uk
Contact: Sarah M Parker (Director).
Products: Greetings cards.
Requirements: Seek high quality colour images of: 1) Florals – contemporary and traditional needed for female-orientated range of greetings cards. Country kitchen type arrangements including china, country dressers etc also needed. 2) Male subjects, eg collection of wine bottles, sporting items, cars etc for male-orientated greetings cards. 3) Gardens and gardening.
Formats: Digital files or colour transparencies. Check website for submission details.
Fees: By negotiation, for worldwide greetings card rights.

PORTFOLIO COLLECTION LTD
105 Golborne Road, London W10 5NL.
Tel: 020 8960 1826/3051. Fax: 020 8960 6570. E-mail: jayne@portfoliocards.com
Contact: Jayne Diggory (Director).
Products: Greetings cards and posters.
Requirements: Specialists in creative black and white photography. Strong, contemporary, expressive images – landscapes, cityscapes, people, etc. Also nostalgic images from the '60s and '70s – pop stars, swinging London, flower power, etc.
Formats: Prints from 10x8in up.
Fees: Usually on royalty basis at 12 per cent of distribution price. Flat fees may be negotiated.

Are you working from the latest edition of The Freelance Photographer s Market Handbook? It s published on 1 October each year. Markets are constantly changing, so it pays to have the latest edition

---

NIGEL QUINEY PUBLICATIONS
Cloudesley House, Shire Hill, Saffron Walden, Essex CB11 3FB.
Tel: 01799 520200. Fax: 01799 520100. E-mail: abutterworth@nigelquiney.com
Web: www.nigelquiney.com
Contact: Alison Butterworth (Creative Director).
Products: Greetings cards.
Requirements: Top quality colour images of animals (domestic and wild) in humorous or interesting situations, and florals – bright, modern, contemporary. Will also consider images suitable for anniversary, new baby, etc.
Formats: Digital files.
Fees: Dependent on product/design, for world rights for five years.

RIVERSIDE CARDS
Jubilee Way, Grange Moor, Wakefield WF4 4TD.
Tel: 01924 840500. Fax: 01924 840600. E-mail: design@riversidecards.com
Web: www.riversidecards.com
Contact: Design Studio.
Products: Greetings cards.
Requirements: B&W and colour images of cute domestic animals (kittens, puppies, etc), landscapes, seascapes, countryside scenes, artistic/natural florals, dramatic/atmospheric sunsets and sunrise.
Formats: Any considered including digital files (low-res JPEG for initial submission; high res TIFF required once order confirmed).
Fees: By negotiation.

ROSE OF COLCHESTER LTD
Clough Road, Severalls Industrial Park, Colchester CO4 9QT.
Tel: 01206 844500. Fax: 01206 845872. E-mail: simon@rosecalendars.co.uk
Web: www.rosecalendars.co.uk/www.reeve-calendars.com
Contact: Simon Williams (Publishing Manager).
Products: Calendars for business promotion.
Requirements: British and worldwide landscapes and wildlife. Also glamour, classic cars and supercars, adventure sport. Submit January for annual selection process, but material accepted throughout the year.
Formats: Full resolution files from high-end digital cameras or professional scans from medium and large format transparencies. All files must have accurate metadata embedded detailing subject matter, with exact location for scenic submissions.
Fees: Negotiable depending on subject matter.

SANTORO GRAPHICS
Rotunda Point, 11 Hartfield Crescent, Wimbledon, London SW19 3RL.
Tel: 020 8781 1100. Fax: 020 8781 1101. E-mail: submissions@santorographics.com
Web: santorographics.com
Contact: J. Freeman
Products: Postcards and greetings cards.
Requirements: Striking and attractive images appealing to the typical young poster and card buyer: nostalgic, retro, contemporary, romantic, humorous and cute images of people, animals and situations. B&W a speciality, but colour images in contemporary styles are also sought.
Formats: Any considered.
Fees: By negotiation for worldwide rights.

AGENCIES

Picture libraries and agencies are in the business of selling pictures. They are not in the business of teaching photography or advising photographers how to produce saleable work – although they can sometimes prove remarkably helpful in the latter respect to those who show promise. Their purpose is strictly a business one: to meet the demand for stock pictures from such markets as magazine and book publishers, advertising agencies, travel operators, greetings card and calendar publishers, and many more.

Many photographers look upon an agency as a last resort; they have been unable to sell their photographs themselves, so they think they might as well try unloading them on an agency. This is the wrong attitude. No agency will succeed in placing pictures which are quite simply unmarketable. In any event, the photographer who has had at least some success in selling pictures is in a far better position to approach an agency.

Agency requirements

If you hope to interest an agency in your work, you must be able to produce pictures which the agency feels are likely to sell to one of their markets. Although the acceptance of your work by an agency is no guarantee that it will sell, an efficient agency certainly will not clutter up its files with pictures which do not stand a reasonably good chance of finding a market.

Agents handle pictures of every subject under the sun. Some specialise in particular subjects – sport, natural history, etc – while others act as general agencies, covering the whole spectrum of subject matter. Any photograph that could be published in one form or another is a suitable picture for an agency.

Even if you eventually decide that you want to place all your potentially saleable material with an agency, you cannot expect to leave every aspect of the business to them. You must continue to study the market, watching for trends; you must continue to study published pictures.

For example, if your speciality is travel material, you should use every opportunity to study the type of pictures published in current travel brochures and other markets using such material. Only by doing this – by being aware of the market – can you hope to continue to provide your agency with marketable pictures.

Nowadays agencies do most of their business online and maintain extensive websites displaying the images they hold. Though some still accept film images, most only want digitally-captured images or high-resolution scans.

Although agency websites are primarily aimed at potential picture buyers, they are equally valuable to the photographer considering an approach since they give a good indication of the type of subject and style of work the agency handles.

Commission and licensing

Agencies generally work on a commission basis, 50 per cent being the most usual rate – if they receive £100 for reproduction rights in a picture, the photographer gets £50 of this. Some agencies have more variable rates, depending on who handles keywording, scanning, etc should these be required.

The percentage taken may seem high, but it should be remembered that a picture agency, like any other business, has substantial overheads to account for.

There can also be high costs involved in making prospective buyers aware of the pictures that are available. Some larger agencies produce lavish colour catalogues featuring selections of their best pictures, while smaller agencies regularly send out flyers. All are involved in constantly maintaining and updating their websites.

Agencies do not normally sell pictures outright. As would the individual photographer, they merely sell reproduction rights, the image being licensed to the buyer for a specific purpose. Images may be licensed by size of reproduction, by territory in which they are published, by the medium in which they are reproduced, by time and/or quantity of reproductions, and can be exclusive or non-exclusive. Selling in this way is known as "rights-managed" licensing.

Other forms of selling undertaken by certain agencies are "royalty-free" and "microstock". Under these methods images are sold for a flat fee and pre-licensed for a specified range of uses. Fees are generally low, but this disadvantage may be offset by multiple sales of the same image.

A long-term investment

When dealing with a photographer for the first time, most agencies require a minimum initial submission – which can consist of anything from a few to 500 or more pictures. Most also stipulate that you must keep your material with them for a minimum period of anything from one to five years.

When an agency takes on the work of a new photographer, they are involved in a lot of work – categorising, filing, keywording, cross-indexing and more.

The next step will be to make it known to picture buyers that these new pictures are available, perhaps including reproductions of them in any new catalogues or publicity material and getting an initial selection onto the website.

Having been involved in all this work and expense, it is not unreasonable for them to want to be given a fair chance to market the pictures. If the photographer were able to demand the withdrawal of the images after only a few months, the agency will have been involved in a lot of work and expense for nothing.

Dealing with an agency must therefore be considered a long-term investment. Having initially placed, say, a few hundred pictures with an agency, it could be at least several months before any are selected by a picture buyer, and even longer before any monies are seen by the photographer.

Normally, the photographer will also be expected to regularly submit new material to the library. Indeed, only when you have several hundred pictures lodged with the library can you hope for regular sales – and a reasonable return on your investment.

Making an approach

When considering placing work with an agency, the best plan is to make an initial short-list of those that seem most appropriate to your work.

Then contact the agency or agencies of your choice outlining the material you have available. It may also be worth mentioning details of any sales you have made yourself. If an agency is interested they will probably ask that you first post or e-mail some samples to them. Later they may suggest an appointment when you can bring a wider selection material to show them in person.

But remember that there is little point in approaching an agency until you have a sizeable collection of potentially saleable material. Most will not feel it worth their while dealing with a photographer who has only a dozen or so marketable pictures to offer – it just wouldn't be worth all the work and expense involved. And the chance of the photographer seeing a worthwhile return on just a dozen pictures placed with an agency are remote indeed; you'd be lucky to see more than one cheque in ten years!

In the listings that follow you'll find information on established agencies seeking work from new contributors: the subjects they handle, the markets they supply, the formats they stock, their terms of business (including any minimum submission quantity and minimum retention period), and their standard commission charged on sales.

Prefacing the listings you'll find an Agency Subject Index. This is a guide to agencies which have a special interest in those subjects, though many other agencies may also cover the same subjects within their general stock.

Remember: simply placing material with an agency doesn't guarantee sales. And no agency can sell material for which there is no market. On the other hand, if you are able to produce good quality, marketable work, and can team up with the right agency, you could see a very worthwhile return from this association.

An asterisk against an agency name in the main listings indicates membership of the British Association of Picture Libraries & Agencies (BAPLA).

Subject Index

Aerial

Geo Aerial Photography
Skyscan Photolibrary

Agriculture

Ecoscene
NHPA/Photoshot
Oxford Scientific (OSF) Ltd
Panos Pictures
Papilio
Royal Geographical Society Picture Library

Architecture

Arcblue
Loop Images
View Pictures Ltd
Elizabeth Whiting & Associates

Botanical/Gardens

FLPA – Images of Nature
Garden Picture Library
Garden World Images
NHPA/Photoshot
Natural Science Photos
Oxford Scientific (OSF) Ltd
Papilio
PictureNature
Shorelark
Elizabeth Whiting & Associates
TTL Plus

Business/Industry

Eye Ubiquitous
Footprint Images
Leslie Garland Picture Library
Getty Images
Robert Harding World Imagery
Impact Photos
Link Picture Library
Newscast Ltd
Photolibrary.com
Panos Pictures
Picturebank Photo Library Ltd
SCR Photo Library
StockScotland.com

Food/Drink

Bubbles Photo Library
Eyecatchers
Food Features
Foodanddrinkphotos.com
Fresh Food Images
Stockfood Ltd
Travel Ink
Elizabeth Whiting & Associates

General (all subjects)

Adams Picture Library
Alamy
Art Directors/TRIP Photo Library
Corbis
Eye Ubiquitous
Getty Images
Robert Harding World Imagery
Imagestate
Photoshot
Pictures Colour Library
TheImagefile.com

Geography/Environment

Allan Cash Picture Library
Ecoscene
Eye Ubiquitous
FLPA – Images of Nature
Impact Photos
Link Picture Library
NHPA/Photoshot
Natural Science Photos
Oxford Scientific (OSF) Ltd
Panos Pictures
Papilio
Picturebank Photo Library Ltd
Royal Geographical Society Picture Library
SCR Photo Library

Glamour

Camera Press Ltd
Picturebank Photo Library Ltd

Historical

Bridgeman Art Library
Royal Geographical Society Picture Library

Landscapes

Arcangel Images
Collections
Cornish Picture Library
Epicscotland
Fotomaze
Loop Images
NHPA/Photoshot
Oxford Scientific (OSF) Ltd
PictureNature
Shorelark
StockScotland
TTL Plus

Music

Arena PAL
Camera Press Ltd
Capital Pictures
Famous
Getty Images
Jazz Index Photo Library
Lebrecht Photo Library
Retna Pictures Ltd

News/Current Affairs

Camera Press Ltd
Express Syndication
Getty Images News & Sport
London Media Press
Press Association Images
Rex Features Ltd
World Picture News
Zenith Image Library

People/Lifestyle

Allan Cash Picture Library
Bizarre Archive
Latitude Stock
PYMCA
Picturebank Photo Library Ltd
Photolibrary.com
Photofusion Picture Library
Retna Pictures Ltd
Shorelark
Socialstock

Personalities/Celebrities

Big Pictures
Camera Press Ltd

Capital Pictures
Eyevine
Express Syndication
Famous
Getty Images News & Sport
Lebrecht Photo Library
London Media Press
Newscast Ltd
Nunn Syndication
Press Association Images
Retna Pictures Ltd
Rex Features Ltd
Writer Pictures

Science/Technology

Camera Press Ltd
Oxford Scientific (OSF) Ltd
Picturebank Photo Library Ltd
Science Photo Library

Social Documentary

Allan Cash Picture Library
Arkreligion
Bubbles Photo Library
Collections
E & E Image Library
Eye Ubiquitous
Impact Photos
Link Picture Library
PYMCA
Panos Pictures
Photofusion Picture Library
Socialstock
Zenith Image Library

Sport

Action Images Ltd
Getty Images News & Sport
Kos Picture Source Ltd
Photolibrary.com
Press Association Images
Skishoot
Skyscan Photolibrary

Transport

Alvey & Towers
Cody Images
Railphotolibrary.com
Skyscan Photolibrary
Slick Stock Images

Travel/Tourist

Andalucia Plus Image Library
Andes Press Agency
Allan Cash Picture Library
Eye Ubiquitous
Eyecatchers
Footprint Images
Fresh Food Images
Kos Picture Source Ltd
Latitude Stock
Photolibrary.com
Picturebank Photo Library Ltd
Pictures Colour Library
Skishoot
Spectrum Colour Library
The Travel Library
World Pictures/Photoshot

Underwater

FLPA – Images of Nature
Kos Picture Source Ltd
Natural Science Photos
Oxford Scientific (OSF) Ltd
Papilio
PictureNature

Wildlife

FLPA – Images of Nature
NHPA/Photoshot
Natural Science Photos
Oxford Scientific (OSF) Ltd
Papilio
PictureNature
TTL Plus

ACTION IMAGES*
1st Floor, Aldgate House, 33 Aldgate High Street, London EC3N 1DL.
Tel: 0845 155 6352 E-mail: info@actionimages.com
Web: www.actionimages.com
Contact: Gavin Clay (Head of Photography and Assignments).
Specialist subjects/requirements: High quality sports pictures, especially of any unusual or spectacular incident.
Markets supplied: Newspapers, magazines, books, etc.
Formats accepted: Digital only; minimum 18MB files.
Usual terms of business: No minimum initial submission, but phone first to discuss possible submissions.
Commission: Negotiable.
Additional information: Operates as the specialist sports arm of the Reuters news agency.

ADAMS PICTURE LIBRARY (APL)*
The Studio, Hillside Cottage, Hessenford, Cornwall PL11 3HH.
Tel: 01503 240475. Fax: 01503 240890. E-mail: tam@adamspicturelibrary.com
Web: www.adamspicturelibrary.com
Contact: Dave Jarvis, Tamsyn Jarvis (Partners).
Specialist subjects/requirements: All subjects, with special interest in retro fashion.
Markets supplied: All markets including advertising, publishing, calendars and posters.
Formats accepted: Digital files preferred (50MB).
Usual terms of business: Minimum initial submission: 100 images. Minimum retention period:
 5 years; 1 year's notice required for withdrawal.
Commission: 50 per cent (for exclusive images).

ALAMY*
127 Milton Park, Abingdon, Oxon OX14 4SA.
Tel: 01235 844640. Fax: 01235 844650. E-mail: memberservices@alamy.com
Web: www.alamy.com
Contact: Alan Capel (Head of Content); Alexandra Bortkiewicz (Director of Photography).
Specialist subjects/requirements: Quality images of all subjects – business, lifestyle, travel, vacations, sports, food, abstracts, concepts, still life, science, wildlife, people, celebrities, historical, reportage.
Markets supplied: Advertising, design, corporate and publishing worldwide.
Formats accepted: Digital files only, usually 48–70MB uncompressed RGB JPEG. See website for full technical requirements.
Usual terms of business: Requires initial test submission of four images; if accepted no minimum submission applies.
Commission: 60 per cent to photographer.
Additional information: Photographers must supply their own digital files and keywording. Alamy do not edit photographers' submissions but files are checked for technical accuracy before being allowed online. For initial approach first register on the website.

ALVEY & TOWERS*
The Springboard Centre, Mantle Lane, Coalville, Leicestershire LE67 3DW.
Tel/fax: 01530 450011. E-mail: office@alveyandtowers.com
Web: www.alveyandtowers.com
Contact: Emma Rowen (Library Manager).
Specialist subjects/requirements: All aspects of transport, air, sea and land, including associated industries and issues worldwide.

Markets supplied: Advertising, books, magazines, corporate brochures, calendars, audio visual.
Formats accepted: Digital only.
Usual terms of business: On application.
Commission: 40 per cent.
Additional information: It is essential that potential contributors make contact prior to making any submission in order to discuss precise requirements. Submission guidelines available via e-mail.

ANDES PRESS AGENCY
26 Padbury Court, London E2 7EH.
Tel: 020 7613 5417. Fax: 020 7739 3159. E-mail: photos@andespressagency.com
Web: www.andespressagency.com
Contact: Val Baker (Picture Editor).
Specialist subjects/requirements: Latin America, including the Caribbean; world religions.
Markets supplied: Books, newspapers, magazines.
Formats accepted: All considered.
Usual terms of business: Minimum initial submission: 100 transparencies. Minimum retention period: 3 years.
Commission: By negotiation.

ARCANGEL IMAGES LTD
Apartado 528, Calle Las Mimosas 85, Campo Mijas, Mijas Costa, 29649, Malaga, Spain.
Tel: 0871 218 1023. E-mail: submissions@arcangel-images.com
Web: www.arcangel-images.com
Contact: Michael Mascaro (Director).
Specialist subjects/requirements: creative and fine art imagery, from nudes to landscapes and with the emphasis on digital capture. Will consider all types of images and styles, from general high-quality stock to personal fine art work.
Markets supplied: Book publishing, music industry, design companies, etc.
Formats accepted: Digital files only (minimum 17MB, preferred 30-40MB).
Usual terms of business: Minimum initial submission: 20 accepted images. Minimum retention period: 3 years.
Commission: 50 per cent.
Additional information: British/Spanish company with head office in Spain. Prefer initial approach by e-mail with a few sample images (totalling no more than 500KB) or a link to a personal website.

ARCBLUE*
93 Gainsborough Road, Richmond, Surrey TW9 2ET.
Tel: 020 8940 2227. Fax: 020 8940 6570. E-mail: info@arcblue.com
Web: www.arcblue.com
Contact: Peter Durant (Library Manager).
Specialist subjects/requirements: Modern contemporary architecture and built environment. Also interiors and landscape.
Markets supplied: General publishing, advertising and design.
Formats accepted: Digital (60MB RGB TIFF).
Usual terms of business: Minimum initial submission: 30 images. Minimum retention period: 2 years.
Commission: 40 per cent.
Additional information: Prefer to see coherent sets of images that work together as well as individually. Send sample set of images in the first instance by e-mail, preferably 20–50 images in digital format.

ARENA PAL*

Thompson House, 42-44 Dolben Street, London SE1 0UQ.

Tel: 020 7403 8542. Fax: 020 7403 8561. E-mail: enquiries@arenapal.com

Web: www.arenapal.com

Contact: Mike Markiewicz (Submissions & Archive Manager).

Specialist subjects/requirements: Performing arts, the entertainment industry and relevant personalities – theatre, music, dance, opera, jazz, TV, film, circus, festivals and venues.

Markets supplied: All media including publishing, arts bodies, advertising, design companies.

Formats accepted: All formats, digital files preferred.

Usual terms of business: No minimum initial submission, but expect around 100 images. Minimum retention period: 3 years.

Commission: 50 per cent.

ARKRELIGION.COM*

57 Burdon Lane, Cheam, Surrey SM2 7BY.

Tel: 020 8642 3593. Fax: 020 8395 7230. E-mail: images@artdirectors.co.uk

Web: www.arkreligion.com

Contact: Helene Rogers (Partner).

Specialist subjects/requirements: All religions worldwide, mainstream to alternate, ceremonies from birth to death, festivals and important events, people (priests, pilgrims, worshippers), artefacts, churches/temples, holy books, worship, meals and food, daily rituals.

Markets supplied: Advertising and editorial.

Formats accepted: All formats, but digital preferred (minimum 50MB 8-bit TIFF).

Usual terms of business: Minimum initial submission: 100 images. Minimum retention period: 3 years.

Commission: 50 per cent.

Additional information: Photographers' Guidelines can be viewed on the website.

ART DIRECTORS/TRIP PHOTO LIBRARY*

57 Burdon Lane, Cheam, Surrey SM2 7BY.

Tel: 020 8642 3593. Fax: 020 8395 7230. E-mail: images@artdirectors.co.uk

Web: www.artdirectors.co.uk

Contact: Bob Turner (Partner).

Specialist subjects/requirements: All subjects and all locations. Art Directors supplies images mainly for advertising; TRIP handles general travel material and in-depth, extensive coverage of all religions.

Markets supplied: Advertising and editorial.

Formats accepted: All formats; digital preferred (minimum 50MB 8-bit TIFF).

Usual terms of business: Minimum initial submission: 100 images. Minimum retention period: 3 years.

Commission: 50 per cent.

Additional information: Ask for Photographers' Guidelines or view them on website.

BIG PICTURES*

50-54 Clerkenwell Road, London EC1M 5PS.

Tel: 020 7250 3555. Fax: 020 7250 0033. E-mail: production@bigpictures.co.uk

Web: www.bigpictures.co.uk/www.mrpaparazzi.com

Contact: Tomasina Brittain (Picture Editor).

Specialist subjects/requirements: Current, well-known and preferably A-list celebrities, mainly informal paparazzi material.

Markets supplied: News media and magazines worldwide.

Formats accepted: Digital files preferred.
Usual terms of business: No minimum submission. Minimum retention period: Exclusive worldwide sales licence for 90 days.
Commission: 50 per cent, or outright purchase.
Additional information: Urgent images can be quickly uploaded via the agency's "Mr Paparazzi" website.

BIZARRE ARCHIVE
30 Cleveland Street, London W1T 4JD.
Tel: 020 7907 6485. E-mail: tom@bizarrearchive.com
Web: www.bizarrearchive.com
Contact: Tom Broadbent (Director).
Specialist subjects/requirements: Photo features on anything weird, quirky or bizarre – pin-up girls, alternative models, fetish and sex material, sideshows, bizarre people, odd animals, lowbrow artists, underground clubs, self-made freaks, alternative fashion, eccentric lifestyles and individuals, extreme tattoos and body modification, counterculture icons of music, performance and film.
Markets supplied: Magazines, newspapers and websites worldwide.
Formats accepted: Digital files preferred.
Usual terms of business: No minimum initial submission. Minimum retention period: None stated.
Commission: 50 per cent.
Additional information: Also stocks, syndicates and sells on material published in Bizarre magazine.

BRIDGEMAN ART LIBRARY*
17-19 Garway Road, London W2 4PH.
Tel: 020 7727 4065. Fax: 020 7792 8509. E-mail: info@bridgeman.co.uk
Web: www.bridgeman.co.uk
Contact: Adrian Gibbs (Collections Manager).
Specialist subjects/requirements: American, European and Oriental paintings and prints, antiques, antiquities, arms and armour, botanical subjects, ethnography, general historical subjects and personalities, maps and manuscripts, natural history, topography, transport, etc.
Markets supplied: Publishing, advertising, television, greetings cards, calendars, etc.
Formats accepted: Minimum 5x4in transparencies or 50MB digital files (RGB TIFF).
Usual terms of business: No minimum initial submission. Retention period negotiable.
Commission: 50 per cent.

BUBBLES PHOTO LIBRARY*
3 Rose Lane, Ipswich IP1 1XE.
Tel: 01473 288605. E-mail: info@bubblesphotolibrary.co.uk
Web: www.bubblesphotolibrary.co.uk
Contact: Sarah Robinson, Loisjoy Thurstun (Partners).
Specialist subjects/requirements: Babies, children, pregnancy, mothercare, child development, education (especially aspects of multiculturalism), teenagers, old age, family life, women's health and medical, still lives of food, vegetables, herbs, etc.
Markets supplied: Books, magazines, newspapers and advertising.
Formats accepted: All formats but digital files preferred (A3 at 300dpi)
Usual terms of business: Minimum initial submission: 100 images. Regular contributions expected. Minimum retention period: 3 years.
Commission: 50 per cent.
Additional information: Attractive women and children sell best. Always looking for multicultural and multiracial children/adults. Photographers must pay close attention to selecting models that are healthy-looking and ensure that backgrounds are uncluttered. Best clothes to wear are light coloured and neutral fashion.

CAMERA PRESS LTD*
21 Queen Elizabeth Street, London SE1 2PD.
Tel: 020 7378 1300. Fax: 020 7407 2635. E-mail: j.wald@camerapress.com
Web: www.camerapress.com
Contact: Jacqui Ann Wald (Editorial Director).
Specialist subjects/requirements: Photographs and illustrated features covering celebrity and personality portraiture, news, reportage, humour, music, food, fashion, beauty and interiors.
Formats accepted: Digital preferred (min 30MB) but scanning still undertaken.
Usual terms of business: By mutual agreement.
Commission: 50 per cent.

CAPITAL PICTURES*
85 Randolph Avenue, London W9 1DL.
Tel: 020 7286 2212. E-mail: sales@capitalpictures.com
Web: www.capitalpictures.com
Contact: Phil Loftus (Manager).
Specialist subjects/requirements: Celebrities and personalities from the worlds of showbusiness, film and TV, rock and pop, politics and royalty.
Markets supplied: UK and international magazines, newspapers, etc.
Formats accepted: Digital only.
Usual terms of business: Minimum initial submission: 100 images. Minimum retention period: 1 year.
Commission: 50 per cent.

THE ALLAN CASH PICTURE LIBRARY*
21 Ceylon Road, London W14 0PY.
Tel: 020 7371 2224. E-mail: david@allancashpicturelibrary.com
Web: www.allancashpicturelibrary.com
Contact: David Bromley (Manager).
Specialist subjects/requirements: Travel and documentary photography from around the world, including culture, industry, native peoples, nature, landmarks and historical images.
Markets supplied: Magazines, newspapers, advertising, travel trade.
Formats accepted: Digital files and film negatives.
Usual terms of business: Minimum initial submission: 100 images. Minimum retention period: 3 months.
Commission: 50 per cent.
Additional information: The library is based on the lifetime's work, covering over 75 countries, of the renowned 20th century travel photographer James Allan Cash FRPS, FIBP.

CLOWNFISHPHOTO
20 Millersdale Drive, West Bromwich, West Midlands B71 3PX.
E-mail: info@clownfishphoto.co.uk
Web: www.clownfishphoto.co.uk
Contact: Craig Stephens (Director).
Specialist subjects/requirements: Displays photographers' personal work for online sales of prints, posters and other items direct to the public. Also markets images to publishing contacts worldwide.
Markets supplied: General public and commercial/publishing industry.
Formats accepted: Digital only. Images for display to be no more than 15MB; if and when an image is sold the agency will contact the photographer and advise what size, format and resolution is required.

Usual terms of business: Minimum six month subscription. No image retention period.
Commission: Photographer receives 80 per cent on sales to commercial clients, 100 per cent on sales to the public.
Additional information: There is a monthly subscription fee of £3.00 for photographers. Subscribers have access to sales reports and hit count statistics for each of their uploaded images enabling monitoring and management of portfolio to maximise sales.

CODY IMAGES*
2 Reform Street, Beith KA15 2AE.
Tel: 0845 2235451. Fax: 0845 2235452. E-mail: ted@codymages.com
Web: www.codyimages.com
Contact: Ted Nevill (Director).
Specialist subjects/requirements: All aspects of aviation and defence – worldwide, historical and modern.
Markets supplied: Books, magazines, newspapers, multi-media, etc.
Formats accepted: All formats, digital files preferred.
Usual terms of business: Minimum initial submission: 200 images. Minimum retention period: 3 years.
Commission: 50 per cent.
Additional information: Ring first to discuss submission and agency requirements.

COLLECTIONS*
13 Woodberry Crescent, London N10 1PJ.
Tel: 020 8883 0083. Fax: 020 8883 9215. E-mail: sal.shuel@btinternet.com
Web: www.collectionspicturelibrary.com/www.collectionspicturelibrary.co.uk
Contact: Brian, Sal and Simon Shuel (Directors).
Specialist subjects: The British Isles and Ireland.
Markets supplied: All, particularly on the editorial side.
Formats accepted: All formats, digital preferred (min 26MB), will consider transparencies and B&W prints, but only in exceptional circumstances
Usual terms of business: By arrangement; "easy going and on the side of the contributor."
Commission: 50 per cent.
Additional information: The library aims to stock quality pictures of as many places, things, happenings on these islands as possible.

CORBIS*
111 Salusbury Road, London NW6 6RG.
Tel: 020 7644 7644. Fax: 020 7644 7645. E-mail: info@corbis.com
Web: www.corbis.com
Contact: Vanessa Kramer (Director of Artistic Relations).
Specialist subjects/requirements: General library handling most subjects, on both a licensed and royalty-free basis.
Markets supplied: Advertising, publishing, design, etc.
Formats accepted: Digital files only, minimum 10MB (current events) or 50MB (editorial/advertising).
Usual terms of business: Minimum initial submission variable. Minimum retention period: 3 years.
Commission: 20–50 per cent, depending on client and use.
Additional information: For detailed contributor submission information see http://studioplus.corbis.com

CORNISH PICTURE LIBRARY*
40b Fore Street, St Columb Major, Cornwall TR9 6RH.
Tel: 01637 880103. E-mail: paul@imageclick.co.uk

Web: www.imageclick.co.uk
Contact: Paul Watts (Proprietor).
Specialist subjects/requirements: Cornwall and the West Country (Devon, Dorset, Somerset, Wiltshire, Isles of Scilly, Channel Isles) – landscapes, historic sites, gardens, people, activities, attractions, wildlife.
Markets supplied: Magazines, books, tourism, etc.
Formats accepted: Digital files from 10MP cameras upwards, minimum 30MB TIFF; must be colour correct preferably with Adobe 1998 profile and with full picture details and keywords in metadata. Top quality medium format or larger transparencies accepted; no 35mm. B&W archive (pre-1960) images of Cornwall.
Usual terms of business: No minimum submission. Minimum retention period: 5 years.
Commission: 50 per cent.
Additional information: Contact by e-mail to request contributors' guidelines before sending submission. Browse website for more info and to view images already held; very similar images not required, only better shots or different views.

THE DEFENCE PICTURE LIBRARY LTD

14 Howeson Court, Mary Seacole Road, The Millfields Business Park, Plymouth PL1 3JY.
Tel: 01752 312061. Fax: 01752 312063. E-mail: dpl@defencepictures.com
Web: www.defencepictures.com
Contact: David Reynolds (Director).
Specialist subjects/requirements: Military images covering all aspects of the armed forces worldwide, in training and on operations. Pictures of UK and international forces across the globe are always of interest.
Markets supplied: Publishers, advertising agencies, national media.
Formats accepted: High-resolution TIFF files preferred, 35mm and medium format trasparencies accepted.
Usual terms of business: Minimum initial submission: 50 quality images. Minimum retention period: 5 years.
Commission: 50 per cent.
Additional information: The library is the UK's leading specialist source of military and defence images.

E & E IMAGE LIBRARY*

Beggars Roost, Woolpack Hill, Brabourne Lees, Nr Ashford, Kent TN25 6RR.
Tel: 01303 812608. E-mail: info@eeimages.co.uk
Web: www.eeimages.co.uk
Contact: Isobel Sindon (Proprietor).
Specialist subjects/requirements: World religions, festivals, manuscripts/illustrations, Biblelands, stained glass, architecture, places of interest, heritage, death (ceremonies, funerals, burials), eccentricities/oddities, transport, nature.
Markets supplied: General publishing, newspapers, TV, merchandising.
Formats accepted: Digital files preferred, with full caption and keywords.
Usual terms of business: Minimum initial submission: 50 images; less if specialist subject matter. Minimum retention period: 5 years.
Commission: 50 per cent.

ECOSCENE*

Empire Farm, Throop Road, Templecombe, Somerset BA8 0HR.
Tel: 01963 371700. E-mail: sally@ecoscene.com
Web: www.ecoscene.com
Contact: Sally Morgan (Proprietor).
Specialist subjects/requirements: Environmental issues worldwide including agriculture, conservation, energy, pollution, transport, sustainable development.

Markets supplied: Books, magazines, organisations, etc.
Formats accepted: Digital files at 50MB.
Usual terms of business: Minimum initial submission: 100 quality images. Minimum retention period: 4 years.
Commission: 55 per cent to photographer.
Additional information: Contributors' guidelines available on request – can also be found on the library's website along with details of specific current requirements.

EPICSCOTLAND
Unit 5, Hathaway Business Centre, 21-29 Hathaway Street, Glasgow G20 8TD.
Tel: 0141 945 0000. Email: info@epicscotland.com
Web: www.epicscotland.com
Contact: Emily Bevan-Pritchard (Picture Editor).
Specialist subjects/requirements: All aspects of Scotland and Scottish life.
Markets supplied: Newspapers, magazines, publishers, design agencies.
Formats accepted: All formats but digital preferred, above 20MB and of high quality.
Usual terms of business: No minimum terms.
Commission: 50 per cent.
Additional information: No submitting without prior contact. Digital files must be checked by e-mail before submission.

EXPRESS SYNDICATION
The Northern & Shell Building, 10 Lower Thames Street, London EC3R 6EN.
Tel: 0870 211 7884. Fax: 0870 211 7871. E-mail: mark.swift@express.co.uk
Web: www.expresspictures.com
Contact: Mark Swift (Syndication Manager).
Specialist subjects/requirements: Current news, features and personalities.
Markets supplied: Magazines and newspapers, UK and overseas.
Formats accepted: All formats.
Usual terms of business: Minimum retention period: 90 days.
Commission: 50 per cent.
Additional information: Represents the Daily and Sunday Express, Daily Star and OK! magazine as well as freelance photographers and other agencies.

EYE UBIQUITOUS & HUTCHISON*
65 Brighton Road, Shoreham, West Sussex BN43 6RE.
Tel: 01273 440113. Fax: 01273 440116. E-mail: library@eyeubiquitous.com
Web: www.eyeubiquitous.com
Contacts: Paul Seheult (Proprietor), Stephen Rafferty (Library Manager).
Specialist subjects/requirements: Material suitable for the travel/tourist industry (scenics, resorts, beaches, major sights), plus general stock and social documentary material (people, lifestyles, work, environment, etc). Also incorporates the Hutchison Picture Library offering in-depth documentary coverage of indigenous cultures worldwide.
Markets supplied: Publishing markets, travel industry, UK and European advertising agencies.
Formats accepted: Digital (50MB TIFF) or colour transparency.
Usual terms of business: Suggested minimum submission 200 images, but terms open to discussion.
Commission: 40 per cent.
Additional information: The collections are run as separate entities, though contributing photographers may have work with more than one.

EYECATCHERS
3 Cobden Road, Midhurst, West Sussex GU29 9JW.
Tel: 01730 812976. E-mail: info@eyecatchersphotopix.com

Web: www. eyecatchersphotopix.com
Contact: Antony Lynn-Hill (Director).
Specialist subjects/requirements: Food and drink, lifestyle images, wildlife, backgrounds, travel, London.
Markets supplied: Magazine and book publishers, web design, advertising.
Formats accepted: Digital.
Usual terms of business: Images are offered on a non-exclusive basis and may be withdrawn by giving 14 days notice in writing.
Commission: 80 per cent to photographer on monthly turnover of up to £1,000; 70 per cent on turnover of £1,000 – £3,000.
Additional information: All sales are on a royalty-free basis but the agency was specifically created to offer photographers a better deal than can be found with other RF-only agencies.

EYEVINE
3 Mills Studios,Three Mill Lane, London E3 3DU.
Tel: 020 8709 8709. E-mail: info@eyevine.com
Web: www.eyevine.com
Contact: Graham Cross (Director).
Specialist subjects/requirements: Portraiture, news and reportage.
Markets supplied: Worldwide editorial publishing (newspapers, magazines, books etc).
Formats accepted: Digital files preferred, minimum 30MB RGB JPEG. Colour/B&W print or transparency also accepted.
Usual terms of business: Minimum initial submission: 1 image. Minimum retention period: 3 years.
Commission rate: 50 per cent.
Additional information: Although a news, feature, personalities and assignments agency we are only looking to take on portraiture at this stage. See website for further information.

FLPA – IMAGES OF NATURE*
Pages Green House, Wetheringsett, Stowmarket, Suffolk IP14 5QA.
Tel: 01728 860789. Fax: 01728 860222. E-mail: pictures@flpa-images.co.uk
Web: www.flpa-images.co.uk
Contact: Jean Hosking, David Hosking (Directors).
Specialist subjects/requirements: Natural history and weather phenomena: birds, clouds, fish, fungi, insects, mammals, pollution, rainbows, reptiles, sea, snow, seasons, trees, underwater, hurricanes, earthquakes, lightning, volcanoes, dew, rain, fog, etc. Ecology and the environment. Horse, dog and cat breeds.
Markets supplied: Book publishers, advertising agencies, magazines.
Formats accepted: Digital files at 50MB (contact agency for guidelines).
Usual terms of business: Minimum initial submission: 20 images for evaluation. Minimum retention period: 4 years.
Commission: 50 per cent.
Additional information: Competition in the natural history field is fierce, so only really sharp, well-composed pictures are needed. Sales are slow to start with, and a really keen photographer must be prepared to invest money in building up stock to the 1,000 mark.

FAMOUS*
13 Harwood Road, London SW6 4QP.
Tel: 020 7731 9333. Fax: 020 7731 9330. E-mail: info@famous.uk.com
Web: www.famous.uk.com
Contact: Rob Howard (Managing Director).
Specialist subjects/requirements: Celebrity photographs, especially personalities in the TV, movie, music, fashion and Royal fields. Taken in any situation: red carpet, paparazzi, party, performance, studio and at home.

Markets supplied: General press and publishing.
Formats accepted: Digital only.
Usual terms of business: No minimum submission or retention period.
Commission: 50 per cent.
Additional information: Always looking for photographers who can supply relevant pictures fast.

FOOD FEATURES*
Beaconhurst, Chestnut Walk,Tangmere,West Sussex, PO20 2HH
Tel: 01243 532240. E-mail: frontdesk@foodpix.co.uk
Web: www.foodfeatures.net
Contact: Steve Moss, Alex Barker (Partners).
Specialist subjects/requirements: Food and drink, especially images involving people – dining, cooking, dinner parties, al fresco, chefs, etc.
Markets supplied: Publishing, advertising, etc.
Formats accepted: Digital files preferred, 30MB minimum, 50MB preferred. 35mm transparencies acceptable for location shots but larger formats preferred.
Usual terms of business: No minimum initial submission. Minimum retention period: 3 years.
Commission: By agreement.

FOODANDDRINKPHOTOS.COM*
Studio 4, Sun Studios, 30 Warple Way, London W3 0RX.
Tel: 020 8740 6610. Fax: 020 8762 9994. E-mail: info@foodanddrinkphotos.com
Web: www.foodanddrinkphotos.com
Contact: Charles Montgomery (Library Manager).
Specialist subjects/requirements: All food and drink related photography, all styles, both traditional and more conceptual.
Markets supplied: Editorial, advertising and design.
Formats accepted: Transparencies or digital files (35–80MB).
usual terms of business: Minimum initial submission: 20 images. Minimum retention period: 3 years.
Commission rate: 50 per cent.
Additional information: Transparencies scanned for free and digitised to high resolution.

FOOTPRINT IMAGES
PO Box 4610, Warwick CV34 9EY.
Tel: 0207 193 1192. E-mail: contributors@footprintimages.com
Web: www.footprintimages.com
Contact: Glyn Thomas, Mike Finn-Kelcey (Partners).
Specialist subjects/requirements: Travel, business, wildlife and conceptual/abstract photography.
Markets supplied: General publishing, advertising.
Formats accepted: Digital; minimum 2400 pixels on longest dimension.
Usual terms of business: Minimum initial submission: 10 sample images. No minimum retention period. Non-exclusive contract.
Commission: 65 per cent to photographer if images fully captioned and keyworded; otherwise 50 per cent.
Additional information: Prospective contributors can register on the website where there are full submission details or send initial samples via e-mail. Rights-managed sales only.

As a member of the Bureau of Freelance Photographers, you'll be kept up-to-date with markets through the BFP Market Newsletter, published monthly. For details of membership, turn to page 9

FOTOMAZE

12 Penlee Street, Penzance, Cornwall TR18 2DE.
Tel: 01736 350192. E-mail: admin@fotomaze.com
Web: www.fotomaze.com
Contact: Lee Searle (Managing Director).
Specialist subjects/requirements: All Cornwall-related subjects – landscapes, seascapes, lifestyle, music, etc. Also creative images suitable for wall display or decoration.
Markets supplied: Tourist/travel trade, publishing, advertising and design. Also sells display prints to business or public.
Formats accepted: Digital files, 300 dpi and over 5MB in size. All images to be uploaded online.
Usual terms of business: Minimum initial submission: 5 sample images. Minimum retention period: None stated.
Commission: 60 per cent to photographer.
Additional information: The agency is particularly interested in new talent. Contributors can choose to sell rights-managed or royalty-free. See website for further details.

FRESH FOOD IMAGES

2nd Floor, Waterside House, 9 Woodfield Road, London W9 2BA.
Tel: 020 7432 8200. Fax: 020 7432 8201. E-mail: creative@freshfoodimages.co.uk
Web: www.freshfoodimages.co.uk
Contact: Lee Wheatley (Creative Director).
Specialist subjects/requirements: Food and wine related images. High quality, original material on all aspects from farming, fishing, country trades, markets and vineyards to raw ingredients, finished dishes, chefs, restaurants and kitchens.
Markets supplied: Publishing, advertising, etc.
Formats accepted: Digital files required, shot on 10MP camera or high-end scans at 50MB.
Usual terms of business: Minimum initial submission: 50+ images for initial evaluation. Minimum retention period: 3 years.
Commission: 40 per cent to photographer.
Additional information: Formerly the Anthony Blake Photo Library, now part of the international Photolibrary Group. Only stocks images of the very highest standard. See www.freshfoodimages.co.uk/photographers.html for full submission details.

GARDEN PICTURE LIBRARY*

2nd Floor, Waterside House, 9 Woodfield Road, London W9 2BA.
Tel: 020 7432 8200. Fax: 020 7432 8201. E-mail: creative@gardenpicture.com
Web: www.gardenpicture.com
Contact: Lee Wheatley (Creative Director).
Specialist subjects/requirements: Gardens, plants (mainly cultivated), people and animals in the garden, practical gardening, food al fresco, outdoor living, flower shows, floral still life, and garden features.
Markets supplied: General publishing, greetings cards and calendars, advertising and design.
Formats accepted: Digital – see website for specifications.
Usual terms of business: Minimum initial submission: 100 images.
Commission: 40 per cent to photographer.
Additional information: Submission guidelines available on request or via website.

GARDEN WORLD IMAGES LTD*

Grange Studio, Woodham Road, Battlesbridge, Wickford, Essex SS11 7QU.
Tel: 01245 325725. Fax: 01245 429198. E-mail: info@gardenworldimages.com
Web: www.gardenworldimages.com
Contact: Tyrone McGlinchey (Director).
Specialist subjects/requirements: All aspects of horticulture, plants, vegetables, fruit, herbs, trees, gardens, pools, patios, etc. Also gardening action shots, people doing things, step-by-step,

making patios, etc. Creative abstract images.
Markets supplied: Publishing, calendars, seed catalogues, etc.
Formats accepted: Digital images preferred, minimum 50MB.
Usual terms of business: Minimum initial submission: 50 images. Minimum retention period: 2 years.
Commission: 50 per cent.
Additional information: Plant portraits must be identified with Latin name.

GEO AERIAL PHOTOGRAPHY*
4 Christian Fields, London SW16 3JZ.
Tel/fax: 020 8764 6292 or 0115 981 9418. E-mail: geo.aerial@geo-group.co.uk
Web: www.geo-group.co.uk
Contact: John Douglas (Director), Kelly White (Consultant).
Specialist subjects/requirements: Worldwide oblique aerial photographs.
Markets supplied: Books, magazines, advertising, etc.
Formats accepted: Digital files preferred, 35mm or larger format transparencies accepted.
Usual terms of business: Negotiable.
Commission: 50 per cent.
Additional information: Locations must be identified in detail. Do not send samples of work but contact by email first.

GETTY IMAGES*
101 Bayham Street, London NW1 0AG.
Tel: 020 7267 8988. Fax: 020 7267 6540. E-mail: editor@gettyartists.com
Web: http://creative.gettyimages.com
Contact: Editorial Submissions Team.
Specialist subjects/requirements: Conceptual and general stock photography on all subjects.
Markets supplied: Advertising, publishing, design agencies, etc.
Formats accepted: Digital.
Usual terms of business: On application, for rights-managed and royalty-free sales.
Commission: Variable.
Additional information: The Getty Images Creative division incorporates several major collections including Digital Vision, The Image Bank, Redferns, Stockbyte, Stone and Photodisc. For contributor information see www.gettyimages.com/contributors

GETTY IMAGES NEWS & SPORT*
116 Bayham Street, London NW1 0AG.
Tel: 0800 376 7981. E-mail: editorialsubmissions@gettyimages.com
Web: http://editorial.gettyimages.com
Contact: Hugh Pinney (Director of Photography).
Specialist subjects/requirements: Contemporary news, sport and entertainment images.
Markets supplied: Newspapers, magazines, television, etc.
Formats accepted: 35mm and digital (for news).
Usual terms of business: Minimum retention period: 3 years.
Commission: 50 per cent.

ROBERT HARDING WORLD IMAGERY*
Berkshire House, Queen Street, Maidenhead, Berkshire SL6 1NF.
Tel: 020 7478 4000. Fax: 020 7478 4161. E-mail: submissions@robertharding.com
Web: www.robertharding.com
Contact: Fraser Hall (Content Manager).
Specialist subjects/requirements: Travel.
Markets supplied: Publishers, advertising agencies, design groups, calendar publishers, etc.
Formats accepted: Digital only (48–52MB uncompressed TIFF).

Usual terms of business: Minimum initial submission: 150–300 images. Minimum retention period: 7 years; 12 months notice of withdrawal.
Commission: As per contract; usually 40% to photographer.
Additional information: For initial submission RAW files must also be included. Will only consider images from professional digital SLR cameras with a minimum data capability of 10 megapixels, shot as RAW files and converted to 16-bit TIFF. Will not accept images shot in TIFF or JPEG mode.

IMAGESTATE*

First Floor, Clerks Court, 18-20 Farringdon Lane, London EC1R 3AU.
Tel: 0207251 7100. E-mail: info@imagestate.com
Web: www.imagestate.com
Contact: Nathan Grainger (Content & Research Manager).
Specialist subjects/requirements: General contemporary stock – lifestyle, business, industry, landscapes, travel, leisure, etc
Markets supplied: Advertising and publishing, marketing, TV and film.
Formats accepted: Digital files preferred, at 50MB. Some transparency, negative and print depending on subject matter.
Usual terms of business: Minimum initial submission dependent on quality. Minimum retention period: 5 years.
Commission: Subject to contract.
Additional information: The agency sells both rights-managed and royalty-free stock. Model releases essential for people pictures.

IMPACT PHOTOS*

First Floor, Clerks Court, 18-20 Farringdon Lane, London EC1R 3AU.
Tel: 020 7251 7100. E-mail: library@impactphotos.com
Web: www.impactphotos.com
Contact: Nathan Grainger (Content & Research Manager).
Specialist subjects/requirements: Worldwide coverage of people in their environment – agriculture, industry, health, religion, transport, modernisation, education, social issues and travel.
Markets supplied: Newspapers, magazines, book, advertising, marketing, TV and film.
Formats accepted: Digital on CD preferred (50MB RGB TIFF uncompressed at 300dpi). Also 35mm transparencies in certain cases.
Usual terms of business: No minimum initial submission. Minimum retention period: 3 years.
Commission: Subject to contract.
Additional information: Digital contributors should also supply low-res images for quick edit.

JAZZ INDEX PHOTO LIBRARY*

26 Fosse Way, London W13 0BZ.
Tel: 020 8998 1232. E-mail: christianhim@jazzindex.co.uk
Web: www.jazzindex.co.uk
Contact: Christian Him (Principal).
Specialist subjects/requirements: Jazz, blues, world music and contemporary music. Good atmospheric shots of musicians (do not have to be well-known). Both contemporary and archive material of interest.
Markets supplied: Newspapers, book publishers, videos, television.
Formats accepted: All transparency formats; B&W prints or negs; digital at 300dpi.
Commission: 50 per cent.
Usual terms of business: No minimum submission.
Additional information: Always interested in jazz and rock photos from the '50s, '60s or '70s. Contributors must phone first to enquire if material is suitable.

KOS PICTURE SOURCE LTD*
PO Box 104, Midhurst, West Sussex GU29 1AS.
Tel: 020 7801 0044. Fax: 020 7801 0055. E-mail: images@kospictures.com
Web: kospictures.com
Contact: Chris Savage (Library Manager).
Specialist subjects/requirements: Water-related images from around the world. International yacht racing, all watersports, seascapes, underwater photography, and general travel.
Markets supplied: Advertising, design, publishing.
Formats accepted: Digital files (min 30MB).
Usual terms of business: No minimum initial submission. Minimum retention period: 2 years.
Commission: Variable.

LATITUDE STOCK*
The Old Coach House, 14 High Street, Goring-on-Thames, Berkshire RG8 9AR.
Tel: 01491 873011. Fax: 01491 875558. E-mail: info@latitudestock.com
Web: www.latitudestock.com
Contact: Felicity Bazell (Collections Manager), Stuart Cox.
Specialist subjects/requirements: All aspects of travel and tourism, from destinations to forms of transport, food, things to buy, famous sights, hotel shots to native lifestyles. All countries including the UK. Particularly interested in travel lifestyle images.
Markets supplied: Travel industry, magazines, books, newspapers, advertising etc.
Formats accepted: Digital only.
Usual terms of business: Minimum initial submission: 200 images. Minimum retention period: 3 years.
Commission: 40 per cent to photographer.
Additional information: Full submissions guidelines on website. If interested in submitting, please e-mail in the first instance.

LEBRECHT PHOTO LIBRARY*
3 Bolton Road, London NW8 0RJ.
Tel: 020 7625 5341. E-mail: pictures@lebrecht.co.uk
Web: www.lebrecht.co.uk; www.authorpictures.co.uk
Contact: Elbie Lebrecht (Proprietor).
Specialist subjects/requirements: Music & Arts Pictures – all aspects of music (classical, opera, jazz, rock) and the performing arts. Instruments, composers, musicians, singers, artists. Interiors and exteriors of concert halls and opera houses, statues and tombs of famous composers in the UK and abroad. Author Pictures – living and dead writers, novelists, politicians, scientists, philosophers, theologians. Playwrights and their plays; historic and modern performances.
Markets supplied: Specialist magazines, national press, book publishers.
Formats accepted: Digital submissions preferred (300dpi 50MB TIFF).
Usual terms of business: No minimum initial submission or retention period.
Commission: 50 per cent.
Additional information: The library has two connected divisions with their own websites – Music & Arts Pictures and Author Pictures.

LINK PICTURE LIBRARY*
41A The Downs, London SW20 8HG.
Tel: 020 8944 6933. E-mail: library@linkpicturelibrary.com
Web: www.linkpicturelibrary.com
Contact: Orde Eliason (Proprietor).
Specialist subjects/requirements: General documentary coverage of countries worldwide, but particularly Africa – communications, culture, education, environment, health, industry, people and politics. Special interest in South Africa, South East Asia, India and Israel.
Markets supplied: Newspapers, general publishing, educational publishing.

Formats accepted: Digital files preferred, at 300dpi for A4 output. 35mm transparencies also considered.

Usual terms of business: Minimum initial submission: 50 images. Minimum retention period: 3 years.

Commission: 50 per cent.

Additional information: Intial submission should be low-res images on CD.

LONDON MEDIA PRESS

11a Printing House Yard, London E2 7PR.

Tel: 020 7613 2548. Fax: 020 7729 9209. E-mail: pictures@london-media.co.uk

Web: www.london-media.co.uk

Contact: Rick Hewett, Andrew Buckwell (Directors).

Specialist subjects/requirements: News pictures, picture stories and features for worldwide syndication, especially celebrity/paparazzi material.

Markets supplied: National and international newspapers and magazines.

Formats accepted: Digital only.

Usual terms of business: No minimum initial submission. Minimum retention period: None stated.

Commission: 60 per cent to contributor.

Additional information: Freelance shift work frequently available.

LOOP IMAGES

The Studio, 61 Park Road, Woking, Surrey GU22 7BZ.

Tel/fax: 01483 830120. E-mail: paul@loopimages.com

Web: www.loopimages.com

Contact: Paul Mortlock (Library Manager).

Specialist subjects/requirments: Contemporary Britain photography (material shot in England, Scotland, Ireland and Wales) – landscape, cityscape, lifestyle, architecture, history, heritage, culture and the arts. Particular need for good town/city imagery.

Markets supplied: Magazine/book/newspaper publishers, design and ad agencies, travel and tourism industry in UK/US and Europe.

Formats accepted: Digital only – A4 300dpi TIFF (33MB) as library master.

Usual terms of business: Minimum initial submission: 50 images. Minimum retention period: Negotiable, but usually 2 years.

Commission rate: 50 per cent.

Additional information: Looking for quality material, not fillers.

MILLENNIUM IMAGES LTD*

17D Ellingfort Road, London, E8 3PA.

Tel: 020 8985 1144. Fax: 020 8525 6647. E-mail: mail@milim.com

Web: www.milim.com

Contact: Niall O'Leary (Art Director).

Specialist subjects/requirements: Creative contemporary photography with a strong individual style.

Markets supplied: Book publishers, advertising and design, general publishing.

Formats accepted: Digital files, 50-60MB TIFF.

Usual terms of business: Minimum initial submission: 20–40 images. Minimum retention period: 3 years.

Commission: 50 per cent.

Additional information: Particularly keen to see work from young innovative photographers. The agency not only sells reproductions rights but also arranges commissions and passes on image requests from picture buyers.

NHPA/PHOTOSHOT*
29-31 Saffron Hill, London EC1N 8SW.
Tel: 020 7421 6003. Fax: 020 7421 6006. E-mail: ldalton@photoshot.com
Web: www.nhpa.co.uk
Contact: Lee Dalton (Picture Editor).
Specialist subjects/requirements: Worldwide wildlife, domestic animals and pets, plants and gardens, landscapes, agriculture and environmental subjects. Endangered and appealing wildlife of particular interest.
Markets supplied: Books, magazines, advertising and design, cards and calendars, electronic publishing, exhibitions, etc (UK and overseas).
Formats accepted: Digital files preferred, transparencies accepted.
Usual terms of business: Minimum initial submission: 200 images.
Commission: 50 per cent.
Additional information: Pictures should be strong, active and well-composed. Full submissions guidelines available on website. NHPA forms the central wildlife and nature collection in the Photoshot group of companies.

NATURAL SCIENCE PHOTOS
PO Box 397, Welwyn Garden City, Herts AL7 9BA.
Tel: 01707 690561. Fax: 01707 690738. E-mail: natasha@naturalsciencephotos.com
Web: www.naturalsciencephotos.com
Contact: Natasha Jones (Partner).
Specialist subjects/requirements: Wildlife and nature, animals and plant life, plus geology, geography, landscape, weather and the environment.
Markets supplied: Books, magazines, newspapers, calendars, advertising, etc.
Formats accepted: Digital files preferred.
Usual terms of business: No minimum submission. Standard contract allows for 3 years retention and is non-exclusive.
Commission: 50 per cent.
Additional information: All material to be clearly captioned and well documented – English and scientific names, locality and photographer; also any useful additional information.

NEWSCAST LTD
First Floor, The Communications Building, 48 Leicester Square, London WC2H 7FG.
Tel: 020 3137 9137. Fax: 020 3137 1553. E-mail: photo@newscast.co.uk
Web: www.newscast.co.uk
Contact: Scott Draper (Head of Client Services).
Specialist subjects/requirements: Corporate, consumer and professional portrait photography.
Markets supplied: Magazines, newspapers, online publications and broadcasting media worldwide.
Formats accepted: Digital files preferred, minimum 18MB JPEG/TIFF.
Usual terms of business: No minimum requirements.
Commission: 50 per cent.
Additional information: This is an entirely Web-based syndication service. For image security the website is password-protected allowing the image owner to track daily downloads. All images are watermarked for protection.

NUNN SYNDICATION*
PO Box 56303, London SE1 2TD.
Tel: 020 7357 9000. Fax: 020 7231 3912. E-mail: production@nunn-syndication.com
Web: www.nunn-syndication.com
Contact: Robin Nunn (Managing Director).
Specialist subjects/requirements: All aspects of the British royal family, including state occasions, foreign tours, informal shots, etc. Also foreign royalty and general celebrities.
Markets supplied: General publishing.

Formats accepted: Digital files and 35mm transparencies.
Usual terms of business: No minimum terms specified.
Commission: 40 per cent.

ONIMAGE*
2 Independent Place, London E8 2HE.
Tel/fax: 020 7249 8384. E-mail: info@onimage.co.uk
Web: www.onimage.co.uk
Contact: Andre Pinkowski (Managing Director).
Specialist subjects/requirements: Contemporary and evocative imagery with a distinctive visual style and character.
Markets supplied: Advertising, design agencies, magazine publishing and book publishing.
Formats accepted: Digital files preferred, shot on at least a 12.5MP camera or scans of near drum scan quality at 50MB (for 35mm). Colour negative and transparency also accepted for in-house scanning.
Usual terms of business: Minimum initial submission: 40 images. Minimum retention period: 3 years.
Commission: 50 per cent.
Additional information: Potential contributors are advised to look at the website to gain an idea of the type and style of material required.

OXFORD SCIENTIFIC (OSF) LTD*
2nd Floor, Waterside House, 9 Woodfield Rd, London W9 2BA.
Tel: 020 7432 8200. Fax: 020 7432 8201. E-mail: creative@osf.co.uk
Web: www.osf.co.uk
Contact: Lee Wheatley (Creative Director).
Specialist subjects/requirements: High quality wildlife photography, plus the environment, botanical, science, travel, pollution and conservation, landscapes, agriculture, high-speed photography, special effects, underwater, creative plant shots, indigenous people, pets.
Markets supplied: Magazines, book publishers, advertising/design companies, merchandising etc.
Formats accepted: Digital (check website for accepted DSLR cameras).
Usual terms of business: Minimum initial submission 50 images. Minimum retention period: 5 years.
Commission: 40 per cent.
Additional information: See contributors' page website for full submission guidelines.

PYMCA*
2nd Floor, 71 St John's Street, London EC1M 4NJ.
Tel: 020 7251 8338. E-mail: james@pymca.com
Web: www.pymca.com
Contact: James Lange (Library Manager).
Specialist subjects/requirements: All images related to youth and subcultures, from the past (1940s/50s) to the present day, UK and abroad. Areas of particular interest: street fashions; lifestyle; social documentary; music/clubbing; recreational sport; related incidental imagery.
Markets supplied: General publishing, editorial, advertising, design, music industry etc.
Formats accepted: All formats, digital files preferred (min 28MB TIFF). Video footage.
Usual terms of business: Minimum initial submission: 20 pictures. Minimum retention period: 3 years.
Commission: 50 per cent.
Additional information: Particularly interested in model-released work for the Model Release collection, which is aimed primarily at commercial advertising and design markets. Also seeking video footage of youth subcultures, plus essays/text about different scenes and stories/experiences about being involved in these.

PANOS PICTURES*
1 Honduras Street, London EC1Y OTH.
Tel: 020 7253 1424. Fax: 020 7253 2752. E-mail: pics@panos.co.uk
Web: www.panos.co.uk
Contact: Adrian Evans (Director).
Specialist subjects/requirements: Documentary coverage of the Third World and Eastern Europe, focusing on global social, economic and political issues and with special emphasis on enviroment and development.
Markets supplied: Newspapers and magazines, book publishers, development agencies.
Formats accepted: Digital only.
Usual terms of business: No minimum initial submission or retention period.
Commission: 50 per cent.
Additional information: 50 per cent of all profits from the library are covenanted to the Panos Institute, an international development studies group.

PAPILIO
155 Station Road, Herne Bay, Kent CT6 5QA.
Tel: 01227 360996. E-mail: library@papiliophotos.com
Web: www.papiliophotos.com
Contact: Justine Pickett or Robert Pickett (Directors).
Specialist subjects/requirements: All aspects of natural history worldwide, including plants, insects, birds, mammals and marine life.
Markets supplied: Books, magazines, advertising, etc.
Formats accepted: Digital preferred (shot as RAW in camera, minimum 18MB TIFF after conversion).
Usual terms of business: Minimum initial submission: 100 images. Minimum retention period: 5 years.
Commission: 50 per cent.
Additional information: Digital files preferred, but contact first before sending digital submissions to obtain full detailed requirements.

PHOTOFUSION PICTURE LIBRARY*
17a Electric Lane, Brixton, London SW9 8LA.
Tel: 020 7733 3500. Fax: 020 7738 5509. E-mail: library@photofusion.org
Web: www.photofusionpictures.org
Contact: Liz Somerville (Library Manager).
Specialist subjects/requirements: All aspects of contemporary life with an emphasis on environmental and social issues. Specialist areas include children, disability, education, environment, the elderly, families, health, housing & homelessness, plus people generally.
Markets supplied: UK book and magazine publishing, newspapers, charities, annual reports, etc.
Formats accepted: Digital files preferred (minimum 30MB TIFF), transparencies and prints accepted.
Usual terms of business: No minimum initial submission. Minimum retention period: 3 years.
Commission: 50 per cent.
Additional information: Particularly looking for photographers who have good access to cover education and health. Also coverage from Scotland and/or Northern Ireland.

PHOTOLIBRARY*
2nd Floor, Waterside House, 9 Woodfield Road, London W9 2BA.
Tel: 020 7432 8200. Fax: 020 7432 8201. E-mail: creative@photolibrary.com
Web: www.photolibrary.com
Contact: Lee Wheatley (UK Creative Director).
Specialist subjects/requirements: High-end, creative imagery primarily oriented to advertising and business-to-business markets. Mainly travel, lifestyle, business, nature and sport.

Markets supplied: Advertising, design agencies, business.
Formats accepted: Digital (30MB TIFF minimum).
Usual terms of business: Minimum initial submission: Up to 50 images for initial assessment. Minimum retention period: 5 years.
Commission: 50 per cent.
Additional information: The Photolibrary Group represents a wide range of individual stock agencies and offers worldwide distribution with offices in 10 countries. Releases always required for people, animals and property. See artists' page on website for full details.

PHOTOSHOT*

29-31 Saffron Hill, London EC1N 8SW.
Tel: 020 7421 6000. Fax: 020 7421 6006. E-mail: info@photoshot.com
Web: www.photoshot.com
Contact: Charles Taylor (Managing Director).
Specialist subjects/requirements: Wide variety of subject matter within various distinct collections including UPPA (news); Starstock and Stay Still (celebrity, entertainment); World Illustrated (culture, environment, heritage); Talking Sport (sport). Also several nature and travel collections including NHPA, PictureNature and World Pictures (see separate listings).
Markets supplied: Newspapers, magazines, book publishers, broadcasting, advertising, etc.
Formats accepted: All formats, digital preferred.
Usual terms of business: Variable.
Commission: Usually 50 per cent.
Additional information: See website for futher details on individual collections.

PICTURE HOOKED*

97 Field Avenue, Canterbury, Kent CT1 1TS.
Tel: 07769 696244. E-mail: info@picturehooked.co.uk
Web: www.picturehooked.co.uk
Contact: Kieran Orwin (Director).
Specialist subjects/requirements: Creative personal photography and artwork on any subject.
Markets supplied: Newspapers, magazines, book publishing. All images are also offered for sale as ready-to-hang canvas prints.
Formats accepted: Digital only, 300dpi RGB 8-bit uncompressed TIFFs.
Usual terms of business: No minimum initial submission. Minimum retention period: 3 years.
Commission: 50 per cent.
Additional information: Simple, standard stock images are not required; images must be able to stand on their own as pieces of "art".

PICTUREBANK PHOTO LIBRARY LTD*

Parman House, 30–36 Fife Road, Kingston-upon-Thames, Surrey KT1 1SY.
Tel: 020 8547 2344. Fax: 020 8974 5652. E-mail: info@picturebank.co.uk
Web: www.picturebank.co.uk
Contact: Martin Bagge (Managing Director).
Specialist subjects/requirements: Worldwide travel and tourism, UK cities and countryside, people (glamour, families, children, ethnic peoples), environment, animals (domestic and wild), business, industry and technology.
Markets supplied: Magazines, calendars, travel industry, advertising, etc.
Formats accepted: Digital files at 50MB+.
Usual terms of business: Minimum initial submission: 100 images. Minimum retention period: 5 years.
Commission: Variable – maximum 50 per cent.

PICTURENATURE*
Lyndhurst, Watson Street, Banchory AB32 5TR.
Tel: 0131 208 2006. E-mail: fenneke@picture-nature.com
Web: www.picture-nature.com
Contact: Fenneke Wolters-Sinke (Founder).
Specialist subjects/requirements: All images involving nature, including landscapes, seascapes, flowers, plants, wildlife, abstracts in nature. Also people interacting with the natural environment, such as outdoor pursuits, natural resources, cultural/traditional celebrations, architecture and outdoors lifestyles.
Markets supplied: General publishing, advertising, etc.
Formats accepted: Digital only.
Usual terms of business: Contact Fenneke Wolters-Sinke for more information.
Commission: By arrangement.
Additional information: The library is now part of the Photoshot group.

PICTURES COLOUR LIBRARY*
10 James Whatman Court, Turkey Mill, Ashford, Kent ME14 5SS.
Tel: 01622 609809. Fax: 01622 609806. E-mail: karen@picturescolourlibrary.co.uk
Web: www.picturescolourlibrary.co.uk
Contact: Karen McCunnall (Submissions Manager).
Specialist subjects/requirements: Travel and travel-related images; food and drink.
Markets supplied: Magazines, newspapers, travel companies, advertising and design, calendars and greetings cards.
Formats accepted: Digital only (minimum file size 50MB).
Usual terms of business: Minimum initial submission: 500 images. Minimum retention period: 3 years.
Commission: 50 per cent.

PRESS ASSOCIATION IMAGES*
Pavilion House, 16 Castle Boulevard, Nottingham NG7 1FL.
Tel: 0115 844 7447. Fax: 0115 844 7448. E-mail: images@pressassociation.com
Web: www.pressassociation.com/images
Contact: Neal Simpson (Photographic Director); Simon Galloway, Scott Wilson (Picture Desk Managers).
Specialist subjects/requirements: Worldwide news, sport and showbusiness, past and present.
Markets supplied: Newspapers, magazines, websites, advertising agencies, etc.
Formats accepted: Digital, film negative and transparency.
Usual terms of business: No minimum terms.
Commission: 50 per cent.
Additional information: Includes pictures from The Press Association, Empics Sport, Empics Entertainment and Associated Press.

RAILPHOTOLIBRARY.COM*
Newton Harcourt, Leicestershire LE8 9FH.
Tel: 0116 259 2068. Fax: 0116 259 3001. E-mail: studio@railphotolibrary.com
Web: www.railphotolibrary.com
Contact: Colin Nash (Library Manager).
Specialist subjects/requirements: Railways – all aspects, national and international, contemporary and archive.
Markets supplied: Advertising, publishing, design, corporate railways.
Formats accepted: Digital preferred (min 25MB JPEG/TIFF); colour transparencies accepted. Archive B&W.
Usual terms of business: Minimum initial submission: 25 pictures. No minimum retention period.
Commission: 50 per cent.

Additional information: All material must be of the highest quality. Transparencies must be mounted and captioned with brief, accurate details.

RETNA PICTURES*
29-31 Saffron Hill, London EC1N 8SW.
Tel: 0845 034 0645. Fax: 020 7421 6006. E-mail: info@retna.co.uk
Web: www.retna.co.uk
Contact: Steve Hodgson (Director).
Specialist subjects/requirements: Lifestyle images: men, women, couples, family life, health and beauty, leisure, babies, children, teenagers, business and food. Celebrity/music images: portraiture, studio and events photography.
Markets supplied: Newspapers, magazines, books, record companies, advertising.
Formats accepted: All formats but digital files preferred.
Usual terms of business: Minimum initial submission: 40–50 images. Minimum retention period: 3 years.
Commission: Negotiable, depending on material.
Additional information: Lifestyle images must be fully model-released.

REX FEATURES*
18 Vine Hill, London EC1R 5DZ.
Tel: 020 7278 7294. Fax: 020 7696 0974. E-mail: photogs@rexfeatures.com
Web: www.rexfeatures.com
Contact: Mike Selby, (Editorial Director), Gretchen Viehmann (Chief Editor).
Specialist subjects/requirements: Human interest and general features, current affairs, personalities, entertainment news, animals (singles and series), humour, travel.
Markets supplied: UK national newspapers and magazines, book publishers, audio visual, television and international press. Daily worldwide syndication.
Formats accepted: Digital preferred.
Usual terms of business: No minimum submission. Preferred minimum retention period: 2 years.
Commission: 50 per cent.

ROYAL GEOGRAPHICAL SOCIETY PICTURE LIBRARY*
1 Kensington Gore, London SW7 2AR.
Tel: 020 7591 3060. Fax: 020 7591 3001. E-mail: images@rgs.org
Web: www.rgs.org/images
Contact: Library Manager.
Specialist subjects/requirements: Exploration and geographical coverage, both historic and current. Travel photography from remote destinations: indigenous peoples and daily life, landscapes, environmental and geographical phenomena, agriculture, crafts, human impact on the environment.
Markets supplied: Commercial publishing and academic research.
Formats accepted: Digital files preferred; minimum 17MB digital capture, 50MB scans.
Usual terms of business: Minimum initial submission: 250 pictures. Minimum retention period: At least 2 years.
Commission: 50 per cent.

SCR PHOTO LIBRARY
Society for Co-operation in Russian and Soviet Studies, 320 Brixton Road, London SW9 6AB.
Tel: 020 7274 2282. Fax: 020 7274 3230. E-mail: ruslibrary@scrss.org.uk
Web: www.scrss.org.uk
Contact: John Cunningham (Librarian).
Specialist subjects/requirements: Pictures from Russia and all Republics of the former Soviet Union. General/everyday scenes, landscapes, architecture, towns and cities, politics, arts, industry, agriculture, science, etc.
Markets supplied: General.

Formats accepted: All formats.
Usual terms of business: No minimum submission. Minimum retention period: 2 years.
Commission: 50 per cent.

SCIENCE PHOTO LIBRARY (SPL)*
327-329 Harrow Road, London W9 3RB.
Tel: 020 7432 1100. Fax: 020 7286 8668. E-mail: info@sciencephoto.com
Web: www.sciencephoto.com
Contact: Rosemary Taylor (Director).
Specialist subjects/requirements: All types of science-related imagery including health and medicine people and lifestyle, flowers and nature, wildlife and environment, technology and industry, astronomy and space, history of science and medicine.
Markets supplied: Books, magazines, advertising, design, corporate, audio visual.
Formats accepted: Digital only, 50MB with no interpolation.
Usual terms of business: No minimum submission. Minimum retention period: 5 years.
Commission: 50 per cent.
Additional information: All photographs must be accompanied by full and accurate caption information.

SHORELARK
The Forum, 277 London Road, Burgess Hill, West Sussex RH15 9QU.
Tel: 01444 240244. E-mail: contributors@shorelark.co.uk
Web: www.shorelark.co.uk
Contact: Christopher Sutton (Director).
Specialist subjects/requirements: Images that celebrate life and the world around us, including landscapes, wildlife, heritage, missionary work, the developing world, major sports and people pictures.
Markets supplied: Editorial, commercial, print and display.
Formats accepted: Digital only, RGB files.
Usual terms of business: Minimum initial submission: 10 sample images on CD. No minimum retention period.
Commission: 50 per cent.
Additional information: Full contributor details available on website. Images are supplied at reduced rates to churches, charities and certain educational organisations.

SKISHOOT
Hall Place, Upper Woodcott, Whitchurch, Hants RG28 7PY.
Tel: 01635 255527. E-mail: pictures@skishoot.co.uk
Web: www.skishoot.co.uk
Contact: Felice Hardy (Partner), Claire Bicknell (Library Manager).
Specialist subjects/requirements: Skiing and snowboarding, ski resorts in Europe, Asia and North America.
Markets supplied: Travel industry, general publishing, and advertising.
Formats accepted: Digital files preferred.
Usual terms of business: Minimum initial submission: 50 images. No minimum retention period.
Commission: 50 per cent.

SKYSCAN PHOTOLIBRARY*
Oak House, Toddington, Cheltenham GL54 5BY.
Tel: 01242 621357. Fax: 01242 621343. E-mail: info@skyscan.co.uk
Web: www.skyscan.co.uk
Contact: Brenda Marks (Library Manager).
Specialist subjects/requirements: Anything aerial – air to ground; aircraft; general aviation; aerial sports (skydiving, ballooning, etc).

Markets supplied: Editorial, advertising, design, calendars.
Formats accepted: Prefer digital files of 28+MB (preferably 50+MB), uninterpolated.
Usual terms of business: Minimum initial submission: 20+ images. Minimum retention period: 2 years.
Commission: 50 per cent.
Additional information: Also operates a brokerage service which is sometimes more appropriate than agency terms. Photographs are retained by the photographer; picture requests are initiated and negotiated by Skyscan and fees split 50/50.

SLICK STOCK IMAGES
Unit 2, 681 Esplanade, Mornington, Victoria 3191, Australia.
Tel: +61 3 5975 1956. E-mail: info@slickstock.com
Web: www.slickstock.com
Contact: Kim Hearn (Partner).
Specialist subjects/requirements: Aviation, including aircraft (civil and military), air travel, passengers, airports, creative images for generic use.
Markets supplied: Worldwide publishing, advertising, design, etc.
Formats accepted: Digital only. 300dpi TIFF from digital origination, or 50MB scans from transparencies. Bulk submissions should be made on CD/DVD but FTP upload is available for urgent or newsworthy images.
Usual terms of business: Minimum initial submission: None specified but prefer to deal with photographers with substantial collections. No minimum retention period.
Commission: 50 per cent, or 55 per cent for exclusive images.
Additional information: Although based in Australia the library sources and sells images worldwide. Partner Kim Hearn was formerly in charge of the Flight Collection, once the UK's leading aviation stock library.

SOCIALSTOCK*
1.11 Paintworks, Bath Road, Bristol BS4 3EH.
Tel: 0117 971 9413. E-mail: nick.cooper@socialstock.co.uk
Web: www.socialstock.co.uk
Contact: Nick Fallowfield-Cooper (Picture Editor).
Specialist subjects/requirements: UK-specific social documentary imagery of all kinds including crime, community, education, healthcare, environment, housing, the elderly and transport. Seeks experienced photographers to provide social documentary images and undertake assignments.
Markets supplied: General publishing and other markets.
Formats accepted: Digital, minimum file size 6MB.
Usual terms of business: Minimum initial submission: None stated. Minimum retention period: 3 years.
Commission: 40 per cent to photographer on "pay-as-you-go" account. 60-80 per cent for assignment work.
Additional information: Photographers are available to clients to shoot on an assigment basis should they require a more bespoke service. A weekly shoot list is available to registered contributors.

SPECTRUM COLOUR LIBRARY
First Floor, Clerks Court, 18-20 Farringdon Lane, London EC1R 3AU.
Tel: 020 7251 7100. E-mail: nathan.grainger@heritage-images.com
Web: www.impactphotos.com
Contact: Nathan Grainger (Content & Research Manager).
Specialist subjects/requirements: Travel, people, culture, places, natural history.
Markets supplied: Advertising, magazines, newspapers, book publishing, travel brochures.
Formats accepted: Digital files preferred, at 50MB.
Usual terms of business: No minimum submission. Minimum retention period: 5 years.

Commission: By negotiation.
Additional information: The library is managed by Imagestate Media Partners Ltd.

STOCKFOOD LTD*
Ground Floor, 24 Conway Sreet, London W1T 6BG.
Tel: +49 89 747 202 22 (Munich); 020 7529 8640 (UK sales). E-mail: photographer@stockfood.com
Web: www.stockfood.com
Contact: Petra Thierry (Manager, Photographers & Art Department, Munich).
Specialist subjects/requirements: All types of food and drink imagery, including people eating and drinking and other food-related lifestyle pictures, as well as interior design.
Markets supplied: Advertising, design, magazine and book publishing, etc.
Formats accepted: Digital (34MB+ from camera, 50MB from scan).
Usual terms of business: Minimum initial submission: 100 images. Minimum retention period: 5 years (exclusive representation required).
Commission: Commission to photographer 40 per cent for rights-managed, 30 per cent royalty-free.
Additional information: With its head office in Munich, Germany, the agency has representation in 80 countries and is the largest source of food-related imagery in the world. All initial photographer contact should be made via the website. UK address is sales office only.

STOCKSCOTLAND*
The Grange House, Lochside, Lairg, Sutherland IV27 4EG.
Tel: 01549 402295. E-mail: info@stockscotland.com
Web: www.stockscotland.com
Contact: Hugh Webster (Library Manager).
Specialist subjects/requirements: All aspects of Scotland and Scottish life – landscapes, castles, Highland games, natural history, industry, whisky, people, lifestyles, etc.
Markets supplied: General publishing, advertising, travel industry.
Formats accepted: All formats. Prefer digital or high-res scans (30MB+).
Usual terms of business: No minimum initial submission. Minimum retention period: 3 years.
Commission: 50 per cent.
Additional information: Images should be edited rigorously before submission. Do not send lots of very similar images. For more submission details see website.

THEIMAGEFILE.COM
3000 Hillswood Drive, Chertsey, Surrey KT16 0RZ.
Tel: 0845 118 0030. E-mail: membership@theimagefile.com
Web: www.theimagefile.com
Contact: James Duncan (Director).
Specialist subjects/requirements: All major commercial subjects.
Markets supplied: Advertising, design agencies, general publishing.
Formats accepted: Digital only.
Usual terms of business: No minimum initial submission or retention period.
Commission: 75 per cent to photographer, but because of the personalised facilities offered (see below) there is a monthly subscription charge (discount to BFP members: 20%).
Additional information: Contributing photographers have their own account through which they set their own prices for images sold. They are able to deal direct with purchasers if they wish and also obtain commissions. Other facilities include direct uploading of images and real time payment tracking.

THE TRAVEL LIBRARY
Unit 7, The Kiln Workshops, Pilcot Road, Crookham Village, Fleet, Hants GU51 5RY.
Tel: 01252 623770. Fax: 01252 812399. E-mail: info@travel-library.co.uk
Web: www.travel-library.co.uk
Contact: Chris Penn (Image Production Manager).

Specialist subjects/requirements: Top quality tourist travel material covering destinations worldwide.
Markets supplied: UK tour operators and travel industry, advertising, design and corporate.
Formats accepted: Digital RAW files saved and submitted as TIFF (minimum 24MB). Transparencies only accepted in exceptional circumstances.
Usual terms of business: Minimum initial submission: 100 images. Minimum retention period: 5 years.
Commission: Exclusive 50 per cent. Non-exclusive 40 per cent.

TRIGGER IMAGE*
Lavender Cottage, Brome Avenue, Eye, Suffolk IP23 7HW.
Tel: 01379 871358. E-mail: studio@triggerimage.co.uk
Web: wwww.triggerimage.co.uk
Contact: Tim Kahane (Director).
Specialist subjects/requirements: Personal, creative photography on any subject, especially images that are atmospheric, emotive or inspiring.
Markets supplied: Art buyers in publishing, design and advertising.
Formats accepted: Digital only, minimum 5100x3000 pixels.
Usual terms of business: Minimum initial submission: 10 sample images. Minimum retention period: 36 months.
Commission: Standard rate 50 per cent.
Additional information: Standard stock images are not accepted; study website first to see the type of work held. Creativity and expression is more important than experience.

TTL PLUS
Unit 7, The Kiln Workshops, Pilcot Road, Crookham Village, Fleet, Hants GU51 5RY.
Tel: 01252 623770. Fax: 01252 812399. E-mail: chris@ttl-plus.com
Web: www.ttl-plus.com
Contact: Chris Penn (Image Production Manager); Elizabeth Cawthorn (Picture Editor).
Specialist subjects/requirements: Professional quality images suitable for use on calendars, greetings cards and posters – cats, kittens, dogs, puppies, florals, nature, landscapes, panoramics, abstracts, railways, the seasons, colours, etc.
Markets supplied: Specialist paper product publishers, as above.
Formats accepted: Digital, minimum 24MB, 50–60MB preferred. Will view transparencies but any selected will require scanning after editing at the cost of the photographer.
Usual terms of business: No minimum initial submission. Minimum retention period: 5 years.
Commission: 50 per cent.
Additional information: Images must be of the highest standard and genuinely suitable for up-market products in relevant fields.

VIEW PICTURES LTD*
2 Whitacre Mews, 26-34 Stannary Street, London SE11 4AB.
Tel: 020 7840 5840. Fax: 020 7840 5841 . E-mail: dg@dennisgilbert.com/yvonne@viewpictures.co.uk
Web:.www.viewpictures.co.uk
Contact: Dennis Gilbert (Director), Yvonne Peeke-Vout (MD).
Specialist subjects/requirements: Top quality images of modern architecture and interior design, with the emphasis on recently-completed projects by leading architects. Classic modern buildings and historic structures also represented.
Markets supplied: Book and magazine publishers, advertising agencies, graphic designers.
Formats accepted: Digital preferred, 48MB TIFF files. Also medium/large format colour transparency.
Usual terms of business: Minimum initial submission: None stated. Minimum retention period: Negotiable.
Commission: 40 per cent to photographer.

Additional information: Seeks only top quality work from experienced architectural photographers. Commissions may also be available.

ELIZABETH WHITING & ASSOCIATES*
70 Mornington Street, London NW1 7QE.
Tel: 020 7388 2828. Fax: 020 7388 7587. E-mail: ewa@elizabethwhiting.com
Web: www.ewastock.com
Contact: Liz Whiting (Director).
Specialist subjects/requirements: Home interest topics – architecture, interiors, design, DIY, crafts, gardens, food. Some travel and scenic material.
Markets supplied: Book and magazine publishers, advertising, design companies.
Formats accepted: Digital files preferred (minimum 50 MB); colour transparencies accepted.
Usual terms of business: No minimum initial submission, but a contract is only entered into if both parties envisage a long-term commitment. Minimum retention period: 1 year.
Commission: 50 per cent.

WORLD PICTURE NETWORK
62 White Street, 3rd Floor, New York 10013, USA.
Tel: +1 212 871 1215. Fax: +1 212 925 4569. E-mail: info@worldpicturenews.com
Web: www.worldpicturenews.com
Contact: Senior Editor.
Specialist subjects/requirements: International news and photojournalism for on-line supply.
Markets supplied: National and international magazines, newspapers, broadcasting organisations.
Formats accepted: Digital.
Usual terms of business: No minimum terms.
Commission: 50 per cent.
Additional information: Originally established in London, HQ is now in New York. Business is conducted entirely on-line and photographers must first register on the website. Contributors must be familiar with scanning procedures, able to process images quickly and have the facility to up-load on-line. For further information see website.

WORLD PICTURES/PHOTOSHOT*
29-31 Saffron Hill, London EC1N 8SW.
Tel: 020 7421 6004. Fax: 020 7421 6006. E-mail: mail@worldpictures.co.uk
Web: www.worldpictures.co.uk
Contact: David Brenes (Library Manager).
Specialist subjects/requirements: Travel material: cities, resorts, hotels worldwide plus girls, couples and families on holiday suitable for travel brochure, magazine and newspaper use.
Markets supplied: Tour operators, airlines, design houses, advertising agencies.
Formats accepted: Digital files, 50MB.
Usual terms of business: No minimum submission but usually like the chance of placing material for minimum period of 2 years.
Commission: 50 per cent.
Additional information: World Pictures forms the central travel collection in the Photoshot group of companies.

WRITER PICTURES LTD*
90 Temple Park Crescent, Edinburgh EH11 1HZ.
Tel: 020 8224 1564. E-mail: info@writerpictures.com
Web: www. writerpictures.com
Contact: Alex Hewitt (Partner).
Specialist subjects/requirements: Photographs of authors and writers, mainly editorial-style portraiture.
Markets supplied: Publishing industry, news media.

Formats accepted: Digital preferred, minimum 30MB, but transparencies/negs always considered.
Usual terms of business: No minimum initial submission. Minimum retention period: 1 year.
Commission: 50 per cent.
Additional information: Commissions to photograph individual writers may also be available.

ZENITH IMAGE LIBRARY

Apollo 11, 18 All Saints Road, London W11 1HH.
Tel: 020 7221 1691. E-mail: info@zenithfoundation.com
Web: www.zenithimagelibrary.com
Contact: Mona Deeley (Director).
Specialist subjects/requirements: The Arab world and the Middle East – current events, historic/recent history events, everyday lives, culture, sport, religion, and other aspects of the unreported Middle East. Both stills and clips. Also interested in private archive collections of images relating to the region.
Markets supplied: Newspapers, magazines, general publishing, etc.
Formats accepted: Digital.
Usual terms of business: No minimum terms stated.
Commission: 50 per cent.
Additional information: All stock is rights-managed, licensed to buyers for specified project uses only and priced according to size.

SERVICES

This section lists companies providing products and services of use to the photographer. A number of those listed offer discounts to BFP members. To obtain the discounts indicated, members should simply produce their current membership card. In the case of mail order transactions, enclose your membership card with your order, requesting that this be returned with the completed order or as soon as membership has been verified. But in all cases, ensure that your membership card is valid: the discount will not be available to those who present an expired card.

Courses & Training

THE BFP SCHOOL OF PHOTOGRAPHY
Focus House, 497 Green Lanes, London N13 4BP.
Tel: 020 8882 3315. Fax: 020 8886 3933. E-mail: course@thebfp.com
Web: www.thebfp.com
Offers a two-year correspondence course in freelance photography and photojournalism. May be undertaken by either post or e-mail.
Discount to BFP members: On application.

NATIONAL COUNCIL FOR THE TRAINING OF JOURNALISTS (NCTJ)
The New Granary, Station Road, Newport, Saffron Walden, Essex CB11 3PL.
Tel: 01799 544014. Fax: 01799 544015. E-mail: info@nctj.com
Web: www.nctj.com
Official training body for the journalism industry. Offers basic journalism training through its accredited colleges/universities and by distance learning. Short mid-term courses are available in various disciplines for journalists wishing to progress their career.

TRAVELLERS' TALES
92 Hillfield Road, London NW6 1QA.
E-mail: info@travellerstales.org
Web: www.travellerstales.org
Training agency dedicated to travel photography and writing, offering masterclasses in London and training holidays around the world. Tutors are top travel photographers, editors and writers. Courses suitable for beginners and professionals. Hosts annual Traveller's Tales Festival featuring the world's leading travel writers and photographers. Details and booking via website.

Equipment Hire

FILM PLUS
77-81 Scrubbs Lane, London, NW10 6QW
Tel/fax: 020 8969 0234. E-mail: neil@filmplus.com
Web: www.filmplus.com
Professional rental and sales. Digital, lighting and camera equipment hire. Film and hardware sales. Also studio hire.
Discount to BFP members: 10%

HIREACAMERA
Unit 5, Wellbrook Farm, Berkeley Road, Mayfield, East Sussex TN20 6EH.
Tel: 01435 873028. E-mail: enquiries@hireacamera.com
Web: www.hireacamera.com
Hire of wide range of digital cameras and camcorders, catering for both private and corporate needs.

THE FLASH CENTRE
68 Brunswick Centre, Marchmont Street, London WC1N 1AE.
Tel: 020 7837 6163. Fax: 020 7833 4882. E-mail: hire@theflashcentre.co.uk
Branches also in Birmingham (0121 327 9220) and Leeds (0113 247 0937).
Web: www.theflashcentre.com
Hire of electronic flash and digital photographic equipment.

SFL
Unit 23 Headley Park 10, Headley Road East, Woodley, Reading RG5 4SW.
Tel: 0118 969 0900. Fax: 0118 969 1397. E-mail: info@sflgroup.co.uk
Web: www.sflgroup.co.uk
Hire and sale of AV equipment, film production and video production equipment.

Equipment Repair

BOURNEMOUTH PHOTOGRAPHIC (REPAIR) SERVICES LTD
251 Holdenhurst Road, Bournemouth, Dorset BH8 8DA.
Tel: 01202 301273. Fax: 01202 301273
Professional repairs to all makes of equipment. Full test facilities including modern electronic diagnostic test equipment.
Discount to BFP members: 5% off labour charges (cash sales).

THE CAMERA REPAIR CENTRE
47 London Road, Southborough,Tunbridge Wells, Kent TN4 0PB.
Tel: 01892 619136. Fax: 01892 540362. E-mail: info@thecameracentre.com
Web: www.camerarepaircentre.com
Repairs to all makes of photographic equipment, including camcorders and digital.

THE FLASH CENTRE
68 Brunswick Centre, Marchmont Street, London WC1N 1AE.
Tel: 020 7883 4737. Fax: 020 7833 4882. E-mail: service@theflashcentre.co.uk
Branches also in Birmingham (0121 327 9220) and Leeds (0113 247 0937).
Web: www.theflashcentre.com
Specialists in electronic flash service and repair.

A J JOHNSTONE & CO LTD
395 Central Chambers, 93 Hope Street, Glasgow G2 6LD.
Tel: 0141 221 2106. Fax: 0141 221 9166. E-mail: ajjohnstone@btconnect.com
Web: www.ajjohnstone.co.uk
All equipment repairs, including AV equipment. Authorised service centre for Canon, Olympus and Nikon. Canon and Nikon warranty repairs.
Discount to BFP members: 10%.

SENDEAN
9–12 St Anne's Court, London W1F 0BB.
22/23 St Cross Street, Clerkenwell, London EC1N 8UH.
Tel: 020 7439 8418. Fax: 0871 528 4582. E-mail: mail@sendeancameras.com
Web: www.sendeancameras.com
General repair service. Estimates free.
Discount to BFP members: 10%.

Insurance

AUA INSURANCE
De Vere House, 90 St Faiths Lane, Norwich NR1 1NL.
Tel: 01603 623227. Fax: 01603 665516. E-mail: sales@aua-insurance.com
Web: www.aua-insurance.com
Insurance for professional and semi-professional photographers. Comprehensive package policies covering equipment, liabilities, loss of income, professional negligence, etc.
Discount to BFP members: 10%.

AADUKI MULTIMEDIA INSURANCE
Bridge House, Okehampton EX20 1DL.
Tel: 0845 838 6933. Fax: 0845 838 6944. E-mail: info@aaduki.com
Web: www.aaduki.com
Specialist service to photographers for the insurance of cameras and other equipment. Range of products suitable for full-time professional, semi-pro or amateur, including liability and indemnity insurance, and high-risk travel. Bespoke policies also available.
Discount to BFP members: 15% (subject to minimum premiums).

E & L INSURANCE
Thorpe Underwood Hall, Ouseburn, York YO26 9SS.
 E-mail: info@eandl.co.uk
Tel: 08449 809 520. Fax: 08449 809 410.
Web: www.eandl.co.uk/leisure-and-lifestyle/camera-insurance
Specialist photographic insurance scheme covering private, domestic or commercial photo equipment. 15% online discount.

GLOVER & HOWE LTD
12 Chapel Street North, Colchester, Essex CO2 7AT.
Tel: 01206 814500. Fax: 01206 814501. E-mail: insurance@gloverhowe.co.uk
Web: www.gloverhowe.co.uk
Insurance for photographic equipment and associated risks, for the amateur, semi-pro or professional.
Discount to BFP members: 10%.

GOLDEN VALLEY INSURANCE
The Olde Shoppe, Ewyas Harold, Herefordshire HR2 0ES.
Tel: 01981 240536. Fax: 01981 240451. E-mail: gvinsurance@aol.com
Web: www.photographicinsurance.co.uk
Comprehensive insurance cover for all photographic, video and sound recording equipment, binoculars and telescopes, computers, home office/studio, all accessories etc.
Discount to BFP members: 10%.

INDEMNITYGUARD
Pavilion Insurance Management Ltd, Pavilion House, Mercia Business Village, Coventry CV4 8HX.
Tel: 02476 851000. Fax: 02476 851080. E-mail: sales@indemnityguard.co.uk
Web: www.indemnityguard.co.uk/bfp
Professional indemnity insurance for photographers and videographers, offering a range of cover levels. Instant quotes, cover, renewals and changes available online.
Discount to BFP members: 10%.

MORGAN RICHARDSON LTD
Freepost CL4071, Westgate Court, Western Road, Billericay, Essex CM12 9ZZ.
Tel: Freecall 0800 731 2940. E-mail: quotes@morganrichardson.co.uk
Web: www.morganrichardson.co.uk
Specialist "Policy Portfolio" and "Photographers' Economy" insurance for photographers. Tailored packages. Professional indemnity automatically insured up to £50,000.
Discount to BFP members: 10%

PHOTOGUARD
Pavilion Insurance Management Ltd, Pavilion House, Mercia Business Village, Coventry CV4 8HX.
Tel: 02476 851000. Fax: 02476 851080. E-mail: sales@photoguard.co.uk
Web: www.photoguard.co.uk/bfp
Specialist insurance cover for photographers and their equipment, offering a range of flexible options. Instant quotes, cover, renewals and changes available online.
Discount to BFP members: 10%.

TOWERGATE CAMERASURE
Funtley Court, Funtley Hill, Fareham, Hampshire PO16 7UY.
Tel: 0870 4115511. Fax: 0870 4115515. E-mail: camerasure@towergate.co.uk
Web: www.towergatecamerasure.co.uk
Range of specialist insurances for amateur, semi-professional and professional photographers, including comprehensive cover for equipment, studios, work in progress and legal liabilities (public, products and employer's).
Discount to BFP members: Up to 40%, subject to minimum premium requirements.

WEALD INSURANCE BROKERS LTD
Falcon House, Black Eagle Square, Westerham, Kent TN16 1SE.
Tel: 01959 565678; freephone 0800 074 7016. Fax: 01959 569988.
Web: www.quoteour.co.uk
Comprehensive specialist insurance policies for professional and semi-pro photographers.
Discount to BFP members: 15% (subject to no claims).

Are you working from the latest edition of The Freelance Photographer's Market Handbook? It's published on 1 October each year. Markets are constantly changing, so it pays to have the latest edition

---

Postcard Printers

ABACUS (COLOUR PRINTERS) LTD
Lowick House, Lowick, Near Ulverston, Cumbria LA12 8DX.
Tel: 01229 885361. Fax: 01229 885348. E-mail: sales@abacusprinters.co.uk
Web: www.abacusprinters.co.uk
Quality printers specialising in colour postcards & greetings cards and promotional card catalogues.
Minimum quantity 500.
Discount for members on production of current membership details.

COLOURCARDS
Unit 2-3 Northfield Industrial Estate, Beresford Avenue, Wembley HA0 1NW.
Tel: 020 8733 9800. E-mail: sales@colourcards.co.uk
Web: www.colourcards.co.uk
7-day postcard and greetings card printing service. Any digital artwork accepted. Card design service also available.

JUDGES POSTCARDS LTD
176 Bexhill Road, St Leonards on Sea, East Sussex TN38 8BN.
Tel: 01424 420919. Fax: 01424 438538. E-mail: sales@judges.co.uk
Web: www.judges.co.uk
Printers of postcards, greetings cards and calendars. Minimum quantity: 100.
Discount to BFP members: 10%.

THE POSTCARD COMPANY
51 Gortin Road, Omagh BT79 7HZ.
Tel: 028 8224 9222. Fax: 028 8224 9886. E-mail: sales@thepostcardcompany.com
Web: www.thepostcardcompany.com
Printers of postcards, greetings cards and product cards. No minimum quantity.

THOUGHT FACTORY
Group House, 40 Waterside Road, Hamilton Industrial Park, Leicester LE5 1TL.
Tel: 0116 276 5302. Fax: 0116 246 0506. E-mail: tara@thoughtfactory.co.uk
Web: www.thoughtfactory.co.uk
Minimum quantity: 100. Price: £50 + VAT.
Discount to BFP members: 10%.

Processing & Finishing

ACTPIX LTD
Trefechan, 2 Dolybont, St Harmon, Rhayader, Powys LD6 5LZ.
Tel: 01597 870017. E-mail: info@actpix.com
Web: www.actpix.com
Picture framing, Giclee printing, image retouching and scanning of commercial images at very high resolution.
Discount to BFP members: 5% on orders over £150.

As a member of the Bureau of Freelance Photographers, you ll be kept up-to-date with markets through the BFP Market Newsletter, published monthly. For details of membership, turn to page 9

ANDREWS IMAGING
Leacon Road, Ashford, Kent TN23 4FB.
Tel: 01233 620764. Fax: 01233 645618. E-mail: info@andrewsimaging.co.uk
Web: www.andrewsimaging.co.uk
Comprehensive range of film and digital processing, scanning and printing services.

BLUE MOON DIGITAL LTD
Davina House, 5th Floor, 137-149 Goswell Road, London EC1V 7ET.
Tel: 020 7253 9993/4. Fax: 020 7253 9995. E-mail: info@bluemoondigital.com
Web: www.bluemoondigital.com
Full film and digital imaging service including printing, processing and duplicating. Other services include mounting, CD/DVD burning and website design.

BLUESKYIMAGES LTD
2 Lakeside, South Cerney, Gloucestershire GL7 5XE.
Tel: 01285 862813. E-mail: info@blueskyimages.co.uk
Web: www.blueskyimages.co.uk
Top-quality film scanning from 35mm up to 5x4in. Also exhibition quality printing services, from film or digital.

CC IMAGING
7 Scala Court, Leathley Road, Leeds LS10 1JD.
Tel: 0113 244 8329. E-mail: ccimaging@btconnect.com
Web: www.ccimaging.co.uk
Comprehensive colour and B&W processing and printing services. E6 specialists. Specialist digital photographic print service. Full mounting and finishing services. Digital scanning, retouching and printing.
Discount to BFP members: 15%.

CPL GRAPHICS & DISPLAY
Head Office: 14 Vale Rise, Tonbridge, Kent TN9 1TB.
Tel: 01732 367222. Fax: 01732 366863. E-mail: info@cpl-graphics.com
Web: www.cpl-graphics.com
Specialist digital printing services. Professional and personal service where the photographer can talk directly to the person printing their work.
Discount to BFP members: 10% on orders over £100.

DUNNS IMAGING GROUP LTD
Chester Road, Cradley Heath, West Midlands B64 6AA.
Tel: 01384 564770. Fax: 01384 637165. E-mail: enquiries@dunns.co.uk
Web: www.dunns.co.uk
Comprehensive printing services, with online ordering. Event photography. Schools package printing and online service.

GENESIS IMAGING
Unit 1, Hurlingham Business Park, Sulivan Road, Fulham, London SW6 3DU.
Tel: 020 7384 6299. Fax: 020 7384 6277. E-mail: info@genesis-digital.net
Web: www.genesis-digital.net
Services: Large Format (Lambda) photographic prints, extra wide Giclee fine art prints, stretched canvas prints, Acrylic face mounts (perspex face mounts), aluminium mounts, Dibond mounts, Foamex mounts, foam board mounts and bespoke framing services. Drum scanning, film outputs, digital image retouching and image composition. E6 & C41 film processing, hand prints and print runs.
Discount to BFP members: 10%.

HMD GROUP PLC
Olympia House, 4 Garnett Close, Watford WD24 7JY.
Tel: 01923 237012. Fax: 01923 817421. E-mail: sales@hmdgroup.com
Web: www.hmdgroup.com
Digital printing services, mounting and finishing.
Discount to BFP members: 15%.

HOME COUNTIES COLOUR SERVICES LTD
Treelands, Oldhill Wood, Studham, Bedfordshire LU6 2NE.
Tel: 01582 873338. E-mail: sales@hccs.co.uk
Web: www.hccs.co.uk
Photographic processing services for photographers, including digital.
Discount to BFP members: On volume work only; open to negotiation.

KAY MOUNTING SERVICE
4c, Athelstane Mews, London N4 3EH.
Tel: 020 7272 7799. Fax: 020 7272 9888. E-mail: info@kaymounting.co.uk
Web: www.kaymounting.co.uk
Specialists in Diasec bonding behind perspex/aluminium with sub-frames; ready to hang frameless
artwork.
Discount to BFP members: 10%

ONE VISION IMAGING LTD
Herald Way, Binley, Coventry CV3 2NY.
Tel: 0845 862 0217. Fax: 024 76 444219. E-mail: info@onevisionimaging.com
Web: www.onevisionimaging.com
Comprehensive colour processing and digital imaging services.

PEAK IMAGING
Unit 6, Flockton Park, Holbrook Avenue, Halfway, Sheffield S20 3PP.
Tel: 01142 243207. Fax: 0114 224 3205. E-mail: info@peak-imaging.com
Web: www.peak-imaging.com.
Mail order pro-am photographic and digital imaging centre.
Discount to BFP members: 10% on pro lab services.

PERFECT PICTURE COMPANY
Welbeck Way, Peterborough PE2 7WH.
Tel: 01733 393383. Fax: 01733 391825. E-mail: sales@perfectpicturecompany.com
Web: www.perfectpicturecompany.com
Specialists in stretch canvas prints. Also supply Image Bloc prints, picture frames and digital image
enhancement services.
Discount to BFP members: 15% on canvas prints; other items according to size and regularity of
orders.

THE PHOTOGRAPHIC CENTRE
Pinewood Studios, Pinewood Road, Iver Heath, Buckinghamshire SL0 0NH.
Tel: 01753 656229. E-mail: info@photographiccentre.com
Web: www.photographiccentre.com
Professional photo lab with full range of conventional and digital services. B&W, colour, processing
and printing, scanning, framing and canvas printing.
Discount to BFP members: 15%.

PROFOLAB IMAGING LTD
Unit 4, Surrey Close, Granby Industrial Estate, Weymouth, Dorset DT4 9TY.
Tel: 01305 774098. Fax: 01305 778746. E-mail: info@profolab.co.uk
Web: www.profolab.co.uk
E6 processing and full digital service.

REDWOOD PRO LAB & WHOLESALER
7 Brunel Court, Severalls Park, Colchester, Essex CO4 9XW.
Tel: 01206 751241. Fax: 01206 855134. E-mail: info@redwoodphoto.com
Web: www.redwoodphoto.com
Colour and B&W processing, electronic imaging, in-house wedding album manufacture.
Discount to BFP members: 5%.

RUSSELL PHOTO IMAGING
17 Elm Grove, Wimbledon, London SE19 4HE. E-mail: info@russellsgroup.co.uk
Tel: 020 8947 6177. Fax: 020 8944 2064.
Web: www.russellsgroup.co.uk
Comprehensive colour processing services; 2-hour E6 processing, C41, machine and hand line printing, exhibition printing and mounting service. Digital services; scanning, digital printing and Giclee printing.
Discount to BFP members: 5%.

SCL
16 Bull Lane, Edmonton, London N18 1SX.
Tel: 020 8807 0725. Fax: 020 8807 2539. E-mail: davids@sclimage.net
Web: www.sclimage.net
Comprehensive colour and B&W processing plus full range of digital output services. Plus mounting and finishing, exhibition graphics, roller banners and display stands.

THE VAULT IMAGING LTD
1 Dorset Place, Brighton BN2 1ST.
Tel: 01273 688733. E-mail: info@thevaultimaging.co.uk
Web: www.thevaultimaging.co.uk
Comprehensive professional processing, scanning and printing services. Specialists in large format printing on a selection of premium papers and canvas, giclee and photo art archival prints.

Specialised Equipment & Materials

COLORAMA
Unit 18, Atlas Road, Hermitage Industrial Estate, Coalville, Leicestershire LE67 3FQ.
Tel: 01530 832570. Fax: 01530 832603. E-mail: info@colorama-photo.com
Web: www.colorama-photo.com
Suppliers of photographic background paper, background support products and light modifying solutions for professionals, including Cove-Lock infinity coving systems.

Are you working from the latest edition of The Freelance Photographer's Market Handbook? It's published on 1 October each year. Markets are constantly changing, so it pays to have the latest edition

THE FLASH CENTRE
68 Brunswick Centre, Marchmont Street, London WC1N 1AE.
Tel: 020 7837 5649. Fax: 020 7833 4882. E-mail: sales@theflashcentre.co.uk
Web: www.theflashcentre.com
2 Mount Street Business Centre, Birmingham B7 5RD.
Tel/fax: 0121 327 9220.
Unit 7 Scala Court, Leathley Road, Leeds LS10 1JD.
Tel: 0113 247 0937. Fax: 0113 247 0038.
Specialist suppliers of electronic flash systems, SLR and medium format digital cameras, and associated colour management and image output services.

JESSOPS
Head Office: Jessop House, 98 Scudamore Road, Leicester LE3 1TZ.
Tel: 0116 232 6000. Fax: 0116 232 0060.
Web: www.jessops.com
Specialist suppliers of all photographic and digital imaging equipment including Portaflash portable studio flash, a full range of darkroom equipment and accessories.

KENRO LTD
Greenbridge Road, Swindon, Wilts SN3 3LH.
Tel: 01793 615836. Fax: 01793 630108. E-mail: sales@kenro.co.uk
Web: www.kenro.co.uk
Wide variety of accessories including camera bags, batteries and chargers, Benbo tripods, Tokina lenses, Nissin flashguns, Marumi filters, flash and lighting kit, background supports, reflector kits, lightboxes and viewers, memory cards.

S.W. KENYON
PO Box 71, Cranbrook, Kent TN18 5ZR.
Tel: 01580 850770. Fax: 01580 850225. E-mail: swkenyon@btinternet.com
Web: www.swkenyon.com
K-Line dulling sprays for reducing glare on objects to be photographed.

OCEAN OPTICS
Archers Field, Burnt Mill Industrial Estate, Basildon, Essex SS13 1DL.
Tel: 01268 523786. Fax: 01268 523795. E-mail: optics@oceanoptics.co.uk
Web: www.oceanoptics.co.uk
Specialist suppliers of underwater photography equipment.

SILVERPRINT LTD
12 Valentine Place, London SE1 8QH.
Tel: 020 7620 0844. Fax: 020 7620 0129. E-mail: sales@silverprint.co.uk
Web: www.silverprint.co.uk
Specialist suppliers of B&W materials. Importers of Maco and Foma fibre-based and RC papers and a wide range of other papers, toners, liquid emulsions, tinting and retouching materials. Products for archival mounting, and archival storage boxes and folio cases. Mail order service.

As a member of the Bureau of Freelance Photographers, you ll be kept up-to-date with markets through the BFP Market Newsletter, published monthly. For details of membership, turn to page 9

Storage & Presentation

ABLE DIRECT CENTRE LTD
5 Mallard Close, Earls Barton, Northampton NN6 0LS.
Tel: 0844 8482733. Fax: 0844 8482766.
Web: www.able-labels.co.uk
Able-Labels – printed self-adhesive labels; rubber stamps.

ARROWFILE
PO Box 637, Wetherby Road, York YO26 0DQ.
Tel: 0844 855 1100. Fax: 0844 855 1101. E-mail: customerservices@arrowfile.com
Web: www.arrowfile.com
Archival photographic storage and presentation specialists. The Arrowfile System organises, stores and protects varying photo sizes, negs, slides, and CDs all in one single binder album.

BRAYTHORN LTD
Phillips Street, Aston, Birmingham B6 4PT.
Tel: 0121 359 8800. Fax: 0121 359 8412. E-mail: sales@braythorn.co.uk
Web: www.braythorn.co.uk
Suppliers of cardboard mailing tubes and polythene envelopes. Minimum quantities: 1000 envelopes, 100 tubes.
Discount to BFP members: 10%.

CHALLONER MARKETING LTD
Raans Road, Amersham, Buckinghamshire HP6 6LL.
Tel: 01494 721270. Fax: 01494 725732. E-mail: info@challoner-marketing.com
Web: www.challoner-marketing.com
Suppliers of Fly-Weight envelope stiffener. Minimum quantity: 100.
Discount to BFP members: 5% on orders over 5,000.

DW GROUP LTD
Unit 7, Peverel Drive, Granby, Milton Keynes MK1 1NL.
Tel: 01908 642323. Fax: 01908 640164. E-mail: sales@dw-view.com
Web: www.photopages.com
Filing and presentation systems, masks for all formats, mounts, wallets, storage cabinets, lightboxes, display boxes, viewing booths, viewtowers, ultra-slim light panels. Also CD-ROM production and replication, CD printers and replication systems, floppy disk duping, poster prints.
Discount to BFP members: 10%.

NICHOLAS HUNTER LTD
Unit 17, Chiltern Business Centre, Garsington Road, Cowley, Oxford OX4 6NG.
Tel: 01865 777365. Fax: 01865 773856. E-mail: office@nicholashunter.com
Web: www.photofiling.com
Plastic wallets for presentation of prints, slides and negatives.
Discount to BFP members: 5% on orders over £100; 10% over £500.

KENRO LTD
Greenbridge Road, Swindon, Wilts SN3 3LH.
Tel: 01793 615836. Fax: 01793 630108. E-mail: sales@kenro.co.uk
Web: www.kenro.co.uk
Professional and retail photo albums and frames, CD storage products, strut mounts and folders, lightboxes and viewers, storage and presentation accessories for digital and film.

LONDON LABELS LTD
20 Oval Road, London NW1 7DJ.
Tel: 020 7267 7105. Fax: 020 7267 1165.
Self-adhesive labels for 35mm slides, printed with name, address or logo. Also plain labels.

RICHFORDS
E M Richford Ltd, Curzon Road, Chilton Industrial Estate, Sudbury, Suffolk CO10 2XW.
Tel: 01787 375241. Fax: 01787 310179. E-mail: sales@richstamp.co.uk
Web: www.richstamp.co.uk
Rubber stamps and inks, including stamps made to order and specialist quick-drying inks.

SECOL LTD
Howlett Way, Thetford, Norfolk IP24 1HZ.
Tel: 01842 752341. Fax: 01842 762159. E-mail: sales@secol.co.uk
Web: www.secol.co.uk
Wide range of photographic storage and display products including sleeves, filing sheets, storage boxes, black card masks, mounting systems, portfolio cases and portfolio boxes.
Discount to BFP members: 10% on prepaid orders of £100 or more.

SLIDEPACKS
1 The Moorings, Aldenham Road, Bushey, Herts WD23 2NR.
Tel: 01923 254790. Fax: 01923 254790. E-mail: sales@slidepacks.com
Web: www.slidepacks.com
Binders, folders, mounts and wallets for transparency presentation, storage and filing. Custom-made service also available. Also supply labels, lightboxes, lupes and other accessories.

Studio Hire & Services

BASE MODELS
PO Box 6709, Bournemouth BH8 0BW.
Tel: 0845 2255015. Fax: 01202 524193. E-mail: info@basemodels.co.uk
Web: www.basemodels.co.uk
Commercial, fashion and glamour model agency supplying models throughout the UK and Portugal.
Discount to BFP members: 10%.

FARNHAM STUDIO
Frampton Cottage, Pankridge Street, Crondall, Near Farnham GU10 5QU.
Tel. 01252 850792. E-mail: enquiries@model-media.co.uk
Web: www.model-media.co.uk
Photographic studio based in an attractive cottage with gardens and three large studio rooms. Studio tuition and models also available.
Discount to BFP members: 20%.

HOLBORN STUDIOS
49/50 Eagle Wharf Road, London N1 7ED.
Tel: 020 7490 4099. Fax: 020 7253 8120. E-mail: studiomanager@holborn-studios.co.uk
Web: www.holborn-studios.co.uk
15 studios to hire, plus very comprehensive equipment hire.
Discount to BFP members: 10% on full week bookings.

SIMULACRA STUDIO

Railway Arch 260, Hardness Street, London SE24 0HN.
Tel: 020 7733 1979. E-mail: info@simulacrastudio.com
Web: www.simulacrastudio.com
Fully equipped studio offering characteful space under a converted railway arch. Wide range of hire equipment available.
Discount to BFP members: 25% on full-day hire

Web Services & Software

AMAZING INTERNET LTD

82 Heath Road, Twickenham, Middlesex TW1 4BW.
Tel: 020 8607 9535. E-mail: contact@amazinginternet.com
Web: www.amazinginternet.com
Website solutions for photographers. Range from fully updateable portfolio websites to large photo library systems, plus full e-commerce facilities and online sales modules for wedding and social photographers.
Discount to BFP members: 10%.

CONTACT

Surrey House, 31 Church Street, Leatherhead, Surrey KT22 8EF.
Tel: 01372 220330. Fax: 01372 220340. E-mail: mail@contact-uk.com
Web: www.contact-uk.com
Low cost web portfolio portal with international art buyer usage, plus optional annual source book.

CRUNCH

Suite 1, Dubarry House, Hove Park Villas, Hove BN3 6HP.
Tel: 0844 500 8000. E-mail: info@crunch.co.uk
Web: www.crunch.co.uk
Online accounting system and accountancy practice dedicated to freelances and other small businesses. Full end-to-end accountancy process backed by qualified Chartered Accountants.
Discount to BFP members: 10% for first two years of service.

IMENSE

William Gates Building, 15 JJ Thomson Avenue, Cambridge CB3 0FD.
3 More London Riverside, London SE1 2RE.
Tel: 020 3283 4225. E-mail: sales@imense.com
Web: www.imense.com
Imense Annotator keywording application aimed at professional and semi-professional photographers. Provides automated kyewording designed to speed up workflow and attract buyers with commercially relevant keywords.

LIGHT BLUE SOFTWARE

101 Teversham Drift, Cambridge CB1 3LL.
Tel: 07881 952510. E-mail: admin@lightbluesoftware.com
Web: www.lightbluesoftware.com
Provider of "Light Blue: Photo" business management software specifically designed for photographers. Includes contacts, shoot records, order and payment tracking, purchases and more. Free 30-day trial version available from website.

MISTERCLIPPING.COM
MisterClipping.com B.V., Hendrik Figeeweg 1M, 2031 BJ Haarlem, The Netherlands.
Tel (UK): 020 3286 9069. E-mail: info@misterclipping.com
www.misterclipping.com
Graphic processing service providing handmade clipping paths to isolate images from their backgrounds. Uploaded images can be downloaded with a path or isolated from their background within 24 hours.

SIGNUM TECHNOLOGIES LTD
Dunraven House, 5 Meadow Court, High Street, Witney, Oxfordshire, OX28 6ER.
Tel: 01933 776929. Fax: 01933 776939. E-mail: signum@signumtech.com
Web: www.signumtech.com
SureSign digital watermarking plug-ins for Photoshop, for copyright protection and notification.

SPANSOFT
8 Juniper Hill, Glenrothes, Fife KY7 5TH.
Tel/fax: 01592 743110. E-mail: support@spansoft.org
Web: www.spansoft.org
Slide Librarian shareware package for cataloguing transparency collections on PC.

THIRD LIGHT
St John's Innovation Centre, Cowley Road, Cambridge CB4 0WS.
Tel: 01223 475674. Fax: 0700 340 1284. E-mail: sales@thirdlight.com
Web: www.thirdlight.com
Provider of Image Management System (IMS), a web-based picture library and e-commerce system enabling photographers to store, display and sell images via internet galleries.

WEBBOUTIQUES LTD
1 Abbey Street, Eynsham, Oxfordshire OX29 4TB.
Tel: 01865 883852 Fax: 01865 883550. E-mail: kimberley@webboutiques.co.uk
Web: www.webboutiques.co.uk
Bespoke web design services to photographers and artists, from standard sites to complex code driven solutions. On-line ordering and printing services and a full on-line portfolio search are available.
Discount to BFP members: On application.

USEFUL ADDRESSES

ASSOCIATION OF MODEL AGENTS
11–29 Fashion Street, London E1 6PX.
Tel: 020 7422 0699. Fax: 020 7247 9230. E-mail: amainfo@btinternet.com
Web: www.associationofmodelagents.org

ASSOCIATION OF PHOTOGRAPHERS (AOP)
81 Leonard Street, London EC2A 4QS.
Tel: 020 7739 6669. Fax: 020 7739 8707. E-mail: general@aophoto.co.uk
Web: www.the-aop.org

BRITISH ASSOCIATION OF PICTURE LIBRARIES AND AGENCIES (BAPLA)
59 Tranquil Vale, Blackheath, London, SE3 0BS
Tel: 020 8852 7211. E-mail: enquiries@bapla.org.uk
Web: www.bapla.org.uk

BRITISH INSTITUTE OF PROFESSIONAL PHOTOGRAPHY (BIPP)
1 Prebendal Court, Oxford Road, Aylesbury, Buckinghamshire HP19 8EY.
Tel: 01296 718530. Fax: 01296 336367. E-mail: info@bipp.com
Web: www.bipp.com

BRITISH PRESS PHOTOGRAPHERS' ASSOCIATION (BPPA)
Suite 219, 2 Lansdowne Crescent, Bournemouth BH1 1SA.
E-mail: info@thebppa.com
Web: www.thebppa.com

BUREAU OF FREELANCE PHOTOGRAPHERS (BFP)
Focus House, 497 Green Lanes, London N13 4BP.
Tel: 020 8882 3315. Fax: 020 8886 3933. E-mail: mail@thebfp.com
Web: www.thebfp.com

CHARTERED INSTITUTE OF JOURNALISTS (CIOJ)
2, Dock Offices, Surrey Quays Road, London SE16 2XU.
Tel: 020 7252 1187. Fax: 020 7232 2302. E-mail: memberservices@cioj.co.uk
Web: www.cioj.co.uk

DESIGN & ARTISTS COPYRIGHT SOCIETY (DACS)
33 Great Sutton Street, London EC1V 0DX.
Tel: 020 7336 8811. Fax: 020 7336 8822. E-mail: info@dacs.org.uk
Web: www.dacs.org.uk

GUILD OF PHOTOGRAPHERS
30 St Edmunds Avenue, Newcastle-Under-Lyme, Staffordshire ST5 0AB.
Tel: 01782 740526. E-mail: info@photoguild.co.uk
Web: www.photoguild.co.uk

MASTER PHOTOGRAPHERS ASSOCIATION (MPA)
Jubilee House, 1 Chancery Lane, Darlington, Co Durham DL1 5QP.
Tel: 01325 356555. Fax: 01325 357813. E-mail: enq@mpauk.com
Web: www.thempa.com

NATIONAL ASSOCIATION OF PRESS AGENCIES (NAPA)
2nd Floor. Contemporary Urban Centre, 41-51, Greenland Street, Liverpool, Liverpool, L1 0BS.
Tel: 0870 609 1935. E-mail: enquiries@napa.org.uk
Web: www.napa.org.uk

NATIONAL UNION OF JOURNALISTS (NUJ)
Headland House, 308-312 Gray's Inn Road, London WC1X 8DP.
Tel: 020 7278 7916. Fax: 020 7837 8143. E-mail: info@nuj.org.uk
Web: www.nuj.org.uk

PRESS ASSOCIATION
292 Vauxhall Bridge Road, London SW1V 1AE.
Tel: 020 7963 7000. Picture Desk: 020 7963 7155.
Web: www.pressassociation.co.uk

REUTERS
Reuters Building, South Colonnade, Canary Wharf, London E14 5EP.
Tel: 020 7542 7949 (picture desk UK news); 020 7542 8088 (international). E-mail:
lon.pictures@reuters.com
Web: http://pictures.reuters.com

ROYAL PHOTOGRAPHIC SOCIETY (RPS)
Fenton House, 122 Wells Road, Bath BA2 3AH.
Tel: 01225 325733. Fax: 01225 448688. E-mail: reception@rps.org
Web: www.rps.org

SOCIETY OF WEDDING & PORTRAIT PHOTOGRAPHERS (SWPP)
6 Bath Street, Rhyl LL16 3EB.
Tel: 01745 356935. Fax: 01745 356953. E-mail: info@swpp.co.uk
Web: www.swpp.co.uk

INDEX

A

B

C

Join the BFP today and get next year's Handbook hot from the press!

As a member of the Bureau of Freelance Photographers, you'll be kept right up to date with market requirements. Every month, you'll receive the BFP *Market Newsletter*, a unique publication telling you what picture buyers are looking for now. It will keep you informed of new markets – including new magazines – as they appear and the type of pictures they're looking for. It also serves to keep *The Freelance Photographer's Market Handbook* up to date between editions, since it reports important changes as they occur.

And as part of membership, you receive the Handbook automatically each year as it is published. For details of some of the other services available to members please see page 9.

Membership currently costs just £54 a year. To join, complete the form below and post with your remittance to the BFP. You'll receive your first Newsletter and membership pack within about seven days.

Please enrol me as a member of the Bureau of Freelance Photographers for 12 months. I understand that if, once I receive my initial membership pack, I decide that membership is not for me, I may return it within 21 days for a full refund.

☐ I enclose cheque/po value £54 *(or £70 Overseas rate*)*

☐ Debit my MASTERCARD/VISA/SWITCH no_____Start_____

Expiry_____ Issue No (Switch only)_____ Security code_____ in the sum of £54.

NAME _____ BLOCK

ADDRESS _____ CAPS PLEASE

_____

_____Postcode_____

Post to:
Bureau of Freelance Photographers,
Focus House, 497 Green Lanes, London N13 4BP.

*Overseas applicants must send cheque/draft drawn on a UK bank; or pay by credit card

H11

Also published by BFP Books

The Freelance Photographer's Project Book is a major new publication from BFP Books. It is designed to help photographers find fresh markets for their work by giving them the inside information on breaking into different sectors of the market. Each of the 20 chapters, or "projects", is written by an experienced and successful freelance who specialises in the market concerned. Each contributor provides the newcomer with the benefit of their long experience in approaching these specific markets.

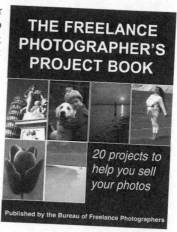

Subjects include Selling family photos; Selling outdoor photos; Selling wildlife photos; Selling country photos; Selling garden photos; Selling boating photos; Selling to photo magazines; Selling to local papers; Selling travel photos; Selling architectural photos; Selling generic photos; Selling transport photos; Selling to home magazines; Selling through libraries; Selling cards & calendars; and Selling stock with articles.

The final two projects cover Mounting an exhibition and Producing a book.

The contributors have been chosen not only for their expertise in their chosen subject but also their ability to impart this knowledge with clarity and precision. A short summary of the contributor's background and experience is appended to each project.

The book is fully illustrated with examples of pictures that sell, all provided by the contributors themselves.

The Freelance Photographer's Project Book will provide invaluable information for anyone who has ever thought of selling their pictures but does not know where to start. Whatever the subject, the *Project Book* offers a fast track to success.

144 pages Hardback £22.50

Please send me a copy of *The Freelance Photographer's Project Book* at £22.50 plus £2.00 p&p. I understand that if I am dissatisfied with the book, I may return it within 14 days for a full refund.

☐ I enclose cheque/po value £24.50

☐ Debit my MASTERCARD/VISA/SWITCH no_____Start_____

Expiry_____ Issue No (Switch only)_____ Security code_____ in the sum of £24.50.

NAME _____ BLOCK CAPS

ADDRESS _____ PLEASE

_____

_____Postcode_____

Post to:
BFP BOOKS
Focus House, 497 Green Lanes, London N13 4BP.

H11

*Overseas readers must send cheque/draft drawn on a UK bank; or pay by credit card

Get a special previous user's discount when you order next year's Handbook direct

Each year's *Handbook* contains hundreds of amended listings as well as new entries. To take the magazine section alone, during the course of the year, new publications launch while existing titles fold. In addition, editors change which often leads to a change in picture requirements. Similar important changes occur in every other section of the book.

the freelance photographer's market handbook

2012 edition out 1 October 2011

It's vital, therefore, to keep up-to-date by working from the latest edition. The *Handbook* is published in October each year, and you can order next year's edition from September onwards. By using this form, you'll benefit from a special previous user's discount, saving you £3 on the usual direct-from-the-publishers price. While the normal price is £16.95 (£14.95 plus £2 p&p), you pay only £13.95.

Complete the details below for your copy of next year's *Freelance Photographer's Market Handbook*.

NB. Offer closes 31 December 2010

Please send me a copy of **The Freelance Photographer's Market Handook 2011** at the special Previous User's Discount price of £11.95 plus £2.00 p&p.

☐ I enclose cheque/po value £13.95

☐ Debit my MASTERCARD/VISA/SWITCH no_____ Start_____

Expiry_____ Issue No (Switch only)_____ Security code_____ in the sum £13.95.

NAME _____ BLOCK CAPS

ADDRESS _____ PLEASE

_____

_____Postcode_____

Post to:
BFP BOOKS
Focus House, 497 Green Lanes, London N13 4BP.

H11

*Overseas readers must send cheque/draft drawn on a UK bank; or pay by credit card